SET THEORY FOR THE MATHEMATICIAN

HOLDEN-DAY SERIES IN MATHEMATICS

Earl E. Coddington and Andrew M. Gleason, Editors

Introductory Calculus
S. Bell, J. R. Blum, J. V. Lewis, and J. Rosenblatt

Modern University Calculus
S. Bell, J. R. Blum, J. V. Lewis, and J. Rosenblatt

Elementary Partial Differential Equations
P. W. Berg and J. L. McGregor

The Structure of Lie Groups
G. Hochschild

Elements of General Topology
Sze-Tsen Hu

Elements of Modern Algebra
Sze-Tsen Hu

Elements of Real Analysis
Sze-Tsen Hu

Introduction to Contemporary Mathematics
Sze-Tsen Hu

Introduction to General Topology
Sze-Tsen Hu

Homology Theory
Sze-Tsen Hu

Abstract Algebra
A. Lindstrum

Set Theory for the Mathematician
J. Rubin

SET THEORY
for the Mathematician

JEAN E. RUBIN
Michigan State University

HOLDEN-DAY
San Francisco, Cambridge, London, Amsterdam

Library of Congress Catalog Card Number 67-13848
Printed in the United States of America

In memory of my father,

Leonard L. Hirsh

Preface

This book is intended as a text in set theory for advanced undergraduate and graduate students in mathematics. There are no formal mathematical prerequisites, but the student should have "mathematical maturity." Essentially, what this means here is that the student is not totally unfamiliar with mathematical abstractions, knows what a mathematical proof is, and can, if pressed, construct a proof himself. (Section 1.2 of Chapter 1 contains in outline form the essential ingredients of a mathematical proof. The amount of time spent on this section depends on the level of mathematical maturity of the student.)

The text is arranged so that it can be used either for a one quarter, one semester, or one year course in set theory. For a short course the more advanced topics may be omitted. The chapters and sections which contain the advanced topics are marked with an asterisk. Chapter 6, on rational and real numbers, is also marked with an asterisk, not so much because it is advanced, but because it can be omitted in a short course without loss of continuity. The same is true for several sections which depend upon Chapter 6, such as sections 7.5 and 10.4. (Chapter 6 contains an axiomatic development of the rational and real numbers which is more an application of set theory than a part of set theory.)

The fundamental concepts of set theory, which are now practically indispensable for all mathematicians, are contained in Chapters 2–5, 7, 8, 10, and 11. Those sections in these chapters which are marked with an asterisk and the remaining chapters which are marked with an asterisk are oriented towards the mathematics student who has more of an intrinsic interest in set theory.

This book could not have been written in its present form without the help of my husband, Herman Rubin. He read the manuscript in detail and made numerous comments and corrections. John G. Hocking rewrote the introduction. Several anonymous reviewers made many suggestions which were incorporated.

JEAN E. RUBIN

January 1967

Contents

Chapter 1: Introduction

1.1. HISTORICAL BACKGROUND

Mathematics is experiencing today the most rapid expansion in its 3000 year old history. Entirely new branches of mathematics, unknown and unexpected 50 years ago, are commonplace today. Applications in the social sciences, in the management sciences, in the biological sciences, in communication and computer techniques, to name a few, have become major fields within the past 25 years. And the so-called "pure mathematics" is expanding at a rate which is unbelievable to the layman.

Still, all known mathematics can be formulated within the framework of set theory. Indeed, all known mathematical concepts can be and have been reduced to the ideas of "set" and "membership in a set". It follows that all known mathematical results eventually can be deduced from the propositions of set theory. As a self-evident corollary, it is essential that every mathematician be familiar with the fundamentals of set theory.

Georg Cantor (1845–1918) is regarded as the founder of modern set theory and the year 1874 saw the publication of his first paper on infinite sets. An *algebraic* number is a real number which is the solution of a polynomial equation with integral coefficients. In 1874 Cantor proved the revolutionary result that the set of all algebraic numbers is the same size as the set of natural numbers (nonnegative integers). That is, there exists a 1–1 correspondence between the two sets. Clearly, every natural number is algebraic, but the algebraic numbers also include all irrational numbers of the form $\sqrt{2}, \sqrt{3}, \sqrt{5}, \ldots, \sqrt[3]{2}, \sqrt[3]{3}, \sqrt[3]{4}, \ldots$, plus many more. Therefore, is it not intuitively clear that there are infinitely many more algebraic numbers than natural numbers? Cantor proved that our intuition is faulty in his bold attack on the concept of infinity.

As if the preceding result were not surprising enough, in the same paper Cantor proved that the set of real numbers is actually larger than the set of algebraic numbers. That is, there does not exist a 1–1 correspondence between the set of real numbers and the set of natural numbers. (Clearly, there does exist a 1–1 correspondence between the set of natural numbers and a subset of the real numbers since each natural number is real.) Consequently, the set of transcendental numbers (real numbers which are not algebraic) is larger than the set of algebraic numbers. Offhand, it is difficult to think of many transcendental numbers. There are, of course, π and e and numbers obtained from π and e by algebraic operations, but what else? Many mathematicians were extremely critical of Cantor's results. Kronecker, in particular, attacked Cantor viciously because the proofs Cantor used were largely nonconstructive.

In spite of the criticism, and in spite of several nervous breakdowns, Cantor continued his work. In 1878 he formalized the notion of equipollence between sets, which led to the concept of cardinal numbers. Two sets have the same cardinal number if there exists a 1–1 correspondence between them. In a true sense, Cantor followed the work of Zeno (495–435 B.C.) and Eudoxus (408–355 B.C.) who first studied the concept of infinity.

In Cantor's "intuitive" or "naive" set theory, a set is anything obtainable from the empty set or the set of integers (or some other such well-defined set of objects) by iterated application of "natural" operations. For instance, we can construct a set of rational numbers by properly defining a set of ordered pairs of integers and the arithmetic operations on such ordered pairs. Similarly, the real numbers are constructed as a set of sets of rational numbers; a set of real-valued functions is a set of sets of ordered pairs of real numbers, and so forth.

The iteration of the "natural" operations may be transfinite. That is, all sets obtained by finite iterations again form a set and the iterative process can then be applied to this new set. It turns out that, when an appropriate definition of an "ordered pair" is made, it is sufficient to start with a *ground set* X, construct the set $\mathcal{P}(X)$ of all subsets of X, construct the set $\mathcal{P}(\mathcal{P}(X))$ of all subsets of $\mathcal{P}(X)$, etc. The collection of all sets formed in this way is then considered to be a set and the construction begins again.

It seems natural to think that Cantor's concept of a set can be generalized in such a way that any collection of sets is again a set. That is, not only should those sets which can be obtained from a ground set by the iteration of natural operations be considered but also any collection which satisfies a given property. It was at this point that set theory ran into serious difficulty. Around the turn of the century several "paradoxes" (contradictions) were discovered in set theory. (There was some controversy on the importance of these paradoxes. In general, mathematicians considered them to be artificial and did not feel that their work was affected. On the other hand, those who worked in the foundations, including Frege and Poincaré, were shattered by these paradoxes!)

A *paradox* or *contradiction* occurs within an axiom system if both a proposition and its negation are deducible from the axioms, or if there is a proposition which is logically equivalent to its negation. Such paradoxes are to be avoided, of course. For if an axiom system results in a paradox, then any statement is provable within the system.[1] This is obviously not a desirable state of affairs!

One of the first paradoxes in set theory was propounded by Russell in 1902. It can be described as follows: In unrestricted set theory it should be meaningful to ask whether or not a given set is a member of itself. For instance, it is obvious that a set of books is not a book. But, in general, a collection of sets should be a set and then it might very well be a member of itself. Thus it seems reasonable to define *the set of all sets which are not members of themselves*. Let us denote this set by S. Thus a set x is a member of S if and only if x is not a member of itself. Now the crucial question arises, Is S a member of itself? If S is a member of itself, then by definition of S, S is not a member of itself. On the other hand, if S is not a member of itself, then again by definition, S must be a member of itself. Thus we have proved the contradictory statement: "S is a member of itself if and only if S is not a member of itself." There is obviously something wrong here! (Other paradoxes in general set theory are mentioned in the text, e.g., Cantor's paradox, § 4.5 and the Burali-Forte paradox, § 8.3.)

An axiom system is said to be *consistent* if it leads to no contradictions.[2] Otherwise the system is called *inconsistent*. Clearly, if the collection S defined above is really a set, then set theory is inconsistent and we would not want our mathematics based upon such a foundation. We point out, however, that all known mathematics can be based upon Cantor's intuitive set theory. And as far as is known, there are no paradoxes there!

Whenever such logical inconsistencies arise, the mathematician and the logician fall back upon the axiomatic approach. Several axiom systems for set theory have been devised in an attempt to retain Cantor's intuitive set theory while avoiding paradoxes. One of the first and most influential of such axiomatizations was given by Russell and Whitehead in their famous *Principia Mathematica* (first edition, 1910–1913). They avoided the

[1] To see this suppose a proposition p and its negation $\neg p$ are both true. Let q be any other proposition in the system. Then since p is true, the proposition p or q is true. But $\neg p$ is also true. Since p or q is true and $\neg p$ is true, it follows from an elementary rule of logic that q is true.

If p is equivalent to its negation $\neg p$, then either p and $\neg p$ are both true, in which case the preceding argument holds; or p and $\neg p$ are both false in which case $\neg p$ and p must both be true. (The negation of a false proposition is true and a double negated proposition is equivalent to a positive proposition.) Thus, the preceding argument holds again.

[2] It was shown by K. Gödel (1931) that the consistency of any mathematical system containing number theory is not provable within the system. For an exposition of Gödel's famous "incompleteness theorem" see, for example, Mostowski (1952) or Kleene (1952).

paradoxes by introducing the so-called "theory of types" in which an infinite number of different types of set variables are defined. For each type of set variable there are an infinite number of variables of the next higher type. The atomic formula "**v** is a member of **u**" is meaningful if and only if **u** is of a type exactly one higher than **v**. In general, a formula is meaningful only if each of its atomic formulae is meaningful. In this way, for instance, Russell's paradox explained above is avoided because the formula "x is a member of x" is meaningless in the theory of types. Because the theory of types is quite difficult and because it is cumbersome to keep track of all of the types of variables, this theory does not lend itself easily to the development of mathematics.

Another axiomatization of set theory was proposed by Quine in 1931. His approach might be said to be semantical. He gives rules for the construction of stratified formulas. An atomic formula "**v** is a member of **u**" is stratified if the variables **v** and **u** can be assigned consecutive levels (which is always the case if **v** and **u** are different variables.) A formula is called stratified if all variables occurring in it can be assigned to levels in such a way that all of the atomic formulae are simultaneously stratified. Finally, a set exists if it can be defined by a stratified formula. That is, if **P** is a stratified formula then there exists a set Y such that

$$X \text{ is a member of } Y \text{ if and only if } \mathbf{P}.$$

The set S of Russell's paradox is not defined by a stratified formula since "x is not a member of x" is not stratified.

Quine's theory is not as unwieldy as the theory of types but it has been found to contain a fatal flaw as far as mathematicians are concerned. It was shown by Specker (1953) that the axiom of choice is inconsistent in the Quine system. (See §3.6 for a discussion of the axiom of choice.)

In current use by mathematicians are two essentially different axiomatic approaches to set theory. One has evolved from the work of E. Zermelo and A. A. Fraenkel so we shall call it the ZF theory. The other has developed from the ideas of von Neumann, Bernays and Gödel, the NBG theory. (It is necessary to keep in mind the fact that these axiomatizations did not develop without good reason. They all had as a model the intuitive set theory of Cantor, of course, but in order to avoid the obvious paradoxes, it was essential to state explicitly what could and what could not be called a set.)

In 1908 Zermelo postulated an axiom system for set theory in which a restriction is placed upon the "size" of sets. He proceeded as follows: If $P(x)$ is a statement about a variable x and if Y is any set, then there exists a subset Z of Y which consists of precisely those elements x of Y for which

$P(x)$ is true. Thus, in order that a set exist, it must be some definite subset of a given set. Again in this system Russell's paradox is avoided because S is not a set.

It turned out however that Zermelo's axioms were not adequate for transfinite induction and ordinal arithmetic. Hence, in 1922 both T. Skolem and Fraenkel (independently) modified Zermelo's axioms to eliminate this difficulty. (Skolem's contributions are not well known. His name rarely appears in discussions of the ZF theory.) Their contribution is the so-called *axiom schema of replacement*. This rule states that if X is a set and ϕ is a binary predicate such that for each set u in X, there is exactly one set v satisfying $\phi(u,v)$, then there is a set Y such that v is a member of Y if and only if there is a u in X satisfying $\phi(u,v)$. In this way the "size" of a set is limited and the obvious paradoxes are avoided.

Again, however, the ZF theory has some disadvantages. For one, it is not finitely axiomatizable. The axiom schema of replacement is not itself an axiom but is a rule which replaces an infinite number of axioms. (Any binary predicate can be substituted for the predicate ϕ.) Moreover, the distinction between those sets which "exist" and those which do not seems rather arbitrary. It seems harmless, for instance, to assume that the collection of all sets, or the collection of all groups, or Russell's set S, exist *as long as they are not elements.*

In the NBG set theory it is essentially true that any meaningful collection of elements exists and forms a *class*. Classes are then subdivided into two types: *sets*, those classes which are members of classes; and *proper classes*, those classes which are not members of any class. Russell's paradox is thus avoided by showing that his set S is a proper class and cannot be a member of any class. One fact in favor of the NBG theory is that Gödel (1940) showed it to be finitely axiomatizable.

The axiomatization of Cantor's intuitive set theory was in itself a very remarkable accomplishment, one of the milestones of twentieth century mathematics. This alone constitutes a justification for the study of axiomatic set theory. Also, starting with Euclid, it has been found that the axiomatic method is perhaps the clearest and most precise way in which to present a body of knowledge.

In this text we shall develop the NBG set theory with modifications due to A. P. Morse. Our approach allows for the existence of *atoms* or *individuals*. Atoms have no members but are themselves members. The class of atoms corresponds to Cantor's ground set—the set of integers or some other well-defined class. This modified system is no longer finitely axiomatizable. However, it does provide, quickly and naturally, a foundation for mathematics which is free of the obvious paradoxes. (We shall cite specifically each instance in which our results differ from those of the standard NBG theory.) Finally, for those interested, an excellent development of the ZF set theory can be found in Suppes (1960).

1.2. MATHEMATICAL LOGIC

The notion of a proof has developed quite naturally in mathematics and most mathematicians can construct proofs without any formal training in mathematical logic. However, nothing in such a precise discipline as mathematics should be taken for granted, so this section is devoted to the concept of a mathematical proof.

We shall use the following symbols for the logical connectives:

$(\neg \mathbf{P})$	It is not the case that **P**,
$(\mathbf{P} \text{ or } \mathbf{Q})$	**P** and/or **Q**,
$(\mathbf{P} \,\&\, \mathbf{Q})$	**P** and **Q**,
$(\mathbf{P} \rightarrow \mathbf{Q})$	If **P** then **Q**,
$(\mathbf{P} \leftrightarrow \mathbf{Q})$	**P** if and only if **Q**.

The quantifiers will be symbolized as follows:

$((\forall \boldsymbol{\nu})\mathbf{P})$	For every $\boldsymbol{\nu}$, **P**,
$((\exists \boldsymbol{\nu})\mathbf{P})$	For some $\boldsymbol{\nu}$, **P**,
$((\exists 1 \boldsymbol{\nu})\mathbf{P})$	There is exactly one $\boldsymbol{\nu}$ such that **P**.

Moreover, the identity relation "=" is considered as a two-place or binary predicate in the logic. The individual variables will be denoted by X, Y, Z, . . . , and these letters with subscripts. (In the text, on occasion we shall use other letters for individual variables like x, y, z, . . . , for set variables, α, β, γ, . . . , for ordinal number variables, etc.) The predicate variables will be denoted by F, G, H, . . . , and these letters with subscripts.

We shall illustrate how the logical symbolism is used in several examples. Let us suppose that in each of the following sentences the range of each of the individual variables is all real numbers. Then the sentence,

(1) There is no largest real number.

can be symbolized as

$$(\forall X)(\exists Y)(X < Y).$$

[If we do not use the convention that the range of each individual variable is all real numbers, then we would have to have a unary predicate "$R(\boldsymbol{\nu})$" to mean "$\boldsymbol{\nu}$ is a real number." Sentence (1) would then be symbolized as,

$$(\forall X)(R(X) \rightarrow (\exists Y)(R(Y) \,\&\, X < Y)). \qquad]$$

The sentence,

There is a real number between each pair of distinct real numbers.

could be symbolized as

$$(\forall X)(\forall Y)(X < Y \rightarrow (\exists Z)(X < Z \,\&\, Z < Y)).$$

And the sentence,

For every X and Y there is exactly one Z such that $X + Z = Y$.

can be symbolized as

$$(\forall X)(\forall Y)(\exists 1Z)(X + Z = Y).$$

There may be several English translations of a given logical symbol. For example, "$(\exists\boldsymbol{\nu})\mathbf{P}$" may be translated as "For some $\boldsymbol{\nu}$, $\mathbf{P}$" or "There is a $\boldsymbol{\nu}$ such that $\mathbf{P}$"; and "$(\forall\boldsymbol{\nu})\mathbf{P}$" may be translated as "For every $\boldsymbol{\nu}$, $\mathbf{P}$", "For all $\boldsymbol{\nu}$, $\mathbf{P}$", or "For each $\boldsymbol{\nu}$, $\mathbf{P}$".

In any formalized system it is important to distinguish between the *object language* and the *metalanguage*. The object language in this case is the logical symbolism described above—the language in which we shall talk about sets. The metalanguage is the language in which we talk about the object language. (There might also be a meta-metalanguage, a meta-meta-metalanguage, etc.) Our metalanguage is English augmented by some mathematical symbols. So, for example, we shall assume that the metalanguage includes the symbols for the positive integers, and sets of positive integers. We shall use: the symbols $\boldsymbol{\nu}$, $\boldsymbol{\mu}$, $\boldsymbol{\lambda}$, and these letters with subscripts for variables each of whose range is all individual variables; the symbols **F**, **G**, **H**, and these letters with subscripts for variables each of whose range is all predicate variables. These metalinguistic or generic variables will not be used in the sections which follow because in this section we shall derive rules of substitution for individual variables, and the only predicates which will occur are constants.

A *term* is an expression which either names or describes an individual or results in a name or description when the variables in the expression are replaced by names or descriptions [Suppes (1957)]. Thus, if the range of each individual variable is all integers, each of the following expressions is a term:

$1, X, X - 2, X^2 + Y^2 + 1,$
The largest integer which is less than 2,
The largest integer which is less than Y.

We shall use the symbols $\boldsymbol{\tau}$, $\boldsymbol{\sigma}$, $\boldsymbol{\rho}$, . . . , and these letters with subscripts for variables each of whose range is all terms.

Any finite sequence of logical connectives, quantifiers, terms, and predicates is a *formula*. But we must distinguish between formulae which make sense and those which do not. This is not a definition of a true formula, but of a *meaningful* one. We shall call a meaningful formula a *well-formed formula* or a *wff* (pronounced "wiff"). We shall use the symbols **P**, **Q**, **R**, . . . , and these symbols with subscripts for variables each of whose range is all wffs.

DEFINITION 1.2.1.

(a) If $\tau_1, \tau_2, \ldots, \tau_n$ are terms and **F** is an n-place predicate, then $\mathbf{F}(\tau_1, \tau_2, \ldots, \tau_n)$ is a wff. [If **F** is a two-place predicate like "$=$" or "$<$", we often write $\tau_1 \mathbf{F} \tau_2$ instead of $\mathbf{F}(\tau_1,\tau_2)$. Also $\neg\tau_1 \mathbf{F} \tau_2$ is often abbreviated by $\tau_1 \not\mathbf{F} \tau_2$. Thus, we usually write "$\tau_1 \neq \tau_2$" instead of "$\neg\tau_1 = \tau_2$", "$\tau_1 \not< \tau_2$" instead of "$\neg\tau_1 < \tau_2$", etc.]

(b) If **P** is a wff so is $(\neg\mathbf{P})$.

(c) If **P** and **Q** are wffs, so are (**P** or **Q**), $(\mathbf{P} \,\&\, \mathbf{Q})$, $(\mathbf{P} \rightarrow \mathbf{Q})$, and $(\mathbf{P} \leftrightarrow \mathbf{Q})$.

(d) If **P** is a wff and ν is an individual variable, then $((\forall\nu)\mathbf{P})$, $((\exists\nu)\mathbf{P})$, and $((\exists 1\nu)\mathbf{P})$ are wffs.

(e) No other formulae are wffs.

It is customary to omit the outermost parentheses in a wff. So, for example, we shall write

$$\begin{array}{rcl} \mathbf{P} \,\&\, \mathbf{Q} & \text{for} & (\mathbf{P} \,\&\, \mathbf{Q}), \\ (\exists\nu)\mathbf{P} & \text{for} & ((\exists\nu)\mathbf{P}), \\ \neg\mathbf{P} & \text{for} & (\neg\mathbf{P}), \end{array}$$

etc. The outermost parentheses around a wff of the form given in 1.2.1(d) is omitted even when the wff is a proper part of another wff. For example, we shall write

$$\begin{array}{rcl} (\forall\nu)(\mathbf{P} \text{ or } (\exists\mu)\mathbf{Q}) & \text{for} & (\forall\nu)(\mathbf{P} \text{ or } ((\exists\mu)\mathbf{Q})), \\ (\exists 1\nu)\mathbf{P} \rightarrow \mathbf{Q} & \text{for} & ((\exists 1\nu)\mathbf{P}) \rightarrow \mathbf{Q}, \\ \neg(\forall\nu)(\exists\mu)\mathbf{P} & \text{for} & \neg((\forall\nu)((\exists\mu)\mathbf{P})), \end{array}$$

etc. Also, by convention, negation is the weakest of the connectives. Without parentheses, it is assumed that it only applies to the smallest wff following it. Thus, we shall write

$$\begin{array}{rcl} \neg\mathbf{P} \leftrightarrow \mathbf{Q} & \text{for} & (\neg\mathbf{P}) \leftrightarrow \mathbf{Q}, \\ \mathbf{P} \,\&\, \neg\mathbf{Q} & \text{for} & \mathbf{P} \,\&\, (\neg\mathbf{Q}), \end{array}$$

etc. For the sake of clarity we shall sometimes use brackets, [ ], in place of parentheses.

The following three formulae are examples of wffs:

(2) $(\exists X)[F(X) \text{ or } (\forall Y)(G(Y) \rightarrow H(X))]$,

(3) $(\exists 1X)[F(X) \mathbin{\&} (\forall Z)(G(Y) \text{ or } \neg F(Z))]$,

(4) $F(X) \rightarrow (\exists Y)(\exists Z)(X = Y \mathbin{\&} X = Z)$.

But the formulae

$$(\exists X)(F(X) \rightarrow (\text{or } G(X)),$$
$$(\forall X)(X \text{ or } F(X)),$$
$$(X = \&),$$

are not wffs.

By the *scope* of a quantifier we mean the quantifier together with the wff of smallest length immediately following the quantifier. So, for example, in formula (2) above the scope of "$(\exists X)$" is the whole formula and the scope of "$(\forall Y)$" is "$(\forall Y)(G(Y) \rightarrow H(X))$." The parentheses in a wff always indicate the scope of each quantifier in the wff.

An occurrence of an individual variable ν in a wff is said to be *bound* if this occurrence is within the scope of one of the quantifiers $(\forall\nu)$, $(\exists\nu)$, or $(\exists 1\nu)$. Otherwise the occurrence of ν is said to be *free*. An individual variable is said to be *bound* in a wff if it has at least one bound occurrence, and it is said to be *free* in a wff if it has at least one free occurrence. It is possible for a variable to be both bound and free in the same wff. For example, in the wff

$$(\exists X)F(X) \mathbin{\&} G(X),$$

X is both bound and free, while in formula (3) above all occurrences of X and Z are bound and all occurrences of Y are free. Similarly in formula (4) all occurrences of X are free and all occurrences of Y and Z are bound.

The truth values of statements built up using the propositional connectives are determined by means of the following table. "T" stands for "true" and "F" for "false."

P	**Q**	$\neg$**P**	**P** or **Q**	**P** & **Q**	**P** $\rightarrow$ **Q**	**P** $\leftrightarrow$ **Q**
T	T	F	T	T	T	T
F	T	T	T	F	T	F
T	F	F	T	F	F	F
F	F	T	F	F	T	T

Thus, $\neg$**P** is true if and only if **P** is false; **P** or **Q** is false if and only if both **P** and **Q** are false; **P** & **Q** is true if and only if both **P** and **Q** are true; etc. Therefore, the truth or falsity of a wff which has no quantifiers in its structure can be determined by a "truth table." As examples, truth tables for the wffs

(5) $$((\mathbf{P} \text{ or } \mathbf{Q}) \ \& \ \neg\mathbf{P}) \rightarrow \mathbf{Q}$$

and

(6) $$((\mathbf{P} \ \& \ \mathbf{Q}) \text{ or } \mathbf{R}) \rightarrow (\mathbf{P} \ \& \ (\mathbf{Q} \text{ or } \mathbf{R}))$$

are given below.

P	Q	P or Q	¬P	(P or Q) & ¬P	(5)
T	T	T	F	F	T
F	T	T	T	T	T
T	F	T	F	F	T
F	F	F	T	F	T

P	Q	R	P & Q	(P & Q) or R	Q or R	P & (Q or R)	(6)
T	T	T	T	T	T	T	T
F	T	T	F	T	T	F	F
T	F	T	F	T	T	T	T
F	F	T	F	T	T	F	F
T	T	F	T	T	T	T	T
F	T	F	F	F	T	F	T
T	F	F	F	F	F	F	T
F	F	F	F	F	F	F	T

Formula (5) is true irrespective of the truth or falsity of **P** and **Q**, while (6) is sometimes true and sometimes false. A wff, like (5), which has all T's in the last column of its truth table is called a *tautology*. Therefore, a tautology is a wff which can be expressed in a logic without quantifiers and is true because of its structure. Formulae (1.2.2)–(1.2.21) below are examples of tautologies:

(1.2.2) $(\mathbf{P} \ \& \ \mathbf{P}) \leftrightarrow \mathbf{P}$,

(1.2.3) $\mathbf{P} \text{ or } \neg\mathbf{P}$,

(1.2.4) $\mathbf{P} \leftrightarrow \neg\neg\mathbf{P}$,

(1.2.5) $(\mathbf{P} \text{ or } \mathbf{Q}) \leftrightarrow (\mathbf{Q} \text{ or } \mathbf{P})$,

(1.2.6) $(\mathbf{P} \ \& \ \mathbf{Q}) \leftrightarrow (\mathbf{Q} \ \& \ \mathbf{P})$,

(1.2.7) $(\mathbf{P} \text{ or } (\mathbf{Q} \text{ or } \mathbf{R})) \leftrightarrow ((\mathbf{P} \text{ or } \mathbf{Q}) \text{ or } \mathbf{R})$,

(1.2.8) $(\mathbf{P} \ \& \ (\mathbf{Q} \ \& \ \mathbf{R})) \leftrightarrow ((\mathbf{P} \ \& \ \mathbf{Q}) \ \& \ \mathbf{R})$,

(1.2.9) $(\mathbf{P} \ \& \ (\mathbf{Q} \text{ or } \mathbf{R})) \leftrightarrow ((\mathbf{P} \ \& \ \mathbf{Q}) \text{ or } (\mathbf{P} \ \& \ \mathbf{R}))$,

(1.2.10) $(\mathbf{P} \text{ or } (\mathbf{Q} \ \& \ \mathbf{R})) \leftrightarrow ((\mathbf{P} \text{ or } \mathbf{Q}) \ \& \ (\mathbf{P} \text{ or } \mathbf{R}))$,

(1.2.11) $\neg(\mathbf{P} \text{ or } \mathbf{Q}) \leftrightarrow (\neg\mathbf{P} \;\&\; \neg\mathbf{Q})$,

(1.2.12) $\neg(\mathbf{P} \;\&\; \mathbf{Q}) \leftrightarrow (\neg\mathbf{P} \text{ or } \neg\mathbf{Q})$,

(1.2.13) $(\mathbf{P} \leftrightarrow \mathbf{Q}) \leftrightarrow ((\mathbf{P} \rightarrow \mathbf{Q}) \;\&\; (\mathbf{Q} \rightarrow \mathbf{P}))$,

(1.2.14) $(\mathbf{P} \rightarrow \mathbf{Q}) \leftrightarrow (\neg\mathbf{P} \text{ or } \mathbf{Q})$,

(1.2.15) $(\mathbf{P} \rightarrow \mathbf{Q}) \leftrightarrow (\neg\mathbf{Q} \rightarrow \neg\mathbf{P})$,

(1.2.16) $((\mathbf{P} \rightarrow \mathbf{Q}) \;\&\; \mathbf{P}) \rightarrow \mathbf{Q}$,

(1.2.17) $((\mathbf{P} \text{ or } \mathbf{Q}) \;\&\; \neg\mathbf{P}) \rightarrow \mathbf{Q}$,

(1.2.18) $\mathbf{P} \rightarrow (\mathbf{P} \text{ or } \mathbf{Q})$,

(1.2.19) $(\mathbf{P} \;\&\; \mathbf{Q}) \rightarrow \mathbf{P}$,

(1.2.20) $\neg(\mathbf{P} \rightarrow \mathbf{Q}) \leftrightarrow (\mathbf{P} \;\&\; \neg\mathbf{Q})$,

(1.2.21) $((\mathbf{P} \rightarrow \mathbf{Q}) \;\&\; (\mathbf{Q} \rightarrow \mathbf{R})) \rightarrow (\mathbf{P} \rightarrow \mathbf{R})$.

[Formula (1.2.2) is called an idempotency law; (1.2.3), the law of the excluded middle; (1.2.4), the law of double negation; (1.2.5) and (1.2.6), commutative laws; (1.2.7) and (1.2.8), associative laws; (1.2.9) and (1.2.10), distributive laws; and (1.2.11) and (1.2.12), De Morgan's laws—named after the English mathematician Augustus De Morgan (1806–1871).]

Moreover, we assume that the identity relation has the following properties.

(1.2.22) $\tau = \tau$,

(1.2.23) $(\sigma = \tau) \leftrightarrow (\tau = \sigma)$,

(1.2.24) $(\rho = \sigma) \;\&\; (\sigma = \tau)) \rightarrow (\rho = \tau)$.

The relationships between the quantifiers are given by the following formulas.

(1.2.25) $\neg(\exists\nu)\mathbf{P} \leftrightarrow (\forall\nu) \neg \mathbf{P}$,

(1.2.26) $\neg(\forall\nu)\mathbf{P} \leftrightarrow (\exists\nu) \neg \mathbf{P}$.

(1.2.27) If $\mathbf{P}(\nu)$ is a wff in which ν is free and μ does not occur, and $\mathbf{P}(\mu)$ is the wff which results from $\mathbf{P}(\nu)$ by substituting μ for ν in all its free occurrences, then

$$(\exists 1\nu)\mathbf{P}(\nu) \leftrightarrow (\exists\nu)(\mathbf{P}(\nu) \;\&\; (\forall\mu)(\mathbf{P}(\mu) \rightarrow \mu = \nu)).$$

In what follows we shall describe a schema for constructing a formal mathematical proof—called a system of *natural deduction.* [It is a modification of a schema which was originally given by J. C. Cooley, (unpublished notes). For other systems of natural deduction see, for example, Gentzen (1934), Quine (1950), Fitch (1952), Copi (1954), or Suppes (1957).]

We shall use the following metalinguistic symbols:

$\mathbf{P}(\nu)$ A wff in which ν is free.

$\mathbf{P}(\boldsymbol{\tau})$	The wff which results from $\mathbf{P}(\boldsymbol{\nu})$ by substituting the term $\boldsymbol{\tau}$ for $\boldsymbol{\nu}$ in all its free occurrences.
$\emptyset$	The empty set—a set which has no members.
$\{\boldsymbol{\tau}_1, \boldsymbol{\tau}_2, \ldots, \boldsymbol{\tau}_n\}$	The set whose only members are $\boldsymbol{\tau}_1, \boldsymbol{\tau}_2, \ldots, \boldsymbol{\tau}_n$.
$\boldsymbol{\tau} \in \boldsymbol{\sigma}$	$\boldsymbol{\tau}$ is a member of $\boldsymbol{\sigma}$.
$\langle\langle \boldsymbol{\tau}, \boldsymbol{\sigma}, \mathbf{P} \rangle\rangle$	An ordered triple whose first member is $\boldsymbol{\tau}$, second $\boldsymbol{\sigma}$, and third $\mathbf{P}$.

A *proof* is a finite sequence of ordered triples such that the nth triple is $\langle\langle n, \mathbf{S}_n, \mathbf{P}_n \rangle\rangle$ (intuitively, $\mathbf{S}_n$ is the set of positive integers which are the numbers of the premises from which the wff $\mathbf{P}_n$ is inferred), and for each n, $\langle\langle n, \mathbf{S}_n, \mathbf{P}_n \rangle\rangle$ satisfies one of the following properties:

T: $\mathbf{S}_n$ is $\emptyset$ and $\mathbf{P}_n$ is a tautology (theorem, or axiom).

Pr: $\mathbf{S}_n$ is $\{n\}$. (The introduction of a premise.)

CP: There exist positive integers $i, j < n$ such that $\mathbf{S}_i$ is $\{i\}$, $\mathbf{S}_n$ is $\mathbf{S}_j$ with i omitted, and $\mathbf{P}_n$ is $\mathbf{P}_i \rightarrow \mathbf{P}_j$. (The rule of *conditional proof*. To prove $\mathbf{P}_i \rightarrow \mathbf{P}_j$, take $\mathbf{P}_i$ as a premise, derive $\mathbf{P}_j$, then apply CP.)

A: There exist positive integers $i, j < n$ such that $k \in \mathbf{S}_n$ if and only if $k \in \mathbf{S}_i$ or $k \in \mathbf{S}_j$, $\mathbf{P}_n$ is $\mathbf{P}_i$ & $\mathbf{P}_j$. (The rule of *adjunction*—from $\mathbf{P}_i$ and $\mathbf{P}_j$ to infer $\mathbf{P}_i$ & $\mathbf{P}_j$.)

MP: There exist positive integers $i, j < n$ such that $k \in \mathbf{S}_n$ if and only if $k \in \mathbf{S}_i$ or $k \in \mathbf{S}_j$, and $\mathbf{P}_j$ is $\mathbf{P}_i \rightarrow \mathbf{P}_n$. (The rule of *modus ponens*—from $\mathbf{P}_i$ and $\mathbf{P}_i \rightarrow \mathbf{P}_n$, to infer $\mathbf{P}_n$.)

SI: There exist positive integers $i, j < n$ such that $k \in \mathbf{S}_n$ if and only if $k \in \mathbf{S}_i$ or $k \in \mathbf{S}_j$, $\mathbf{P}_i$ is $\boldsymbol{\sigma} = \boldsymbol{\tau}$, $\mathbf{P}_j$ is $\mathbf{P}(\boldsymbol{\sigma})$, and $\mathbf{P}_n$ is $\mathbf{P}(\boldsymbol{\tau})$, as long as no free occurrence of a variable in $\boldsymbol{\tau}$ and $\boldsymbol{\sigma}$ is bound in $\mathbf{P}(\boldsymbol{\tau})$ and $\mathbf{P}(\boldsymbol{\sigma})$, respectively. The substitution of $\boldsymbol{\tau}$ for $\boldsymbol{\sigma}$ need not be made at all occurrences of $\boldsymbol{\sigma}$. [The rule of *substitution for identical terms*. Formulas (1.2.23) and (1.2.24) may be inferred using SI. Also, "$=$" may be replaced by "$=_{\mathrm{Df}}$" (see § 1.3).]

SE: There are positive integers $i, j < n$ such that $k \in \mathbf{S}_n$ if and only if $k \in \mathbf{S}_i$ or $k \in \mathbf{S}_j$, $\mathbf{P}_i$ is $\mathbf{Q} \leftrightarrow \mathbf{R}$, and $\mathbf{P}_n$ is obtained from $\mathbf{P}_j$ by substituting $\mathbf{R}$ for $\mathbf{Q}$ in one or more of its occurrences, as long as no free occurrence of a variable in $\mathbf{Q}$ and $\mathbf{R}$ is bound in $\mathbf{P}_j$ and $\mathbf{P}_n$, respectively. (The rule of *substitution for equivalent wffs*. Actually, this rule is a consequence of the other rules. It can be derived using mathematical induction, but we shall not give this derivation here.)

US: There is a positive integer $i < n$ such that $\mathbf{S}_n$ is $\mathbf{S}_i$, $\mathbf{P}_i$ is $(\forall \boldsymbol{\nu})\mathbf{P}(\boldsymbol{\nu})$ and $\mathbf{P}_n$ is $\mathbf{P}(\boldsymbol{\tau})$, as long as no free occurrence of a variable in $\boldsymbol{\tau}$ is bound in $\mathbf{P}(\tau)$. [The rule of *universal specification*. For example, from

$$(\forall x)(\exists y)(x < y)$$

we can infer

$$(\exists y)(1 < y)$$

or

$$(\exists y)(x < y).$$

UG: There is a positive integer $i < n$ such that $\mathbf{S}_n$ is $\mathbf{S}_i$, and $\mathbf{P}_n$ is $(\forall \nu)\mathbf{P}_i$, as long as ν is not free in any $\mathbf{P}_j$ such that $j \in \mathbf{S}_i$. [The rule of *universal generalization*. For example, from

$$(\exists y)(x < y)$$

we can infer

$$(\forall x)(\exists y)(x < y).$$

However, one cannot generalize on any variable ν in a wff $\mathbf{P}$ if ν is free in any premise from which $\mathbf{P}$ is inferred.]

EG: There is a positive integer $i < n$ such that $\mathbf{S}_n$ is $\mathbf{S}_i$, $\mathbf{P}_i$ is $\mathbf{P}(\tau)$, and $\mathbf{P}_n$ is $(\exists \nu)\mathbf{P}(\nu)$ as long as either $\tau = \nu$ or there are no free occurrences of ν in $\mathbf{P}(\tau)$, and no free occurrence of ν in $\mathbf{P}(\tau)$, and no free occurrence of a variable in τ is bound in $\mathbf{P}(\tau)$. If $\tau \neq \nu$ the substitution of ν for τ need not be made at all occurrences of τ. [The rule of *existential generalization*. For example, from

$$x < 2$$

we can infer

$$(\exists y)(x < y)$$

or

$$(\exists x)(x < 2).$$

But we cannot infer $(\exists x)(x < x)$ from $x < 2$.]

EP: There are positive integers $i, j, k < n$ such that $\mathbf{S}_j$ is $\{j\}$, $l \in \mathbf{S}_n$ if and only if $l \in \mathbf{S}_i$ or $l \in \mathbf{S}_k$ but $l \neq j$, $\mathbf{P}_i$ is $(\exists \nu)\mathbf{P}_j$, $\mathbf{P}_n$ is $\mathbf{P}_k$, and ν is not free in any $\mathbf{P}_l$ such that $l \in \mathbf{S}_k$ and $l \neq j$. (The rule of *existential proof*.)

The following example of a proof illustrates the use of EP:

To prove: $(\exists \nu)(\forall \mu)\mathbf{P} \rightarrow (\forall \mu)(\exists \nu)\mathbf{P}$

Proof:

1. $\{1\}$ $(\exists \nu)(\forall \mu)\mathbf{P}$ (Pr)

2. $\{2\}$ $(\forall\mu)\mathbf{P}$ (Pr)
3. $\{2\}$ $\mathbf{P}$ (2,US)
4. $\{2\}$ $(\exists\nu)\mathbf{P}$ (3,EG)
5. $\{2\}$ $(\forall\mu)(\exists\nu)\mathbf{P}$ (4,UG)
6. $\{1\}$ $(\forall\mu)(\exists\nu)\mathbf{P}$ (1,2,5,EP)
7. $\emptyset$ $(\exists\nu)(\forall\mu)\mathbf{P} \rightarrow (\forall\mu)(\exists\nu)\mathbf{P}$. (1,6,CP)

Thus, in this proof $i = 1, j = 2$, and $k = 5$. The rule EP allows us to infer $(\forall\mu)(\exists\nu)\mathbf{P}$ from premise 1 instead of 2. There will be additional illustrations below.

A wff $\mathbf{P}$ is said to be a *theorem* if there is a positive integer n such that $\langle\langle n, \emptyset, \mathbf{P}\rangle\rangle$ is the last line of a proof. In rule T above, the word "tautology" may be replaced by "theorem."

We shall illustrate various types of proofs below.

(1.2.28) $$(\forall\nu)(\forall\mu)\mathbf{P} \leftrightarrow (\forall\mu)(\forall\nu)\mathbf{P}$$

Proof:

1. $\{1\}$ $(\forall\nu)(\forall\mu)\mathbf{P}$ (Pr)
2. $\{1\}$ $(\forall\mu)\mathbf{P}$ (1,US)
3. $\{1\}$ $\mathbf{P}$ (2,US)
4. $\{1\}$ $(\forall\nu)\mathbf{P}$ (3,UG)
5. $\{1\}$ $(\forall\mu)(\forall\nu)\mathbf{P}$ (4,UG)
6. $\emptyset$ $(\forall\nu)(\forall\mu)\mathbf{P} \rightarrow (\forall\mu)(\forall\nu)\mathbf{P}$. (1,5,CP)

The *converse* is proved in an analogous way. [The *converse* of the conditional statement $\mathbf{P} \rightarrow \mathbf{Q}$ is $\mathbf{Q} \rightarrow \mathbf{P}$. The *inverse* is $\neg\mathbf{P} \rightarrow \neg\mathbf{Q}$ and the *contrapositive* is $\neg\mathbf{Q} \rightarrow \neg\mathbf{P}$. It follows from (1.2.15) that a conditional statement is equivalent to its contrapositive and its converse is equivalent to its inverse. $\mathbf{P}$ is said to be *sufficient* for $\mathbf{Q}$ if $\mathbf{P} \rightarrow \mathbf{Q}$ and $\mathbf{P}$ is said to be *necessary* for $\mathbf{Q}$ if $\mathbf{Q} \rightarrow \mathbf{P}$.]

After proving the converse, use rule A and (1.2.13) to obtain the desired result. The details are left to the reader.

(1.2.29) $$(\exists\nu)(\exists\mu)\mathbf{P} \leftrightarrow (\exists\mu)(\exists\nu)\mathbf{P}.$$

Proof:

1. $\{1\}$ $(\exists\nu)(\exists\mu)\mathbf{P}$ (Pr)
2. $\{2\}$ $(\exists\mu)\mathbf{P}$ (Pr)
3. $\{3\}$ $\mathbf{P}$ (Pr)
4. $\{3\}$ $(\exists\nu)\mathbf{P}$ (3,EG)
5. $\{3\}$ $(\exists\mu)(\exists\nu)\mathbf{P}$ (4,EG)
6. $\{2\}$ $(\exists\mu)(\exists\nu)\mathbf{P}$ (2,3,5,EP)
7. $\{1\}$ $(\exists\mu)(\exists\nu)\mathbf{P}$ (1,2,6,EP)
8. $\emptyset$ $(\exists\nu)(\exists\mu)\mathbf{P} \rightarrow (\exists\mu)(\exists\nu)\mathbf{P}$. (1,7,CP)

The remaining part of the proof is left as an exercise.

The reader may notice at this point that a formal proof is quite detailed and repetitious. Consequently, it is customary merely to outline a formal proof and give what is called an *informal proof.* An informal proof omits many of the repetitious details of a formal proof and telescopes many of the steps. In what follows, all our proofs will be informal.

(1.2.30) $$(\forall\nu)(\mathbf{P} \,\&\, \mathbf{Q}) \leftrightarrow ((\forall\nu)\mathbf{P} \,\&\, (\forall\nu)\mathbf{Q}).$$

Proof: Assume $(\forall\nu)(\mathbf{P} \,\&\, \mathbf{Q})$. Then by US we can infer $\mathbf{P} \,\&\, \mathbf{Q}$. Therefore, by (1.2.19), we can infer $\mathbf{P}$, and by UG, $(\forall\nu)\mathbf{P}$. Similarly, we obtain $(\forall\nu)\mathbf{Q}$. Therefore, by A we obtain $(\forall\nu)\mathbf{P} \,\&\, (\forall\nu)\mathbf{Q}$.

Conversely, assume $(\forall\nu)\mathbf{P} \,\&\, (\forall\nu)\mathbf{Q}$. Then, by (1.2.19), we can infer $(\forall\nu)\mathbf{P}$, and by US, $\mathbf{P}$. Similarly, we obtain, $\mathbf{Q}$. Then use A to obtain $\mathbf{P} \,\&\, \mathbf{Q}$, and UG to obtain $(\forall\nu)(\mathbf{P} \,\&\, \mathbf{Q})$. ■[3]

(1.2.31) $$(\exists\nu)(\mathbf{P} \,\&\, \mathbf{Q}) \rightarrow ((\exists\nu)\mathbf{P} \,\&\, (\exists\nu)\mathbf{Q}).$$

Proof: Suppose $(\exists\nu)(\mathbf{P} \,\&\, \mathbf{Q})$. Then $\mathbf{P} \,\&\, \mathbf{Q}$ holds for some ν. So by (1.2.19) we obtain $\mathbf{P}$, and by EG, $(\exists\nu)\mathbf{P}$. Similarly, we obtain $(\exists\nu)\mathbf{Q}$. Hence, by A, EP, and CP we obtain the desired result. ■

We claim that the converse of (1.2.31) is not a theorem. To demonstrate this we construct what is called a *counterexample*, that is, an instance in which the wff is false. In this case, let the range of each individual variable be all real numbers, let ν be "X", $\mathbf{P}$ be "$X = 1$", and $\mathbf{Q}$ be "$X \neq 1$". Then the hypothesis of the converse, $(\exists\nu)\mathbf{P} \,\&\, (\exists\nu)\mathbf{Q}$, is

$$(\exists X)(X = 1) \,\&\, (\exists X)(X \neq 1),$$

which is true, and the conclusion of the converse, $(\exists\nu)(\mathbf{P} \,\&\, \mathbf{Q})$, is

$$(\exists X)(X = 1 \,\&\, X \neq 1),$$

which is false. Thus, in this example, the converse of (1.2.31) is false, which implies that the converse is not a theorem. For if a wff is a theorem, it must be true for all values of its variables, otherwise the system would be inconsistent.

The proofs of the following theorems are left as exercises:

(1.2.32) $$(\exists\nu)(\mathbf{P} \text{ or } \mathbf{Q}) \leftrightarrow ((\exists\nu)\mathbf{P} \text{ or } (\exists\nu)\mathbf{Q}).$$

(1.2.33) $$((\forall\nu)\mathbf{P} \text{ or } (\forall\nu)\mathbf{Q}) \rightarrow (\forall\nu)(\mathbf{P} \text{ or } \mathbf{Q}).$$

(The converse is not a theorem.)

(1.2.34) If ν is not free in $\mathbf{P}$ then
$$(\exists\nu)(\mathbf{P} \,\&\, \mathbf{Q}) \leftrightarrow (\mathbf{P} \,\&\, (\exists\nu)\mathbf{Q}).$$

[3] The symbol ■ designates the end of a proof.

(1.2.35) If ν is not free in **P** then
$(\forall\nu)(\mathbf{P} \text{ or } \mathbf{Q}) \leftrightarrow (\mathbf{P} \text{ or } (\forall\nu)\mathbf{Q})$.

(1.2.36) If ν is not free in **P** then
(a) $\mathbf{P} \leftrightarrow (\forall\nu)\mathbf{P}$.
(b) $\mathbf{P} \leftrightarrow (\exists\nu)\mathbf{P}$.

(1.2.37) If ν is not free in **P** then
$(\exists\nu)(\mathbf{P} \to \mathbf{Q}) \leftrightarrow (\mathbf{P} \to (\exists\nu)\mathbf{Q})$.

(1.2.38) If ν is not free in **P** then
$(\forall\nu)(\mathbf{P} \to \mathbf{Q}) \leftrightarrow (\mathbf{P} \to (\forall\nu)\mathbf{Q})$.

(1.2.39) If ν is not free in **Q** then
$(\exists\nu)(\mathbf{P} \to \mathbf{Q}) \leftrightarrow ((\forall\nu)\mathbf{P} \to \mathbf{Q})$.

(1.2.40) If ν is not free in **Q** then
$(\forall\nu)(\mathbf{P} \to \mathbf{Q}) \leftrightarrow ((\exists\nu)\mathbf{P} \to \mathbf{Q})$.

(1.2.41) $(\exists\nu)(\mathbf{P} \to \mathbf{Q}) \leftrightarrow ((\forall\nu)\mathbf{P} \to (\exists\nu)\mathbf{Q})$.

(1.2.42) $(\exists\nu)(\forall\mu)\mathbf{P} \to (\forall\mu)(\exists\nu)\mathbf{P}$.

(The converse is not a theorem.)

Certain proofs can be given in a more brief and a more precise form than the proofs of (1.2.30) and (1.2.31), by displaying a series of implications or equivalences. We illustrate this in the following proof of (1.2.41):

(1.2.41) $(\exists\nu)(\mathbf{P} \to \mathbf{Q}) \leftrightarrow ((\forall\nu)\mathbf{P} \to (\exists\nu)\mathbf{Q})$.

Proof:

$$\begin{aligned}(\exists\nu)(\mathbf{P} \to \mathbf{Q}) &\leftrightarrow (\exists\nu)(\neg\mathbf{P} \text{ or } \mathbf{Q}) && (1.2.14)\\ &\leftrightarrow ((\exists\nu)\neg\mathbf{P} \text{ or } (\exists\nu)\mathbf{Q}) && (1.2.32)\\ &\leftrightarrow (\neg(\forall\nu)\mathbf{P} \text{ or } (\exists\nu)\mathbf{Q}) && (1.2.26)\\ &\leftrightarrow ((\forall\nu)\mathbf{P} \to (\exists\nu)\mathbf{Q}). && (1.2.14)\ \blacksquare\end{aligned}$$

Notice that the rule of substitution for equivalent wffs, SE, is used without any explicit reference. In the following, in most instances, we shall omit explicit references to all the rules of natural deduction. Before this comes to pass, however, we would like to add two derived rules which are often useful in practice—the rule of substitution for free variables, SF, and the rule of substitution for bound variables, SB.

SF: There is an $i < n$ such that $\mathbf{S}_n$ is $\mathbf{S}_i$, $\mathbf{P}_i$ is $\mathbf{P}(\nu)$ and $\mathbf{P}_n$ is $\mathbf{P}(\tau)$, as long as ν is not free in any $\mathbf{P}_j$ such that $j \in \mathbf{S}_i$ and no free occurrence of a variable in τ is bound in $\mathbf{P}(\tau)$. (A substitution for a variable in a wff cannot be made if the variable is free in a premise from which the wff is derived.)

Proof: Suppose $\mathbf{P}(\nu)$ holds. Then by UG we obtain $(\forall\nu)\mathbf{P}(\nu)$ and by US, $\mathbf{P}(\tau)$. ■

SB: There is an $i < n$ such that $\mathbf{S}_n$ is $\mathbf{S}_i$, $\mathbf{P}_i$ is $(\forall\nu)\mathbf{P}(\nu)$, $(\exists\nu)\mathbf{P}(\nu)$, or $(\exists 1\nu)\mathbf{P}(\nu)$, and $\mathbf{P}_n$ is $(\forall\mu)\mathbf{P}(\mu)$, $(\exists\mu)\mathbf{P}(\mu)$, or $(\exists 1\mu)\mathbf{P}(\mu)$, respectively, as long as μ does not occur in $\mathbf{P}(\nu)$.

Proof: The proof for the universal quantifier follows from US and UG. Then, using this result and SE, the proofs for the existential quantifiers follow from (1.2.26) and (1.2.27). ■

Next, we shall illustrate several types of proofs which are common in mathematics. The first type is a proof that one statement implies a conditional statement. That is, to prove a statement of the form

$$\mathbf{P} \rightarrow (\mathbf{Q} \rightarrow \mathbf{R}).$$

The procedure is to take **P** and **Q** as premises and derive **R** because

$$\begin{aligned}
(\mathbf{P} \rightarrow (\mathbf{Q} \rightarrow \mathbf{R})) &\leftrightarrow (\neg\mathbf{P} \text{ or } (\mathbf{Q} \rightarrow \mathbf{R})) && (1.2.14)\\
&\leftrightarrow (\neg\mathbf{P} \text{ or } (\neg\mathbf{Q} \text{ or } \mathbf{R})) && (1.2.14)\\
&\leftrightarrow ((\neg\mathbf{P} \text{ or } \neg\mathbf{Q}) \text{ or } \mathbf{R})) && (1.2.7)\\
&\leftrightarrow (\neg(\mathbf{P} \mathbin{\&} \mathbf{Q}) \text{ or } \mathbf{R}) && (1.2.12)\\
&\leftrightarrow ((\mathbf{P} \mathbin{\&} \mathbf{Q}) \rightarrow \mathbf{R}). && (1.2.14)
\end{aligned}$$

Therefore, we have

(1.2.43) $$(\mathbf{P} \rightarrow (\mathbf{Q} \rightarrow \mathbf{R})) \leftrightarrow ((\mathbf{P} \mathbin{\&} \mathbf{Q}) \rightarrow \mathbf{R}).$$

As an illustration of this type of proof, we shall prove the first half of (1.2.40). That is,

If ν is not free in **Q** then
$(\forall\nu)(\mathbf{P} \rightarrow \mathbf{Q}) \rightarrow ((\exists\nu)\mathbf{P} \rightarrow \mathbf{Q})$.

Proof: Assume $(\exists\nu)\mathbf{P}$. Then **P** holds for some ν. From the hypothesis and US we obtain $\mathbf{P} \rightarrow \mathbf{Q}$. Thus, from **P**, $\mathbf{P} \rightarrow \mathbf{Q}$, and MP we obtain **Q**. Since ν is not free in **Q** we can apply EP and the theorem follows. ■

We have actually shown that

$$((\forall\nu)(\mathbf{P} \rightarrow \mathbf{Q}) \mathbin{\&} (\exists\nu)\mathbf{P}) \rightarrow \mathbf{Q},$$

but it follows from (1.2.43) that this is equivalent to

$$(\forall\nu)(\mathbf{P} \rightarrow \mathbf{Q}) \rightarrow ((\exists\nu)\mathbf{P} \rightarrow \mathbf{Q}).$$

Another type of proof which is used frequently in mathematics is the *indirect proof*. An indirect proof has the following structure. Suppose we want to prove **P**. Take $\neg\mathbf{P}$ as a premise and derive a contradiction **C**. So we have

$$\neg\mathbf{P} \rightarrow \mathbf{C}$$

or, equivalently,

$$\neg \mathbf{C} \rightarrow \mathbf{P}.$$

But since **C** is a contradiction, $\neg$**C** must be a theorem. Therefore, using T and MP, **P** follows. In practice, the negation of a theorem or premise is derived from $\neg$**P** and the proof ends there, because from this point a contradiction can easily be derived.

To illustrate this notion we shall give an indirect proof of (1.2.42).

$$(\exists \nu)(\forall \mu)\mathbf{P} \rightarrow (\forall \mu)(\exists \nu)\mathbf{P}.$$

Proof: Suppose the theorem is false. Then,

$$\neg[(\exists \nu)(\forall \mu)\mathbf{P} \rightarrow (\forall \mu)(\exists \nu)\mathbf{P}].$$

By (1.2.20), this is equivalent to

$$(\exists \nu)(\forall \mu)\mathbf{P} \ \& \ \neg(\forall \mu)(\exists \nu)\mathbf{P},$$

which, in turn, by (1.2.25) and (1.2.26), is equivalent to

$$(\exists \nu)(\forall \mu)\mathbf{P} \ \& \ (\exists \mu)(\forall \nu)\neg\mathbf{P}.$$

This latter wff implies a contradiction since we can derive **P** from the first conjunct and $\neg$**P** from the second. ■

Alternatively, an indirect proof of a conditional statement, **P** → **Q**, is often given by proving the contrapositive, $\neg$**Q** → $\neg$**P**. Thus, for example, let us prove (1.2.33).

$$((\forall \nu)\mathbf{P} \text{ or } (\forall \nu)\mathbf{Q}) \rightarrow (\forall \nu)(\mathbf{P} \text{ or } \mathbf{Q}).$$

Proof: Take

$$\neg(\forall \nu)(\mathbf{P} \text{ or } \mathbf{Q})$$

as a premise. From this, using (1.2.26), (1.2.11), and (1.2.31), we obtain

$$(\exists \nu) \neg\mathbf{P} \ \& \ (\exists \nu) \neg\mathbf{Q},$$

which, by (1.2.26) and (1.2.11), is equivalent to

$$\neg((\forall \nu)\mathbf{P} \text{ or } (\forall \nu)\mathbf{Q}).$$

Hence, by (1.2.15), (1.2.33) follows. ■

Often the hypothesis of a conditional statement is a conjunction of several wffs. In this case, to prove the conditional statement it is sufficient to prove that the denial of the conclusion along with all but one of the conjuncts in the hypothesis implies the denial of the remaining conjunct. For example, to prove

$$(\mathbf{P} \ \& \ \mathbf{Q}) \rightarrow \mathbf{R}$$

it is sufficient to prove

$$(\neg \mathbf{R} \ \& \ \mathbf{P}) \rightarrow \neg \mathbf{Q},$$

because

$$\begin{aligned}
(\neg \mathbf{R} \ \& \ \mathbf{P}) \rightarrow \neg \mathbf{Q}) &\leftrightarrow (\neg(\mathbf{R} \text{ or } \neg \mathbf{P}) \rightarrow \neg \mathbf{Q}) && (1.2.11)\\
&\leftrightarrow ((\mathbf{R} \text{ or } \neg \mathbf{P}) \text{ or } \neg \mathbf{Q}) && (1.2.14)\\
&\leftrightarrow (\mathbf{R} \text{ or } \neg(\mathbf{P} \ \& \ \mathbf{Q})) && [(1.2.7), (1.2.12)]\\
&\leftrightarrow (\neg(\mathbf{P} \ \& \ \mathbf{Q}) \text{ or } \mathbf{R}) && (1.2.5)\\
&\leftrightarrow ((\mathbf{P} \ \& \ \mathbf{Q}) \rightarrow \mathbf{R}). && (1.2.14)
\end{aligned}$$

The last type of proof to be considered in this section is the *alternative proof*. An alternative proof is used to prove a conditional statement in which the hypothesis is a disjunction of two or more wffs:

(7) $$(\mathbf{P} \text{ or } \mathbf{Q}) \rightarrow \mathbf{R}.$$

To prove (7) it is sufficient to prove $\mathbf{P} \rightarrow \mathbf{R}$ and $\mathbf{Q} \rightarrow \mathbf{R}$ because we have

(1.2.44) $$((\mathbf{P} \rightarrow \mathbf{R}) \ \& \ (\mathbf{Q} \rightarrow \mathbf{R})) \leftrightarrow ((\mathbf{P} \text{ or } \mathbf{Q}) \rightarrow \mathbf{R}).$$

Proof:

$$\begin{aligned}
((\mathbf{P} \rightarrow \mathbf{R}) \ \& \ (\mathbf{Q} \rightarrow \mathbf{R})) &\leftrightarrow ((\neg \mathbf{P} \text{ or } \mathbf{R}) \ \& \ (\neg \mathbf{Q} \text{ or } \mathbf{R})) && (1.2.14)\\
&\leftrightarrow ((\neg \mathbf{P} \ \& \ \neg \mathbf{Q}) \text{ or } \mathbf{R}) && [(1.2.5), (1.2.10)]\\
&\leftrightarrow (\neg(\mathbf{P} \text{ or } \mathbf{Q}) \text{ or } \mathbf{R}) && (1.2.11)\\
&\leftrightarrow ((\mathbf{P} \text{ or } \mathbf{Q}) \rightarrow \mathbf{R}). && (1.2.14) \ ■
\end{aligned}$$

To illustrate this we give an alternative proof of (1.2.33).

$$[(\forall \nu)\mathbf{P} \text{ or } (\forall \nu)\mathbf{Q}] \rightarrow (\forall \nu)(\mathbf{P} \text{ or } \mathbf{Q}).$$

Proof: Suppose $(\forall \nu)\mathbf{P}$. Then by US we obtain $\mathbf{P}$. By (1.2.18), $\mathbf{P} \rightarrow (\mathbf{P} \text{ or } \mathbf{Q})$. Thus, using MP and UG, we obtain $(\forall \nu)(\mathbf{P} \text{ or } \mathbf{Q})$. In an analogous manner we obtain $(\forall \nu)\mathbf{Q} \rightarrow (\forall \nu)(\mathbf{P} \text{ or } \mathbf{Q})$.

We have actually shown

$$[(\forall \nu)\mathbf{P} \rightarrow (\forall \nu)(\mathbf{P} \text{ or } \mathbf{Q})] \ \& \ [(\forall \nu)\mathbf{Q} \rightarrow (\forall \nu)(\mathbf{P} \text{ or } \mathbf{Q})].$$

However, it follows from (1.2.44) that this is equivalent to (1.2.33). ■

To conclude this section, we insert a word of warning on the use of the rules of natural deduction. If the restrictions on their use are not heeded, trouble may result. For example, it is easy to show that the converse of (1.2.42) is not a theorem. (Counterexample: For each real number there is a larger real number, but there is no largest real number.) Examine the following "proof" and find the error.

$$(\forall \mu)(\exists \nu)\mathbf{P} \rightarrow (\exists \nu)(\forall \mu)\mathbf{P}$$

1.	{1}	$(\forall\mu)(\exists\nu)\mathbf{P}$	(Pr)
2.	{1}	$(\exists\nu)\mathbf{P}$	(1,US)
3.	{3}	$\mathbf{P}$	(Pr)
4.	{3}	$(\forall\mu)\mathbf{P}$	(3,UG)
5.	{3}	$(\exists\nu)(\forall\mu)\mathbf{P}$	(4,EG)
6.	{1}	$(\exists\nu)(\forall\mu)\mathbf{P}$	(2,3,5,EP)
7.	$\emptyset$	$(\forall\mu)(\exists\nu)\mathbf{P} \rightarrow (\exists\nu)(\forall\mu)\mathbf{P}$.	(1,6,CP)

The answer will be found in the footnote below.[4]

1.3. AXIOMATIC SYSTEMS

Each mathematical system has as its foundation some system of logic. That is, the mathematical system incorporates the logical symbols, theorems, and rules as its own. The logical system we are presupposing is, as you might guess, the system described in the preceding section. We shall refer to it as *mathematical logic*. In everything that follows, it is assumed that mathematical logic is at the foundation of the structure.

To obtain a mathematical system, we must add *content* to the logical structure. This means terms and predicates which have some intuitive mathematical meaning. To avoid circular definitions, some of these terms and/or predicates must be undefined. We call these the *undefined notions*.

Additional terms and predicates can be introduced by means of *definitions*. A definition is considered as an abbreviation. Thus, for example, if conjunction, "&," were not introduced as an undefined connective in the logic in § 1.2, it could have been defined by

$$(\mathbf{P}\ \&\ \mathbf{Q}) =_{\mathrm{Df}} \neg(\neg\mathbf{P} \text{ or } \neg\mathbf{Q}).$$

This means that "**P** & **Q**" is an abbreviation for "$\neg(\neg\mathbf{P}$ or $\neg\mathbf{Q})$". [5]

After introducing the undefined and defined notions, their properties are described by means of *axioms* and/or *axiom schemata*. An axiom is a wff containing undefined notions, which is intuitively considered to be "true." An axiom schema is a procedure for producing axioms. An axiom is a wff in the system, but an axiom schema is a rule about the system.[6]

To illustrate these ideas we shall give as an example the *Peano Axioms*, an axiom system for defining the natural numbers 0, 1, 2, ... (discovered by Giuseppe Peano in 1889).

UNDEFINED NOTIONS: 0, an individual; N, a unary or one-place predicate; and S, a binary or two-place predicate.

[4] The error is in line 4. It is an incorrect use of UG because universal generalization was used on a variable which was free in a premise.
[5] In SI "=" may be replaced by "$=_{\mathrm{Df}}$."
[6] In T the word "tautology" may be replaced by "axiom."

Intuitively these symbols have the following meaning: 0 is the smallest natural number. "$N(X)$" means "X is a natural number." "$S(X, Y)$" means "Y is the successor of X" or "$Y = X + 1$."

AXIOMS

A1: $$N(0).$$
(0 is a natural number.)

A2: $$(\forall X)(\forall Y)(N(X) \,\&\, S(X, Y) \rightarrow N(Y)).$$
(The successor of each natural number is a natural number.)

Note that because of the rules of substitution, SF and SB, it is not necessary to use general individual variables in the axioms.

We shall use the convention that the range of each individual variable is all natural numbers. Thus, we hereafter omit hypotheses of the form $N(X)$.

A3: $$(\forall X)(\exists 1\, Y)S(X, Y).$$
(Each natural number has exactly one successor.)

In general, if F is an $(n + 1)$-place predicate such that for each set of n terms $\tau_1, \tau_2, \ldots, \tau_n$, there is exactly one term σ such that $\mathbf{F}(\tau_1, \tau_2, \ldots, \tau_n, \sigma)$, then the predicate $\mathbf{F}$ is often expressed by means of an *n-ary operation* $\mathbf{G}$ which is defined by the formula

$$\sigma = \mathbf{G}(\tau_1, \tau_2, \ldots, \tau_n) =_{\mathrm{Df}} \mathbf{F}(\tau_1, \tau_2, \ldots, \tau_n, \sigma).$$

Therefore, we make the following definition.

DEFINITION 1.3.1. $(Y = X^+) =_{\mathrm{Df}} S(X, Y).$

Thus X^+ is the successor of X.

Because of US and UG, it is customary to omit universal quantifiers at the beginning of a formula. We shall, in general, follow this custom. Thus A2 could have been stated as $(N(X) \,\&\, S(X, Y)) \rightarrow N(Y)$, and A3 as $(\exists 1 Y)S(X, Y)$.

A4: $$X^+ \neq 0.$$
(0 is not the successor of any natural number.)

A5: $$X^+ = Y^+ \rightarrow X = Y.$$
(If two natural numbers have the same successor, they are identical.)

A6: $$[\mathbf{P}(0) \,\&\, (\forall X)(\mathbf{P}(X) \rightarrow \mathbf{P}(X^+))] \rightarrow (\forall X)\mathbf{P}(X).$$
(Mathematical induction.)

A1–A5 are axioms, but A6 is an axiom schema. $\mathbf{P}(\boldsymbol{\nu})$ can be replaced by any meaningful statement about $\boldsymbol{\nu}$. Thus, A6 is a rule which replaces an infinite number of axioms.

As examples of theorems in the system we take the following.

THEOREM 1.3.2. $X \neq Y \rightarrow X^+ \neq Y^+$.

Proof: (Indirect proof.) Suppose $X^+ = Y^+$. Then by A5, $X = Y$. This contradicts the hypothesis. Hence, $X \neq Y \rightarrow X^+ \neq Y^+$. ■

THEOREM 1.3.3. $X^+ \neq X$.

Proof: (Mathematical induction.) We have $0^+ \neq 0$ by A3.

Suppose $X^+ \neq X$. Then by theorem 1.3.2 $(X^+)^+ \neq X^+$. Consequently, by A6, $X^+ \neq X$ for all X. ■

In theorem 1.3.3, $\mathbf{P}(X)$ is "$X^+ \neq X$." So in the proof of the theorem, we first prove $0^+ \neq 0$ ($\mathbf{P}(0)$). Then using a conditional proof we show $X^+ \neq X \rightarrow (X^+)^+ \neq X^+$ ($\mathbf{P}(X) \rightarrow \mathbf{P}(X^+)$). Consequently, it follows from A6 that $(\forall X)X^+ \neq X$ ($(\forall X)\mathbf{P}(X)$).

This, then, is an example of a mathematical axiom system, the ingredients of which are: Mathematical logic, undefined and defined notions, axioms and axiom schemata, and theorems. We shall now go on to the subject matter of this text—set theory. (For further theorems concerning natural numbers, the reader is referred to Landau (1946). See also Chapter 4 of this text.)

Chapter 2: Class Algebra

2.1. ATOMS, CLASSES, SETS, AND THE $\in$-RELATION

We start our description of an axiom system for set theory with the undefined notions. It is customary to take as undefined the intuitive notions the axiom system is attempting to make precise. In geometry, for example, points, lines, and the relations of "incidence" and "between" are natural choices for undefined notions. However, there are other considerations in choosing undefined notions. A less natural choice may greatly simplify the axioms and therefore be more desirable. In some instances, the primary consideration is to have as few undefined notions as possible. Some mathematicians will make artificial choices of undefined notions in order to make the number a minimum. However, we shall make a relatively natural choice and take the following as undefined.

UNDEFINED NOTIONS

1. A—a unary predicate.

The symbol "A(X)" is read "X is an *atom*." Atoms contain no elements but they are elements.

2. Cl—a unary predicate.

"Cl(X)" is read "X is a *class*." Classes are collections of elements.

3. $\in$—a binary relation.

The relation $\in$ is called the *element* or *membership relation*. The formula "$X \in Y$" is read "X is an element of Y," "X is a member of Y," or "X belongs to Y," and "$X \notin Y$" is read "X is not an element of Y," "X is not a member of Y," or "X does not belong to Y." As long as Cl(X) or A(X), and Cl(Y) or A(Y), both $X \in Y$ and $X \notin Y$ are *meaningful*, but only one of them is *true*. The formula $X \in Y$ is called an *atomic formula*. If there is a class Y such that $X \in Y$, X is called an *element*. The symbol "$X_1, X_2, \ldots, X_n \in Y$" will mean "$X_1 \in Y, X_2 \in Y, \ldots$, and $X_n \in Y$."

We shall distinguish between two types of classes—those which are elements and those which are not.

DEFINITION 2.1.1. Sets and proper classes

(a) $S(X) =_{Df} [Cl(X) \;\&\; (\exists Y)(Cl(Y) \;\&\; X \in Y)]$

(b) $Pr(X) =_{Df} [Cl(X) \;\&\; (\forall Y)(Cl(Y) \rightarrow X \notin Y)]$.

"S(X)" is read "X is a *set*" and "Pr(X)" is read "X is a *proper class*." Thus, a set is a class which is an element of some class, and a proper class is a class which is not an element of any class.

It follows directly from definition 2.1.1 that a class is either a set or a proper class, but not both. Thus we have

THEOREM 2.1.2. $\mathrm{Cl}(X) \rightarrow [(\mathrm{S}(X) \text{ or } \mathrm{Pr}(X))\ \&\ \neg(\mathrm{S}(X)\ \&\ \mathrm{Pr}(X))]$.

Curly braces are used to denote classes. If X is a class whose only elements are u, v, and w we write,

$$X = \{u,v,w\}.$$

Or if $\mathbf{P}(x)$ is the sentence "x is a point in the plane" and Y is the class of all points in the plane we write,

$$Y = \{x : \mathbf{P}(x)\}$$

which is read, in general, "Y is the class of all elements x such that $\mathbf{P}(x)$." Moreover, we shall use the convention that capital letters, $X, Y, Z, \ldots$, and these letters with subscripts denote variables each of whose range is all classes and atoms, while lower case letters, $x, y, z, \ldots$, and these letters with subscripts denote variables each of whose range is all sets and atoms.

2.2. THE AXIOM OF EXTENSIONALITY

The properties of the undefined notions will be described by means of axioms and axiom schemata. The first axiom characterizes an atom.

A1: $\mathrm{A}(X) \rightarrow [\neg \mathrm{Cl}(X)\ \&\ (\forall Y)(Y \notin X)]$.
(An atom is not a class and it has no elements.)

The following theorem follows from A1 and definition 2.1.1.

THEOREM 2.2.1. $(X \in Y) \rightarrow (\mathrm{S}(X) \text{ or } \mathrm{A}(X))$.

Proof: If $X \in Y$ then by A1, Y is not an atom. X is a class or an atom. Since $X \in Y$, it follows from definition 2.1.1 that X is not a proper class. Therefore, X is a set or an atom. ■

Axiom 2 is called the *Axiom of Extensionality*.

A2: $(\mathrm{Cl}(X)\ \&\ \mathrm{Cl}(Y)) \rightarrow [(\forall u)(u \in X \leftrightarrow u \in Y) \rightarrow X = Y]$.
(If two classes have the same elements then they are identical.)

It follows from the properties of the identity relation (SI, §1.2) that if two classes are identical, then they have the same elements. Hence, *two classes are identical if and only if they have the same elements.* For example, it follows from A2 that if

$$X = \{u,v,w\},$$
$$Y = \{u,u,v,w,w,w,\},$$
$$Z = \{w,u,v\},$$

then

$$X = Y \quad \text{(repetitions do not count)}$$

and

$$X = Z \quad \text{(order does not matter).}$$

The word "extension" is used here in its logical sense. The extension of a term is the class of things to which the term is applicable. For example, the extension of the term "man" consists of the class of such individuals as "Socrates," "Plato," "Aristotle," etc. The antonym of extension is *intension*. The intension of a term is the sum of the attributes contained in or connoted by the term. So that the intension of the term "man" could be "an intelligent featherless biped." If in A2 two classes were said to be identical, if they had the same shape or color, A2 might have been called the Axiom of Intensionality rather than the Axiom of Extensionality.

2.3. SUBCLASSES

Using the $\in$-relation, we can define what it means for one class to be a *subclass* of another class.

DEFINITION 2.3.1. Subclasses

(a) $(\mathrm{Cl}(X) \mathbin{\&} \mathrm{Cl}(Y)) \rightarrow (X \subseteq Y =_{\mathrm{Df}} (\forall u)(u \in X \rightarrow u \in Y))$

(b) $(\mathrm{Cl}(X) \mathbin{\&} \mathrm{Cl}(Y)) \rightarrow (X \subset Y =_{\mathrm{Df}} (X \subseteq Y \mathbin{\&} X \neq Y))$.

If $X \subseteq Y$, then X is said to be a *subclass* of Y; if $X \subset Y$, then X is said to be a *proper subclass* of Y. We use the symbols "$X \nsubseteq Y$" and "$X \not\subset Y$" to mean "X is not a subclass of Y" and "X is not a proper subclass of Y," respectively. If X is a set and $X \subseteq Y$ $(X \subset Y)$, then X is said to be a *subset* (*proper subset*) of Y.

For example, the class of even integers is a proper subclass of the class of all integers—every even integer is an integer, but not conversely; the class of all points in the first quadrant of a plane is a proper subclass of the class of all points in the plane—each point in the first quadrant is a point in the plane, but not conversely; but the class of rational numbers is not a subclass of the class of integers—there is at least one rational number which is not an integer.

We shall assume that X and Y are classes whenever we write "$X \subseteq Y$" and "$X \subset Y$."

The following theorems are consequences of definition 2.3.1.

THEOREM 2.3.2. $X \subset Y \to X \subseteq Y.$

Proof: By definition 2.3.1(b).

THEOREM 2.3.3. $X \subseteq X.$

Proof: By definition 2.3.1(a).

THEOREM 2.3.4. $(X \subseteq Y \;\&\; Y \subseteq Z) \to X \subseteq Z.$

Proof: Suppose $u \in X$. Then, since $X \subseteq Y$, it follows from 2.3.1(a) that $u \in Y$. By hypothesis $Y \subseteq Z$. So, by 2.3.1(a), we obtain $u \in Z$. ∎

THEOREM 2.3.5. $(X \subseteq Y \;\&\; Y \subseteq X) \to X = Y.$

Proof: By hypothesis and 2.3.1(a), $u \in X \to u \in Y$ and $u \in Y \to u \in X$. Hence, $u \in X \leftrightarrow u \in Y$. Therefore, by A2, $X = Y$. ∎

EXERCISES 2.3

1. Prove $X \not\subset X$.
2. Prove $X \subset Y \leftrightarrow (X \subseteq Y \;\&\; (\exists u)(u \in Y \;\&\; u \notin X))$.
3. Prove each of the following:
   (a) $(X \subset Y \;\&\; Y \subseteq Z) \to X \subset Z$
   (b) $(X \subseteq Y \;\&\; Y \subset Z) \to X \subset Z$
   (c) $(X \subset Y \;\&\; Y \subset Z) \to X \subset Z$.
4. Prove $X \subseteq Y \leftrightarrow (X \subset Y$ or $X = Y)$.

2.4. MODELS

In order to illustrate the concepts developed in §§2.1–2.3 we shall give several *models*. A model for an axiomatic system is a system in which the undefined notions are given an interpretation which satisfies the axioms. Often in models and examples, well-known concepts like points in a plane, integers, etc., will be used for illustrative purposes without definition, but they will play no part in the formal development.

M1: Atoms—Points in a plane (ordered pairs of real numbers).
Classes—Collections of points.
$\in$-relation—Incidence between atoms and classes.
That is, $X \in Y$ if and only if X is a point and is a member of the collection of points Y.

Two classes are equal in this model if they contain the same points. It is clear that axioms A1 and A2 are true. (Points are not classes and they

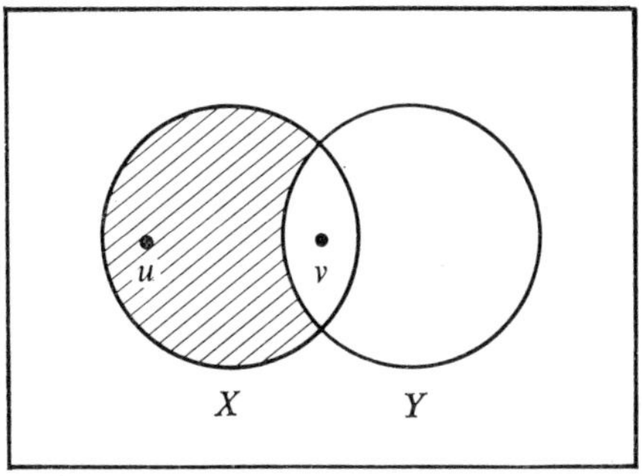

FIGURE 2.4.1

have no elements, and if two classes contain the same points then they are equal.) In this model every class is a proper class.

In Figure 2.4.1, X is the class which contains as elements all points inside the circle on the left, and Y is the class which contains as elements all points inside the circle on the right. Also, $u \in X$, $u \notin Y$, $v \in X$, and $v \in Y$. The shaded area, the class of all points which belong to X but do not belong to Y, is an example of a subclass of X. Figure 2.4.1 is called a *Venn diagram*, after the English logician, John Venn (1834–1923).

In the next model the classes are *dyadic expansions*, both finite and infinite. Each positive integer can be uniquely expressed as a finite sum of non-negative, integral powers of 2 which is called its dyadic expansion. For example,

$$7 = 2^2 + 2 + 1,$$
$$18 = 2^4 + 2,$$

etc. Each finite dyadic expansion is identified with a positive integer. An infinite dyadic expansion is considered as a formal entity.

M2: Atoms—None.
Sets—Non-negative integers.
Proper Classes—Infinite dyadic expansions.
$\in$-relation—$u \in X$ if and only if u is an exponent in the dyadic expansion of X.

In M2, $X = Y$ if and only if the dyadic expansions for X and Y contain the same terms irrespective of order.

We have, for example, $u \in 7$ if and only if $u = 2$, $u = 1$, or $u = 0$. Similarly, $u \in 18$ if and only if $u = 4$ or $u = 1$. The number 0 has no elements. Every non-negative integer is an element of the infinite dyadic expansion

$$1 + 2 + 2^2 + 2^3 + 2^4 + \cdots.$$

It is easy to verify that A1 and A2 are true in this model.

Another method for constructing a model is to take the atoms and classes of some given model and change the element relation. For example, let M be some given model and let a and b be two given sets or atoms in M. Let $\in$ be the element relation in M. Then we define a new element relation $\in'$ as follows. For any u and X in M,

(1)
$$u \in' X =_{\text{Df}} [(u = a \;\&\; b \in X) \text{ or } (u = b \;\&\; a \in X) \text{ or } (u \neq a \;\&\; u \neq b \;\&\; u \in X)].$$

Thus, for example, if $\{a\}$, $\{a,\{b\}\}$, and $\{c\}$, are sets in M such that $c \neq a$ and $c \neq b$, then

$$u \in \{a\} \leftrightarrow u = a$$
$$u \in \{a,\{b\}\} \leftrightarrow (u = a \text{ or } u = \{b\})$$
$$u \in \{c\} \leftrightarrow u = c,$$
$$u \in' \{a\} \leftrightarrow u = b$$
$$u \in' \{a,\{b\}\} \leftrightarrow (u = b \text{ or } u = \{b\})$$
$$u \in' \{c\} \leftrightarrow u = c.$$

Now we define a new model M3 as follows.

M3: Atoms—Same as the atoms in M.
Classes—Same as the classes in M.
$\in$-relation—$\in'$ as defined in (1).

Two classes are identical in M3 if and only if they are identical in M. It is easy to verify that A1 and A2 hold in M3.

The next model to be discussed in this section is called an *inner model*. That is, a model which is a submodel of some given model which has the added property that whenever a class is in the submodel all elements of the class are also in the submodel. Let M be some model and suppose a is an atom in M. The model M4 is an inner model which is generated by the atom a.

M4: Atoms—a.
Classes—All classes in M which are generated by a.

We shall assume that $\{a\}$ is a set and, in general, if $x_1, x_2, \ldots, x_n$ are sets or individuals then $\{x_1, x_2, \ldots, x_n\}$ is a set. Therefore, each of the following are examples of sets in M4.

$$\{a\},\ \{a,\{a\}\},\ \{\{a,\}\{a,\{a\}\}\},\ \text{etc.}$$

$\in$-relation—Same as in M.

For example, if

$$x = \{a,\{a\},\{a,\{a\}\}\},$$

then $u \in x$ if and only if $u = a$, $u = \{a\}$, or $u = \{a,\{a\}\}$. Also $\{a,\{a\}\} \subset x$ because a, $\{a\} \in x$, but $\{a,\{a\}\} \in x$ and $\{a,\{a\}\} \notin \{a,\{a\}\}$.

Two classes are identical in M4 if and only if they are identical in M. Since A1 and A2 are true in M, they must also be true in M4.

As our last model in this section we consider a simplification of the natural model described in the introduction—all sets built up in a finite number of steps from a ground set. This is a generalization of M4. For any set x let $\mathcal{P}(x)$ be the set of all subsets of x.

$$u \in \mathcal{P}(x) \leftrightarrow u \subseteq x.$$

Also, for all sets x and y let $x \cup y$ be the set of all elements which belong either to x or to y. Thus,

$$u \in x \cup y \leftrightarrow (u \in x \text{ or } u \in y).$$

Let x_0 be an arbitrary set of elements—the ground set. Define

$$x_1 = x_0 \cup \mathcal{P}(x_0),\ x_2 = x_1 \cup \mathcal{P}(x_1), \text{ etc.}$$

In general, for any positive natural number n, $x_n = x_{n-1} \cup \mathcal{P}(x_{n-1})$. The universe, V, is $x_0 \cup x_1 \cup x_2 \cup \ldots$. That is,

$$u \in V \leftrightarrow (\exists n)(n \text{ is a natural number and } u \in x_n).$$

The atoms of the model are the elements of x_0 and the classes are the subclasses of V.

EXERCISES 2.4

1. Consider the Venn diagram in Figure 2.4.2. X is the class of points inside the circle on the left, Y is the class of points inside the circle on the right, and Z

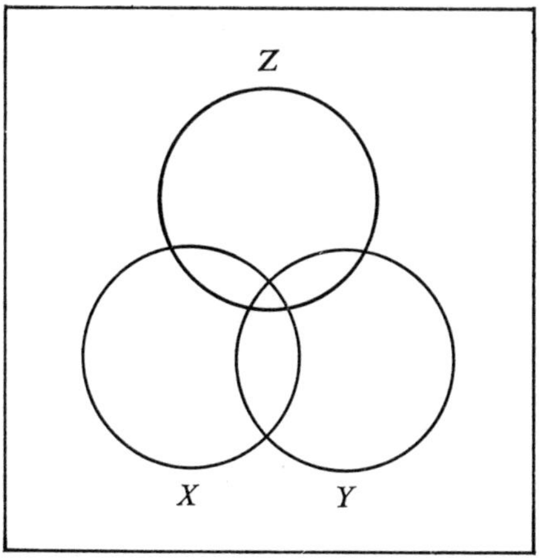

FIGURE 2.4.2

is the class of points inside the circle on top. For each of the following problems draw a Venn diagram similar to Figure 2.4.2 and shade the indicated area.

The class of points which are

(a) in both Y and Z
(b) in X and not in Z
(c) in either X, Y, or Z
(d) in Y or not in X
(e) not in X, Y, and Z
(f) in Z and X, or Y
(g) in Z, and X or Y.

2. In M2 determine which of the following are true.

(a) $4 \in 24$
(b) $3 \in 23$
(c) $1 \notin 7$
(d) $1 \in 9$
(e) $0 \in 11$
(f) $0 \notin 12$
(g) $9 \subseteq 13$
(h) $9 \subseteq 14$
(i) $11 \not\subseteq 14$
(j) $12 \subseteq 13$
(k) $20 \subset 24$
(l) $17 \subset 20$.

3. In M3 determine which of the following are true. All classes given are assumed to be classes in M and $c \neq a$, $c \neq b$.

(a) $a \in' \{a,c\}$
(b) $b \in' \{a,c\}$
(c) $a \in \{\{a\},b\}$
(d) $b \in' \{\{a\},b\}$
(e) $a \in' \{b\}$
(f) $c \in \{c,\{a\}\}$
(g) $c \in' \{c,\{b\}\}$
(h) $\{a\} \in' \{a,\{b\}\}$
(i) $\{a\} \in' \{\{a\},b,c\}$
(j) $\{b\} \in \{a,\{b\}\}$.

4. In M4 let

$$
\begin{aligned}
x_1 &= \{a\},\\
x_2 &= \{\{a\}\},\\
x_3 &= \{a,\{a\}\},\\
x_4 &= \{a,\{\{a\}\}\},\\
x_5 &= \{\{a\},\{\{a\}\}\},\\
x_6 &= \{a,\{a\},\{\{a\}\}\},\\
x_7 &= \{\{a,\{a\}\},\{a,\{\{a\}\}\}\},\\
x_8 &= \{a,\{a\},\{\{a\}\},\{a,\{a\}\},\{\{a\},\{\{a\}\}\}\}.
\end{aligned}
$$

Which of the following relations are true?

(a) $x_1 \in x_2$
(b) $x_1 \subseteq x_2$
(c) $x_1 \in x_3$
(d) $x_1 \subseteq x_3$
(e) $x_2 \in x_3$
(f) $x_2 \subseteq x_3$
(g) $x_2 \in x_4$
(h) $x_2 \subseteq x_4$
(i) $x_1 \in x_5$
(j) $x_1 \subseteq x_5$
(k) $x_5 \in x_6$
(l) $x_5 \subseteq x_6$
(m) $x_4 \in x_7$
(n) $x_4 \subseteq x_7$
(o) $x_4 \in x_8$
(p) $x_4 \subseteq x_8$
(q) $x_5 \in x_8$
(r) $x_5 \subseteq x_8$
(s) $x_6 \in x_8$
(t) $x_6 \subseteq x_8$.

2.5. CLASSES

Axiom A1 describes atoms. But what can be said of classes? Intuitively, a class is any collection of elements. Thus, we give the following general rule for the existence of classes:

A3: If **P** is a wff in which X is not a free variable then the following statement is an axiom[7,8]:

$$(\exists X)(\mathrm{Cl}(X) \;\&\; (\forall u)(u \in X \leftrightarrow \mathbf{P})).$$

A3 is an axiom schema—a rule for producing axioms (see §1.3). As an immediate consequence of A3 and A2 we have,

THEOREM 2.5.1. If **P** is a wff in which X is not a free variable, then the following statement is a theorem:

$$(\exists 1 X)(\mathrm{Cl}(X) \;\&\; (\forall u)(u \in X \leftrightarrow \mathbf{P})).$$

Proof: Suppose both X and Y satisfy A3. Then

$$u \in X \leftrightarrow \mathbf{P}$$

and

$$u \in Y \leftrightarrow \mathbf{P}.$$

Thus,

$$u \in X \leftrightarrow u \in Y.$$

Therefore, A2 implies $X = Y$. ■

Theorem 2.5.1 is called a *meta-theorem* or *theorem schema*, that is, a rule for producing theorems. For example, it follows from theorem 2.5.1, that each of the following formulae are theorems.

(1) $$(\exists 1 X_1)(\mathrm{Cl}(X_1) \;\&\; (\forall u)(u \in X_1 \leftrightarrow u \neq u)).$$

(X_1 has no elements.)

(2) $$(\exists 1 X_2)(\mathrm{Cl}(X_2) \;\&\; (\forall u)(u \in X_2 \leftrightarrow u = u)).$$

[7] In the **NBG** theory a slight restriction is placed on **P**. Namely, it is specified that **P** contains no bound class variables. (No capital letters are bound in **P**.) The reason for this restriction on **P** is briefly discussed in §14.2. In this text, A3 is seldom applied with a **P** which has bound class variables, but when it is we shall make a note of it in the text.

[8] See §1.2 for the definition of wff and free variable. We remind the reader that capital letters, X, Y, Z, . . . , and these letters with subscripts denote variables each of whose range is all classes and atoms, while lower case letters, x, y, z, u, v, w, . . . , and these letters with subscripts denote variables each of whose range is all sets and atoms.

(Every atom and set is an element of X_2.)

(3) $$(\exists 1 X_3)(\mathrm{Cl}(X_3) \ \&\ (\forall u)(u \in X_3 \leftrightarrow u \notin u).$$

(X_3 is Russell's class. See §1.1.)

(4) $$(\exists 1 X_4)(\mathrm{Cl}(X_4) \ \&\ (\forall u)(u \in X_4 \leftrightarrow u \notin Y).$$

(For any class Y there is a unique class X_4 such that $u \in X_4$ if and only if $u \notin Y$.)

(5) $$(\exists 1 X_5)(\mathrm{Cl}(X_5) \ \&\ (\forall u)(u \in X_5 \leftrightarrow u \subseteq Y)).$$

(X_5 is the class of all subsets of Y.)

(6) $$(\exists 1 X_6)(\mathrm{Cl}(X_6) \ \&\ (\forall u)(u \in X_6 \leftrightarrow (u \in Y \text{ or } u \in Z))).$$

(For any two classes Y and Z there is a unique class X_6 such that $u \in X_6$ if and only if $u \in Y$ or $u \in Z$.)

The two classes which are defined by (1) and (2) are given special names. The first class is called the *empty class* and is denoted by $\emptyset$,[9] and the second is called the *universal class* and is denoted by V. Thus, we have

DEFINITION 2.5.2.
(a) $\mathrm{Cl}(\emptyset) \ \&\ (u \in \emptyset \leftrightarrow u \neq u)$
(b) $\mathrm{Cl}(V) \ \&\ (u \in V \leftrightarrow u = u)$.

Therefore,

$$\emptyset = \{u : u \neq u\}$$

and

$$V = \{u : u = u\}.$$

As a direct consequence of definition 2.5.2 and (1.2.22) we have,

THEOREM 2.5.3.
(a) $u \notin \emptyset$
(b) $u \in V$.

The empty class has no elements and every set and atom is an element of the universal class. It follows immediately from theorem 2.5.3 that

THEOREM 2.5.4.
(a) $\emptyset \subseteq X$
(b) $X \subseteq V$.

[9] Some mathematicians take $\emptyset$ and $\in$ as the undefined terms in set theory and then define,

$$\mathrm{A}(x) =_{\mathrm{Df}} (X \neq \emptyset \ \&\ (\forall Y)(Y \notin X))$$

and

$$\mathrm{Cl}(X) =_{\mathrm{Df}} (X = \emptyset \text{ or } (\exists Y)(Y \in X)).$$

EXERCISES 2.5

1. Prove Theorems 2.5.3 and 2.5.4.
2. Prove that the class X_3 defined in (3) above is a proper class (Hint: See Russell's paradox in §1.1.)

2.6. CLASS ALGEBRA

The following theorem follows immediately from theorem 2.5.1.

THEOREM 2.6.1.
(a) $(\exists 1 Z_1)(\forall u)(u \in Z_1 \leftrightarrow (u \in X \text{ or } u \in Y))$
(b) $(\exists 1 Z_2)(\forall u)(u \in Z_2 \leftrightarrow (u \in X \;\&\; u \in Y))$
(c) $(\exists 1 Z_3)(\forall u)(u \in Z_3 \leftrightarrow (u \in X \;\&\; u \notin Y))$
(d) $(\exists 1 Z_4)(\forall u)(u \in Z_4 \leftrightarrow (u \notin X)$.

The classes defined by theorems 2.6.1 (a), (b), and (c) are given special names.

DEFINITION 2.6.2. Union, Intersection, and Complement
(a) $u \in (X \cup Y) =_{\text{Df}} (u \in X \text{ or } U \in Y)$
(b) $u \in (X \cap Y) =_{\text{Df}} (u \in X \;\&\; u \in Y)$
(c) $u \in (X \sim Y) =_{\text{Df}} (u \in X \;\&\; u \notin Y)$
(d) $u \in (X') =_{\text{Df}} (u \notin X)$.

Thus, Z_1 is denoted by $(X \cup Y)$ and is called the *union* of X and Y; Z_2 by $(X \cap Y)$, the *intersection* of X and Y; Z_3 by $(X \sim Y)$, the *relative complement* of Y with respect to X; and Z_4 by (X'), the *complement* of X. Therefore, we have

$$\begin{aligned}(X \cup Y) &= \{u : u \in X \text{ or } u \in Y\},\\ (X \cap Y) &= \{u : u \in X \;\&\; u \in Y\},\\ (X \sim Y) &= \{u : u \in X \;\&\; u \notin Y\},\\ (X') &= \{u : u \notin X\}.\end{aligned}$$

(Parentheses are often omitted from the expressions on the left side of the preceding identities and we shall always assume that X and Y are classes whenever we write "$X \cup Y$," "$X \cap Y$," "$X \sim Y$," and "X'".)

To illustrate these operations let

$$X = \{a,b,c\}$$

and

$$Y = \{a,c,d,e\}.$$

Then

$$X \cup Y = \{a,b,c,d,e\},$$
$$X \cap Y = \{a,c\},$$
$$X \sim Y = \{b\}.$$

Alternatively, these concepts can be illustrated by Venn diagrams. The class of points in the shaded area in each of the Figures 2.6.1, 2.6.2, and 2.6.3, is the indicated class.

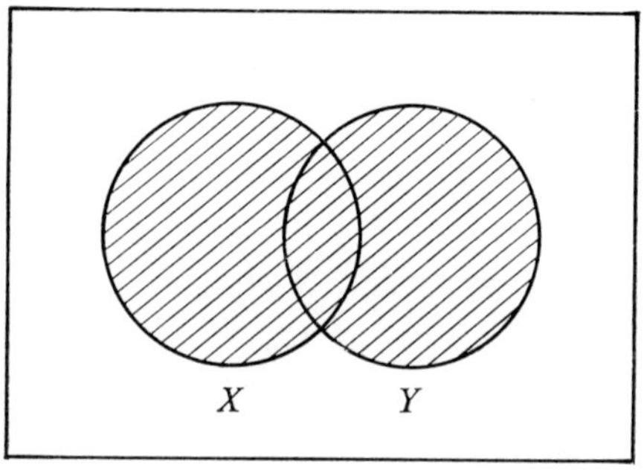

$X \cup Y$

FIGURE 2.6.1

The remaining part of this section is devoted to the properties of these operations. The proofs of the first four theorems are left as exercises.

THEOREM 2.6.3. Commutative Laws
(a) $X \cup Y = Y \cup X$
(b) $X \cap Y = Y \cap X$.

THEOREM 2.6.4. Associative Laws
(a) $(X \cup Y) \cup Z = X \cup (Y \cup Z)$
(b) $(X \cap Y) \cap Z = X \cap (Y \cap Z)$.

THEOREM 2.6.5. Distributive Laws
(a) $X \cap (Y \cup Z) = (X \cap Y) \cup (X \cap Z)$
(b) $X \cup (Y \cap Z) = (X \cup Y) \cap (X \cup Z)$.

THEOREM 2.6.6. Idempotency Laws
(a) $X \cup X = X$
(b) $X \cap X = X$.

THEOREM 2.6.7.
(a) $X \subseteq X \cup Y$
(b) $X \cap Y \subseteq X$.

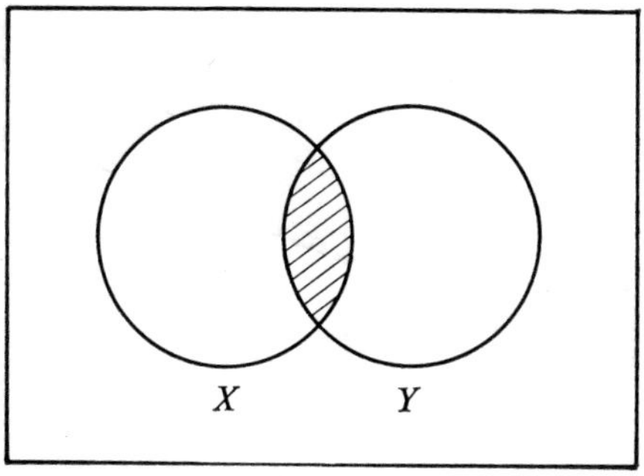

$X \cap Y$

FIGURE 2.6.2

Proof:

(a) $(u \in X) \rightarrow (u \in X \text{ or } u \in Y)$ (1.2.18)

$\hookrightarrow (u \in X \cup Y).$ (2.6.2a)

So, $X \subseteq X \cup Y$.

(b) $(u \in X \cap Y) \rightarrow (u \in X \;\&\; u \in Y)$ (2.6.2b)

$\rightarrow u \in X.$ (1.2.19)

Therefore, $X \cap Y \subseteq X$. ■

The next theorem tells us how to operate with $\emptyset$ and V.

THEOREM 2.6.8.

(a) $X \cup \emptyset = X$

(b) $X \cap \emptyset = \emptyset$

(c) $X \cup V = V$

(d) $X \cap V = X$.

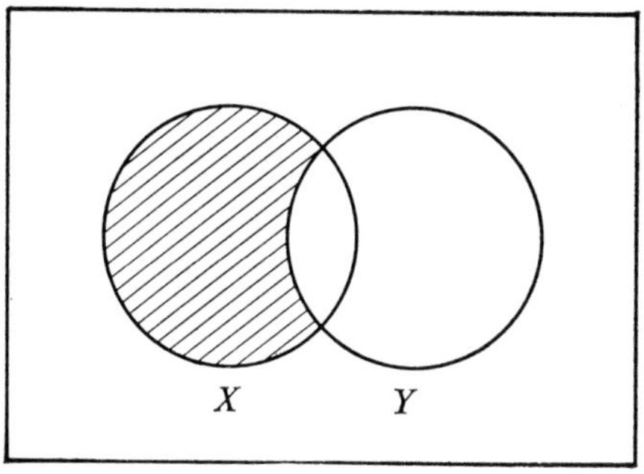

$X \sim Y$

FIGURE 2.6.3

Proof:

(a) $X \subseteq X \cup \emptyset$ by 2.6.7(a). Suppose $u \in X \cup \emptyset$, then $u \in X$ or $u \in \emptyset$. But, by 2.5.3(a), $u \notin \emptyset$, so $u \in X$. This implies $X \cup \emptyset \subseteq X$. The desired result now follows from 2.3.5.

(b) $X \cap \emptyset \subseteq \emptyset$ by 2.6.7(b) and $\emptyset \subseteq X \cap \emptyset$ by 2.5.4(a).

(c) $V \subseteq X \cup V$ by 2.6.7(a) and $X \cup V \subseteq V$ by 2.5.4(b).

(d) $X \cap V \subseteq X$ by 2.6.7(b). Suppose $u \in X$. From 2.5.3(b), we obtain $u \in V$. Therefore, $u \in X \cap V$ and $X \subseteq X \cap V$. ∎

The next theorem gives necessary and sufficient conditions for one class to be a subclass of another.

THEOREM 2.6.9.

(a) $X \subseteq Y \leftrightarrow (X \cup Y = Y)$

(b) $X \subseteq Y \leftrightarrow (X \cap Y = X)$.

Proof:

(a) Suppose $X \subseteq Y$. It follows from 2.6.7(a) that $Y \subseteq X \cup Y$. Suppose then, that $u \in X \cup Y$. Then $u \in X$ or $u \in Y$. Since $X \subseteq Y$, if $u \in X$ then $u \in Y$. Therefore, if $u \in X \cup Y$, then $u \in Y$. So $X \cup Y = Y$.

Conversely, suppose $X \cup Y = Y$ and $u \in X$. By 2.6.7(a), $X \subseteq X \cup Y$ so $u \in X$ implies $u \in X \cup Y$. But $X \cup Y = Y$, so $u \in Y$. Therefore, $X \subseteq Y$.

The proof of (b) is analogous and is left as an exercise. ∎

The proof of the next theorem, on complements, is also left as an exercise.

THEOREM 2.6.10.

(a) $(X')' = X$

(b) $X \cup X' = V$

(c) $X \cap X' = \emptyset$.

THEOREM 2.6.11.

(a) $V \sim X = X'$

(b) $X \sim Y = X \cap Y'$

(c) $X \subseteq Y \leftrightarrow Y' \subseteq X'$

(d) $X \subset Y \leftrightarrow Y' \subset X'$.

Proof:

(a) $u \in V \sim X \leftrightarrow (u \in V \ \&\ u \notin X)$ (2.6.2c)
$\leftrightarrow (u \notin X)$ (2.5.3b)
$\leftrightarrow u \in X'$. (2.6.2d)

(b) $u \in X \sim Y \leftrightarrow (u \in X \ \&\ u \notin Y)$ (2.6.2c)
$\leftrightarrow (u \in X \ \&\ u \in Y')$ (2.6.2d)
$\leftrightarrow u \in X \cap Y'$. (2.6.2b)

(c) Suppose $X \subseteq Y$ and $u \in Y'$. Then $u \notin Y$, so $u \notin X$. (Since $X \subseteq Y$, $u \in X$ implies $u \in Y$.) Therefore, $u \in X'$ and $Y' \subseteq X'$.

Conversely, suppose $Y' \subseteq X'$. Then, as before, we obtain $(X')' \subseteq (Y')'$. Applying 2.6.10(a) we get the desired result.

(d) Suppose $X \subset Y$. Then $X \subseteq Y$. So by part (c), $Y' \subseteq X'$. If $Y' = X'$, then $Y = X$ (2.6.10a), which contradicts $X \subset Y$. Therefore, $Y' \subseteq X'$ and $Y' \neq X'$, so $Y \subset X'$.

The proof of the converse is analogous. ∎

THEOREM 2.6.12. De Morgan's Laws

(a) $(X \cup Y)' = X' \cap Y'$

(b) $(X \cap Y)' = X' \cup Y'$.

Proof: [We shall prove (a) and leave the proof of (b) as an exercise.]

$$\begin{aligned} u \in (X \cup Y)' &\leftrightarrow (u \notin (X \cup Y)) && (2.6.2d)\\ &\leftrightarrow \neg(u \in X \text{ or } u \in Y) && (2.6.2a)\\ &\leftrightarrow (u \notin X \ \&\ u \notin Y) && (1.2.11)\\ &\leftrightarrow (u \in X' \ \&\ u \in Y') && (2.6.2d)\\ &\leftrightarrow u \in X' \cap Y'. && (2.6.2b) \end{aligned}$$ ∎

The preceding theorems give the basic properties of the operations of union, intersection, and complement. However, a word of warning, the cancellation laws do not hold for union and intersection. That is, the two formulae

(1) $$X \cup Y = X \cup Z \rightarrow Y = Z$$

and

(2) $$X \cap Y = X \cap Z \rightarrow Y = Z$$

do not hold in general. To see this, take X in formula (1) to be V and X in formula (2) to be $\emptyset$. Then the equation on the left side of both formulae (1) and (2) hold for all Y and Z.

Further properties of the class operations are given in the exercises

EXERCISES 2.6

1. Draw a Venn diagram similar to Figure 2.4.2 for each of the following classes and shade the area which represents the given class:

(a) $Y \cap Z$
(b) $X \sim Z$
(c) $X \cup Y \cup Z$
(d) $Y \cup X'$
(e) $(X \cap Y \cap Z)'$
(f) $(Z \cap X) \cup Y$
(g) $Z \cap (X \cup Y)$.

2. In model M2 § 2.4, calculate each of the following:
   (a) $2 \cup 13$
   (b) $5 \cap 12$
   (c) $7 \sim 17$
   (d) $(12 \cup 17) \cap 11$
   (e) $20' \cap 23$
   (f) $(12 \cup 18) \sim 27$
   (g) $9 \cap (16 \cup 5)'$
   (h) $(9 \cap 12 \cap 20)'$.
3. Let the classes x_1–x_8 be defined as in exercise 2.4.4. Calculate each of the following classes:
   (a) $x_1 \cup x_4$
   (b) $x_2 \cup x_6$
   (c) $x_4 \cap x_5$
   (d) $x_4 \cap x_7$
   (e) $x_7 \cap x_8$
   (f) $x_6 \sim x_4$
   (g) $x_7 \sim x_8$
   (h) $(x_5 \cup x_7) \sim x_8$
   (i) $(x_3 \cap x_4) \sim x_6$
   (j) $(x_5 \cap x_6) \sim (x_8 \sim x_4)$.
4. Prove each of the following:
   (a) $X \cap (Y \cup Z)' = (X \sim Y) \sim Z$
   (b) $[(X \cap Y) \cup Z = X \cap (Y \cup Z)] \leftrightarrow Z \subseteq X$
   (c) $X \subseteq Y \leftrightarrow X \cap Y' = \emptyset$.
5. The *symmetric difference* or *Boolean sum* of two classes X and Y, $X \square Y$, is defined as follows:

$$X \square Y =_{\text{Df}} (X \cup Y) \sim (X \cap Y).$$

   (Named after the English mathematician George Boole, 1815–1864.)
   (a) Draw a Venn diagram for $X \square Y$.
   Prove each of the following:
   (b) $X \square Y = Y \square X$
   (c) $X \square (Y \square Z) = (X \square Y) \square Z$
   (d) $X \cap (Y \square Z) = (X \cap Y) \square (X \cap Z)$
   (e) $X \square Y = (X \cap Y') \cup (X' \cap Y)$
   (f) $(X \square Y)' = X \square Y'$
   (g) $X = Y \leftrightarrow X \square Y = \emptyset$
   (h) $X \square Y = X \square Z \rightarrow Y = Z$.
6. For each of the following formulae if it is true prove it, if false give a counter-example:
   (a) $(X \sim Y) \sim Z = X \sim (Y \sim Z)$
   (b) $Y \subseteq Z \rightarrow (X \sim Z \subseteq X \sim Y)$
   (c) $(X \cap Y = X \cap Z) \rightarrow Y = Z$
   (d) $(X \cup Y = X \cup Z \;\&\; X \cap Y = X \cap Z) \rightarrow Y = Z$
   (e) $(X \cap Y = X \cap Z \;\&\; X' \cap Y = X' \cap Z) \rightarrow Y = Z$
   (f) $(X \sim Y') \cup (Y' \sim X) = (X' \cap Y)' \sim (X' \cup Y)'$.

2.7. A DECISION PROCEDURE FOR CLASS ALGEBRA

Suppose we were asked to determine whether or not the equation

$$(X \sim Y)' = X' \cup Y \tag{1}$$

holds for all classes X and Y. In other words, is equation (1) an identity? In this case it is quite easy to get the answer:

$$
\begin{aligned}
(X \sim Y)' &= (X \cap Y')' && (2.6.11b)\\
&= X' \cup (Y')' && (2.6.12b)\\
&= X' \cup Y. && (2.6.10a)
\end{aligned}
$$

Therefore, (1) is an identity.

Now, let us attack this problem in a slightly different way. It follows from A2 that (1) is an identity if and only if the class $(X \sim Y)'$ has the same elements as the class $X' \cup Y$ irrespective of the choice of the classes X and Y. For any two classes X and Y and for any element u the following four possibilities are mutually exclusive and exhaustive:

(a) $u \in X$ and $u \in Y$,
(b) $u \in X$ and $u \notin Y$,
(c) $u \notin X$ and $u \in Y$,
(d) $u \notin X$ and $u \notin Y$.

If case (a) holds then by 2.6.2(c), since $u \in Y$, $u \notin X \sim Y$. Consequently by 2.6.2(d) $u \in (X \sim Y)'$. Since $u \in Y$ it follows from 2.6.2(a) that $u \in X' \cup Y$.

If case (b) is true then by 2.6.2(c), since $u \in X$ and $u \notin Y$, $u \in X \sim Y$. So by 2.6.2(d), $u \notin (X \sim Y)'$. Also, since $u \in X$ and $u \notin Y$, it follows from 2.6.2(d) that $u \notin X'$ and $u \notin Y$, so by 2.6.2(a), $u \notin X' \cup Y$.

Similarly, for cases (c) and (d) we obtain $u \in (X \sim Y)'$ and $u \in X' \cup Y$. Therefore, $u \in (X \sim Y)'$ if and only if $u \in X' \cup Y$, so that again we obtain $(X \sim Y)' = X' \cup Y$.

This procedure can be greatly shortened by using a table. In the following table we write a "T" whenever u is an element of the indicated class and "F" when it is not.

TABLE 2.7.1

	1	2	3	4	5	6
	X	Y	$X \sim Y$	$(X \sim Y)'$	X'	$X' \cup Y$
1	T	T	F	T	F	T
2	T	F	T	F	F	F
3	F	T	F	T	T	T
4	F	F	F	T	T	T

Row 1 represents case (a) above; row 2 case (b); and so on. Hence, we see equation (1) is an identity because columns 4 and 6 are identical. Table 2.7.1 is an example of a truth table.

Let us consider another equation:

(2) $$X \sim (Y \sim Z) = (X \sim Y) \sim Z.$$

This time there will be eight mutually exclusive, exhaustive cases to consider. (If there were n distinct class variables in the equation then there would be 2^n cases to consider.) A truth table for equation (2) will therefore have eight rows.

TABLE 2.7.2

	1	2	3	4	5	6	7
	X	Y	Z	$Y \sim Z$	$X \sim (Y \sim Z)$	$X \sim Y$	$(X \sim Y) \sim Z$
1	T	T	T	F	T	F	F
2	T	T	F	T	F	F	F
3	T	F	T	F	T	T	F
4	T	F	F	F	T	T	T
5	F	T	T	F	F	F	F
6	F	T	F	T	F	F	F
7	F	F	T	F	F	F	F
8	F	F	F	F	F	F	F

We see equation (2) is not an identity because column 5 is not identical with column 7. They differ in row 1 and row 3. In fact, with the aid of the truth table it is relatively easy to find classes X, Y, and Z for which the equation does not hold. From row 1 of Table 2.7.2 we can infer that if $u \in X$, $u \in Y$, and $u \in Z$, then u is an element of the left side of equation (2), but is not an element of the right side. Therefore, take $X = Y = Z = \{u\}$ then $X \sim (Y \sim Z) = \{u\}$ and $(X \sim Y) \sim Z = \emptyset$. In an analogous manner, we can construct a counterexample from row 3. Take $X = Z = \{u\}$ and $Y = \emptyset$, then $X \sim (Y \sim Z) = \{u\}$ and $(X \sim Y) \sim Z = \emptyset$.

The truth table gives us a mechanical procedure for determining whether or not an equation is an identity. Such a mechanical procedure is called a *decision procedure.*

It is also possible by means of truth tables to determine whether or not one class is a subclass of another. We have $X \subseteq Y$ if and only if $u \in X$ implies $u \in Y$. Therefore, by the truth table method $X \subseteq Y$ if and only if whenever there is a T in the column under X there is also a T in the same row in the column under Y. However, if there is an F in the column under X, then either a T or an F may occur in the corresponding place in the column under Y.

It follows from Table 2.7.2 that $((X \sim Y) \sim Z) \subseteq (X \sim (Y \sim Z))$ for all classes X, Y, and Z.

As another illustration let us determine whether or not the following relation is true.

(3) $$[X \cap (Y \cup Z)] \subseteq [(X \cap Y) \cup Z].$$

The truth table for (3) will have 8 rows.

TABLE 2.7.3

	1	2	3	4	5	6	7
	X	Y	Z	$Y \cup Z$	$X \cap (Y \cup Z)$	$X \cap Y$	$(X \cap Y) \cup Z$
1	T	T	T	T	T	T	T
2	T	T	F	T	T	T	T
3	T	F	T	T	T	F	T
4	T	F	F	F	F	F	F
5	F	T	T	T	F	F	T
6	F	T	F	T	F	F	F
7	F	F	T	T	F	F	T
8	F	F	F	F	F	F	F

Therefore, it follows that (3) is true for all classes X, Y, and Z because whenever there is a T in column 5 (rows 1–3) there is also a T in column 7. In other words, whenever $u \in (X \cap (Y \cup Z))$ it is also true that $u \in ((X \cap Y) \cup Z)$. Therefore, it follows from 2.3.1(a) that $X \cap (Y \cup Z) \subseteq (X \cap Y) \cup Z$.

EXERCISES 2.7

1. Do exercise 2.6.4 using truth tables.
2. Do exercise 2.6.6 using truth tables.
3. Use truth tables to determine which of the following are theorems (see exercise 2.6.5 for the definition of $\square$):

   (a) $(X \cup (Y \square Z) = (X \cup Y) \square (X \cup Z)$
   (b) $X \cap (Y \square Z) = (X \cap Y) \square (X \cap Z)$
   (c) $X \square (Y \cap Z) = (X \square Y) \cap (X \square Z)$
   (d) $X \square (Y \sim Z) = (X \square Y) \sim (X \square Z)$.

   For each of the above equations which are not theorems, construct a counterexample. Also, for each of the above equations which are not theorems, determine whether or not one side is a subclass of the other.

2.8. SETS

It is clear that not every class can be a set. For if this were the case, then Russell's class, $\{u : u \notin u\}$ would be a set and Russell's paradox would hold in the system (see § 1.1). Intuitively, a set is a class which isn't "too large." Therefore, it seems reasonable that if X is a class and is a subclass of some set then X should be a set. We shall take this as a temporary axiom. (We shall see later that it is a consequence of A6. See theorem 3.3.8. None of the consequences which we derive from T1 will be used to prove 3.3.8.)

T1: $$[\mathrm{Cl}(X) \ \& \ (\exists u)(\mathrm{S}(u) \ \& \ X \subseteq u)] \rightarrow \mathrm{S}(X).$$

It follows immediately from 2.5.4(a) and T1 that if there is a set then $\emptyset$, the empty class, is a set.

The following theorem is a consequence of T1 and 2.5.1.

THEOREM 2.8.1. If **P** is a wff in which X is not a free variable, then the following statement is a theorem:

$$(\forall v)(\exists 1 X)[\mathrm{S}(X) \ \& \ (\forall u)(u \in X \leftrightarrow (u \in v \ \& \ \mathbf{P}))].$$

Proof: It follows from 2.5.1 that there exists a unique *class* X satisfying the conditions. But we also have

$$u \in X \rightarrow u \in v$$

for some set v. This implies that

$$X \subseteq v.$$

Therefore the theorem follows from T1. ■

Theorem 2.8.1 states that if **P** is any meaningful statement (in which X is not free) and v is a set, then there exists a unique set X such that X is a subset of v and the elements of X satisfy **P**. A class is a set if it is a subclass of a set. The following theorem is also a consequence of T1.

THEOREM 2.8.2. $(\mathrm{Cl}(X) \ \& \ \mathrm{Cl}(Y)) \rightarrow$
(a) $(\mathrm{S}(X)$ or $\mathrm{S}(Y)) \rightarrow \mathrm{S}(X \cap Y)$
(b) $\mathrm{S}(X) \rightarrow \mathrm{S}(X \sim Y)$.

Proof:
(a) It follows from 2.6.7(b) that

$$X \cap Y \subseteq X \quad \text{and} \quad X \cap Y \subseteq Y.$$

Therefore, if either X or Y are sets, then so is $X \cap Y$.
(b) By 2.6.11(b)

$$X \sim Y = X \cap Y'.$$

Therefore, the result follows from part (a). ■

It is also reasonable for the union of two sets to be a set. But this does not follow from the axioms so we shall postulate it as a temporary axiom.

(It is a special case of A7 and no consequence of T2 is needed to prove this.)

T2: $$(\mathrm{S}(X) \,\&\, \mathrm{S}(Y)) \rightarrow \mathrm{S}(X \cup Y).$$

It follows from 2.5.1 that

THEOREM 2.8.3. $$(\exists 1\, Y)(\mathrm{Cl}(Y) \,\&\, (\forall u)(u \in Y \leftrightarrow u \subseteq X)).$$

The unique class Y whose existence is guaranteed by 2.8.3 is called the *power class* of X and is denoted by $\mathcal{P}(X)$.

DEFINITION 2.8.4. Power Class

$$u \in \mathcal{P}(X) =_{\mathrm{Df}} u \subseteq X.$$

Thus, we have

$$\mathcal{P}(X) = \{u : u \subseteq X\}.$$

For example, if $\emptyset$ is a set, then $\mathcal{P}(\emptyset) = \{\emptyset\}$. If $\{1,2\}$ is a set, then $\mathcal{P}(\{1,2\}) = \{\emptyset, \{1\}, \{2\}, \{1,2\}\}$.

It is also natural in a system of set theory that if X is a set, so is $\mathcal{P}(X)$. This does not follow from the axioms so we must postulate it.

A4: $$\mathrm{S}(X) \rightarrow \mathrm{S}(\mathcal{P}(X)).$$

Thus, we have:

a subclass of a set is a set
the union of two sets is a set
the power class of a set is a set.

We shall postulate the existence of additional sets in subsequent chapters.

EXERCISES 2.8

1. Prove $(\mathrm{Pr}(X) \,\&\, \mathrm{Cl}(Y) \,\&\, X \subseteq Y) \rightarrow \mathrm{Pr}(Y)$.
2. Prove $(\mathrm{Pr}(X)$ or $\mathrm{Pr}(Y)) \rightarrow \mathrm{Pr}(X \cup Y)$.
3. Calculate $\mathcal{P}(x_i)$ for each of the sets x_i, $i = 1, 2, \ldots, 8$, given in exercise 2.4.4.
4. For each of the following, if it is a theorem prove it, if not give a counterexample:

   (a) $\mathcal{P}(X \cup Y) = \mathcal{P}(X) \cup \mathcal{P}(Y)$
   (b) $\mathcal{P}(X \cap Y) = \mathcal{P}(X) \cap \mathcal{P}(Y)$
   (c) $\mathcal{P}(X \sim Y) = \mathcal{P}(X) \sim \mathcal{P}(Y)$.

   For each of the above equations which are not identities, determine whether or not one side is a subclass of the other.

2.9. SUMMARY OF THE AXIOMS

A1: Characterization of Atoms

$$A(X) \to (\neg Cl(X) \;\&\; (\forall Y)(Y \notin X)).$$

A2: Axiom of Extensionality

$$(Cl(X) \;\&\; Cl(Y)) \to ((\forall u)(u \in X \leftrightarrow u \in Y) \to X = Y).$$

A3: Axiom Schema for Construction of Classes

If **P** is a wff in which X is not a free variable then the following statement is an axiom:

$$(\exists X)[Cl(X) \;\&\; (\forall u)(u \in X \leftrightarrow \mathbf{P})].$$

T1: Subclass Axiom

$$(Cl(X) \;\&\; (\exists u)(S(u) \;\&\; X \subseteq u)) \to S(X).$$

T2: Union Axiom

$$(S(X) \;\&\; S(Y)) \to S(X \cup Y).$$

A4: Power Set Axiom

$$S(X) \to S(\mathcal{P}(X)).$$

Chapter 3: Functions and Relations

3.1. UNORDERED PAIRS, ORDERED PAIRS, AND DIRECT PRODUCTS

We are working under the assumption that a set is a class which is an element, or intuitively, a set is a class which isn't "too big." Therefore, if a class only has one, two, three, or some finite number of elements we would expect it to be a set. However, this does not follow from any of the axioms which have previously been stated, so if we want it to be true we have to postulate it. It so happens that with the other axioms it is sufficient to postulate this for a class which has at most two elements. Thus, the axiom is called the *pairing axiom.*

A5: $$(\exists x)[S(x) \;\&\; (\forall u)(u \in x \leftrightarrow (u = v \text{ or } u = w))].$$

It follows immediately from A2, the axiom of extensionality, that given v and w, the set x of A5 is unique. That is,

THEOREM 3.1.1.

$$(\exists 1x)(S(x) \;\&\; (\forall u)(u \in x \leftrightarrow (u = v \text{ or } u = w))).$$

This unique set x is called an *unordered pair* and is denoted by $\{v,w\}$. Thus,

DEFINITION 3.1.2. Unordered Pair

$$u \in \{v,w\} =_{\mathrm{Df}} (u = v \text{ or } u = w).$$

In other words,

$$\{v,w\} = \{u : u = v \text{ or } u = w\}.$$

As a consequence of A5 we have

THEOREM 3.1.3. $S(\{v,w\})$.

(Note that it follows from 2.5.1 that $\{v,w\}$ is a class, but A5 is needed to guarantee that it is a set.)

If in 3.1.1, we take $v = w$ we get as a corollary,

COROLLARY 3.1.4. $(\exists 1x)(S(x) \;\&\; (\forall u)(u \in x \leftrightarrow u = v)).$

This unique set x is called a *unit* set or a *singleton* and is denoted by $\{v\}$.

DEFINITION 3.1.5. Unit Set

$$u \in \{v\} =_{\mathrm{Df}} u = v.$$

Equivalently,

$$\{v\} = \{u : u = v\},$$

and we have as a theorem,

THEOREM 3.1.6. $\mathrm{S}(\{v\})$.

Also it follows from 3.1.2 and 3.1.5 that,

THEOREM 3.1.7. $\{u,u\} = \{u\}$.

The unordered pair $\{x,y\}$ is a set whose elements are x and y, irrespective of the order. This is stated in the next theorem.

THEOREM 3.1.8.

$$\{x,y\} = \{u,v\} \rightarrow ((x = u \;\&\; y = v) \text{ or } (x = v \;\&\; y = u)).$$

Proof: By 3.1.2, $x \in \{x,y\}$. By hypothesis, $\{x,y\} = \{u,v\}$, therefore, $x \in \{u,v\}$. So, by 3.1.2, $x = u$ or $x = v$. By an analogous argument we obtain $y = u$ or $y = v$. There are four cases to consider:

(1) $x = u \;\&\; y = u$
(2) $x = u \;\&\; y = v$
(3) $x = v \;\&\; y = u$
(4) $x = v \;\&\; y = v$.

If (1) holds, then $\{x,y\} = \{u,u\}$. By 3.1.7 $\{u,u\} = \{u\}$. Thus, using the hypothesis, we obtain $\{u,v\} = \{u\}$. Therefore, by 3.1.2, $v \in \{u\}$, and by 3.1.5, $v = u$. Hence, in this case we have $x = y = u = v$.

Similarly in case (4) the same result is obtained. ■

As an immediate consequence of 3.1.7 and 3.1.8, we have,

THEOREM 3.1.9. $\{u\} = \{v\} \rightarrow u = v$.

The converses of 3.1.8 and 3.1.9 also hold. They follow immediately from A2.

The concept of an unordered pair can easily be extended to an unordered triple, unordered quadruple, etc.

DEFINITION 3.1.10. Unordered Triple and Quadruple

(a) $\{u,v,w\} =_{\mathrm{Df}} \{u,v\} \cup \{w\}$
(b) $\{u,v,w,x\} =_{\mathrm{Df}} \{u,v,w\} \cup \{x\}$.

It follows from A5 and T2 that the unordered triple, $\{u,v,w\}$, and the unordered quadruple, $\{u,v,w,x\}$, are sets. (We note again that neither this result nor any other consequence of T2 is used to prove that T2 is a consequence of A7. See §3.5). It is easy to prove that

$$y \in \{u,v,w\} \leftrightarrow (y = u \text{ or } y = v \text{ or } y = w)$$

and

$$y \in \{u,v,w,x\} \leftrightarrow (y = u \text{ or } y = v \text{ or } y = w \text{ or } y = x).$$

Also, a theorem similar to 3.1.8 holds for the unordered triplet and the unordered quadruple. (We shall see later, in exercise 4.3.1, how an unordered n-triple is defined for any positive integer n.)

Now, what we would like to do is to define some order on a set of elements. Which element is first? Second? etc. Suppose u and v are two elements which are to be ordered in such a way that u is first and v second. One way to do this with the tools available would be to form two sets $\{u\}$ and $\{u,v\}$. Then let

$$x = \{\{u\},\{u,v\}\}.$$

The set x itself is an unordered pair. But given x we can distinguish between the elements u and v because u is an element of both sets in x while v is an element of only one if $u \neq v$. We shall use this as the definition of an ordered pair.

Definition 3.1.11. Ordered Pair

$$\langle u,v\rangle =_{\text{Df}} \{\{u\},\{u,v\}\}.$$

It immediately follows from 3.1.11, 3.1.3, and 3.1.6 that,

Theorem 3.1.12. $S(\langle u,v\rangle)$.

The actual technique used to define an ordered pair is unimportant. (For example, it is not particularly significant that $\{u\} \in \langle u,v\rangle$ or $\{u,v\} \in \langle u,v\rangle$.) What is important, however, is that it is a set and it has the one property that an ordered pair must have to deserve its name. That is,

Theorem 3.1.13. $\langle x,y\rangle = \langle u,v\rangle \rightarrow (x = u \,\&\, y = v)$.

Proof: If $\langle x,y\rangle = \langle u,v\rangle$ it follows from 3.1.11 that

$$\{\{x\},\{x,y\}\} = \{\{u\},\{u,v\}\}.$$

Therefore, by 3.1.8 either

(1) $\{x\} = \{u\}$ and $\{x,y\} = \{u,v\}$

or

(2) $\{x\} = \{u,v\}$ and $\{x,y\} = \{u\}$.

If (1) occurs, then by 3.1.9,

(3) $$x = u,$$

and by 3.1.8,

(4) $$x = u \text{ and } y = v$$

or

(5) $$x = v \text{ and } y = u.$$

If (3) and (5) hold, we have $x = y = u = v$. Consequently, (4) must hold. If (2) occurs, then we easily obtain $x = u = v$ and $x = y = u$. So the theorem holds in this case also. ■

If $\langle u,v\rangle$ is an ordered pair, u is called the *first coordinate* and v the *second coordinate*. The notion of an ordered pair can be extended to an ordered triple, an ordered quadruple, etc.

DEFINITION 3.1.14. Ordered Triple and Quadruple

(a) $\langle u,v,w\rangle =_{\mathrm{Df}} \langle u,\langle v,w\rangle\rangle$

(b) $\langle u,v,w,x\rangle =_{\mathrm{Df}} \langle u,\langle v,w,x\rangle\rangle$.

Therefore we have,

$$\begin{aligned}\langle u,v,w\rangle &= \langle u,\langle v,w\rangle\rangle && (3.1.14)\\ &= \{\{u\},\{u,\langle v,w\rangle\}\} && (3.1.11)\\ &= \{\{u\},\{u,\{v,\{v,w\}\}\}\}. && (3.1.11)\end{aligned}$$

The theorem analogous to 3.1.13 for ordered triples and quadruples is

THEOREM 3.1.15.

(a) $\langle x_1,x_2,x_3\rangle = \langle y_1,y_2,y_3\rangle \rightarrow (x_1 = y_1 \;\&\; x_2 = y_2 \;\&\; x_3 = y_3)$

(b) $\langle x_1,x_2,x_3,x_4\rangle = \langle y_1,y_2,y_3,y_4\rangle$
$\rightarrow (x_1 = y_1 \;\&\; x_2 = y_2 \;\&\; x_3 = y_3 \;\&\; x_4 = y_4)$.

The proof is left as an exercise.

The following theorem follows from 2.5.1.

THEOREM 3.1.16.

$$(\exists 1 Z)(\mathrm{Cl}(Z) \;\&\; (\forall u)(u \in Z \leftrightarrow (\exists v)(\exists w)(u = \langle v,w\rangle \;\&\; v \in X \;\&\; w \in y))).$$

This unique Z is denoted by $X \times Y$ and is called the *direct* or *Cartesian product* of X and Y. [Named after René Descartes (1596–1650), the French philosopher and mathematician.] Just as for $\subseteq$, $\cup$, $\cap$, $\sim$, and $'$, we assume that X and Y are classes whenever we write "$X \times Y$."

DEFINITION 3.1.17. Direct Product

$$u \in X \times Y =_{\mathrm{Df}} (\exists v)(\exists w)(u = \langle v,w\rangle \;\&\; v \in X \;\&\; w \in Y).$$

Therefore,

$$X \times Y = \{u : (\exists v)(\exists w)(u = \langle v,w\rangle \;\&\; v \in X \;\&\; w \in Y\}.$$

This brings up another type of notation that is often convenient to use. If for each $u_1, u_2, \ldots, u_n$ there is exactly one v such that $v = \mathbf{F}(u_1, u_2, \ldots, u_n)$, then we denote

$$\{v : (\exists u_1)(\exists u_2) \cdots (\exists u_n)(v = \mathbf{F}(u_1, u_2, \ldots, u_n) \;\&\; \mathbf{P})\}$$

by

$$\{\mathbf{F}(u_1, u_2, \ldots, u_n) : \mathbf{P}\}.$$

In particular, we write

$$X \times Y = \{\langle u,v\rangle : u \in X \;\&\; v \in Y\}.$$

If

$$X = \{1,2\}$$

and

$$Y = \{2,3,4\},$$

then

$$X \times Y = \{\langle 1,2\rangle, \langle 1,3\rangle, \langle 1,4\rangle, \langle 2,2\rangle, \langle 2,3\rangle, \langle 2,4\rangle\}$$

and

$$Y \times X = \{\langle 2,1\rangle, \langle 2,2\rangle, \langle 3,1\rangle, \langle 3,2\rangle, \langle 4,1\rangle, \langle 4,2\rangle\}.$$

If

$$X = Y = \{u : u \text{ is a real number } \& \; 0 \leqq u \leqq 1\},$$

then

$$X \times Y = \{\langle u,v\rangle : u \;\&\; v \text{ are real numbers } \& \; 0 \leqq u, v \leqq 1\}.$$

In other words, if X and Y are each the unit interval, then $X \times Y$ is the unit square.

It was necessary to postulate that the subclass of a set is a set, the union of two sets is a set, and the power class of a set is a set. However, using these three results, we can prove as a theorem that the direct product of two sets is a set.

THEOREM 3.1.18. $(S(X) \;\&\; S(Y)) \rightarrow S(X \times Y)$.

Proof: Suppose $\langle u,v\rangle \in X \times Y$. Then by 3.1.17, $u \in X$ and $v \in Y$. Therefore, $\{u\} \subseteq X \cup Y$ and $\{u,v\} \subseteq X \cup Y$. So, by 2.8.4, $\{u\} \in \mathcal{P}(X \cup Y)$ and $\{u,v\} \in \mathcal{P}(X \cup Y)$. Therefore, it follows from 3.1.11 that $\langle u,v\rangle \subseteq \mathcal{P}(X \cup Y)$. So by 2.8.4 again, $\langle u,v\rangle \in \mathcal{P}(\mathcal{P}(X \cup Y))$. This implies that $X \times Y \subseteq \mathcal{P}(\mathcal{P}(X \cup Y))$. Therefore, if X and Y are sets, so are $X \cup Y$ (T2), $\mathcal{P}(\mathcal{P}(X \cup Y))$ (A4), and $X \times Y$ (T1). ■

To conclude this section we shall discuss some of the algebraic properties of the direct product. We shall assume in this discussion that capital letters denote variables each of whose range is all classes.

THEOREM 3.1.19. $X \times Y = \emptyset \leftrightarrow (X = \emptyset \text{ or } Y = \emptyset)$

Proof: Suppose $X \times Y = \emptyset$, $X \neq \emptyset$, and $Y \neq \emptyset$. The latter two conditions imply that there are elements u and v such that $u \in X$ and $v \in Y$. So, by 3.1.17, $\langle u,v \rangle \in X \times Y$ which contradicts the hypothesis $X \times Y = \emptyset$.

Conversely, suppose $X = \emptyset$ and $X \times Y \neq \emptyset$. Then, by 3.1.17, there are elements u and v such that $\langle u,v \rangle \in X \times Y$. This implies $u \in X$, contradicting the assumption that $X = \emptyset$. The proof is analogous if $Y = \emptyset$. ■

In general, the direct product is not commutative. The following theorem gives necessary and sufficient conditions for the commutative law to hold.

THEOREM 3.1.20.

$$X \times Y = Y \times X \leftrightarrow (X = \emptyset \text{ or } Y = \emptyset \text{ or } X = Y).$$

Proof: If $X = \emptyset$ or $Y = \emptyset$, then by 3.1.19 $X \times Y = \emptyset = Y \times X$. Clearly, if $X = Y$, then $X \times Y = Y \times X$.

Conversely, suppose $X \neq \emptyset$, $Y \neq \emptyset$, and $X \neq Y$. If $X \neq Y$, then either

(1) $$(\exists u)(u \in X \ \&\ u \notin Y), \text{ or}$$

(2) $$(\exists u)(u \in Y \ \&\ u \notin X).$$

We shall assume (1) holds. [The proof follows the same pattern if (2) holds.] Suppose then that $u \in X$ and $u \notin Y$. Since $Y \neq \emptyset$, there is a $v \in Y$. Therefore, by 3.1.17 $\langle u,v \rangle \in X \times Y$. But $\langle u,v \rangle \notin Y \times X$ because $u \notin Y$. Consequently, $X \times Y \neq Y \times X$. ■

The proofs of the next two theorems are left as exercises.

THEOREM 3.1.21.

$$Y \subseteq Z \rightarrow (X \times Y \subseteq X \times Z \ \&\ Y \times X \subseteq Z \times X).$$

THEOREM 3.1.22.

$$(X \neq \emptyset \ \&\ (X \times Y \subseteq X \times Z \text{ or } Y \times X \subseteq Z \times X)) \rightarrow Y \subseteq Z.$$

The next theorem gives distributive laws for the direct product. We shall prove one of them and the others are left as exercises.

THEOREM 3.1.23.

(a) $X \times (Y \cup Z) = (X \times Y) \cup (X \times Z)$

(b) $(X \cup Y) \times Z = (X \times Z) \cup (Y \times Z)$

(c) $X \times (Y \cap Z) = (X \times Y) \cap (X \times Z)$
(d) $(X \cap Y) \times Z = (X \times Z) \cap (Y \times Z)$
(e) $X \times (Y \sim Z) = (X \times Y) \sim (X \times Z)$
(f) $(X \sim Y) \times Z = (X \times Z) \sim (Y \times Z)$.

Proof: [We shall prove (a).]

$$\begin{aligned} &\langle u,v\rangle \in X \times (Y \cup Z) \\ &\quad \leftrightarrow u \in X \;\&\; v \in Y \cup Z && (3.1.17) \\ &\quad \leftrightarrow u \in X \;\&\; (v \in Y \text{ or } v \in Z) && (2.6.2a) \\ &\quad \leftrightarrow (u \in X \;\&\; v \in Y) \text{ or } (u \in X \;\&\; v \in Z) && (1.2.9) \\ &\quad \leftrightarrow (\langle u,v\rangle \in X \times Y) \text{ or } (\langle u,v\rangle \in X \times Z) && (3.1.17) \\ &\quad \leftrightarrow (\langle u,v\rangle \in (X \times Y) \cup (X \times Y). && (2.6.2a) \; \blacksquare \end{aligned}$$

EXERCISES 3.1

1. Give a counterexample to show that the following formula is not a theorem:

$$X \cup (Y \times Z) = (X \cup Y) \times (X \cup Z).$$

2. For each of the following, if it is a theorem prove it, if not give a counterexample.
   (a) $X \cap (Y \times Z) = (X \cap Y) \times (X \cap Z)$
   (b) $(X \times X) \cap (Y \times Z) = (X \cap Y) \times (X \cap Z)$
   (c) $(X \times X) \cup (Y \times Z) = (X \cup Y) \times (X \cup Z)$
   (d) $(X \times X) \sim (Y \times Z) = (X \sim Y) \times (X \sim Z)$
   (e) $(X \times Y) \sim (Z \times Z) = ((X \sim Z) \times Y) \cup (X \times (Y \sim Z))$.

3.2. RELATIONS

Using the notion of an ordered pair, we can formulate the theory of relations in set-theoretic language. By a relation here we mean a *binary* relation—a relation between two terms. Examples of binary relations are well known: "=" (between two classes or atoms); "<" (between two real numbers); etc.

One way to describe a relation (for example, "<" between two real numbers) is to give examples of ordered pairs $\langle u,v\rangle$ such that $u < v$. If the class of *all* such ordered pairs, call it X, were given, then the relation would be completely determined. For then we could say

$$u < v \leftrightarrow \langle u,v\rangle \in X.$$

A relation, then, will be defined as a class of ordered pairs. We shall use the symbol "Rel(R)" to mean "R is a (binary) relation."

DEFINITION 3.2.1. (Binary) Relation

$$\mathrm{Rel}(R) =_{\mathrm{Df}} (\mathrm{Cl}(R) \;\&\; (x \in R \rightarrow (\exists u)(\exists v)(x = \langle u,v\rangle))).$$

The notion of a binary relation can easily be extended to a ternary relation—a class of ordered triples; a quaternary relation—a class of ordered quadruples; etc. The relation "betweenness" on the set of real numbers is an example of a ternary relation. The relation which holds between four points in a plane if and only if they form the vertices of a parallelogram is an example of a quaternary relation. However, our primary interest here is with binary relations.

The following theorem follows immediately from 3.2.1.

THEOREM 3.2.2.

$$(\mathrm{Rel}(R)\ \&\ \mathrm{Rel}(S)) \rightarrow (\mathrm{Rel}(R \cup S)\ \&\ \mathrm{Rel}(R \cap S)\ \&\ \mathrm{Rel}(R \sim S)).$$

It follows from 2.5.1 that we can make the following definition. (In the future we shall usually omit explicit references to 2.5.1 preceding definitions and implicitly assume that the classes which are defined exist. The reader can verify it for himself.)

DEFINITION 3.2.3. Domain, Range, and Field

(a) $\mathfrak{D}(R) =_{\mathrm{Df}} \{u : (\exists v)(\langle u,v\rangle \in R)\}$

(b) $\mathfrak{R}(R) =_{\mathrm{Df}} \{v : (\exists u)(\langle u,v\rangle \in R)\}$

(c) $\mathfrak{F}(R) =_{\mathrm{Df}} (\mathfrak{D}(R) \cup \mathfrak{R}(R))$.

"$\mathfrak{D}(R)$" is called the "*domain* of R," "$\mathfrak{R}(R)$," the "*range* of R" and "$\mathfrak{F}(R)$," the "*field* of R." Even though it is not specified that R is a relation in 3.2.3, these concepts are only of interest when R is a relation. The same is true in 3.2.11, 3.2.12, 3.2.16, and 3.2.23.

If R is a relation, we often write

$$u\,R\,v \quad \text{to mean} \quad \langle u,v\rangle \in R.$$

A trivial example of a relation is the empty class, $\emptyset$. It can easily be verified that $\emptyset$ is a relation and $\mathfrak{D}(\emptyset) = \mathfrak{R}(\emptyset) = \mathfrak{F}(\emptyset) = \emptyset$. Another example is the identity relation

$$I = \{\langle u,v\rangle : u = v\}.$$

Another less trivial example of a relation is the following: Let X be a non-empty class. Define a relation R such that

$$R = \{\langle u,x\rangle : u \in x\ \&\ x \subseteq X\}.$$

Then it can easily be verified that $\mathfrak{D}(R) = X$ and $\mathfrak{R}(R) = \mathcal{P}(X) \sim \{\emptyset\}$. (The range of R is the class of non-empty subsets of X.)

If R is a relation such that $X = \mathfrak{F}(R)$, R is said to be a relation *on* X.

There are certain special types of relations which are of importance and they will be defined next.

DEFINITION 3.2.4.

(a) R is *reflexive* $=_{\text{Df}} (\forall u)(u \in \mathfrak{F}(R) \rightarrow \langle u,u\rangle \in R)$

(b) R is *irreflexive* $=_{\text{Df}} (\forall u)(u \in \mathfrak{F}(R) \rightarrow \langle u,u\rangle \notin R)$

(c) R is *symmetric* $=_{\text{Df}} (\forall u)(\forall v)(u,v \in \mathfrak{F}(R) \rightarrow (\langle u,v\rangle \in R \rightarrow \langle v,u\rangle \in R))$

(d) R is *asymmetric* $=_{\text{Df}} (\forall u)(\forall v)(u,v \in \mathfrak{F}(R) \rightarrow (\langle u,v\rangle \in R \rightarrow \langle v,u\rangle \notin R))$

(e) R is *antisymmetric* $=_{\text{Df}} (\forall u)(\forall v)(u,v \in \mathfrak{F}(R) \rightarrow (\langle u,v\rangle,\langle v,u\rangle \in R \rightarrow u = v))$

(f) R is *transitive* $=_{\text{Df}} (\forall u)(\forall v)(\forall w)(u,v,w \in \mathfrak{F}(R) \rightarrow (\langle u,v\rangle,\langle v,u\rangle \in R \rightarrow \langle u,w\rangle \in R))$

(g) R is *intransitive* $=_{\text{Df}} (\forall u)(\forall v)(\forall w)(u,v,w \in \mathfrak{F}(R) \rightarrow (\langle u,v\rangle,\langle v,w\rangle \in R \rightarrow \langle u,w\rangle \notin R))$

(h) R is an *equivalence relation* $=_{\text{Df}}$ R is reflexive, symmetric, and transitive.

The relation of $\leqq$ defined on the class of real numbers is an example of a relation which is reflexive, antisymmetric, and transitive. The relation $<$ on the class of all real numbers is irreflexive, asymmetric, and transitive. The relation $=$ on V is reflexive, symmetric, and transitive and is therefore an equivalence relation. A relation may be neither reflexive nor irreflexive. For example, the relation

$$R = \{\langle 1,1\rangle, \langle 1,2\rangle\}$$

is not reflexive because $2 \in \mathfrak{F}(R)$, but $\langle 2,2\rangle \notin R$ and it is not irreflexive because $\langle 1,1\rangle \in R$. Similarly, it is possible to construct relations which are neither symmetric nor asymmetric, or which are neither transitive nor intransitive.

THEOREM 3.2.5.

$$(\text{Rel}(R)\ \&\ (R \text{ is reflexive or symmetric})) \rightarrow \mathfrak{D}(R) = \mathfrak{R}(R).$$

Proof: If R is reflexive and $u \in \mathfrak{D}(R)$, then $\langle u,u\rangle \in R$, so $u \in \mathfrak{R}(R)$. Similarly, if $u \in \mathfrak{R}(R)$, then $\langle u,u\rangle \in R$, so $u \in \mathfrak{D}(R)$.

Suppose R is symmetric. If $u \in \mathfrak{D}(R)$, then there is a $v \in \mathfrak{R}(R)$ such that $\langle u,v\rangle \in R$. But since R is symmetric, $\langle u,v\rangle \in R$ implies $\langle v,u\rangle \in R$, so that $u \in \mathfrak{R}(R)$. Therefore, $\mathfrak{D}(R) \subseteq \mathfrak{R}(R)$. The proof that $\mathfrak{R}(R) \subseteq \mathfrak{D}(R)$ is analogous. ■

THEOREM 3.2.6.

$$(\text{Rel}(R)\ \&\ R \text{ is symmetric } \&\ \text{transitive}) \rightarrow R \text{ is reflexive.}$$

Proof: Suppose $u \in \mathfrak{D}(R)$. Then there is a $v \in \mathfrak{R}(R)$ such that

$\langle u,v\rangle \in R$. Since R is symmetric, this implies that $\langle v,u\rangle \in R$. Since R is transitive,

$$\langle u,v\rangle, \langle u,u\rangle \in R \rightarrow \langle u,u\rangle \in R.$$

The proof is analogous if $u \in \mathcal{R}(R)$. ∎

Now, we shall turn our attention to equivalence relations. First, some preliminary definitions.

DEFINITION 3.2.7. Disjoint Classes
(a) $(\mathrm{Cl}(X)\ \&\ \mathrm{Cl}(Y)) \rightarrow (\mathrm{Dis}(X,Y) =_{\mathrm{Df}} X \cap Y = \emptyset)$
(b) $(\mathrm{Cl}(X)\ \&\ (u \in X \rightarrow \mathrm{S}(u))) \rightarrow$
$$(\mathrm{Pr\ Dis}(X) =_{\mathrm{Df}} (\forall u)(\forall v)(u,v \in X \rightarrow \mathrm{Dis}(u,v)).$$

"$\mathrm{Dis}(X,Y)$" is read "X and Y are *disjoint*" and "$\mathrm{Pr\ Dis}(X)$" is read "the elements of X are *pairwise disjoint*." If $X = \{0,1,3,4\}$ and $Y = \{2,5\}$, then X and Y are disjoint. Similarly, if X is the class of odd integers and Y is the class of even integers, then X and Y are disjoint. However, if X is the class of all primes (positive integers larger than 1 which have no factors besides 1 and themselves) and Y is the class of all positive even integers, then X and Y are not disjoint because $X \cap Y = \{2\}$.

DEFINITION 3.2.8. $\mathrm{Rel}(R) \rightarrow$
(a) $[u]_R =_{\mathrm{Df}} \{v : u\ R\ v\}$
(b) $(\forall u)(u \in \mathfrak{D}(R) \rightarrow \mathrm{S}([u]_R)) \rightarrow \mathfrak{D}(R)/R =_{\mathrm{Df}} \{[u]_R : u \in \mathfrak{D}(R)\}$.

If R is an equivalence relation, then $[u]_R$ is called an *equivalence class* and $\mathfrak{D}(R)/R$, the class of all equivalence classes.

THEOREM 3.2.9. $(\mathrm{Cl}(X)\ \&\ R$ is an equivalence relation on $X) \rightarrow$
(a) $(\forall u)(u \in X \rightarrow u \in [u]_R)$
(b) $(\forall u)(\forall v)((u,v \in X\ \&\ [u]_R \neq [v]_R) \rightarrow \mathrm{Dis}([u]_R,[v]_R))$
(c) $(\forall u)(u \in X \rightarrow \mathrm{S}([u]_R)) \rightarrow \mathrm{Pr\ Dis}(X/R)$.

Proof: (a) Let $u \in X$. Since R is an equivalence relation on X, $\mathfrak{F}(R) = X$ and R is reflexive. So, by 3.2.5, $\mathfrak{D}(R) = \mathcal{R}(R) = \mathfrak{F}(R) = X$. Therefore, $u \in X$ implies $u\ R\ u$. Consequently, by 3.2.8a, $u \in [u]_R$.

(b) Suppose $w \in [u]_R \cap [v]_R$. Then $w \in [u]_R$ and $w \in [v]_R$. Therefore, by definition 3.2.8(a)

(1) $$u\ R\ w$$
and
(2) $$v\ R\ w.$$
Since R is symmetric, it follows from (1) that
(3) $$w\ R\ u.$$
Since R is transitive, (2) and (3) imply
(4) $$v\ R\ u.$$

Now, suppose $s \in [u]_R$. Then

(5) $$u\ R\ s.$$

By (4), (5), and the transitivity of R, we obtain

(6) $$v\ R\ s,$$

which implies $s \in [v]_R$. Therefore, we have shown that if $[u]_R$ and $[v]_R$ have an element in common, then $[u]_R \subseteq [v]_R$. But this argument is perfectly symmetric in u and v, so in an analogous manner we can show $[v]_R \subseteq [u]_R$. Hence, we have shown that if $[u]_R$ and $[v]_R$ have an element in common, then they are identical.

(c) follows from (b). ■

A relation R is said to *partition* a class if it satisfies (a) and (b) of 3.2.9.

DEFINITION 3.2.10. $(\mathrm{Rel}(R)\ \&\ \mathrm{Cl}(X)) \rightarrow$

$$R \textit{ partitions } X =_{\mathrm{Df}} [\mathfrak{F}(R) = X\ \&\ (\forall u)(u \in X \rightarrow u \in [u]_R)\ \& \\ (\forall u)(\forall v)(u,v \in X\ \&\ [u]_R \neq [v]_R \rightarrow \mathrm{Dis}([u]_R,[v]_R))].$$

To illustrate this concept, let

In = class of all integers,
Y_1 = class of negative integers,
Y_2 = class of positive even integers,
Y_3 = class of positive odd integers,
$Y_4 = \{0\}$.

Then define R_1, R_2, and R_3 as follows:

$$u\ R_1\ v =_{\mathrm{Df}} u,v \in In,$$
$$u\ R_2\ v =_{\mathrm{Df}} (u,v \in In\ \&\ u = v),$$
$$u\ R_3\ v =_{\mathrm{Df}} (u,v \in Y_1 \text{ or } u,v \in Y_2 \text{ or } u,v \in Y_3 \text{ or } u,v \in Y_4).$$

R_1 and R_2 trivially partition In and it is easy to show that R_3 partitions In because

$$Y_1 \cup Y_2 \cup Y_3 \cup Y_4 = In$$

and

$$Y_i \cap Y_j = \emptyset \text{ if } i \neq j, \text{ for } i,j = 1,2,3,4.$$

It follows from 3.2.9 that if R is an equivalence relation on X, then R partitions X. We shall show that the converse is also true.

THEOREM 3.2.11.

$(\mathrm{Rel}(R)\ \&\ \mathrm{Cl}(X)\ \&\ R \text{ partitions } X) \rightarrow R$ is an equivalence relation on X.

Proof: It follows from 3.2.6 that it is sufficient to prove R is symmetric and transitive. Suppose $u\ R\ v$ then $v \in [u]_R$. Since R partitions X,

$v \in [v]_R$. Consequently, $[u]_R = [v]_R$. Since $u \in [u]_R$, $u \in [v]_R$. Therefore, $v \; R \; u$. Hence, R is symmetric.

Suppose $u \; R \; v$ and $v \; R \; w$. Since R is symmetric, we obtain $u \; R \; v$ and $w \; R \; v$, and this implies that $v \in [u]_R$ and $v \in [w]_R$. Therefore, $[u]_R = [w]_R$. Since $w \in [w]_R$, we must have $w \in [u]_R$. Hence, $u \; R \; w$. ■

Thus, we have shown that each equivalence relation on a class partitions the class, and conversely, each relation which partitions a class is an equivalence relation.

Next, we shall define several operations on relations.

DEFINITION 3.2.12. Inverse or Converse

$$R^{-1} =_{\mathrm{Df}} \{\langle u,v\rangle : \langle v,u\rangle \in R\}.$$

Clearly, R^{-1} is a relation. Also if R is a relation, it is very easy to show that

$$\mathfrak{D}(R^{-1}) = \mathfrak{R}(R), \quad \mathfrak{R}(R^{-1}) = \mathfrak{D}(R),$$

and

$$(R^{-1})^{-1} = R.$$

(The inverse of R is sometimes denoted by "$\breve{R}$.")

DEFINITION 3.2.13. Composite or Relative Product

$$R \circ S =_{\mathrm{Df}} \{\langle u,v\rangle : (\exists w)(\langle u,w\rangle \in S \;\&\; \langle w,v\rangle \in R)\}.$$

Clearly $R \circ S$ is a relation, and if R and S are relations, then

$$\mathfrak{D}(R \circ S) \subseteq \mathfrak{D}(S)$$

and

$$\mathfrak{R}(R \circ S) \subseteq \mathfrak{R}(R).$$

For example, if

$$R = \{\langle 2,5\rangle, \langle 2,6\rangle, \langle 3,7\rangle, \langle 4,8\rangle\}$$

and

$$S = \{\langle 1,2\rangle, \langle 1,3\rangle, \langle 2,5\rangle\},$$

then

$$R \circ S = \{\langle 1,5\rangle, \langle 1,6\rangle, \langle 1,7\rangle\}.$$

Or if $R = Y \times Z$ and $S = X \times Y$, then $R \circ S = X \times Y$.

THEOREM 3.2.14. $(R \circ S) \circ T = R \circ (S \circ T)$.

Proof: $\langle u,v \rangle \in (R \circ S) \circ T$

$\leftrightarrow (\exists w)(\langle u,w \rangle \in T \ \& \ \langle w,v \rangle \in R \circ S)$	(3.2.13)
$\leftrightarrow (\exists w)(\langle u,w \rangle \in T \ \& \ (\exists x)(\langle w,x \rangle \in S \ \& \ \langle x,v \rangle \in R))$	(3.2.13)
$\leftrightarrow (\exists w)(\exists x)(\langle u,w \rangle \in T \ \& \ \langle w,x \rangle \in S \ \& \ \langle x,v \rangle \in R)$	(1.2.34)
$\leftrightarrow (\exists x)(\exists w)(\langle u,w \rangle \in T \ \& \ \langle w,x \rangle \in S \ \& \ \langle x,v \rangle \in R)$	(1.2.29)
$\leftrightarrow (\exists x)((\exists w)(\langle u,w \rangle \in T \ \& \ \langle w,x \rangle \in S) \ \& \ \langle x,v \rangle \in R)$	(1.2.34)
$\leftrightarrow (\exists x)(\langle u,x \rangle \in S \circ T \ \& \ \langle x,v \rangle \in R)$	(3.2.13)
$\leftrightarrow \langle u,v \rangle \in R \circ (S \circ T).$	(3.2.13) ∎

Thus, the composite product is associative. Next, it is shown that the composite product is distributive over union.

THEOREM 3.2.15. $R \circ (S \cup T) = (R \circ S) \cup (R \circ T).$

Proof: $\langle u,v \rangle \in R \circ (S \cup T)$

$\leftrightarrow (\exists w)(\langle u,w \rangle \in S \cup T \ \& \ \langle w,v \rangle \in R)$	(3.2.13)
$\leftrightarrow (\exists w)((\langle u,w \rangle \in S \text{ or } \langle u,w \rangle \in T) \ \& \ \langle w,v \rangle \in R)$	(2.6.2a)
$\leftrightarrow (\exists w)((\langle u,w \rangle \in S \ \& \ \langle w,v \rangle \in R) \text{ or } (\langle u,w \in T \ \& \ \langle w,v \rangle \in R))$	(1.2.9)
$\leftrightarrow ((\exists w)(\langle u,w \rangle \in S \ \& \ \langle w,v \rangle \in R) \text{ or }$	
$\qquad\qquad\qquad (\exists w)(\langle u,w \rangle \in T \ \& \ \langle w,v \rangle \in R))$	(1.2.32)
$\leftrightarrow (\langle u,v \rangle \in R \circ S \text{ or } \langle u,v \rangle \in R \circ T)$	(3.2.13)
$\leftrightarrow \langle u,v \rangle \in (R \circ S) \cup (R \circ T).$	(2.6.2a) ∎

We have partial distributive laws for intersection and relative complement.

THEOREM 3.2.16.

    (a) $R \circ (S \cap T) \subseteq (R \circ S) \cap (R \circ T)$

    (b) $(R \circ S) \sim (R \circ T) \subseteq R \circ (S \sim T).$

Proof: (a) $\langle u,v \rangle \in R \circ (S \cap T)$

$\leftrightarrow (\exists w)(\langle u,w \rangle \in S \cap T \ \& \ \langle w,v \rangle \in R)$	(3.2.13)
$\leftrightarrow (\exists w)(\langle u,w \rangle \in S \ \& \ \langle u,w \rangle \in T \ \& \ \langle w,v \rangle \in R)$	(2.6.2b)
$\leftrightarrow (\exists w)((\langle u,w \rangle \in S \ \& \ \langle w,v \rangle \in R) \ \& \ (\langle u,w \rangle \in T \ \& \ \langle w,v \rangle \in R))$	(1.2.2)
$\rightarrow ((\exists w)(\langle u,w \rangle \in S \ \& \ \langle w,v \rangle \in R) \ \& \ (\exists w)(\langle u,w \rangle \in T \ \& \ \langle w,v \rangle \in R))$	
	(1.2.31)
$\leftrightarrow (\langle u,v \rangle \in R \circ S \ \& \ \langle u,v \rangle \in R \circ T)$	(3.2.13)
$\leftrightarrow (\langle u,v \rangle \in (R \circ S) \cap (R \circ T).$	(2.6.2b)
(b) $\langle u,v \rangle \in (R \circ S) \sim (R \circ T)$	
$\leftrightarrow (\langle u,v \rangle \in R \circ S \ \& \ \langle u,v \rangle \notin R \circ T)$	(2.6.2c)
$\leftrightarrow [(\exists w)(\langle u,w \rangle \in S \ \& \ \langle w,v \rangle \in R) \ \& \ \neg(\exists w)(\langle u,w \rangle \in T \ \& \ \langle w,v \rangle \in R)]$	
	(3.2.13)
$\leftrightarrow [(\exists w)(\langle u,w \rangle \in S \ \& \ \langle w,v \rangle \in R) \ \& \ (\forall w)(\langle w,v \rangle \in R \rightarrow \langle u,w \rangle \notin T)]$	
	(1.2.25, 1.2.20)
$\rightarrow (\exists w)(\langle u,w \rangle \in S \ \& \ \langle u,w \rangle \notin T \ \& \ \langle w,v \rangle \in R)$	(1.2.16)

$\leftrightarrow (\exists w)(\langle u,w\rangle \in S \sim T \;\&\; \langle w,v\rangle \in R)$ (2.6.2c)
$\leftrightarrow \langle u,v\rangle \in R \circ (S \sim T).$ (3.2.13) ■

Notice that in the proof of (a) we cannot replace the one "→" by "↔" because the converse of 1.2.31 is not a theorem. Similarly for (b), because the converse of 1.2.16 is not a theorem. Moreover, we cannot prove that the right side of (a) is a subclass of the left side. For, let

$$R = \{\langle w_1,v\rangle, \langle w_2,v\rangle\},$$
$$S = \{\langle u,w_1\rangle\},$$
$$T = \{\langle u,w_2\rangle\}.$$

Then

$$S \cap T = \emptyset,$$

so

$$R \circ (S \cap T) = \emptyset.$$

But

$$R \circ S = R \circ T = \{\langle u,v\rangle\},$$

so

$$(R \circ S) \cap (R \circ T) = \{\langle u,v\rangle\}.$$

The preceding example also shows that in (b) inclusion cannot be strengthened to identity for

$$(R \circ S) \sim (R \circ T) = \emptyset$$

and

$$R \circ (S \sim T) = \{\langle u,v\rangle\}.$$

There are occasions when it is convenient to restrict the domain of a relation. For example, if

$$R = \{\langle 1,1\rangle, \langle 2,2\rangle, \langle 3,4\rangle\},$$

then R is not reflexive. However, if 3 is omitted from $\mathfrak{D}(R)$, the new relation,

$$S = \{\langle 1,1\rangle, \langle 2,2\rangle\} \subset R$$

is reflexive. We shall use the symbol "$R|X$" to mean "R restricted to X."

Definition 3.2.17.

$$R|X =_{\mathrm{Df}} \{\langle u,v\rangle : u \in X \;\&\; \langle u,v\rangle \in R\}.$$

Clearly $R|X$ is a relation and $R|X \subseteq R$. It is assumed in the following six theorems that X and Y are classes, and the proofs of the theorems are left as exercises.

THEOREM 3.2.18. $R|X = R \cap (X \times \mathcal{R}(R))$.

THEOREM 3.2.19. $X \subseteq Y \rightarrow R|X \subseteq R|Y$.

THEOREM 3.2.20. $R|(X \cup Y) = (R|X) \cup (R|Y)$.

THEOREM 3.2.21. $R|(X \cap Y) = (R|X) \cap (R|Y)$.

THEOREM 3.2.22. $R|(X \sim Y) = (R|X) \sim (R|Y)$.

THEOREM 3.2.23. $(R \circ S)|X = R \circ (S|X)$.

The next notion to be defined is that of the image of a class X under a relation R, symbolically $R''X$.

DEFINITION 3.2.24.

$$R''X =_{\mathrm{Df}} \{v : (\exists u)(u \in X \;\&\; \langle u,v \rangle \in R\}.$$

For example, if

$$R = \{\langle 1,1 \rangle, \langle 1,2 \rangle, \langle 2,3 \rangle, \langle 3,1 \rangle, \langle 3,4 \rangle, \langle 4,4 \rangle\}$$

and

$$X = \{1,2\},$$

then

$$R''X = \{1,2,3\}.$$

Or if R is the relation "<" on the class of integers and $X = \{0\}$, then $R''X =$ the class of positive integers.

THEOREM 3.2.25. $R''X = \mathcal{R}(R|X)$.

Proof:

$$\begin{aligned} v \in R''X &\leftrightarrow (\exists u)(u \in X \;\&\; \langle u,v \rangle \in R) && (3.2.24)\\ &\leftrightarrow (\exists u)(\langle u,v \rangle \in R|X) && (3.2.17)\\ &\leftrightarrow v \in \mathcal{R}(R|X). && (3.2.3b) \blacksquare \end{aligned}$$

In the last three theorems of this section, it is assumed that X and Y are classes.

THEOREM 3.2.26. $R''(X \cup Y) = (R''X \cup R''Y)$.

Proof: Similar to proof of 3.2.15.

THEOREM 3.2.27. $R''(X \cap Y) \subseteq (R''X \cap R''Y)$.

Proof: Similar to the proof of 3.2.16(a).

The following example shows that inclusion cannot be strengthened to identity in 3.2.27. Let

$$\begin{aligned} R &= \{\langle 1,3\rangle, \langle 2,3\rangle\}, \\ X &= \{1\}, \\ Y &= \{2\}, \end{aligned}$$

then

$$R''(X \cap Y) = \emptyset,$$

but

$$(R''X) \cap (R''Y) = \{3\}.$$

THEOREM 3.2.28. $(R''X \sim R''Y) \subseteq R''(X \sim Y)$.

Proof: Similar to the proof of 3.2.16(b).

Moreover, the same example following 3.2.27 may be used to show that inclusion cannot be strengthened to identity since

$$(R''X) \sim (R''Y) = \emptyset$$

and

$$R''(X \sim Y) = \{3\}.$$

EXERCISES 3.2

1. Prove $X \subseteq Y \to R''X \subseteq R''Y$.
2. Prove $(R \circ S)^{-1} = S^{-1} \circ R^{-1}$.
3. Prove each of the following $\text{Rel}(R) \to$
   (a) R is reflexive $\leftrightarrow I|\mathfrak{F}(R) \subseteq R$. ($I$ is the identity relation, $\langle u,v\rangle \in I \leftrightarrow u = v$.)
   (b) R is irreflexive $\leftrightarrow R \cap I = \emptyset$
   (c) R is symmetric $\leftrightarrow R = R^{-1}$
   (d) R is asymmetric $\leftrightarrow R \cap R^{-1} = \emptyset$
   (e) R is antisymmetric $\leftrightarrow R \cap R^{-1} \subseteq I$
   (f) R is transitive $\leftrightarrow R \circ R \subseteq R$
   (g) R is intransitive $\leftrightarrow (R \circ R) \cap R = \emptyset$
   (h) R is an equivalence relation $\leftrightarrow R \circ R^{-1} = R$
4. Prove each of the following: $\text{Rel}(R) \to$
   (a) (R is reflexive & irreflexive) $\to R = \emptyset$
   (b) (R is symmetric & asymmetric) $\to R = \emptyset$
   (c) $\neg$((R is transitive & intransitive) $\to R = \emptyset$).
5. Prove $X \subseteq \mathfrak{D}(R) \to X \subseteq (R^{-1} \circ R)''X$. Give an example to show that inclusion cannot be strengthened to identity.
6. Prove $\text{Rel}(R) \to (\exists X)(\exists Y)(R \subseteq X \times Y)$.

7. Prove $(X \times Y)^{-1} = Y \times X$.
8. Prove $(\mathrm{Cl}(X)\ \&\ \mathrm{Cl}(Y)) \rightarrow (R''X \cap S''Y = \emptyset \leftrightarrow (S^{-1} \circ R) \cap (X \times Y) = \emptyset)$.
9. The *ordinal sum* of two relations R and S is the relation $R + S$ defined as follows:

$$R + S = R \cup S \cup (\mathfrak{F}(R) \times \mathfrak{F}(S)).$$

(a) If $R = \{\langle 1,2\rangle,\langle 1,3\rangle\}$ and $S = \{\langle 3,3\rangle\}$, calculate $R + S$ and $S + R$.
(b) What is the domain, range, and field of $R + S$?
(c) Determine which, if any, of the following distributive laws hold:

$$R + (S \cup T) = (R + S) \cup (R + T)$$
$$R + (S \cap T) = (R + S) \cap (R + T)$$
$$R \cup (S + T) = (R \cup S) + (R \cup T)$$
$$R \cap (S + T) = (R \cap S) + (R \cap T).$$

(d) Prove that if R and S are reflexive relations, then so is $R + S$. Give an example to show that the converse does not hold. State a simple condition to impose on R and S so that the converse does hold.
(e) Prove (R,S,T, & U are reflexive relations & $R + S = T + U$ & $\mathfrak{F}(R) \cap \mathfrak{F}(S) = \emptyset) \rightarrow (R = (R \cap T) + (R \cap U)\ \&\ S = (S \cap T) + (S \cap U))$.

3.3. FUNCTIONS

By a *function* we shall mean a *many–one relation*, or what is often called a *single-valued function.*

DEFINITION 3.3.1. Function

$$\mathrm{Func}(F) =_{\mathrm{Df}} (\mathrm{Rel}(F)\ \&\ (\langle u,v\rangle, \langle u,w\rangle \in F \rightarrow v = w)).$$

Clearly the identity relation

$$I = \{\langle u,v\rangle : u = v\}$$

is a function. Also, if $\mathfrak{F}(F)$ = the class of real numbers and $\langle u,v\rangle \in F$ if and only if $v = u^2$, then F is a function. But if $\mathfrak{F}(G)$ = class of real numbers and $\langle u,v\rangle \in G$ if and only if $u = v^2$, then G is not a function.

If F is a function, instead of writing

$$\langle u,v\rangle \in F \text{ or } u\,F\,v$$

we shall often write

$$v = F(u) \text{ or } v = F_u.$$

If F is a function and the domain of F is a class of ordered pairs, F is said to be a *function of two variables*. In this case instead of writing

$$F(\langle u,v\rangle) = w,$$

it is customary to omit the angular brackets and write

$$F(u,v) = w.$$

The following are examples of functions of two variables:

$$F_1(u,v) = u,$$
$$F_2(u,v) = \langle u,v \rangle,$$

or if u and v are real numbers,

$$F_3(u,v) = u^2 + v^2.$$

Functions of three or more variables are defined analogously.

THEOREM 3.3.2.

(a) $(\text{Func}(F) \ \& \ G \subseteq F) \rightarrow \text{Func}(G)$

(b) $\text{Func}(F) \rightarrow \text{Func}(F|X)$

(c) $(\text{Func}(F) \ \& \ \text{Func}(G)) \rightarrow [\text{Func}(F \circ G) \ \& \ (F \circ G)(u) = F(G(u))]$

(d) $\text{Func}(I)$.

Proof:

(a) Suppose F is a function and $G \subseteq F$. Suppose also that $\langle u,v \rangle$, $\langle u,w \rangle \in G$. Then, since $G \subseteq F$, $\langle u,v \rangle$, $\langle u,w \rangle \in F$ and since F is a function, $v = w$. Therefore, G is a function.

(b) Since $F|X \subseteq F$, (b) follows from (a).

(c) Suppose F and G are functions and $\langle u,v \rangle$, $\langle u,w \rangle \in F \circ G$. Then there are x and y such that

$$\langle u,x \rangle \in G \text{ and } \langle x,v \rangle \in F,$$
$$\langle u,y \rangle \in G \text{ and } \langle y,w \rangle \in F.$$

Since G is a function, $x = y$. And since $x = y$ and F is a function, $v = w$. Therefore, $F \circ G$ is a function.

To prove the last part of (c) we have

$$\begin{aligned} v = (F \circ G)(u) &\leftrightarrow \langle u,v \rangle \in F \circ G \\ &\leftrightarrow (\exists w)(\langle u,w \rangle \in G \ \& \ \langle w,v \rangle \in F) \\ &\leftrightarrow (\exists w)(w = G(u) \ \& \ \langle w,v \rangle \in F) \\ &\leftrightarrow \langle G(u),v \rangle \in F \\ &\leftrightarrow v = F(G(u)). \end{aligned}$$

(d) Suppose $\langle u,v \rangle$, $\langle u,w \rangle \in I$, then $u = v$ and $u = w$. Therefore, $v = w$. ■

A 1–1 *function* is a function whose inverse is also a function.

DEFINITION 3.3.3. 1–1 Function

$$\text{1–1 Func}(F) =_{\text{Df}} (\text{Func}(F) \ \& \ \text{Func}(F^{-1})).$$

Therefore F is a 1–1 function if

(1) F is a relation—a class of ordered pairs,

(2) F is a function—if $\langle u,v\rangle, \langle u,w\rangle \in F$, then $v = w$,

and

(3) F^{-1} is a function—if $\langle u,w\rangle, \langle v,w\rangle \in F$, then $u = v$.

The identity function is an example of a 1–1 function. Any linear function of a real number is 1–1. That is, if $\mathfrak{D}(F) =$ the class of real numbers and a and b are real numbers, $a \neq 0$, then

$$F(x) = ax + b$$

is a linear function and is 1–1. Another example of a 1–1 function is the function G such that

$$\mathfrak{D}(G) = \{u_1, u_2, \ldots, u_n\},$$

$$G(u_i) = \begin{cases} u_{i+1} & \text{if } 1 \leqq i \leqq n-1 \\ u_1 & \text{if } i = n. \end{cases}$$

A 1–1 function on a finite set is often called a *permutation*.

THEOREM 3.3.4.

(a) $1\text{–}1 \operatorname{Func}(F) \leftrightarrow 1\text{–}1 \operatorname{Func}(F^{-1})$

(b) $1\text{–}1 \operatorname{Func}(F) \rightarrow (F(x) = y \leftrightarrow F^{-1}(y) = x)$

(c) $(1\text{–}1 \operatorname{Func}(F)\ \&\ G \subseteq F) \rightarrow 1\text{–}1 \operatorname{Func}(G)$

(d) $1\text{–}1 \operatorname{Func}(F) \rightarrow 1\text{–}1 \operatorname{Func}(F|X)$

(e) $(1\text{–}1 \operatorname{Func}(F)\ \&\ 1\text{–}1 \operatorname{Func}(G)) \rightarrow 1\text{–}1 \operatorname{Func}(F \circ G)$

(f) $1\text{–}1 \operatorname{Func}(F) \leftrightarrow (F \circ F^{-1} \subseteq I\ \&\ F^{-1} \circ F \subseteq I)$

(g) $1\text{–}1 \operatorname{Func}(I)$.

The proof is left as an exercise.

We shall introduce some mathematical notation which will simplify the discussion of functions.

DEFINITION 3.3.5.

(a) $F: X \rightarrow Y =_{\mathrm{Df}} (\operatorname{Func}(F)\ \&\ \mathfrak{D}(F) = X\ \&\ \mathfrak{R}(F) \subseteq Y)$. ($F$ is a function from X into Y.)

(b) $F: X \xrightarrow{\text{onto}} Y =_{\mathrm{Df}} (\operatorname{Func}(F)\ \&\ \mathfrak{D}(F) = X\ \&\ \mathfrak{R}(F) = Y)$. (F is a function from X onto Y.)

(c) $F: X \xrightarrow{1\text{–}1} Y =_{\mathrm{Df}} (1\text{–}1 \operatorname{Func}(F)\ \&\ \mathfrak{D}(F) = X\ \&\ \mathfrak{R}(F) \subseteq Y)$. ($F$ is a 1–1 function from X into Y.)

(d) $F: X \xrightarrow[1\text{–}1]{\text{onto}} Y =_{\mathrm{Df}} (1\text{–}1 \operatorname{Func}(F)\ \&\ \mathfrak{D}(F) = X\ \&\ \mathfrak{R}(F) = Y)$.

If $F: X \rightarrow Y$, we often say F *maps* X *into* Y and if $F: X \rightarrow X$, we say F is a function *on* X.

The following theorem is often useful when it is necessary to prove that some function is 1–1 or onto.

THEOREM 3.3.6.

$$((F: X \to Y) \; \& \; (G: Y \to X) \; \& \; (G \circ F = I|X)) \\ \to ((F: X \xrightarrow{1\text{-}1} Y) \; \& \; (G: Y \xrightarrow{\text{onto}} X)).$$

Proof: We shall show first that F is 1–1. Suppose

$$\langle u,w \rangle, \langle v,w \rangle \in F.$$

Since $G \circ F = I|X$, there is an s and t such that

$$\langle u,s \rangle \in F \text{ and } \langle s,u \rangle \in G,$$
$$\langle v,t \rangle \in F \text{ and } \langle t,v \rangle \in G.$$

Since $\langle u,w \rangle, \langle u,s \rangle \in F$ and F is a function, $w = s$. And since $\langle v,w \rangle, \langle v,t \rangle \in F$, $w = t$. Therefore, $s = t$. Now we have $\langle s,u \rangle, \langle t,v \rangle \in G$, $s = t$, and G is a function, therefore $u = v$, which implies F is 1–1.

To show G maps Y onto X, let $u \in X$. Then, since $G \circ F = I|X$, there is a $v \in Y$ such that $\langle u,v \rangle \in F$ and $\langle v,u \rangle \in G$. The latter condition implies that G maps Y onto X. ■

It does not follow from 3.3.6 that G is 1–1 or that F maps X onto Y. To see this let

$$X = \{1\}, \qquad Y = \{2,3\},$$
$$F = \{\langle 1,2 \rangle\}, \qquad G = \{\langle 2,1 \rangle, \langle 3,1 \rangle\}.$$

Then F, G, X, and Y satisfy the hypothesis of 3.3.6, but F does not map X onto Y and G is not 1–1.

Theorems 3.2.27 and 3.2.28 can be strengthened when R^{-1} is a function.

THEOREM 3.3.7.

(a) $\text{Func}(R^{-1}) \leftrightarrow (\forall X)(\forall Y)(R''(X \cap Y) = (R''X \cap R''Y))$

(b) $\text{Func}(R^{-1}) \leftrightarrow (\forall X)(\forall Y)(R''(X \sim Y) = (R''X \sim R''Y))$.

Proof:

(a) It follows from 3.2.27 that

$$R''(X \cap Y) \subseteq (R''X \cap R''Y)$$

for all R, X, and Y. Suppose R^{-1} is a function. Then

$$w \in (R''X \cap R''Y)$$
$$\leftrightarrow w \in R''X \;\&\; w \in R''Y \qquad (2.6.2b)$$
$$\leftrightarrow (\exists u)(u \in X \;\&\; \langle u,w \rangle \in R) \;\&\; (\exists v)(v \in Y \;\&\; \langle v,w \rangle \in R). \qquad (3.2.24)$$

Since R^{-1} is a function, $\langle u,w \rangle$, $\langle v,w \rangle \in R$ implies $u = v$. Thus, we have

$$\begin{aligned} w \in (R''X \cap R''Y) &\rightarrow (\exists u)(u \in X \;\&\; u \in Y \;\&\; \langle u,w \rangle \in R) \\ &\leftrightarrow (\exists u)(u \in X \cap Y \;\&\; \langle u,w \rangle \in R) && (2.6.2b) \\ &\leftrightarrow w \in R''(X \cap Y). && (3.2.24) \end{aligned}$$

Therefore, $R''(X \cap Y) = (R''X \cap R''Y)$ for all X and Y.

Conversely, suppose $R''(X \cap Y) = (R''X \cap R''Y)$ for all X and Y and suppose $\langle u,w \rangle$, $\langle v,w \rangle \in R$. Let

$$X = \{u\} \text{ and } Y = \{v\}.$$

Then, if $u \neq v$,

$$R''(X \cap Y) = \emptyset,$$

but

$$w \in R''X \cap R''Y,$$

which contradicts the hypothesis that $R''(X \cap Y) = (R''X \cap R''Y)$ for all X and Y. Thus, we must have $u = v$, which implies that R^{-1} is a function.

(b) From 3.2.28 we obtain

$$(R''X \sim R''Y) \subseteq R''(X \sim Y)$$

for all R, X, and Y. Suppose, then, that R^{-1} is a function.

$$\begin{aligned} w \in R''(X \sim Y) &\leftrightarrow (\exists u)(u \in X \sim Y \;\&\; \langle u,w \rangle \in R) && (3.2.24) \\ &\leftrightarrow (\exists u)(u \in X \;\&\; u \notin Y \;\&\; \langle u,w \rangle \in R) && (2.6.2c) \\ &\rightarrow w \in R''X. && (3.2.24) \end{aligned}$$

We wish to show that $w \notin R''Y$. So suppose $w \in R''Y$, then by 3.2.24

$$(\exists v)(v \in Y \;\&\; \langle v,w \rangle \in R).$$

Since R^{-1} is a function, $\langle u,w \rangle$, $\langle v,w \rangle \in R$ implies $u = v$. But $u \notin Y$, therefore, $w \notin R''Y$. So we have

$$w \in R''X \;\&\; w \notin R''Y.$$

Consequently,

$$w \in R''X \sim R''Y.$$

Hence, we have shown $R''(X \sim Y) = (R''X \sim R''Y)$ for all X and Y under the assumption that R^{-1} is a function.

Conversely, suppose $R''(X \sim Y) = (R''X \sim R''Y)$ for all X and Y and $\langle u,w \rangle$, $\langle v,w \rangle \in R$. Let

$$X = \{u\} \text{ and } Y = \{v\}.$$

Then, if $u \neq v$,

$$w \in R''(X \sim Y),$$

but

$$w \notin R''X \sim R''Y,$$

contradicting the hypothesis. Therefore $u = v$ and R^{-1} is a function. ■

If F is a function, then in a certain manner of speaking the range of F is no bigger than the domain, because for each element in the domain there is one and only one element in the range which corresponds to it, while one element in the range may correspond to many elements in the domain. Therefore, one would expect that if the domain of a function is a set, then so is the range. We take this as an axiom.

A6: $$(\text{Func}(F) \ \& \ \text{S}(\mathfrak{D}(F))) \rightarrow \text{S}(\mathfrak{R}(F)).$$

A6 is called the *Axiom of replacement* and is due to A. Fraenkel. However, A6 is not necessarily true if F is not a function. The range of a relation may be larger than its domain. For example, let

$$R = \{\langle u,v\rangle : v \in V\},$$

then

$$\mathfrak{D}(R) = \{u\} \ \& \ \mathfrak{R}(R) = V.$$

We shall show now that the temporary axiom T1 is a consequence of A6.

THEOREM 3.3.8. $[\text{Cl}(X) \ \& \ (\exists u)(S(u) \ \& \ X \subseteq u)] \rightarrow S(X).$

Proof: Suppose $X \subseteq u$. By 3.3.2(d), I, the identity relation, is a function and by 3.3.2(b), $I|X$ is also a function. Since $X \subseteq u$, $(I|X)''u = X$. Therefore, if u is a set, it follows from A6 that X is a set. ■

EXERCISES 3.3

1. Prove:
   (a) $(\text{Func}(F) \ \& \ \text{Func}(G)) \rightarrow (\text{Func}(F \cap G) \ \& \ \text{Func}(F \sim G))$
   (b) $(1\text{–}1 \ \text{Func}(F) \ \& \ 1\text{–}1 \ \text{Func}(G)) \rightarrow (1\text{–}1 \ \text{Func}(F \cap G) \ \& \ 1\text{–}1 \ \text{Func}(F \sim G))$.
2. If F and G are functions, give necessary and sufficient conditions for $F \cup G$ to be a function.
3. Give an example of a function F such that $F = F^{-1}$ where F is not an identity function.
4. Prove $(F : X_1 \xrightarrow[\text{onto}]{1\text{–}1} X_2 \ \& \ G : Y_1 \xrightarrow[\text{onto}]{1\text{–}1} Y_2) \rightarrow$
   (a) $(\text{Dis}(X_1, Y_1) \ \& \ \text{Dis}(X_2, Y_2)) \rightarrow (\exists H)(H : (X_1 \cup Y_1) \xrightarrow[\text{onto}]{1\text{–}1} (X_2 \cup Y_2))$

(b) $(\exists H)(H{:}(X_1 \times Y_1) \xrightarrow[\text{onto}]{1-1} (X_2 \times Y_2))$.

5. Which of the following relations are functions? Which are 1–1 functions? (*Re* = class of real numbers and *In* = class of integers.)
   (a) $u\ R\ v \leftrightarrow (u,v \in Re\ \&\ u < v < u + 1)$
   (b) $u\ R\ v \leftrightarrow (u,v \in In\ \&\ u < v < u + 2)$
   (c) $u\ R\ v \leftrightarrow (u,v \in Re\ \&\ u^2 + v^2 = 1)$
   (d) $u\ R\ v \leftrightarrow (u,v \in \mathrm{Re}\ \&\ u = v^2)$
   (e) $u\ R\ v \leftrightarrow (u,v \in \mathrm{Re}\ \&\ v = u^2)$
   (f) $u\ R\ v \leftrightarrow \left(u,v \in Re\ \&\ 0 \leqq u < 1\ \&\ v = \dfrac{u}{1-u}\right)$
   (g) $\langle u,v\rangle\ R\ w \leftrightarrow \left(u,v,w \in Re\ \&\ w = \dfrac{u+v}{2}\right)$
   (h) $\langle u,v\rangle\ R\ w \leftrightarrow (u,v,w \in In\ \&\ 0 \leqq u,v \leqq 9\ \&\ w = 10\cdot u + v)$.
6. Prove $(F{:}X \xrightarrow{1-1} Y\ \&\ (\forall u)(u \subseteq X \rightarrow G(u) = F''u)) \rightarrow G{:}\mathcal{P}(X) \xrightarrow{1-1} \mathcal{P}(Y)$.
7 Prove each of the following:
   (a) $(1\text{–}1\ \mathrm{Func}(F)\ \&\ \mathrm{Pr}(X)\ \&\ X \subseteq \mathfrak{D}(F)) \rightarrow \mathrm{Pr}(F''X)$
   (b) $\mathrm{Pr}(X) \rightarrow \mathrm{Pr}(\mathcal{P}(X))$
   (c) $(\mathrm{Pr}(X)\ \&\ Y \neq \emptyset) \rightarrow \mathrm{Pr}(X \times Y)$
   (d) $(\mathrm{Func}(F)\ \&\ \mathrm{S}(\mathfrak{D}(F))) \rightarrow \mathrm{S}(F)$
   (e) $(1\text{–}1\ \mathrm{Func}(F)\ \&\ (\mathrm{S}(\mathfrak{D}F))$ or $\mathrm{S}(\mathfrak{R}(F))) \rightarrow \mathrm{S}(F)$.

3.4. EQUIPOLLENCE

It is possible to determine whether two classes have the same number of elements without knowing how to count. This is done by matching or pairing the elements of the two classes. Thus, for example, to determine whether there are the same number of students and chairs in a given classroom, let each student sit in one chair. Then, if there are no empty chairs and no students standing there must be the same number of students and chairs. If two classes have the same number of elements we shall call them *equipollent*.

DEFINITION 3.4.1. Equipollence

$$X \approx Y =_{\mathrm{Df}} (\exists F)(F{:}X \xrightarrow[\text{onto}]{1-1} Y).$$

Since the domain and range of a function are classes if $X \approx Y$ then both X and Y are classes. The following theorem also follows easily from 3.4.1.

THEOREM 3.4.2.
(a) $\mathrm{Cl}(X) \rightarrow X \approx X$
(b) $X \approx Y \rightarrow Y \approx X$
(c) $(X \approx Y\ \&\ Y \approx Z) \rightarrow X \approx Z$.

Thus $\approx$ is an equivalence relation on the class of all sets. (We also have that 3.4.2 holds if X, Y, and Z are proper classes, but a proper class cannot be an element of the field of a relation.)

DEFINITION 3.4.3. Dominance

(a) $X \precsim Y =_{\text{Df}} (\exists F)(F: X \xrightarrow{1-1} Y)$

(b) $X \prec Y =_{\text{Df}} (X \precsim Y \; \& \; X \not\approx Y)$.

"$X \precsim Y$" is read "X is *dominated* by Y" and "$X \prec Y$" is read "X is *strictly dominated* by Y." The proof of the following theorem follows easily from definition 3.4.3 and is left as an exercise.

THEOREM 3.4.4.

(a) $\text{Cl}(X) \rightarrow X \precsim X$

(b) $(X \precsim Y \; \& \; Y \precsim Z) \rightarrow X \precsim Z$

(c) $X \not\prec X$

(d) $X \subseteq Y \rightarrow X \precsim Y$

(e) $X \precsim Y \leftrightarrow (X \prec Y \text{ or } X \approx Y)$

(f) $X \precsim Y \leftrightarrow (\exists Z)(Z \subseteq Y \; \& \; X \approx Z)$.

The proof of the following theorem follows directly from A6, and definitions 3.4.1 and 3.4.3. It is left as an exercise.

THEOREM 3.4.5.

(a) $(\text{S}(X) \; \& \; X \approx Y) \rightarrow \text{S}(Y)$

(b) $(\text{S}(X) \; \& \; Y \precsim X) \rightarrow \text{S}(Y)$

(c) $(\text{Pr}(X) \; \& \; X \approx Y) \rightarrow \text{Pr}(Y)$

(d) $(\text{Pr}(X) \; \& \; X \precsim Y) \rightarrow \text{Pr}(Y)$.

The next important result is due to Cantor. Its proof is based on the same principle as Russell's paradox, but it precedes Russell's paradox.

THEOREM 3.4.6. $\text{S}(x) \rightarrow x \prec \mathcal{P}(x)$.

Proof: It is clear that $x \precsim \mathcal{P}(x)$, for define a function F such that for each $u \in x$, $F(u) = \{u\}$. F is clearly a 1–1 function mapping x into $\mathcal{P}(x)$.

Suppose $x \approx \mathcal{P}(x)$. Let G be a 1–1 function mapping x onto $\mathcal{P}(x)$. For each $u \in x$, $G(u) \in \mathcal{P}(x)$, so $G(u) \subseteq x$. Let y be a set defined as follows:

$$y = \{u : u \in x \; \& \; u \notin G(u)\}.$$

Clearly, $y \subseteq x$ so $y \in \mathcal{P}(x)$. Therefore, there must be a $v \in x$ such that $G(v) = y$. But this is where the trouble lies. If $v \in y$, then by the definition of y, $v \notin G(v) = y$. On the other hand, if $v \notin y$ then $v \notin G(v)$. So again by the definition of y, $v \in y$. So we have $v \in y$ if and only if $v \notin y$. This is a contradiction so $x \not\approx \mathcal{P}(x)$. Therefore, we must have $x \prec \mathcal{P}(x)$. ■

There are two additional results concerning 1–1 functions which are not surprising but which are difficult to prove. The first, called the Schröder–Bernstein theorem, states

$$(x \lesssim y \;\&\; y \lesssim x) \rightarrow x \approx y \qquad \text{(see § 4.5).}$$

The other, called the trichotomy, states

$$x \prec y \text{ or } x \approx y \text{ or } y \prec x \qquad \text{(see § 10.2).}$$

The proofs of these theorems require more tools than have been developed up to this point. In fact, we have to introduce another axiom before we can prove the trichotomy.

EXERCISES 3.4

1. Prove
   $(X_1 \approx X_2 \;\&\; Y_1 \approx Y_2 \;\&\; X_1 \cap Y_1 = \emptyset \;\&\; X_2 \cap Y_2 = \emptyset) \rightarrow (X_1 \cup Y_1) \approx (X_2 \cup Y_2)$
2. Prove $(X_1 \approx X_2 \;\&\; Y_1 \approx Y_2) \rightarrow (X_1 \times Y_1) \approx (X_2 \times Y_2)$.
3. Prove:
   (a) $(X \times Y) \approx (Y \times X)$
   (b) $((X \times Y) \times Z) \approx (X \times (Y \times Z))$.
4. Prove $(\exists F)(F : X \xrightarrow{\text{onto}} Y) \leftrightarrow (\mathcal{P}(Y) \lesssim \mathcal{P}(X))$.

3.5. "INFINITE" OPERATIONS

If F is a function from X into Y, then for each $u \in X$, F_u is the unique v such that $\langle u,v \rangle \in F$. In fact,

$$\mathcal{R}(F) = \{F_u : u \in X\}.$$

The class X, the domain of F, is often called an *index class.* This notation permits us to generalize the operations of union and intersection.

DEFINITION 3.5.1. Union and Intersection

$$(\text{Func}(F) \;\&\; X \subseteq \mathcal{D}(F)) \rightarrow$$

(a) $\bigcup_{u \in X} F_u =_{\text{Df}} \{x : (\exists u)(u \in X \;\&\; x \in F_u)\}$
(b) $\bigcap_{u \in X} F_u =_{\text{Df}} \{x : (\forall u)(u \in X \rightarrow x \in F_u)\}$.

Thus, the union is the class of all elements which belong to at least *one* of the F_u's, and the intersection is the class of all elements which belong to *all* of the F_u's. In case F is the identity function, we use a slightly different notation.

DEFINITION 3.5.2. Union and Intersection

(a) $\bigcup X =_{\text{Df}} \bigcup_{u \in X} I_u$
(b) $\bigcap X =_{\text{Df}} \bigcap_{u \in X} I_u$.

Thus, we have

THEOREM 3.5.3.
(a) $\bigcup X = \{x:(\exists u)(u \in X \;\&\; x \in u)\}$
(b) $\bigcap X = \{x:(\forall u)(u \in X \rightarrow x \in u)\}$.

The proof follows immediately from 3.5.1 and 3.5.2.

There is a further generalization of 3.5.1 which is of some interest—namely the union and intersection of classes which are not necessarily sets. Definitions 3.5.1 and 3.5.2 both define union and intersection for a class of sets. A class of proper classes, of course, does not exist since a proper class cannot be an element of any class. However, if R is a relation, then $R''\{u\}$ could be a proper class. For example, if

$$R = \{\langle u,v\rangle : v \in V\},$$

then

$$R''\{u\} = V.$$

This is the device we shall use to define union and intersection of classes.

DEFINITION 3.5.4. Union and Intersection of Classes

$$(\mathrm{Rel}(R) \;\&\; X \subseteq \mathfrak{D}(R)) \rightarrow$$

(a) $\bigcup_{u\in X} R''\{u\} = \{x:(\exists u)(u \in X \;\&\; x \in R''\{u\})\}$
(b) $\bigcap_{u\in X} R''\{u\} = \{x:(\forall u)(u \in X \rightarrow x \in R''\{u\})\}$.

Definition 3.5.1 is a special case of 3.5.4.

It is clear that the union and intersection defined in this section is a generalization of that defined in §2.6. The proof of the next theorem is left as an exercise.

THEOREM 3.5.5. $\mathrm{S}(u) \;\&\; \mathrm{S}(v) \rightarrow$
(a) $\bigcup \{u,v\} = u \cup v$
(b) $\bigcap \{u,v\} = u \cap v$.

The following examples illustrate these notions. It

$$Y = \{\{1,2\}, \{1,2,3\}, \{2,4,6\}\},$$

then

$$\bigcup Y = \{1,2,3,4,6\}$$

and

$$\bigcap Y = \{2\}.$$

If

$$X = \text{set of positive integers}$$

and for each $u \in X$

$$F_u = \{u, u + 1, u + 2, \ldots\},$$

then, if $u \leqq v$,

$$F_u \cup F_v = F_u,\ F_u \cap F_v = F_v,\ \bigcup_{u \in X} F_u = X,\ \bigcap_{u \in X} F_u = \emptyset.$$

Finally, if

$$Re = \text{set of real numbers}$$

and a relation R is defined by

$$u\ R\ v \leftrightarrow (\exists w)(v = \langle u, w \rangle),$$

then

$$R''\{u\} = \{u\} \times V$$

and

$$\bigcup_{u \in Re} R''\{u\} = Re \times V$$

and since, if $u \neq v$, $R''\{u\} \cap R''\{v\} = \emptyset$,

$$\bigcap_{u \in Re} R''\{u\} = \emptyset.$$

Now we shall replace the temporary axiom T2 by a stronger axiom.

A7: $$\mathrm{S}(X) \rightarrow \mathrm{S}(\bigcup X).$$

The union of any set is a set. Clearly T2 follows from A7. Also the following theorem is a result of A7.

THEOREM 3.5.6.

$$(\mathrm{Func}(F)\ \&\ X \subseteq \mathfrak{D}(F)\ \&\ \mathrm{S}(X)) \rightarrow \mathrm{S}(\bigcup_{u \in X} F_u).$$

It is necessary to be somewhat more careful in the case of intersection because of the following result.

THEOREM 3.5.7. $\bigcap \emptyset = V.$

Proof: Clearly,

$$\bigcap \emptyset \subseteq V$$

since every class is a subclass of V. Suppose $u \in V$. Since $\emptyset$ has no elements $v \in \emptyset$ is false for all v. Consequently,

$$v \in \emptyset \rightarrow u \in v$$

is true for all v. Therefore, $u \in \bigcap \emptyset$ and

$$V \subseteq \bigcap \emptyset. \blacksquare$$

COROLLARY 3.5.8. $\text{Func}(F) \to \bigcap_{u \in \emptyset} F_u = V$.

(What can be said about $\bigcup \emptyset$ and $\bigcup_{u \in \emptyset} F_u$?)

We can prove that the intersection of a non-empty class is a set or is empty.

THEOREM 3.5.9. $X \neq \emptyset \to (\text{S}(\bigcap X) \text{ or } \bigcap X = \emptyset)$.

Proof: Since $X \neq \emptyset$, there is an element $w \in X$. By 3.5.2(b)

$$u \in \bigcap X \leftrightarrow (\forall v)(v \in X \to u \in v).$$

But $w \in X$, therefore, $u \in \bigcap X$ implies $u \in W$. If w is a set, then $\bigcap X \subseteq w$. Therefore, by 3.3.8, $\bigcap X$ is a set. If all elements of X are atoms, then $\bigcap X = \emptyset$, which may or may not be a set. ■

Since the intersection is a subclass of each class in the intersection, we can generalize 3.5.9.

THEOREM 3.5.10. $[\text{Rel}(R) \ \& \ X \subseteq \mathfrak{D}(R) \ \& \ (\exists u)(u \in X \ \& \ \text{S}(R''\{u\})] \to \text{S}(\bigcap_{u \in X} R''\{u\})$.

That is, if at least one of the classes $R''\{u\}$ is a set, then the intersection of all of them is a set. The proof of this theorem is left as an exercise.

The following theorem gives generalizations of the distributive laws and De Morgan's laws.

THEOREM 3.5.11. $(\text{Func}(F) \ \& \ \text{Func}(G) \ \& \ X \subseteq \mathfrak{D}(F) \ \& \ Y \subseteq \mathfrak{D}(G) \ \& \ X \neq \emptyset \ \& \ Y \neq \emptyset \ \& \ \text{S}(Z)) \to$

(a) $Z \cap \bigcup_{u \in X} F_u = \bigcup_{u \in X} (Z \cap F_u)$
(b) $Z \cup \bigcap_{u \in X} F_u = \bigcap_{u \in X} (X \cup F_u)$
(c) $\bigcup_{u \in X} F_u \cap \bigcup_{v \in Y} G_v = \bigcup_{\langle u,v \rangle \in X \times Y} (F_u \cap G_v)$
(d) $\bigcap_{u \in X} F_u \cup \bigcap_{v \in Y} G_v = \bigcap_{\langle u,v \rangle \in X \times Y} (F_u \cup G_u)$
(e) $(\bigcup_{u \in X} F_u)' = \bigcap_{u \in X} F'_u$
(f) $(\bigcap_{u \in X} F_u)' = \bigcup_{u \in X} F'_u$.

Proof: We shall prove (a) and (f) and leave the proof of the others as exercises.

(a)

$$\begin{aligned} w \in Z \cap \textstyle\bigcup_{u \in X} F_u &\leftrightarrow (w \in Z \ \& \ w \in \textstyle\bigcup_{u \in X} F_u) && (2.6.2\text{b}) \\ &\leftrightarrow (w \in Z \ \& \ (\exists u)(u \in X \ \& \ w \in F_u)) && (3.5.1\text{a}) \\ &\leftrightarrow (\exists u)(w \in Z \ \& \ u \in X \ \& \ w \in F_u) && (1.2.34) \\ &\leftrightarrow (\exists u)(u \in X \ \& \ w \in Z \cap F_u) && (2.6.2\text{b}) \\ &\leftrightarrow w \in \textstyle\bigcup_{u \in X} (Z \cap F_u). && (3.5.1\text{a}) \end{aligned}$$

(f)

$$
\begin{aligned}
w \in (\textstyle\bigcap_{u\in X} F_u)' &\leftrightarrow w \notin \textstyle\bigcap_{u\in X} F_u && \text{(2.6.2d)}\\
&\leftrightarrow \neg(\forall u)(u \in X \rightarrow w \in F_u) && \text{(3.5.1b)}\\
&\leftrightarrow (\exists u)(u \in X \,\&\, w \notin F_u) && \text{(1.2.26, 1.2.20)}\\
&\leftrightarrow (\exists u)(u \in X \,\&\, w \in F_u') && \text{(2.6.2d)}\\
&\leftrightarrow w \in \textstyle\bigcup_{u\in X} F_u'. && \text{(3.5.1a)} \blacksquare
\end{aligned}
$$

The following two theorems are generalizations of 3.2.26 and 3.3.7(a). The proofs are left as exercises for the reader.

THEOREM 3.5.12.

$(\mathrm{Func}(F) \,\&\, X \subseteq \mathfrak{D}(F) \,\&\, X \neq \emptyset \,\&\, \mathrm{Rel}(R)) \rightarrow R''(\bigcup_{u\in X} F_u) = \bigcup_{u\in X} R''F_u.$

THEOREM 3.5.13.

$(\mathrm{Func}(F) \,\&\, X \subseteq \mathfrak{D}(F) \,\&\, X \neq \emptyset \,\&\, \mathrm{Rel}(R) \,\&\, \mathrm{Func}(R^{-1})) \rightarrow$
$R''(\bigcap_{u\in X} F_u) = \bigcap_{u\in X} R''F_u.$

Theorems 3.5.11–13 may be generalized to include the union and intersection of proper classes by using the technique given in 3.5.4.

The generalization of the direct product to a class of sets is a bit more tricky than the generalization of union and intersection. The direct product of two classes X and Y,

$$X \times Y = \{\langle u,v\rangle : u \in X \text{ and } v \in Y\}.$$

So it would not be unreasonable to expect that the direct product of n classes would be a class of ordered n-tuples. However, if n is infinite, generalizations along this line are not feasible, so we approach the problem from a slightly different angle.

Let $\{a,b\}$ be an unordered pair with $a \neq b$ and let

$$Z = \{\{\langle a,u\rangle, \langle b,v\rangle\} : u \in X \text{ and } v \in Y\}.$$

Let us compare Z with $X \times Y$. We note that

$$\langle u,v\rangle \in X \times Y \leftrightarrow \{\langle a,u\rangle, \langle b,v\rangle\} \in Z,$$

so that the only difference between Z and $X \times Y$ is the names which are given their elements. While $X \times Y$ is a class of ordered pairs, Z is a class of functions. The notion of an infinite ordered tuple cannot easily be defined, but the notion of a function with an infinite domain has already been defined. Therefore, to generalize the definition of a direct product, we shall generalize Z instead of $X \times Y$.

DEFINITION 3.5.14. Direct Product

$(\mathrm{Func}(F)\ \&\ X \subseteq \mathfrak{D}(F)) \rightarrow$
$\times_{u \in X} F_u =_{\mathrm{Df}} \{g{:}\mathrm{Func}(g)\ \&\ \mathfrak{D}(g) = X\ \&\ (\forall u)(u \in X \rightarrow g(u) \in F_u\}.$

If "F_u" is replaced by "$R''\{u\}$" where R is a relation, then 3.5.14 can be generalized to a direct product of proper classes. We note that if X is a proper class, then

$$\times_{u \in X} F_u = \emptyset,$$

because any function whose domain is a proper class is a proper class itself and no proper class can be an element of a class.

As an illustration, let

$$F_a = \{1,2\} \text{ and } F_b = \{2,3\}.$$

Then

$$F_a \times F_b = \{\langle 1,2\rangle, \langle 1,3\rangle, \langle 2,2\rangle, \langle 2,3\rangle\}$$

while

$$\times_{u \in \{a,b\}} F_u = \{f_1, f_2, f_3, f_4\},$$

where

$$\begin{aligned} f_1 &= \{\langle a,1\rangle, \langle b,2\rangle\} \\ f_2 &= \{\langle a,1\rangle, \langle b,3\rangle\} \\ f_3 &= \{\langle a,2\rangle, \langle b,2\rangle\} \\ f_4 &= \{\langle a,2\rangle, \langle b,3\rangle\}. \end{aligned}$$

As another illustration, take

$$X = \text{set of positive integers}$$

and

$$F_u = \{0,u\} \text{ for each } u \in X.$$

Then

$$\times_{u \in X} F_u = \{g{:}\mathrm{Func}(g)\ \&\ (\forall u)(u \in X \rightarrow (g(u) = 0 \text{ or } g(u) = u)\}.$$

Thus, for example, $I|X \in \times_{u \in X} F_u$ and the function g, such that $g(u) = 0$ for all $u \in X$, is also a member of $\times_{u \in X} F_u$.

If in 3.5.14 F is the identity function, we make the following definition.

DEFINITION 3.5.15. Direct Product

$$\mathrm{Cl}(X) \rightarrow \times X =_{\mathrm{Df}} \times_{u \in X} I_u.$$

It follows immediately from 3.5.14 and 3.5.15 that

THEOREM 3.5.16.

$\mathrm{Cl}(X) \rightarrow \times X = \{g: \mathrm{Func}(g) \ \&\ \mathfrak{D}(g) = X \ \&\ (\forall u)(u \in X \rightarrow g(u) \in u)\}.$

For the special case that $F_u = Y$ for all $u \in X$, we shall denote $\times_{u \in X} F_u$ by Y^X.

DEFINITION 3.5.17. Exponentiation

$$(\mathrm{Cl}(X) \ \&\ \mathrm{Cl}(Y)) \rightarrow Y^X =_{\mathrm{Df}} \{g: \mathrm{Func}(g) \ \&\ \mathfrak{D}(g) = X \ \&\ \mathfrak{R}(g) \subseteq Y\}.$$

Then we clearly have

THEOREM 3.5.18.

$$[\mathrm{Func}(F) \ \&\ X \subseteq \mathfrak{D}(F) \ \&\ (\forall u)(u \in X \rightarrow F_u = Y)] \rightarrow \times_{u \in X} F_u = Y^X.$$

The proof of the following theorem is left as an exercise.

THEOREM 3.5.19. $\mathrm{Cl}(X) \rightarrow$

(a) $\times \emptyset = \{\emptyset\}$

(b) $X \neq \emptyset \rightarrow \emptyset^X = \emptyset.$

Thus we have,

THEOREM 3.5.20.

$$(\mathrm{Cl}(X) \ \&\ \mathrm{Cl}(Y)) \rightarrow (X^Y = \emptyset \leftrightarrow [(X = \emptyset \ \&\ Y \neq \emptyset) \text{ or } \mathrm{Pr}(Y)].$$

Next, we shall prove that the direct product of a set of sets is a set.

THEOREM 3.5.21. $\mathrm{S}(X) \rightarrow (\mathrm{S}(\times X) \text{ or } \times X = \emptyset).$

Proof: Suppose $g \in \times X$ and $\langle u,v \rangle \in g$. Then, using an argument similar to that given in the proof of 3.1.18, we obtain

$$\langle u,v \rangle \in \mathcal{P}(\mathcal{P}(X \cup \bigcup X))$$

since $u \in X$ and $v \in \bigcup X$. Therefore,

$$g \in \mathcal{P}(\mathcal{P}(\mathcal{P}(X \cup \bigcup X))).$$

Hence, $\times X \subseteq \mathcal{P}(\mathcal{P}(\mathcal{P}(X \cup \bigcup X)))$.
Consequently, it follows from hypothesis (X is a set), A7 ($\bigcup X$ is a set), A4 ($\mathcal{P}(\mathcal{P}(\mathcal{P}(X \cup \bigcup X))$ is a set) and 3.3.8 that $\times X$ is a set. ■

COROLLARY 3.5.22. $(\mathrm{S}(X) \ \&\ \mathrm{S}(Y)) \rightarrow \mathrm{S}(X^Y).$

The last theorem to be proved in this section gives a relationship between the power set and exponentiation.

THEOREM 3.5.23. $(\mathrm{S}(x) \ \&\ y = \{u,v\} \ \&\ u \neq v) \rightarrow y^x \approx \mathcal{P}(x).$

Proof: Let $g \in y^x$, then $\mathfrak{D}(g) = x$ and for all $w \in x$

$$g(w) = u \text{ or } g(w) = v.$$

Define

$$\psi(g) = \{w : w \in x \ \& \ g(w) = u\}.$$

Clearly, ψ is a function, $\mathfrak{D}(\psi) = y^x$ and $\mathfrak{R}(\psi) \subseteq \mathcal{P}(x)$. We shall prove that ψ is 1–1 and onto.

Suppose $\psi(g) = \psi(h)$, then

$$g(w) = u \leftrightarrow h(w) = u.$$

Since v is the only other value either of these functions has, we have also

$$g(w) = v \leftrightarrow h(w) = v.$$

Therefore, $g = h$ and ψ is 1–1.

Let $z \in \mathcal{P}(x)$. Define a function g as follows

$$g(w) = \begin{cases} u & \text{if } w \in z \\ v & \text{if } w \in x \sim z. \end{cases}$$

Then $g \in y^x$, and it follows from the definition of ψ that $\psi(g) = z$. Thus, ψ maps y^x onto $\mathcal{P}(x)$.

Hence, we have shown that ψ is a 1–1 function mapping y^x onto $\mathcal{P}(x)$. Therefore, $y^x \approx \mathcal{P}(x)$. ∎

EXERCISES 3.5

1. Let $X = \{\langle u,v\rangle : u,v \in Y\}$. Determine the relationship between Y and $\bigcup\bigcup X$.
2. Prove each of the following:
   (a) $(\text{Func}(F) \ \& \ X \subseteq \mathfrak{D}(F) \ \& \ X \neq \emptyset) \rightarrow ((\bigcap_{u\in X} F_u \subseteq F_v) \ \& \ (F_v \subseteq \bigcup_{u\in X} F_u))$
   (b) $(\text{Func}(F) \ \& \ \text{Func}(G) \ \& \ X \subseteq \mathfrak{D}(F) \ \& \ Y \subseteq \mathfrak{D}(G) \ \& \ X \neq \emptyset \ \& \ Y \neq \emptyset) \rightarrow$
   (i) $(\bigcup_{u\in X} F_u) \times (\bigcup_{v\in Y} G_v) = \bigcup_{\langle u,v\rangle\in X\times Y} (F_u \times G_v)$
   (ii) $(\bigcap_{u\in X} F_u) \times (\bigcap_{v\in Y} G_v) = \bigcap_{\langle u,v\rangle\in X\times Y} (F_u \times G_v)$
   (c) $\text{Cl}(X) \rightarrow X = \bigcup \mathcal{P}(X)$
   (d) $(\text{Cl}(X) \ \& \ X \neq \emptyset) \rightarrow \bigcap \mathcal{P}(X) = \emptyset$
3. For each of the following, if it is a theorem prove it, if not give a counterexample.

   It is assumed that X, Y, and Z are classes and in (a) Z is a set. It is also assumed that F and G are functions such that $F''X$ and $G''Y$ are classes of sets.
   (a) $Y \subseteq Z \rightarrow X^Y \subseteq X^Z$
   (b) $X \subseteq Y \rightarrow X^Z \subseteq Y^Z$
   (c) $X \subseteq \mathcal{P}(\bigcup X)$
   (d) $\mathcal{P}(\bigcup X) \subseteq X$
   (e) $X \subseteq \mathcal{P}(\bigcap X)$
   (f) $\mathcal{P}(\bigcap X) \subseteq X$

(g) $(\times_{u \in X} F_u) \cup (\times_{v \in Y} G_v) = \times_{\langle u,v \rangle \in X \times Y} (F_u \cup G_v)$
(h) $(\times_{u \in X} F_u) \cap (\times_{v \in Y} G_v) = \times_{\langle u,v \rangle \in X \times Y} (F_u \cap G_v)$.

4 Prove each of the following:
(a) $(X_1 \approx X_2 \; \& \; Y_1 \approx Y_2) \rightarrow X_1^{Y_1} \approx X_2^{Y_2}$
(b) $X_1 \precsim X_2 \rightarrow X_1^Y \precsim X_2^Y$
(c) $X_1 \precsim X_2 \rightarrow Y^{X_1} \precsim Y^{X_2}$.

5. Prove:

$$[\mathrm{Cl}(X) \; \& \; (\forall f)(f \in X \rightarrow \mathrm{Func}(f)) \; \& \; (\forall f_1)(\forall f_2)(f_1, f_2 \in X \rightarrow (f_1 \subseteq f_2 \text{ or } f_2 \subseteq f_1))] \rightarrow \mathrm{Func}(\bigcup X).$$

3.6. THE AXIOMS OF CHOICE AND REGULARITY[10]

There are three additional axioms to consider to complete the list of axioms. Two of them will be discussed in this section and the third, the axiom of infinity, will be discussed in Chapter 4.

The axiom of choice has caused a lot of controversy because of its non-constructive character. It asserts the existence of a certain class but gives no rule of construction. It was shown by Gödel in 1939 that the axiom of choice is relatively consistent with the other axioms of set theory. That is, if we assume that axioms A1–A7 are consistent, then the system remains consistent if the axiom of choice is added [see Gödel (1940)]. More recently it was shown by Cohen (1963) that the axiom of choice is independent of the other axioms—which means that if we want to use it we have to postulate it. It is not a consequence of the other axioms.

It turns out that this axiom is quite useful, in fact almost indispensable, in many branches of mathematics. The form of the axiom of choice given here is due to Russell.

A8: The Axiom of Choice

$$[\mathrm{Cl}(X) \; \& \; X \neq \emptyset \; \& \; (\forall u)(u \in X \rightarrow (\mathrm{S}(u) \; \& \; u \neq \emptyset)) \; \& \; \mathrm{Pr\,Dis}(X)] \rightarrow (\exists C)[C \subseteq \bigcup X \; \& \; (\forall u)(u \in X \rightarrow (\exists v)(v \in u \; \& \; C \cap u = \{v\}))].$$

That is, if X is a non-empty class of non-empty pairwise disjoint sets, then there exists a class C which consists of one and only one element from each set in X. The class C is called a *choice class*. Note that if X is not a class of unit sets, then C is not unique.

As a simple example of a choice class let

$$X = \{x_1, x_2, x_3\},$$

[10] The axioms of choice and regularity will be specifically cited when used as opposed to the other axioms which are often implicitly used. Each theorem in which the axiom of choice is used in the proof will be marked with a "Ⓒ" and each theorem in which the axiom of regularity is used in the proof will be marked with an "Ⓡ."

where

$$x_1 = \{1,2,3\}, x_2 = \{4\},\ x_3 = \{5,6\}.$$

Then each of the following six classes are choice classes.

$$C_1 = \{1,4,5\}$$
$$C_2 = \{2,4,5\}$$
$$C_3 = \{3,4,5\}$$
$$C_4 = \{1,4,6\}$$
$$C_5 = \{2,4,6\}$$
$$C_6 = \{3,4,6\}.$$

However, the axiom of choice need only be applied to construct a choice class when there is no other rule available. If X is the class of all sets of pairs of shoes, then a choice class could be the class of all right (or left) shoes. The axiom of choice is not needed to construct such a class since there is a rule for choosing an element from each set. But if, for instance, X is the class of all sets of pairs of socks, then the axiom of choice is needed to construct a choice class.

We shall state several equivalent formulations of the axiom of choice.

AC1: $$[\mathrm{Cl}(X)\ \&\ X \neq \emptyset\ \&\ (\forall u)(u \in X \rightarrow (\mathrm{S}(u)\ \&\ u \neq \emptyset))] \rightarrow (\exists F)[\mathrm{Func}(F)\ \&\ \mathfrak{D}(F) = X\ \&\ (\forall u)(u \in X \rightarrow F(u) \in u)].$$

If X is a non-empty class of non-empty sets, then there is a function F such that the domain of F is X and for each $u \in X$, $F(u) \in u$. A function which satisfies the conditions of AC1 is called a *choice function.*

AC2: $$[\mathrm{Rel}(R)\ \&\ (\forall u)(u \in \mathfrak{D}(R) \rightarrow \mathrm{S}(R''\{u\}))] \rightarrow (\exists F)(\mathrm{Func}(F)\ \&\ \mathfrak{D}(F) = \mathfrak{D}(R)\ \&\ F \subseteq R).$$

AC3: $$[\mathrm{Func}(F)\ \&\ (\forall u)(u \in \mathfrak{R}(F) \rightarrow \mathrm{S}(F^{-1''}\{u\}))] \rightarrow (\exists G)(\mathrm{Func}(G)\ \&\ \mathfrak{D}(G) = \mathfrak{R}(F)\ \&\ G \subseteq F^{-1}).$$

AC1 is due to E. Zermello, and AC2 and AC3 to P. Bernays. At first glance, it looks as if A8 is a special case of AC1, and AC3 is a special case of AC2. However, we shall prove that they are all equivalent, that is we shall prove

$$(\mathrm{A1}\ \&\ \mathrm{A2}\ \&\ \ldots\ \&\ \mathrm{A7}) \rightarrow (\mathrm{A8} \leftrightarrow \mathrm{AC}n) \text{ for } n = 1, 2, 3.$$

THEOREM 3.6.1. $\mathrm{A8} \leftrightarrow \mathrm{AC1}$.

Proof: It is clear that AC1 implies A8, for suppose X satisfies the hypothesis of A8. Then by AC1, there exists a function F such that $\mathfrak{D}(F) = X$ and for each $u \in X$, $F(u) \in u$. The range of F is the required choice class.

Conversely, suppose A8 holds and X satisfies the hypothesis of AC1. Define

$$Y = \{\{u\} \times u : u \in X\}.$$

Then Y is a non-empty class of non-empty pairwise disjoint sets. Therefore, by A8 there exists a choice class, F, which consists of one and only one element from each set in Y. F is the required choice function on X. ■

THEOREM 3.6.2. A8 $\leftrightarrow$ AC2.

Proof: First we shall show that A8 implies AC2. Suppose R is a relation satisfying the hypothesis of AC2. Let

$$X = \{\{u\} \times R''\{u\} : u \in \mathfrak{D}(R)\}.$$

Then X satisfies the hypothesis of A8, and a choice class for X is the required function.

Conversely, suppose AC2 holds. Let X be a class satisfying the hypothesis of A8. Define a relation R on X as follows:

$$u\ R\ v \leftrightarrow (u \in X \ \&\ v \in u).$$

R is a relation and $R''\{u\} = u$ is a set. Therefore, R satisfies the hypothesis of AC2, so there exists a function F such that $\mathfrak{D}(F) = \mathfrak{D}(R) = X$ and $F \subseteq R$. Clearly, $\mathfrak{R}(F)$ is a choice class for X. ■

THEOREM 3.6.3. AC2 $\leftrightarrow$ AC3.

Proof: First to show AC2 implies AC3, let F be a function satisfying the hypothesis of AC3. Then F^{-1} is a relation satisfying the hypothesis of AC2. Therefore, there exists a function G such that $\mathfrak{D}(G) = \mathfrak{D}(F^{-1}) = \mathfrak{R}(F)$ and $G \subseteq F^{-1}$. (If F is 1–1, then $G = F^{-1}$.)

Conversely, let R be a relation satisfying the hypothesis of AC2. Define a function H as follows:

$$H = \{\langle\langle u,v\rangle,u\rangle : u\ R\ v\}.$$

H is a function and for each $u \in \mathfrak{R}(H)$

$$H^{-1''}\{u\} = \{\langle u,v\rangle : u\ R\ v\}.$$

Therefore, since $R''\{u\}$ is a set, so is $H^{-1''}\{u\}$. Therefore, H satisfies the hypothesis of AC3. Consequently, there is a function G such that $\mathfrak{D}(G) = \mathfrak{R}(H)$ and $G \subseteq H^{-1}$. For each $u \in \mathfrak{D}(G)$, $G(u)$ is an ordered pair $\langle u,v\rangle$. Define a function F such that for each $u \in \mathfrak{D}(G) = \mathfrak{D}(R)$, $F(u)$ is the second coordinate of the ordered pair $G(u)$. Since G is a function, F is also a function. It follows from the definitions of G and H, that $\mathfrak{D}(F) = \mathfrak{D}(R)$ and $F \subseteq R$. ■

Notice the non-constructive nature of AC1–AC3. Each states that some function exists, but no method to construct the function is given.

The form of the axiom of choice given here is a strong form. Weaker forms may be obtained by replacing the word "class" by "set." Thus, four weaker forms of A8 and AC1–AC3 are given below.

a8: $[\mathrm{S}(x) \;\&\; x \neq \emptyset \;\&\; (\forall u)(u \in x \rightarrow (\mathrm{S}(u) \;\&\; u \neq \emptyset)) \;\&\; \mathrm{Pr\ Dis}(x)] \rightarrow$
$(\exists c)[c \subseteq \bigcup x \;\&\; (\forall u)(u \in x \rightarrow (\exists v)(v \in u \;\&\; c \cap u = \{v\}))]$.

ac1: $[\mathrm{S}(x) \;\&\; x \neq \emptyset \;\&\; (\forall u)(u \in x \rightarrow (\mathrm{S}(u) \;\&\; u \neq \emptyset)] \rightarrow$
$(\exists f)[\mathrm{Func}(f) \;\&\; \mathfrak{D}(f) = x \;\&\; (\forall u)(u \in x \rightarrow f(u) \in u)]$.

ac2: $\mathrm{Rel}(r) \rightarrow (\exists f)(\mathrm{Func}(f) \;\&\; \mathfrak{D}(f) = \mathfrak{D}(r) \;\&\; f \subseteq r)$.

ac3: $\mathrm{Func}(f) \rightarrow (\exists g)(\mathrm{Func}(g) \;\&\; \mathfrak{D}(g) = \mathfrak{R}(f) \;\&\; g \subseteq f^{-1})$.

It is clear that the class forms imply the set forms. So, we have

THEOREM 3.6.4.
(a) A8 $\rightarrow$ a8
(b) AC1 $\rightarrow$ ac1
(c) AC2 $\rightarrow$ ac2
(d) AC3 $\rightarrow$ ac3.

It is also clear that the four set forms of the axiom of choice are equivalent. That is,

$$(\mathrm{A1} \;\&\; \mathrm{A2} \;\&\; \ldots \;\&\; \mathrm{A7}) \rightarrow (\mathrm{a8} \leftrightarrow \mathrm{ac}n) \text{ for } n = 1, 2, 3.$$

Therefore, we have

THEOREM 3.6.5.
(a) a8 $\leftrightarrow$ ac1
(b) a8 $\leftrightarrow$ ac2
(c) ac2 $\leftrightarrow$ ac3.

There is one additional set form of the axiom of choice which was impossible even to state as a class form. Namely,

ac4: $[\mathrm{S}(x) \;\&\; x \neq \emptyset \;\&\; (\forall u)(u \in x \rightarrow (\mathrm{S}(u) \;\&\; u \neq \emptyset))] \rightarrow \times\, x \neq \emptyset$.

The direct product of a non-empty set of non-empty sets is non-empty. (The direct product of a proper class of sets is always empty.) Actually ac4 is just a restatement of ac1.

THEOREM 3.6.5. ac4 $\leftrightarrow$ ac1.

Proof: To show ac4 implies ac1, let x satisfy the hypothesis of ac1. Then, by ac4, $\times\, x \neq \emptyset$. So, there is an $f \in \times\, x$. It follows from 3.5.15 that f is a choice function on x.

Conversely, if f is a choice function on a non-empty set of non-empty sets x, then by 3.5.15, $f \in \times x$. Thus, $\times x \neq \emptyset$. ■

The second axiom we wish to consider in this section is the *axiom of regularity* or, as it is sometimes called, the *axiom of foundation*. The form given here is due to J. von Neumann and P. Bernays.

A9: $(\mathrm{Cl}(X) \;\&\; X \neq \emptyset \;\&\; (\forall u)(u \in X \rightarrow \mathrm{S}(u)) \rightarrow (\exists u)(u \in X \;\&\; u \cap X = \emptyset)$.

Each non-empty class of sets has an element which is disjoint with it. Axiom A9 is not indispensable, but it implies a number of properties that are intuitively expected to be true in a system of set theory. However, like the axiom of choice, it is non-constructive. No rule is given for choosing the element u.

The following three theorems are examples of such properties.

THEOREM 3.6.7.® $x \notin x$.

Proof: Clearly, if x is an atom, the theorem is true since an atom has no elements. Suppose, then, that x is a set and $x \in x$. Let $X = \{x\}$. Then for all $u \in X$, $u \cap X \neq \emptyset$ because x is the only element of X and $x \cap X = x$. This contradicts A9. ■

THEOREM 3.6.8.® $x \notin y$ or $y \notin x$.

Proof: Clearly, if either x or y is an atom, the theorem is true. So suppose x and y are sets such that $x \in y$ and $y \in x$. Let

$$X = \{x, y\},$$

then

$$x \cap X = y \text{ and } y \cap X = x.$$

This again violates A9. ■

THEOREM 3.6.9.® $\mathrm{Pr}(V)$.

Proof: Since V is a class, V is either a proper class or a set. Suppose V is a set. Then from the definition of V, $V \in V$, contradicting 3.6.7. Therefore, V must be a proper class. ■

We shall prove that V is a proper class in §4.5 without using the axiom of regularity. Also, in §5.4, we shall prove that the axiom of regularity is equivalent to the statement: There does not exist an infinite descending chain of sets—that is, sets $f(1), f(2), \ldots$, such that $f(n) \in f(n + 1)$ for all n.

EXERCISES 3.6

1. Prove $[\text{Func}(F) \mathbin{\&} x \subseteq \mathfrak{D}(F)] \to F''x \precsim x$. (The axiom of choice is used in the proof.)
2. Prove $[\text{Cl}(X) \mathbin{\&} X \neq \emptyset \mathbin{\&} (\forall u)(u \in X \to (\text{S}(u) \mathbin{\&} u \neq \emptyset))] \to X \precsim \bigcup X$. (The axiom of choice is used in the proof.)
3. Prove that the following statement is equivalent to AC1.

AC5: $(\text{Cl}(X) \mathbin{\&} X \neq \emptyset) \to (\exists F)[\text{Func}(F) \mathbin{\&} \mathfrak{D}(F) = \mathcal{P}(X) \sim \{\emptyset\} \mathbin{\&} (\forall u)(u \in \mathfrak{D}(F) \to F(u) \in u)]$.

4. Prove:

$$[\text{S}(x) \mathbin{\&} x \neq \emptyset \mathbin{\&} C(x) = \{f{:}\,\text{Func}(f) \mathbin{\&} \mathfrak{D}(f) = x \mathbin{\&} (\forall u)(u \in x \to f(u) \in u)\}] \to \bigcap_{u \in x} \bigcup_{v \in u} v = \bigcup_{f \in C(x)} \bigcap_{u \in x} f(u).$$

(The set form of the axiom of choice is used in the proof. This statement is actually equivalent to the set form of the axiom of choice. See Rubin [1963].)

5. Prove that the following statement is equivalent to ac1.

ac5: $\text{Func}(f) \to (\exists g)[\text{Func}(g) \mathbin{\&} (\forall u)((u \in \mathfrak{D}(f) \mathbin{\&} f(u) \neq \emptyset) \to g(u) \in f(u))]$.

6. In model M3 of § 2.4, take $a = x$ and $b = x \cup \{x\}$. Show that if model M satisfies A1–A9, then model M3 satisfies A1–A8 but does not satisfy A9.

3.7. SUMMARY OF THE AXIOMS

A1: Characterization of Atoms

$\text{A}(X) \to (\neg\text{Cl}(X) \mathbin{\&} (\forall Y)(Y \notin X))$.

A2: Axiom of Extensionality

$(\text{Cl}(X) \mathbin{\&} \text{Cl}(Y)) \to ((\forall u)(u \in X \leftrightarrow u \in Y) \to X = Y)$.

A3: Axiom Schema for Construction of Classes

If **P** is a wff in which X is not a free variable, then the following statement is an axiom:

$(\exists X)(\text{Cl}(X) \mathbin{\&} (\forall u)(u \in X \leftrightarrow \mathbf{P}))$.

A4: Power Set Axiom

$\text{S}(X) \to \text{S}(\mathcal{P}(X))$.

A5: Pairing Axiom

$(\exists x)(\text{S}(x) \mathbin{\&} (\forall u)(u \in x \leftrightarrow (u = v \text{ or } u = w))$.

A6: Axiom of Replacement

$(\text{Func}(F) \mathbin{\&} \text{S}(\mathfrak{D}(F)) \to \text{S}(\mathfrak{R}(F))$.

A7: Union Axiom

$$S(X) \rightarrow S(\bigcup X).$$

A8: Axiom of Choice

$$[\mathrm{Cl}(X) \;\&\; X \neq \emptyset \;\&\; (\forall u)(u \in X \rightarrow (S(u) \;\&\; u \neq \emptyset)) \;\&\; \mathrm{Pr\ Dis}(X)] \rightarrow (\exists C)[C \subseteq \bigcup X \;\&\; (\forall u)(u \in X \rightarrow (\exists v)(v \in u \;\&\; C \cap u = \{v\}))].$$

A9: Axiom of Regularity

$$[\mathrm{Cl}(X) \;\&\; X \neq \emptyset \;\&\; (\forall u)(u \in X \rightarrow S(u))] \rightarrow (\exists u)(u \in X \;\&\; u \cap X = \emptyset).$$

Chapter 4: Natural Numbers

4.1. NATURAL NUMBERS

In this chapter and in Chapter 6, we shall formally develop the real number system starting with the natural numbers. Even though numbers are being defined within the framework of abstract set theory, in order for them to be of any use to mathematicians, all their arithmetical properties must be preserved. Even with this limitation, there are two standard ways for defining a natural number. One is to define the number n to be the class of all sets which have n distinct elements. (It is possible to define what it means for a set to have n elements without defining the number n. For example, the set u has two distinct elements x and y if

$$u = \{v : (v = x \text{ or } v = y) \ \& \ x \neq y\}.$$

Any set which is equipollent to u has two distinct elements.) One disadvantage of this method of defining the natural numbers is that each natural number, except possibly 0, is a proper class. Therefore, the class of natural numbers does not exist.

The method we shall use is to define the natural number n to be some fixed set which has n elements. It is natural to let the natural number 0 be the empty class. Therefore, we define

$$0 = \emptyset.$$

The natural number 1 will be some set which has one element. Which element shall we choose? Why not the element 0? Therefore, define

$$1 = \{0\}.$$

Now the rest is easy. Define

$$2 = \{0,1\},$$
$$3 = \{0,1,2\}, \text{ etc.}$$

In general, the natural number n is the set of n natural numbers which precede n.

But at this point in the development of set theory, we do not know whether or not $\emptyset$ is a set. Even if $\emptyset$ is a set, there is no guarantee that the class of natural numbers, if it exists, is a set. In order to guarantee the existence of the set of natural numbers, we shall introduce another axiom called the Axiom of Infinity. First we need some notation to simplify the discussion.

DEFINITION 4.1.1. $S(x) \to (x^+ =_{\mathrm{Df}} x \cup \{x\})$.

x^+ is called the *successor* of x.

Thus, using the successor symbol, we have

$$\begin{aligned} 0 &=_{\mathrm{Df}} \emptyset, \\ 1 &=_{\mathrm{Df}} 0^+, \\ 2 &=_{\mathrm{Df}} 1^+, \\ 3 &=_{\mathrm{Df}} 2^+, \end{aligned}$$

etc. Some simple consequences of 4.1.1 are:

THEOREM 4.1.2. $S(x) \to$

(a) $u \in x^+ \leftrightarrow (u \in x \text{ or } u = x)$

(b) $x \in x^+$

(c) $x \subseteq x^+$.

Next, the Axiom of Infinity.

A10: $(\exists x)(S(x) \;\&\; \emptyset \in x \;\&\; (\forall u)(u \in x \to u^+ \in x))$.

The axiom of infinity is the only axiom which postulates the unconditional existence of a set. One obvious consequence of it is that $\emptyset$ is a set.

THEOREM 4.1.3. $S(\emptyset)$.

Proof: By 2.5.2, $\emptyset$ is a class and by A10, $\emptyset$ is an element. Therefore, by 2.1.1(a), $\emptyset$ is a set. ■

DEFINITION 4.1.4. Successor Class

X is a *successor class* $=_{\mathrm{Df}} [\mathrm{Cl}(X) \;\&\; \emptyset \in X \;\&\; (\forall u)(u \in X \to u^+ \in X)]$. (If X is also a set, it is called a *successor set*.)

It follows from A10 that there is at least one successor set and from 4.1.4, that no successor class is empty. Moreover, it is easy to show that the intersection of successor sets is a successor set.

THEOREM 4.1.5.

$$[\mathrm{Cl}(X) \;\&\; X \neq \emptyset \;\&\; (\forall u)(u \in X \to u \text{ is a successor set})] \to \bigcap X \text{ is a successor set.}$$

The proof is left as an exercise.

Now we define the class of natural numbers, ω, to be the *smallest* successor class, that is, the intersection of all successor sets.

DEFINITION 4.1.6. The Class of Natural Numbers

$$\omega =_{\mathrm{Df}} \bigcap \{x : x \text{ is a successor set}\}.$$

THEOREM 4.1.7. $S(\omega)$ & ω is a successor class.

Proof: By A10, there is a successor set; therefore, it follows from 4.1.5 that ω is a successor set. ■

Next we shall show that the elements of ω satisfy the well-known properties of natural numbers. The first theorem states that the elements of ω satisfy the Peano Axioms (see §1.3). (When discussing natural numbers we shall denote "$\emptyset$" by "0", "0^+" by "1", "1^+" by "2", etc.)

THEOREM 4.1.8.
(a) $0 \in \omega$
(b) $n \in \omega \to n^+ \in \omega$
(c) $n \in \omega \to n^+ \neq 0$
(d) $(x \subseteq \omega \;\&\; 0 \in x \;\&\; (\forall n)(n \in x \to n^+ \in x)) \to x = \omega$
(Mathematical induction)
(e)® $(n,m \in \omega \;\&\; n^+ = m^+) \to n = m$.

Proof: (a) and (b) follow from the fact that ω is a successor set.

By 4.1.2(b), $n \in n^+$. Therefore $n^+ \neq 0$, proving (c).

The hypothesis of (d) implies that x is a successor set. Since ω is the intersection of all successor sets, $\omega \subseteq x$. But by hypothesis, $x \subseteq \omega$. Therefore, we must have $x = \omega$.

To prove (e) we shall use the axiom of regularity A9, but we shall show below how it could have been avoided (see 4.1.15 ff.). Suppose $n^+ = m^+$ and $n \neq m$. Since $n \in n^+$ and $n^+ = m^+$, $n \in m^+$. But since $n \neq m$, $n \in m$. By symmetry we obtain $m \in n$. But $n \in m$ and $m \in n$ contradicts 3.6.8. ■

Some further properties of the natural numbers are given by the following definitions and theorems. In what follows we shall use the letters "n", "m", "p", "q", and these letters with subscripts to denote variables, each of whose range is ω.

THEOREM 4.1.9. $n \neq 0 \to 0 \in n$.

Proof: The proof is by induction. Let x be a set defined as follows:

$$x = \{n : n \in \omega \;\&\; 0 \in n\} \cup \{0\}.$$

We shall show that x is a successor set. First, $0 \in x$ by construction. Suppose that $n \in x$. If $n = 0$, then $n^+ = \{0\}$, so that $0 \in n^+$. If $n \neq 0$, then $0 \in n$ since $n \in x$. But $n \subseteq n^+$. Therefore, $0 \in n$ implies $0 \in n^+$. Hence, $n^+ \in x$. ■

THEOREM 4.1.10. $n \neq 0 \rightarrow (\exists m)(m^+ = n)$.

Proof: The proof is again by induction on n; the details are left as an exercise.

Theorem 4.1.10 states that every natural number except 0 has an immediate predecessor. It follows from 4.1.8(e) that the immediate predecessor is unique.

DEFINITION 4.1.11. Transitive Class

$$\mathrm{Cl}(X) \rightarrow (X \text{ is } \textit{transitive} =_{\mathrm{Df}} (\forall u)(u \in X \rightarrow u \subseteq X)).$$

The terms "*full*" and "*complete*" are sometimes used instead of "transitive." We use the term "transitive" because the definition can be rewritten as:

$$(v \in u \ \&\ u \in X) \rightarrow v \in X.$$

Thus, $\in$ appears to be similar to a transitive relation.

THEOREM 4.1.12. $n \in \omega \rightarrow n$ is transitive.

Proof: The proof is by induction. Let x be the set of transitive elements in ω. Since 0 has no elements, $0 \in x$. Suppose that $n \in x$. We shall show that $n^+ \in x$. Let $u \in n^+$, then $u \in n$ or $u = n$. Since $n \subseteq n^+$, it follows that $u = n$ implies $u \subseteq n^+$. Since $n \in x$, it follows that $u \in n$ implies $u \subseteq n \subseteq n^+$. Hence, in either case $u \subseteq n^+$, so that $n^+ \in x$. Consequently, $x = \omega$. ■

THEOREM 4.1.13. ω is transitive.

Proof: The proof is by induction. Let

$$x = \{n : n \in \omega \ \&\ n \subseteq \omega\}.$$

First, $0 \in x$ because $0 \in \omega$ and $0 \subseteq \omega$. Suppose that $n \in x$. Then $n \in \omega$ and $n \subseteq \omega$. Since $n \in \omega$, $n^+ \in \omega$. Let $u \in n^+$, then $u \in n$ or $u = n$. Since $n \subseteq \omega$, it follows that $u \in n$ implies $u \in \omega$, and since $n \in \omega$, it follows that $u = n$ implies $u \in \omega$. Consequently, $n^+ \in x$ so that $x = \omega$ and ω is transitive. ■

It follows from the transitivity of ω that every element of a natural number is a natural number.

The following two theorems are direct consequences of A9, the axiom of regularity. But we will prove them for natural numbers without the use of this axiom.

THEOREM 4.1.14. $n \notin n$.

Proof: The proof is by mathematical induction. Let

$$x = \{n : n \in \omega \;\&\; n \notin n\}.$$

First we have $0 \notin 0$ because 0 has no elements. Therefore $0 \in x$. Suppose that $n \in x$ and $n^+ \in n^+$. Then $n^+ \in n$ or $n^+ = n$. If $n^+ \in n$, then $n^+ \subseteq n$ since n is transitive. But $n \in n^+$, which implies that $n \in n$, a contradiction. If $n^+ = n$, then since $n \in n^+$, we have again the contradiction $n \in n$. Hence, $n^+ \in x$. ■

THEOREM 4.1.15. $n \notin m$ or $m \notin n$.

Proof: Suppose $n \in m$ and $m \in n$. By transitivity this implies $n \subseteq m$ and $m \subseteq n$. Consequently, $n = m$. Therefore $n \in n$, which contradicts 4.1.14. ■

Therefore, using 4.1.14 and 4.1.15 we can prove 4.1.8(e) without using the axiom of regularity.

A further result which is quite useful is the following.

THEOREM 4.1.16. $n \in m \rightarrow (n^+ \in m$ or $n^+ = m)$.

Proof: The proof is by induction on m. Let

$$x = \{m : (\forall n)[n \in m \rightarrow (n^+ \in m \text{ or } n^+ = m)]\}.$$

First $0 \in x$ because 0 has no elements. Suppose that $m \in x$ and $n \in m^+$. Then either $n \in m$ or $n = m$. If $n \in m$, since $m \in x$, it follows that $n^+ \in m$ or $n^+ = m$. In either case, $n^+ \in m^+$. If $n = m$, then $n^+ = m^+$. Consequently, $m^+ \in x$, so that $x = \omega$. ■

THEOREM 4.1.17. The Trichotomy for Natural Numbers

$$n \in m \text{ or } n = m \text{ or } m \in n.$$

Proof: The proof is by induction. Let

$$x = \{n : (\forall m)(n \in m \text{ or } n = m \text{ or } m \in n)\}.$$

It follows from 4.1.9 that $0 \in x$. Suppose that $n \in x$. If $n \in m$, then by 4.1.16 either $n^+ \in m$ or $n^+ = m$. If $n = m$, then $n^+ = m^+$, so that $m \in n^+$. Finally, if $m \in n$, then $m \in n^+$ since $n \subseteq n^+$. Thus $n^+ \in x$. Consequently, $x = \omega$. ■

The results given in theorems 4.1.9, 4.1.12, 4.1.14-4.1.17 may seem artificial at first and may not seem to be properties of the natural numbers as we know them. But if the $\in$-relation between natural numbers is conceived as strict inequality, $<$, then everything is clear. Theorem 4.1.9 merely states that 0 is the smallest natural number; theorem 4.1.12, that $<$ is a transitive relation; theorem 4.1.14, that $n \not< n$; theorem 4.1.15, that $n < m$ implies $m \nless n$; theorem 4.1.16, that $n < m$ implies $n^+ \leqq m$, ($n^+ = n + 1$); and theorem 4.1.17, that either $n < m$, $n = m$, or $m < n$.

EXERCISES 4.1

1. Prove $(m \in n \;\&\; n \in p) \rightarrow m \in p$.
2. Prove $(x \in m \;\&\; m \in \omega) \rightarrow x \in \omega$.
3. Prove $(m, n \in \omega \;\&\; m \subseteq n) \rightarrow (m \in n \text{ or } m = n)$.
4. Prove $m \in n \rightarrow m^+ \in n^+$.
5 Prove:

(a) $m \cup n = \begin{cases} m \text{ if } n \in m \text{ or } n = m \\ n \text{ if } m \in n \end{cases}$

(b) $m \cap n = \begin{cases} m \text{ if } m \in n \text{ or } m = n \\ n \text{ if } n \in m. \end{cases}$

6. Prove $\bigcup n^+ = n$.
7. Prove $(x \subseteq \omega \;\&\; x \neq \emptyset \;\&\; \bigcup x = x) \rightarrow x = \omega$.
8. Prove (X & Y are transitive) $\rightarrow$ ($X \cup Y$ & $X \cap Y$ are transitive).
9. Prove (Cl(X) & $(\forall u)(u \in X \rightarrow u$ is transitive)) $\rightarrow$
   (a) $\bigcup X$ is transitive
   (b) $X \neq \emptyset \rightarrow \bigcap X$ is transitive.

4.2. MATHEMATICAL INDUCTION

In this section we shall examine the principle of mathematical induction and derive additional consequences from it.

DEFINITION 4.2.1. $x \subseteq \omega \rightarrow$

(a) (n is the *smallest* or *first* element of x) $=_{\text{Df}}$
$[n \in x \;\&\; (\forall m)(m \in x \rightarrow (n \in m \text{ or } n = m))]$

(b) (n is the *largest* or *last* element of x) $=_{\text{Df}}$
$[n \in x \;\&\; (\forall m)(m \in x \rightarrow (m \in n \text{ or } m = n))]$.

It follows from 4.1.15 that if a first or last element exists, it is unique (exercise 4.2.1).

Theorem 4.1.9 implies that every natural number except 0 has a first element, namely 0. It is also easy to prove that every natural number except 0 has a last element (exercise 4.2.2).

The following principle is often used in proofs instead of the principle of mathematical induction. It states that every non-empty set of natural numbers has a smallest element.

THEOREM 4.2.2.

$$(x \subseteq \omega \;\&\; x \neq \emptyset) \rightarrow (\exists n)(n \text{ is the smallest element of } x.)$$

Proof: Suppose the theorem is false. Let x be a non-empty set of natural numbers such that x has no smallest element. Let y be the set of all natural numbers which precede every element of x. That is,

$$y = \{n : n \in \omega \ \& \ (\forall m)(m \in x \rightarrow n \in m)\}.$$

We shall show that $y = \omega$. First, we have $0 \in y$ because of 4.1.9 and the assumption that x has no first element. Suppose that $n \in y$. Then $n \in m$ for all $m \in x$. Thus by 4.1.16, either $n^+ \in m$ or $n^+ = m$. If $n^+ \in m$ for all $m \in x$, then $n^+ \in y$. Suppose that $n^+ = m$ for some $m \in x$. In this case n^+ would be the smallest element of x, contrary to our assumption. Hence, $n^+ \in y$ and it follows by mathematical induction that $y = \omega$. But this implies that $x = \emptyset$, which contradicts the hypothesis. Therefore x must have a smallest element. ■

Another principle often used to replace the principle of mathematical induction is the following.

THEOREM 4.2.3. $(x \subseteq \omega \ \& \ (\forall n)(n \subseteq x \rightarrow n \in x)) \rightarrow x = \omega.$

Proof: The proof is again by contradiction. Let x be a set which satisfies the hypothesis, and suppose that $x \subset \omega$. Let $z = \omega \sim x$. Then z is a non-empty subset of ω so that, by 4.2.2, z has a smallest element, say n. Suppose that $m \in n$. Then, since ω is transitive, $m \in \omega$. And since n is the smallest element of $z = \omega \sim x$, $m \in x$. Consequently, $n \subseteq x$. Therefore, by hypothesis, $n \in x$, which contradicts the definition of n. Therefore $x = \omega$. ■

When using mathematical induction it is necessary to show that a number is in a set if its immediate predecessor is in the set. On the other hand, when using 4.2.3 it is necessary to show that a number is in a set if all its predecessors are in the set. Theorem 4.2.3 has a stronger hypothesis than the hypothesis of mathematical induction and is, therefore, a weaker theorem. However, we shall show later that 4.2.3 has a wider application than mathematical induction (see §7.3).

EXERCISES 4.2

1. Prove $(x \subseteq \omega \ \& \ (\exists n)(n$ is the first (last) element of $x)) \rightarrow (\exists 1 n)(n$ is the first (last) element of $x)$.
2. Prove $(n \in \omega \ \& \ n \neq 0) \rightarrow (\exists m)(m$ is the last element of $n)$.
3. If x and y are non-empty sets of natural numbers such that $x \subseteq y$ and if n is the smallest element of x and m the smallest element of y, what is the relationship between m and n? Give reasons for your answer. State and prove a similar result for the largest elements.

4. Use 4.1.10 and 4.2.2 to prove the principle of mathematical induction.
5. Use 4.1.10 and 4.2.3 to prove the principle of mathematical induction.

4.3. THE RECURSION THEOREM

Mathematical induction is often used as a method of definition as well as a method of proof. For example, once multiplication of natural numbers has been defined we could define a function, f, on ω as follows:

$$f(0) = 1 \ \& \ (\forall n)(f(n^+) = 2 \cdot f(n)).$$

Then we may say that it follows by mathematical induction, that there exists a unique function f satisfying the given conditions. It seems reasonable because we have

$$\begin{aligned} f(0) &= 1 \\ f(1) &= f(0^+) = 2 \cdot 1 = 2 \\ f(2) &= f(1^+) = 2 \cdot 2 = 4 \\ f(3) &= f(2^+) = 2 \cdot 4 = 8 \end{aligned}$$

etc. Using this schema we can find the value of $f(n)$ for any given n. (In fact, $f(n) = 2^n$.) However, some effort is required to show that the set of ordered pairs which is the function f does exist and is unique. The following theorem demonstrates that this is so. It is called the *recursion theorem.*

THEOREM 4.3.1. The Recursion Theorem I

$$(\text{Func}(F) \ \& \ \mathfrak{D}(F) = V \ \& \ u \in V) \rightarrow (\exists 1 f)[\text{Func}(f) \ \&$$

(a) $\mathfrak{D}(f) = \omega$
(b) $f(0) = u$
(c) $(\forall n)(f(n^+) = F(f(n))]$.

Proof: Let us first prove the uniqueness of the function f. Suppose that f and g are two functions which satisfy (a)–(c). Let

$$x = \{n : n \in \omega \ \& \ f(n) = g(n)\}.$$

It follows from (b) that $0 \in x$. Suppose that $n \in x$. Then

$$\begin{aligned} f(n^+) &= F(f(n)) && \text{(c)} \\ &= F(g(n)) && (n \in x) \\ &= g(n^+) && \text{(c).} \end{aligned}$$

Therefore, $n^+ \in x$. So by mathematical induction $x = \omega$, which implies that $f = g$.

To construct the function f which satisfies (a)–(c) we construct the class of all functions, each of which has a natural number for its domain and each satisfies (a)–(c) on its domain. The class of all such functions is equipollent to ω and is therefore a set. Further, each pair of functions in the class has the property that one is a subset of the other. Then f will be defined to be the union of this class of functions, and it will be easy to show that f is a function satisfying (a)–(c).

Formally, define

$$H = \{h\colon \text{Func}(h) \ \&\ (\exists n)[n \in \omega \ \&\ n \neq 0 \ \&\ \mathfrak{D}(h) = n \ \&\ h(0) = u \ \&\ (\forall m)(m^+ \in n \rightarrow h(m^+) = F(h(m)))]\}.$$

In other words, $h \in H$ if h is a function, the domain of h is a natural number different from 0, and h satisfies (b) and (c) on its domain. For example:

$$\text{if } \mathfrak{D}(h) = 1, \text{ then } h = \{\langle 0,u\rangle\},$$
$$\text{if } \mathfrak{D}(h) = 2, \text{ then } h = \{\langle 0,u\rangle, \langle 1, F(u)\rangle\}, \text{ etc.}$$

Next we shall prove,

(1) $$(\forall n)((n \in \omega \ \&\ n \neq 0) \rightarrow (\exists 1 h)(h \in H \ \&\ \mathfrak{D}(h) = n)).$$

The proof of uniqueness is left as an exercise. It is analogous to the proof of the uniqueness of f which appears at the beginning of this proof. The proof of existence is by mathematical induction. Let

$$y = \{n\colon n \in \omega \ \&\ (\exists h)(h \in H \ \&\ \mathfrak{D}(h) = n)\} \cup \{0\}.$$

First, $0 \in y$ by construction. Suppose that $n \in y$. If $n = 0$, then let $h = \{\langle 0,u\rangle\}$. Then $h \in H$, so that $n^+ \in y$. If $n \neq 0$, then there is an m such that $m^+ = n$ and there is a $g \in H$ such that $\mathfrak{D}(g) = n$. Let

$$h = g \cup \{\langle n, F(g(m))\rangle\}.$$

[That is, $h|n = g$ and $h(n) = F(g(m))$.] It is easy to show that $h \in H$ and $\mathfrak{D}(h) = n^+$. Therefore, $n^+ \in y$ and it follows by mathematical induction that (1) holds.

Suppose that $h_1,h_2 \in H$, $\mathfrak{D}(h_1) = m$, and that $\mathfrak{D}(h_2) = n$. If $m = n$, then it follows from (1) that $h_1 = h_2$. Suppose that $m \in n$. Then it is easy to show that $h_2|m \in H$, and since $\mathfrak{D}(h_2|m) = m$, it follows from (1) that $h_2|m = h_1$. Therefore, $h_1 \subseteq h_2$. Hence we have shown,

(2) $$h_1,h_2 \in H \rightarrow (h_1 \subseteq h_2 \text{ or } h_2 \subseteq h_1).$$

Now define

$$f = \bigcup H.$$

It follows from (1) that there exists a 1–1 function mapping H into ω. Therefore, since ω is a set, it follows from 3.4.5(b) that H is a set. Consequently, by the union axiom, A7, f is a set. Also, since H is a set of functions, it is clear that f is a relation. We shall show f is a function. Suppose that $\langle n,u\rangle$, $\langle n,v\rangle \in f$. Then there exist functions $h_1,h_2 \in H$ such that $\langle n,u\rangle \in h_1$ and $\langle n,v\rangle \in h_2$. By (2), either $h_1 \subseteq h_2$ or $h_2 \subseteq h_1$. Consequently, both of the ordered pairs, $\langle n,u\rangle$ and $\langle n,v\rangle$, are elements of *one* of the functions, h_1 or h_2. Thus, $u = v$ and f is a function (see exercise 3.5.5). The proof that f satisfies conditions (a)–(c) of the theorem is left as an exercise. ■

Note that in the hypothesis of the recursion theorem I, the domain of the function F need not be V. The only requirement on the function F is that it be defined where necessary. That is, $f(n) \in \mathfrak{D}(F)$ for all $n \in \omega$.

There are two other forms of the recursion theorem which are often useful in practice.

THEOREM 4.3.2. The Recursion Theorem II

$$(\text{Func}(G)\ \&\ \mathfrak{D}(G) = V) \rightarrow (\exists 1 g)(\text{Func}(g)\ \&$$

(a) $\mathfrak{D}(g) = \omega$
(b) $(\forall n)(g(n) = G(g|n))$.

THEOREM 4.3.3. The Recursion Theorem III

$$(\text{Func}(H)\ \&\ \mathfrak{D}(H) = V) \rightarrow (\exists 1 h)(\text{Func}(h)\ \&$$

(a) $\mathfrak{D}(h) = \omega$
(b) $(\forall n)(h(n) = H(h''n))$.

Here again, it is not necessary for the domains of the functions, G and H, to be V. We require only that $g|n \in \mathfrak{D}(G)$ for all $n \in \omega$, and that $h''n \in \mathfrak{D}(H)$ for all $n \in \omega$.

We shall show that 4.3.1 implies 4.3.2 and 4.3.3. First, it is clear that 4.3.2 implies 4.3.3 because $h''n = \mathfrak{R}(h|n)$. Thus we have

$$G(x) = \begin{cases} H(\mathfrak{R}(x)) & \text{if Func}(x) \\ 0 & \text{otherwise.} \end{cases}$$

Then, by 4.3.2, there is a unique function h such that

$$\mathfrak{D}(h) = \omega$$
$$h(n) = G(h|n) = H(h''n).$$

Next we shall show that 4.3.1 implies 4.3.2.

Suppose G satisfies the hypotheses of 4.3.2. We shall construct a function f using 4.3.1 by choosing F and u appropriately so that for each $n \in \omega$, $f(n) = g|n$. By 4.3.1, there exists a unique function f such that

$$\mathfrak{D}(f) = \omega$$
$$f(0) = 0$$
$$(\forall n)(f(n^+) = f(n) \cup \{\langle n, G(f(n))\rangle\}).$$

It follows by mathematical induction that

$$(\forall n)(\mathrm{Func}(f(n))$$
$$(\forall n)(\mathfrak{D}(f(n)) = n)$$
$$(\forall m)(\forall n)(m \in n \rightarrow f(m) \subseteq f(n)).$$

Define

$$g = \bigcup_{n \in \omega} f(n).$$

Now it is easy to see that g is a function, $\mathfrak{D}(g) = \omega$, and for each $n \in \omega$, $g(n) = G(g|n)$. The uniqueness of g follows from 4.2.2.

At this point we have shown that 4.3.1 implies 4.3.2, and that 4.3.2 implies 4.3.3. The proof of 4.3.1 is sufficient to prove the three theorems. A further step will show that the three forms of the recursion theorem are equivalent by proving that 4.3.3 implies 4.3.1.

Let F and u satisfy the hypothesis of 4.3.1. We shall construct the function H so that $f|n = h''n$. Define H as follows:

$$H(x) = \begin{cases} \langle 0,u\rangle, & \text{if } x = 0 \\ \langle n^+, F(x(n))\rangle, & \text{if Func}(x) \ \&\ \mathfrak{D}(x) = n^+ \\ 0, & \text{otherwise.} \end{cases}$$

Then, by 4.3.3, there exists a unique function h such that

$$\mathfrak{D}(h) = \omega$$
$$(\forall n)(h(n) = H(h''n)).$$

It follows by induction that for each $n \in \omega$,

$$\mathrm{Func}(H''n) \ \&\ \mathfrak{D}(h''n) = n.$$

Then define

$$f = \bigcup_{n \in \omega} h''n.$$

Now it is easy to show that f is the required function. (Again use mathematical induction to prove uniqueness.)

By a slight modification of the preceding proof, it can be shown directly that 4.3.3 implies 4.3.2. We leave this as an exercise.

The form of the recursion theorem given in 4.3.1 compares with either of the other forms in the same way that mathematical induction (4.1.8d) compares with 4.2.3. In 4.3.1 the value of the function at each natural number n^+ is determined by its value at n. While in 4.3.2 and

4.3.3, the value of the function at each natural number n is determined by its values on the set of predecessors of n. The form which is used depends on the context. For example, 4.3.1 is applied to define addition and multiplication of natural numbers in the next section, while 4.3.3 is used in the proof of 5.2.3.

EXERCISES 4.3

1. Use the recursion theorem I to define an unordered n-tuple so that the definition coincides with 3.1.5, 3.1.2, and 3.1.10 when $n = 1, 2, 3$, and 4.
2. Use the recursion theorem I to define an ordered n-tuple so that the definition coincides with 3.1.11 and 3.1.14 when $n = 2, 3$, and 4.
3. We use the recursion theorem I to define a function f. Let x be any element. Then define

$$f(0) = x$$
$$f(n^+) = \bigcup f(n).$$

Now the *ancestral* of x, $N(x)$, is defined as follows.

$$N(x) =_{\mathrm{Df}} \bigcup_{n\in\omega} f(n).$$

Prove each of the following:
(a) $\mathrm{S}(N(x))$
(b) $\mathrm{Cl}(x) \to x \subseteq N(x)$
(c) $(\forall u)(\forall v)[(u \in N(x) \;\&\; v \in u) \to v \in N(x)]$
(d) $(\forall Y)[\mathrm{Cl}(Y) \;\&\; x \subseteq Y \;\&\; (\forall u)(\forall v)((u \in Y \;\&\; v \in u) \to v \in Y) \to N(x) \subseteq Y$
(e) $\mathrm{A}(x) \to N(x) = \emptyset$.
[Thus if x is a set, then $N(x)$ is the smallest set which contains x as a subset and satisfies (c). Note that $N(x)$ is not necessarily transitive since it might have atoms as elements.]

4. Prove that a function can be defined by a double induction. That is, prove:

$(\mathrm{Func}(F) \;\&\; \mathrm{Func}(G) \;\&\; \mathfrak{D}(F) = V \;\&\; \mathfrak{D}(g) = V \;\&\; u \in V) \to (\exists 1h)(\mathrm{Func}(h) \;\&$

(a) $\mathfrak{D}(h) = \omega \times \omega$
(b) $h(0,0) = u$
(c) $(\forall n)[h(0,n^+) = F(h(0,n))]$
(d) $(\forall n)(\forall m)[h(m^+,n) = G(h(m,n))]$.

5. Prove:
$(\mathrm{Func}(F) \;\&\; \mathrm{Func}(G) \;\&\; \mathfrak{D}(F) = V \;\&\; \mathfrak{D}(G) = V \;\&\; u,v \in V) \to$
$(\exists 1h_1)(\exists 1h_2)(\mathrm{Func}(h_1) \;\&\; \mathrm{Func}(h_2) \;\&$

(a) $\mathfrak{D}(h_1) = \mathfrak{D}(h_2) = \omega$
(b) $h_1(0) = u \;\&\; h_2(0) = v$
(c) $h_1(n^+) = F(h_1(n), h_2(n))$
(d) $h_2(n^+) = G(h_1(n), h_2(n))$.

4.4. ADDITION AND MULTIPLICATION

The definitions of addition and multiplication of natural numbers are typical applications of the recursion theorem.

DEFINITION 4.4.1. Addition

(a) $(\forall m)(s_m(0) = m)$
(b) $(\forall m)(\forall n)[s_m(n^+) = (s_m(n))^+]$.

It follows from the recursion theorem I that for each $m \in \omega$ there exists a unique function s_m satisfying (a) and (b). We shall use the customary notation for addition.

DEFINITION 4.4.2. $(m + n) =_{\mathrm{Df}} s_m(n)$.

We shall usually omit the parentheses around "$(m + n)$." Using this notation, definition 4.4.1 can be rewritten as follows.

THEOREM 4.4.3.

(a) $(\forall m)(m + 0 = m)$
(b) $(\forall m)(\forall n)(m + n^+ = (m + n)^+)$.

We shall next derive some properties of addition.

THEOREM 4.4.4. $m^+ = m + 1$.

Proof:

$$\begin{aligned} m + 1 &= m + 0^+ && (1 = 0^+) \\ &= (m + 0)^+ && (4.4.3\text{b}) \\ &= m^+. && (4.4.3\text{a}) \ \blacksquare \end{aligned}$$

THEOREM 4.4.5. Associative Law for Addition

$$(m + n) + p = m + (n + p).$$

Proof: The proof is by induction on p.

$$\begin{aligned} (m + n) + 0 &= m + n && (4.4.3\text{a}) \\ m + (n + 0) &= n + n. && (4.4.3\text{a}) \end{aligned}$$

Therefore, the associative law holds when $p = 0$.

Suppose that

(1) $$(m + n) + p = m + (n + p),$$

then

$$\begin{aligned} (m + n) + p^+ &= ((m + n) + p)^+ && (4.4.3\text{b}) \\ &= (m + (n + p))^+ && (1) \\ &= m + (n + p)^+ && (4.4.3\text{b}) \\ &= m + (n + p^+). && (4.4.3\text{b}) \end{aligned}$$

Therefore, it follows by mathematical induction that the associative law holds for addition. ■

The proof of the commutative law is more difficult. First we give two preliminary lemmas.

LEMMA 4.4.6. $0 + n = n.$

Proof: The proof, which is by induction, is left as an exercise.

LEMMA 4.4.7. $m^+ + n = (m + n)^+.$

Proof: By induction on n.

$$m^+ + 0 = m^+ \qquad (4.4.3a)$$
$$(m + 0)^+ = m^+. \qquad (4.4.3a)$$

Therefore, the lemma is true when $n = 0$. Suppose that

(1) $$m^+ + n = (m + n)^+.$$

Then

$$\begin{aligned} m^+ + n^+ &= (m^+ + n)^+ && (4.4.3b) \\ &= (m + n)^{++} && (1) \\ &= (m + n^+)^+. && (4.4.3b) \end{aligned}$$

The lemma follows by mathematical induction. ■

THEOREM 4.4.8. Commutative Law for Addition

$$m + n = n + m.$$

Proof: The proof is again by induction. If $m = 0$ the theorem follows from 4.4.3(a) and 4.4.6. Suppose that

(1) $$m + n = n + m.$$

Then

$$\begin{aligned} m^+ + n &= (m + n)^+ && (4.4.7) \\ &= (n + m)^+ && (1) \\ &= n + m^+. && (4.4.3b) \end{aligned}$$

Thus the commutative law for addition follows by mathematical induction. ■

Next, multiplication.

DEFINITION 4.4.9. Multiplication

(a) $(\forall m)(p_m(0) = 0)$

(b) $(\forall m)(\forall n)(p_m(n^+) = p_m(n) + m).$

The recursion theorem I implies that for each $m \in \omega$, p_m exists and is unique.

DEFINITION 4.4.10. $(m \cdot n) =_{\mathrm{Df}} p_m(n)$.

Often the symbol "$\cdot$" is omitted and we usually omit the parentheses from "$(m \cdot n)$." Moreover, the operation "$\cdot$" is considered more binding than "$+$." For example, "$m \cdot n + m$" stands for "$(m \cdot n) + m$."

We now rewrite 4.4.9 using the standard notation.

THEOREM 4.4.11.

(a) $(\forall m)(m \cdot 0 = 0)$

(b) $(\forall m)(\forall n)(m \cdot n^+ = m \cdot n + m)$.

THEOREM 4.4.12. Distributive Law

(a) $m \cdot (n + p) = m \cdot n + m \cdot p$

(b) $(n + p) \cdot m = n \cdot m + p \cdot m$.

Proof:

(a) The proof is by induction on p. First, if $p = 0$ then

$$m(n + 0) = mn \qquad (4.4.3a)$$

and

$$\begin{aligned} mn + m0 &= mn + 0 && (4.4.11a) \\ &= mn. && (4.4.3a) \end{aligned}$$

Thus the theorem holds if $p = 0$.

Suppose that

(1) $$m(n + p) = mn + mp.$$

Then

$$\begin{aligned} m(n + p^+) &= m(n + p)^+ && (4.4.3b) \\ &= m(n + p) + m && (4.4.11b) \\ &= (mn + mp) + m && (1) \\ &= mn + (mp + m) && (4.4.5) \\ &= mn + mp^+. && (4.4.11b) \end{aligned}$$

The proof of (b) is similar. Use induction on m. The details are left as an exercise. ∎

THEOREM 4.4.13. Associative Law for Multiplication

$$(m \cdot n) \cdot p = m \cdot (n \cdot p).$$

Proof: The proof is by induction on p. If $p = 0$, then it follows from 4.4.11(a) that

$$(mn)p = m(np) = 0.$$

Therefore, suppose that

(1) $$(mn)p = m(np).$$

Then

$$\begin{aligned} (mn)p^+ &= (mn)p + mn && (4.4.11b) \\ &= m(np) + mn && (1) \\ &= m(np + n) && (4.4.12) \\ &= m(np^+). && (4.4.11b) \ \blacksquare \end{aligned}$$

The following two lemmas will be used in the proof of the commutative law for multiplication. The proofs of the lemmas are left as an exercise.

LEMMA 4.4.14. $0 \cdot n = 0.$

LEMMA 4.4.15. $n \cdot 1 = 1 \cdot n = n.$

THEOREM 4.4.16. Commutative Law for Multiplication

$$m \cdot n = n \cdot m.$$

Proof: The proof is again by induction.
If $m = 0$, then the theorem follows from 4.4.11(a) and 4.4.14.
Suppose that

(1) $$nm = mn.$$

Then

$$\begin{aligned} nm^+ &= nm + n && (4.4.11b) \\ &= mn + n && (1) \\ &= mn + 1n && (4.4.15) \\ &= (m + 1)n && (4.4.12) \\ &= m^+n. && (4.4.4) \ \blacksquare \end{aligned}$$

Next we shall define exponentiation and subtraction of natural numbers, but leave their properties for the exercises.

DEFINITION 4.4.17. Exponentiation
(a) $(\forall m)(e_m(0) = 1)$
(b) $(\forall m)(\forall n)(m \neq 0 \rightarrow e_m(n^+) = e_m(n) \cdot m)$
(c) $(\forall n)(n \neq 0 \rightarrow e_0(n) = 0)$.

It follows from the recursion theorem I that for each m there exists a unique function e_m satisfying (a)–(c).

DEFINITION 4.4.18. $m^n =_{\text{Df}} e_m(n).$

Note that m^n is defined to be 1 if both m and n are 0. While this does not conform with its usual definition in analysis (0^0 is not defined in analysis), it does conform with class exponentiation ($\emptyset^{\emptyset} = \{\emptyset\}$). Thus, in this text we assume $0^0 = 1$. Unfortunately, exponentiation of natural numbers in general is not the same as exponentiation of classes (3.5.17), even though the same symbol is used in both cases. However, whenever m and n are natural numbers we shall assume that $m^n = e_m(n)$. Further properties of exponentiation are given in exercise 4.4.5.

Next, we define the inequality relation.

DEFINITION 4.4.19. Inequality

(a) $m < n =_{\text{Df}} m \in n$

(b) $m > n =_{\text{Df}} n < m$

(c) $m \leqq n =_{\text{Df}} (m < n \text{ or } m = n)$

(d) $m \geqq n =_{\text{Df}} (n \leqq m)$.

Some properties of the inequality relation are given in the next theorem (see also exercises 4.4.3).

THEOREM 4.4.20.

(a) $p < q \rightarrow (m + p < m + q)$

(b) $m + p = m + q \rightarrow p = q$.

Proof:

(a) The proof is by induction on m. If $m = 0$, the theorem is true by 4.4.6. Suppose that

$$\begin{aligned} p < q \rightarrow m + p &< m + q \\ &\rightarrow (m+p)^+ < (m+q)^+ && \text{(ex. 4.1.4)} \\ &\rightarrow m^+ + p < m^+ + q. && \text{(4.4.7)} \end{aligned}$$

(b) Suppose that $m + p = m + q$. By 4.1.17, either $p < q$, $p = q$, or $q < p$. Suppose that $p < q$. Then by part (a), $m + p < m + q$, contradicting the hypothesis. Similarly, if $q < p$, then $m + q < m + p$, again contradicting the hypothesis. Hence, we must have $p = q$. ■

Theorem 4.4.20(a) is called the *monotonicity law* for addition and (b) is called the *cancellation law* for addition. Similar laws are given for multiplication in exercises 4.4.3 (b) and (c).

We require an additional preliminary result before defining subtraction.

THEOREM 4.4.21. $m \leqq n \rightarrow (\exists 1 p)(m + p = n)$.

Proof: First, to prove uniqueness suppose that $m + p = n$ and $m + q = n$. Then $m + p = n + q$. Therefore, by 4.4.20(b), $p = q$.

The proof of existence is by mathematical induction on m. If $m = 0$, then take $p = n$. Next suppose that there is a p such that

$$m + p = n.$$

If $p = 0$, then $m = n$, so that $m^+ \nleqq n$. If $p \neq 0$, then there is a q such that $q^+ = p$ (by 4.1.10). Moreover,

$$\begin{aligned} m + q^+ &= (m + q)^+ && (4.4.3b) \\ &= m^+ + q. && (4.4.7) \end{aligned}$$

Thus, $m^+ + q = n$. The theorem has been established by induction. ■

DEFINITION 4.4.22. Subtraction

$$m \leqq n \rightarrow (n - m = p =_{\mathrm{Df}} m + p = n).$$

It follows from 4.4.21 that if $m \leqq n$, then there is one and only one p such that $m + p = n$. Thus, whenever $m \leqq n$, subtraction is uniquely defined. The properties of subtraction are given in the exercises (see exercise 4.4.4).

EXERCISES 4.4

1 Prove:
   (a) $m + n = 0 \leftrightarrow (m = 0 \;\&\; n = 0)$
   (b) $m \cdot n = 0 \leftrightarrow (m = 0 \text{ or } n = 0)$.
2. Prove $(\exists p)(m = 2p \text{ or } m + 1 = 2p)$. (Either m or $m + 1$ is divisible by 2.)
3. Prove each of the following:
   (a) $(m < n \;\&\; p \leqq q) \rightarrow m + p < n + q$
   (b) $(m < n \;\&\; p \neq 0) \rightarrow m \cdot p < n \cdot p$
   (c) $(m < n \;\&\; p \leqq q \;\&\; q \neq 0) \rightarrow m \cdot p < n \cdot q$
   (d) $m + p < n + p \rightarrow m < n$
   (e) $(m \cdot p = n \cdot p \;\&\; p \neq 0) \rightarrow m = n$
   (f) $m \cdot p < n \cdot p \rightarrow m < n$
   (g) $(\exists p)(m + p = n \rightarrow m \leqq n)$.
4. Prove each of the following:
   (a) $n - 0 = n$
   (b) $n - n = 0$
   (c) $m^+ = n \rightarrow m = n - 1$
   (d) $(p \leqq m \;\&\; m < n) \rightarrow m - p < n - p$
   (e) $(p \leqq m \;\&\; p \leqq n \;\&\; m - p = n - p) \rightarrow m = n$
   (f) $p < m \rightarrow (n^+ = m - p \leftrightarrow n = m - p^+)$.
5. Prove each of the following:
   (a) $m^{n+p} = m^n \cdot m^p$
   (b) $(m \cdot n)^p = m^p \cdot n^p$
   (c) $(m^n)^p = m^{n \cdot p}$
   (d) $m \cdot n \approx m \times n$
   (e) $m^n \approx \{f\colon \mathrm{Func}(f) \;\&\; \mathfrak{D}(f) = n \;\&\; \mathfrak{R}(f) \subseteq m\}$.
6. Prove $m,n \in \omega \rightarrow (m + n \in \omega \;\&\; m \cdot n \in \omega \;\&\; m^n \in \omega)$.

4.5. THE SCHRÖDER–BERNSTEIN THEOREM

The following theorem states an important result about equipollent classes. The theorem seems obvious, but its proof is somewhat difficult. It depends quite heavily on properties of the natural numbers. The theorem was conjectured by Cantor and proved independently by E. Schröder and F. Bernstein. It is commonly called the Schröder–Bernstein theorem.

THEOREM 4.5.1. The Schröder–Bernstein Theorem

$$(X \lesssim Y \;\&\; Y \lesssim X) \to X \approx Y.$$

Proof: Suppose that $X \lesssim Y$. Then there is a subclass Y_1 of Y such that

$$X \approx Y_1.$$

And if $Y \lesssim X$, there is a subclass X_1 of X such that

$$Y \approx X_1.$$

Since $Y_1 \subseteq Y$ and $Y \approx X_1$, there is a subclass X_2 of X_1 such that

$$Y_1 \approx X_2.$$

Thus, we have

(1) $$X_2 \subseteq X_1 \subseteq X$$
(2) $$X \approx X_2.$$

We shall complete the proof by showing that $X \approx X_1$.

It follows from (2) that there exists a 1–1 function F mapping X onto X_2.

$$F\colon X \xrightarrow[\text{onto}]{1-1} X_2.$$

It follows from the recursion theorem I (4.3.1), that for each u there exists a unique function G_u such that

(3) $$\mathfrak{D}(G_u) = \omega$$
(4) $$G_u(0) = u$$
(5) $$G_u(n^+) = F(G_u(n)).$$

Let

$$F^{(n)}(u) = G_u(n).$$

Then $F^{(0)}(u) = u$, $F^{(1)}(u) = F(u)$, and in general, $F^{(n^+)}(u) = F(F^{(n)}(u))$. Now we shall define a function H on X as follows: For each $u \in X$

$$H(u) = \begin{cases} F(u), & \text{if } (\exists n)(\exists v)(v \in X \sim X_1 \ \& \ u = F^{(n)}(v)) \\ u, & \text{otherwise.} \end{cases}$$

At this point let us illustrate what we are doing by a diagram. In Figure 4.5.1,

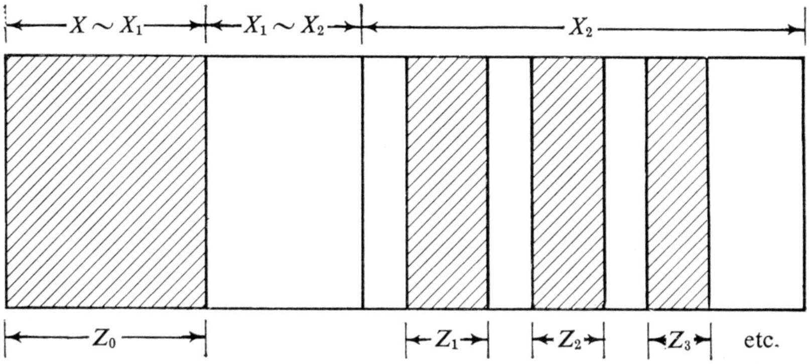

FIGURE 4.5.1

$$\begin{aligned} Z_0 &= X \sim X_1 \\ Z_1 &= F''Z_0 \\ Z_2 &= F''Z_1 \\ Z_3 &= F''Z_2, \end{aligned}$$

etc. Thus in Figure 4.5.1, if u is in one of the shaded areas, $H(u) = F(u)$ (H maps u to the next shaded area); if u is not in one of the shaded areas, $H(u) = u$.

We shall show that H is a 1–1 function mapping X onto X_1. It follows from the definition of H that H is a function and $\mathfrak{D}(H) = X$. Suppose that $H(u) = H(v)$.

Case 1. If $H(u) = u$ and $H(v) = v$, then clearly $u = v$.

Case 2. If $H(u) = F(u)$ and $H(v) = F(v)$, then $F(u) = F(v)$. But since F is 1–1, we obtain $u = v$.

Case 3. If $H(u) = F(u)$ and $H(v) = v$, then there is a $w \in X \sim X_1$ and an $n \in \omega$ such that

$$u = F^{(n)}(w).$$

Therefore,

$$F(u) = F^{(n^+)}(w).$$

But, since $H(v) = v$, $v \neq F^{(n^+)}(w)$. Hence, $v \neq F(u)$ and case 3 is impossible. The proof is analogous if $H(u) = u$ & $H(v) = F(v)$. Thus we have shown that if $H(u) = H(v)$, then $u = v$, so that H is 1–1.

Finally, we shall prove that H maps X onto X_1. Clearly $\mathfrak{R}(H) \subseteq X_1$, for if $u \in X \sim X_1$, then $H(u) = F(u) \in X_2 \subseteq X_1$, and if $u \in X_1$, then $H(u) = u$ or $H(u) = F(u)$, so that in either case, $H(u) \in X_1$. Let $v \in X_1$. If

$$(6) \qquad (\exists u)(u \in X \sim X_1 \ \&\ v = F^{(n^+)}(u)),$$

then by the definition of H, $H(F^{(n)}(u)) = v$. If (6) does not hold, then $H(v) = v$. Thus for each $v \in X_1$ there is a $u \in X$ such that $H(u) = v$. Therefore, H maps X onto X_1.

We have shown that H is a 1–1 function mapping X onto X_1. Thus $X \approx X_1$, which implies that $X \approx Y$. ■

The proof of the Schröder–Bernstein theorem does not depend on the axiom of choice.

Some consequences of the Schröder–Bernstein theorem are stated in the next theorem.

THEOREM 4.5.2.

(a) $X \precsim Y \rightarrow Y \nprec X$
(b) $X \prec Y \rightarrow Y \nprec X$
(c) $(X \precsim Y \ \&\ Y \prec Z) \rightarrow X \prec Z$
(d) $(X \prec Y \ \&\ Y \precsim Z) \rightarrow X \prec Z$
(e) $(X \prec Y \ \&\ Y \prec Z) \rightarrow X \prec Z$.

Proof:

(a) Suppose $X \precsim Y$ and $Y \prec X$. But $Y \prec X$ implies $Y \precsim X$. Therefore, the Schröder–Bernstein theorem implies $X \approx Y$. But $X \approx Y$ contradicts $Y \prec X$.

(b) This proof follows immediately from (a) because $X \prec Y$ implies $X \precsim Y$.

(c) Suppose that $X \precsim Y$ and $Y \prec Z$. Then it follows from theorem 3.4.4(b) that $X \precsim Z$. Suppose that $X \approx Z$. Then we have $Z \precsim Y$ and $Y \prec Z$. But this contradicts (a).

The proofs of (d) and (e) are analogous to the proof of (c). ■

Cantor's theorem, 3.4.6, states that for each set x, $x \prec \mathcal{P}(x)$. Let us suppose for a moment that V is a set. Then we would have

$$(1) \qquad V \prec \mathcal{P}(V).$$

However, $\mathcal{P}(V) \subseteq V$ (2.5.4b), so by 3.4.4(d),

$$(2) \qquad \mathcal{P}(V) \precsim V.$$

Formulas (1) and (2) contradict 4.5.2(a): consequently, V is not a set. But since V is a class, V must be a proper class. Thus, we have

THEOREM 4.5.3. $\quad \Pr(V)$.

In intuitive set theory, the preceding argument led to a contradiction which is often referred to as *Cantor's paradox*. In our system of set theory, the paradox is easily resolved by inferring that V is a proper class. In the Zermelo–Fraenkel system, the paradox does not arise (if the system is consistent) because it cannot be proved that V is a set (see §1.1).

EXERCISES 4.5

1. Considering $\lesssim$ as a relation between sets, decide whether or not the relation is
   (a) reflexive
   (b) symmetric
   (c) antisymmetric
   (d) asymmetric
   (e) not symmetric
   (f) transitive.
   If the answer is yes, prove it; if no, give a counterexample.
2. Answer question 1 for the relation $\prec$.

Chapter 5: Finite and Infinite Classes

5.1. FINITE CLASSES

We shall define a class as *finite* if it has the same number of elements as some natural number. Otherwise, it shall be called an *infinite* class.

DEFINITION 5.1.1. Finite and Infinite Classes
$\mathrm{Cl}(X) \rightarrow$
(a) X is *finite* $=_{\mathrm{Df}} (\exists n)(n \in \omega \;\&\; X \approx n)$
(b) X is *infinite* $=_{\mathrm{Df}} X$ is not finite.

Clearly, if X is a finite class, then X is a set. Also, if X is finite and $Y \approx X$, then Y is finite. Moreover, each natural number is finite.

THEOREM 5.1.2.
(a) $(\mathrm{Cl}(X) \;\&\; X$ is finite$) \rightarrow \mathrm{S}(X)$
(b) $(\mathrm{Cl}(X) \;\&\; X$ is finite $\&\; Y \approx X) \rightarrow Y$ is finite
(c) $n \in \omega \rightarrow n$ is finite.

In what follows we shall prove some additional properties of finite sets. Since properties of finite sets correspond to properties of natural numbers, we shall first prove a result for natural numbers and then state the corresponding result for finite sets as a corollary.

THEOREM 5.1.3. $(n \in \omega \;\&\; x \subseteq n) \rightarrow x$ is finite.

Proof: The proof is by induction. Let

$$y = \{n : n \in \omega \;\&\; (\forall u)(u \subseteq n \rightarrow u \text{ is finite})\}.$$

Clearly, $0 \in y$. Suppose that $n \in y$ and $x \subseteq n^+$. Then either $x \subseteq n$ or $n \in x$. If $x \subseteq n$, then x is finite since $n \in y$. Suppose that $n \in x$ and $x \subset n^+$. (If $x = n^+$, then x is a natural number and therefore finite.) Then there is an element $m \in n^+$ such that $m \notin x$. Let

$$z = (x \sim \{n\}) \cup \{m\}.$$

Then $x \approx z$ and $z \subseteq n$. Since $n \in y$, z is finite. Therefore, $x \approx z$ implies that x is also finite. Therefore, $n^+ \in y$. ■

COROLLARY 5.1.4. $(\mathrm{Cl}(X) \;\&\; X$ is finite $\&\; Y \subseteq X) \rightarrow Y$ is finite.

COROLLARY 5.1.5. $(\text{Cl}(X)\ \&\ X \text{ is finite } \&\ Y \precsim X) \to Y \text{ is finite.}$

The next theorem states that no natural number is equipollent to a proper subset of itself.

THEOREM 5.1.6. $n \in \omega \to \neg(\exists x)(x \subset n\ \&\ x \approx n).$

The proof is by induction and similar to the proof of 5.1.3. It is left as an exercise.

COROLLARY 5.1.7. $(\text{Cl}(X)\ \&\ X \text{ is finite}) \to \neg(\exists Y)(Y \subset X)\ \&\ Y \approx X).$

It follows immediately from 5.1.7 that ω is not finite. [The set ω is equipollent to $\omega \sim \{0\}$, for if $f(n) = n^+$ for all $n \in \omega$, then f is a 1–1 function mapping ω onto $\omega \sim \{0\}$.]

COROLLARY 5.1.8. ω is infinite.

THEOREM 5.1.9. $(m,n \in \omega\ \&\ m \approx n) \to m = n.$

Proof: Suppose $m \approx n$ and $m \neq n$. Then by 4.1.17, either $m \in n$ or $n \in m$. Because of symmetry, it will not matter which we choose. Suppose that $m \in n$. Then by 4.1.12 and hypothesis, $m \subset n$. But $m \subset n$ and $m \approx n$ contradicts 5.1.6. ∎

COROLLARY 5.1.10. $(\text{Cl}(X)\ \&\ X \text{ is finite}) \to (\exists 1 n)(X \approx n).$

Because of this corollary, if x is finite and $x \approx n$, it can be said without ambiguity that *x has n elements.*

EXERCISES 5.1

1. Give an example of a class which has both a smallest and a largest element with respect to some ordering, but which is not finite.
2. Prove: (X is finite & Y is finite) $\to$
   (a) $X \cap Y$ is finite, (b) $X \cup Y$ is finite,
   (c) $X \times Y$ is finite, (d) X^Y is finite.
3. Prove $x \subseteq \omega \to (x \text{ is finite} \leftrightarrow (\exists m)(m \text{ is the largest element of } x)).$

5.2. DENUMERABLE CLASSES

Since ω is not finite, no class which is equipollent to ω is finite either. Such classes are important enough to deserve a special name.

DEFINITION 5.2.1. Denumerable and Countable Classes

(a) X is *denumerable* $=_{\text{Df}} X \approx \omega$

(b) X is *countable* $=_{\text{Df}}$ (X is denumerable or X is finite).

Often in mathematics the terms "denumerable" and "countable" are used interchangeably. For the sake of clarity we distinguish between them here. The terms "enumerable" and "countably infinite" are sometimes used instead of "denumerable."

Clearly, a denumerable class is an infinite set.

THEOREM 5.2.2. X is denumerable $\rightarrow$ (S(X) & X is infinite).

Proof: The proof follows from 5.2.1, 4.1.7, 3.4.5(a), 5.1.8, and 5.1.1. Details of the proof are left to the reader.

Another term frequently used in mathematics for a countable set is *sequence*. In general, when a mathematician discusses a sequence of elements he symbolizes it thus:

$$x_0, x_1, x_2, \ldots .$$

But what does the symbolization mean? Does it mean that the sequence is $\{x_n : n \in \omega\}$? No. The sequence

$$1, 0, 0, 0, \ldots$$

is not the same as the sequence

$$0, 1, 1, 1, \ldots .$$

While order and repetitions do not affect sets, they do affect sequences. Therefore, we should like to define a sequence as an ordered tuple. This is accomplished in the following way:

DEFINITION 5.2.3. Sequences

$$u \subseteq \omega \rightarrow (X \text{ is a } u\text{-}sequence =_{\text{Df}} (\text{Func}(X) \ \& \ \mathfrak{D}(X) = u).$$

Clearly, for each countable set x there is a $u \subseteq \omega$ such that x is equipollent to a u-sequence. The converse is true also, namely, that if $u \subseteq \omega$, then each u-sequence is countable. The proof follows from the next theorem.

THEOREM 5.2.4. $x \subseteq \omega \rightarrow x$ is countable.

Proof: It follows from 3.4.4(d) that if $x \subseteq \omega$, then $x \lesssim \omega$. If $x \approx \omega$, then x is denumerable. We shall show that if $x < \omega$, then x is finite.

Suppose that $x \subseteq \omega$, $x < \omega$, and x is infinite. It follows from 4.2.2, the recursion theorem III, 4.3.3, and the remarks following 4.2.1 that there exists a unique function f such that $\mathfrak{D}(f) = \omega$ and for each $n \in \omega$,

$$f(n) = \begin{cases} \text{smallest element of } (x \sim f''n), & \text{if } x \sim f''n \neq \emptyset \\ \emptyset, & \text{if } x \sim f''n = \emptyset. \end{cases}$$

However if $x \sim f''n = \emptyset$, then $x \subseteq f''n$. This implies that x is finite, contradicting our assumption that x is infinite. Consequently,

$$(1) \qquad f(n) = \text{smallest element of } (x \sim f''n),$$

for all $n \in \omega$. Moreover f is 1–1, for suppose $n, m \in \omega$ and $m \in n$. Then $f(m) \notin x \sim f''n$ because $f(m) \in f''n$. But, by (1), $f(n) \in x \sim f''n$. Therefore, $f(n) \neq f(m)$, so that f is 1–1 and $\omega \precsim x$. This contradicts the fact that $x \prec \omega$. Consequently x must be finite. ■

COROLLARY 5.2.5. $(x \text{ is denumerable } \& \ y \subseteq x) \rightarrow y$ is countable.

COROLLARY 5.2.6. $(x \text{ is denumerable } \& \ y \precsim x) \rightarrow y$ is countable.

COROLLARY 5.2.7. $(x \text{ is denumerable } \& \ y \prec x) \rightarrow y$ is finite.

Next, we shall prove that the union of a denumerable number of pairwise disjoint denumerable sets is denumerable. The proof uses Cantor's diagonal procedure and the axiom of choice.

THEOREM 5.2.8.©

$$(\forall n)[x_n \text{ is denumerable } \& \ (\forall m)(m \neq n \rightarrow x_n \cap x_m = \emptyset)] \rightarrow \bigcup_{n \in \omega} x_n \text{ is denumerable.}$$

Proof: The intuitive idea of the proof is as follows. Since $x_n \approx \omega$ for each $n \in \omega$, the set x_n can be expressed in the following form.

$$(1) \qquad x_n = \{x_{np} : p \in \omega\}.$$

Then the elements of $\bigcup_{n \in \omega} x_n$ can be written as an "infinite matrix" such that the first row consists of the elements of x_0; the second row, of the elements of x_1; etc.

$$\begin{matrix} x_{00} & x_{01} & x_{02} & x_{03} & \cdots \\ x_{10} & x_{11} & x_{12} & x_{13} & \cdots \\ x_{20} & x_{21} & x_{22} & x_{23} & \cdots \\ x_{30} & x_{31} & x_{32} & x_{33} & \cdots \\ \cdot & \cdot & \cdot & \cdot & \cdots \end{matrix}$$

It follows from the hypotheses and (1) that

$$(2) \qquad x_{nm} = x_{pq} \text{ if and only if } n = p \text{ and } m = q.$$

Moreover, every element of $\bigcup_{n \in \omega} x_n$ appears in the infinite matrix.

We construct a 1–1 correspondence between $\bigcup_{n \in \omega} x_n$ and ω by counting the elements of the infinite matrix along the diagonals. That is, define a function f such that

$$\begin{aligned} f(x_{00}) &= 0 \\ f(x_{10}) &= 1 \\ f(x_{01}) &= 2 \\ f(x_{20}) &= 3 \\ f(x_{11}) &= 4 \\ f(x_{02}) &= 5 \\ f(x_{30}) &= 6, \end{aligned}$$

etc. But what must be done to make the proof rigorous? First we must be sure that the "infinite matrix" exists. While it is true that x_n is denumerable for each $n \in \omega$, in order to construct the "infinite matrix" we must be able to choose an enumeration of x_n for each $n \in \omega$. That is, for each $n \in \omega$ we must choose a function f_n such that f_n is a 1–1 correspondence from x_n onto ω. If there were only a finite number of choices to be made, this could be done without difficulty. However, since an infinite number of choices must be made, the aid of the axiom of choice is needed. The axiom of choice is used as follows. For each $n \in \omega$ we define a set y_n as follows:

$$f \in y_n \leftrightarrow f: x_n \xrightarrow[\text{onto}]{1\text{–}1} \omega.$$

Let

$$Y = \{y_n : n \in \omega\}.$$

The set Y is a non-empty set of non-empty sets. Therefore, by the axiom of choice, ac1, there is a function F on Y such that for each $y_n \in Y$, $F(y_n) \in y_n$. Let

$$F(y_n) = f_n.$$

Thus, for each $n \in \omega$, f_n is a 1–1 function mapping x_n onto ω. Thus we have constructed a denumerable number of enumerations simultaneously. (There are numerous instances in mathematics where some form of the axiom of choice is needed in a similar capacity.)

The other point of the proof which is not rigorous is the assumption that f is a 1–1 correspondence from $\bigcup_{n \in \omega} x_n$ onto ω. We shall give a rigorous proof of this theorem here.

Define a function f on $\bigcup_{n \in \omega} x_n$ as follows:

(3) $$f(x_{mp}) = \tfrac{1}{2}(m + p + 1)(m + p) + p.$$

It follows from exercise 4.4.2 that either $m + p + 1$ or $m + p$ is divisible by two, so for each $m,p \in \omega$, $f(x_{mp}) \in \omega$.

We shall show first that f is 1–1. Suppose that $f(x_{mp}) = f(x_{nq})$.

Case 1. $m + p = n + q$. Then it follows from (3) that $m = n$ and $p = q$.

Case 2. $m + p \neq n + q$. Then because of symmetry and the trichotomy we may assume that

(4) $$m + p < n + q \qquad (\text{that is, } m + p \in n + q)$$

$$\begin{aligned} f(x_{mp}) &= \tfrac{1}{2}(m + p + 1)(m + p) + p && (3) \\ &< \tfrac{1}{2}(m + p + 1)(m + p) + p + m + 1 && (\text{exercise 4.4.3a}) \\ &= \tfrac{1}{2}(m + p + 2)(m + p + 1) \\ &\leqq \tfrac{1}{2}(n + q + 1)(n + q) + q && (4, \text{exercise 4.4.3j, d}) \\ &= f(x_{nq}). \end{aligned}$$

This is a contradiction since we assumed that $f(x_{mp}) = f(x_{nq})$. Hence, f is 1–1.

To show that f maps $\bigcup_{n\in\omega} x_n$ onto ω, we shall define a function g from ω to $\bigcup_{n\in\omega} x_n$ and prove that $f \circ g = I|\mathfrak{D}(g)$ (see 3.3.6).

With this in mind, we define g inductively as follows:

$$g(0) = x_{00}.$$

(5) If $g(n) = x_{mp}$ and $m = 0$, then $g(n^+) = x_{p^+0}$.
If $g(n) = x_{mp}$ and $m \neq 0$, then there is an r such that $r^+ = m$ and $g(n^+) = x_{rp^+}$.

We shall prove by induction that $f(g(n)) = n$ for each $n \in \omega$. By (5), $g(0) = x_{00}$ and by (3), $f(x_{00}) = 0$; therefore, $f(g(0)) = 0$. Suppose that

(6) $$f(g(n)) = n \text{ and } g(n) = x_{mp}.$$

Case 1. $m = 0$. Then by (5), $g(n^+) = x_{p^+0}$ and by (3),

$$\begin{aligned} f(x_{p^+0}) &= \tfrac{1}{2}(p^+ + 1)(p^+) \\ &= \tfrac{1}{2}(p + 1)p + p + 1 \\ &= f(x_{0p}) + 1 && (3) \\ &= n + 1 && (6) \\ &= n^+. \end{aligned}$$

Case 2. $m \neq 0$. Then there is an r such that $r^+ = m$ and by (5), $g(n^+) = x_{rp^+}$. By (3),

$$\begin{aligned} f(x_{rp^+}) &= \tfrac{1}{2}(r + p^+ + 1)(r + p^+) + p^+ \\ &= \tfrac{1}{2}(m + p + 1)(m + p) + p + 1 \\ &= f(x_{mp}) + 1 && (3) \\ &= n + 1 && (6) \\ &= n^+. \end{aligned}$$

It follows by mathematical induction that $f(g(n)) = n$ for all $n \in \omega$. Therefore, by 3.3.6, f maps $\bigcup_{n\in\omega} x_n$ onto ω. ■

See exercise 5.2.5 for an alternative proof of theorem 5.2.8.

We have shown with the aid of the axiom of choice that the union of a denumerable number of pairwise disjoint sets is denumerable. There follows a list of several corollaries to this theorem.

COROLLARY 5.2.9.©

$$(\forall n)(x_n \text{ is denumerable}) \rightarrow \bigcup_{n\in\omega} x_n \text{ is denumerable.}$$

Proof: Use 5.2.8 and the Schröder–Bernstein theorem.

The axiom of choice is *not* used to prove the remaining corollaries.

COROLLARY 5.2.10.

$$(\forall n)(n \in m \rightarrow x_n \text{ is denumerable}) \rightarrow \bigcup_{n\in m} x_n \text{ is denumerable.}$$

COROLLARY 5.2.11.

$$(x \text{ is finite } \& \ y \text{ is denumerable}) \rightarrow x \cup y \text{ is denumerable.}$$

COROLLARY 5.2.12. $\omega \times \omega \approx \omega.$

Proof: Arrange the elements of $\omega \times \omega$ in an infinite matrix:

$$\begin{matrix} \langle 0,0\rangle, & \langle 0,1\rangle, & \langle 0,2\rangle, & \cdots \\ \langle 1,0\rangle, & \langle 1,1\rangle, & \langle 1,2\rangle, & \cdots \\ \langle 2,0\rangle, & \langle 2,1\rangle, & \langle 2,2\rangle, & \cdots \\ \cdot & \cdot & \cdot & \cdots. \end{matrix}$$

Count them along the diagonals:

$$\begin{aligned} f(0,0) &= 0 \\ f(1,0) &= 1 \\ f(0,1) &= 2 \\ f(2,0) &= 3 \\ f(1,1) &= 4, \end{aligned}$$

etc. The function f is a 1–1 function mapping $\omega \times \omega$ onto ω. The proof is similar to the proof of 5.2.8, but here the axiom of choice is *not* needed. ■

COROLLARY 5.2.13. $n \neq 0 \rightarrow \omega^n \approx \omega.$

Proof: Use 5.2.11 and induction. ■

However, if $2 \leq n$, then n^ω is not countable because it follows from 3.5.23 that

$$2^\omega \approx \mathcal{P}(\omega);$$

from theorem 3.4.6, that

$$\omega \prec \mathcal{P}(\omega);$$

and from exercise 3.5.4(b), that

$$2 \leqq n \rightarrow 2^{\omega} \precsim n^{\omega}.$$

COROLLARY 5.2.14.

(X is denumerable & Y is denumerable) $\rightarrow X \times Y$ is denumerable.

Proof: By theorem 5.2.12.

COROLLARY 5.2.15.

(X is denumerable & Y is finite & $Y \neq \emptyset$) $\rightarrow X^Y$ is denumerable.

Proof: By corollary 5.2.13.

From the remarks following 5.2.13 it follows also that Y^X is not countable if $2 \precsim Y$.

We shall show that each infinite set contains a denumerable subset. Let X be an infinite set. Since $X \neq \emptyset$, there is an element $y_0 \in X$. But $X \sim \{y_0\} \neq \emptyset$ because X is infinite; thus there is an element $y_1 \in X \sim \{y_0\}$. Moreover, $X \sim \{y_0, y_1\} \neq \emptyset$; thus there is an element $y_2 \in X \sim \{y_0, y_1\}$. It seems intuitively clear that by continuing this process we could construct a denumerable subset of X. But again we are in a situation where we must make a denumerable number of choices. Therefore, just as in the proof of 5.2.8, the axiom of choice is used to prove that every infinite set has a denumerable subset.

THEOREM 5.2.16.©

$$(\mathrm{S}(X) \ \&\ X \text{ is infinite}) \rightarrow (\exists Y)(Y \subseteq X \ \&\ Y \text{ is denumerable}).$$[11]

Proof: Let X be an infinite set and F a choice function on $\mathcal{P}(X) \sim \{\emptyset\}$. That is, F is a function, the domain of F is the set of non-empty subsets of X, and for each $u \subseteq X$, if $u \neq \emptyset$ then $F(u) \in u$. If u is a finite subset of X, since X is infinite, then $X \sim u \neq \emptyset$, so that $X \sim u \in \mathfrak{D}(F)$.

Using the recursion theorem I, define a function G as follows:

$$G(0) = \emptyset$$
$$G(n^+) = G(n) \cup \{F(X \sim G(n))\}.$$

It follows easily by induction that $G(n)$ is finite for each $n \in \omega$ so that $X \sim G(n) \in \mathfrak{D}(F)$ for each $n \in \omega$.

[11] In order to prove this theorem in the case that X is a proper class it is necessary to use a stronger form of the axiom of choice than is available at this time. The stronger forms of the axiom of choice will be discussed in Chapter 10. See also theorem 5.3.2, section 8.6 and exercise 8.6.12.

[Comparing this formal construction with the informal discussion preceding the theorem, we have

$$F(X \sim G(n)) = y_n$$

and

$$G(n^+) = \{y_0, y_1, \ldots, y_n\}. \qquad]$$

Now we shall show that

(1) $$\{F(X \sim G(n)) : n \in \omega\} \subseteq X$$

and

(2) $$\{F(X \sim G(n)) : n \in \omega\} \approx \omega.$$

Since F is a choice function, then

(3) $$F(X \sim G(n)) \in X \sim G(n)$$

and clearly $X \sim G(n) \subseteq X$. Therefore (1) holds. To prove (2), for each $n \in \omega$ let

(4) $$H(n) = F(X \sim G(n)).$$

Then $\mathfrak{D}(H) = \omega$. It will be shown that H is 1–1. Suppose that $m < n$. Then it follows from the definition of G that

(5) $$H(m) \in G(n).$$

But by (3) and (4),

(6) $$H(n) \notin G(n).$$

Thus, by (5) and (6), $H(m) \neq H(n)$. This proves (2). ∎

As a consequence of 5.2.16 and 5.1.7, we can formulate a necessary and sufficient condition for a class to be infinite.

THEOREM 5.2.17.© x is infinite $\leftrightarrow (\exists y)(y \subset x \;\&\; y \approx x)$.

Proof: If a class is equipollent to a proper subclass of itself, then it follows from 5.1.7 that it is infinite.

Conversely, suppose that x is infinite. Then, by 5.2.16, x contains a denumerable subset

$$z = \{y_n : n \in \omega\}.$$

Define a function F on x as follows:

$$(\forall n)(u \neq y_n \rightarrow F(u) = u)$$
$$(\exists n)(u = y_n \rightarrow F(u) = y_{n^+}).$$

Thus,

$$\begin{aligned} F(u) &= u, \qquad \text{if } u \neq y_n \\ F(y_0) &= y_1 \\ F(y_1) &= y_2 \\ F(y_2) &= y_3 \end{aligned}$$

etc. It is clear that F is a 1–1 function mapping x onto $x \sim \{y_0\}$. Therefore, x is equipollent to a proper subclass of itself. ■

Corollary 5.2.18.© $\quad x$ is infinite $\leftrightarrow x \approx x^+$.

EXERCISES 5.2

1. Give several examples of denumerable sets and several examples of classes which are not countable.
2. Prove $u \notin x \rightarrow (x$ is infinite $\leftrightarrow x \approx x \cup \{u\})$. (The proof uses the axiom of choice.)
3. Prove (y is finite & $y \cap x = \emptyset) \rightarrow (x$ is infinite $\leftrightarrow x \approx x \cup y)$. (The proof uses the axiom of choice.)
4. What changes would you make in the proof of 5.2.8 if the elements of $\bigcup_{n \in \omega} x_n$ were counted down the diagonals instead of up? That is, if the function f had the property that $f(x_{00}) = 0, f(x_{01}) = 1, f(x_{10} = 2, f(x_{02}) = 3, f(x_{11}) = 4, f(x_{20}) = 5, f(x_{03}) = 6$, etc.
5. In the proof of 5.2.8, replace the function f by the function g defined as follows:

$$\begin{aligned} \mathfrak{D}(g) &= \textstyle\bigcup_{n \in \omega} x_n \\ (\forall m)(\forall n)(g(x_{mn}) &= 2^{m+n+1} + 2^m). \end{aligned}$$

   Prove that g is a 1–1 function mapping $\bigcup_{n \in \omega} x_n$ into ω, thereby giving an alternative proof of theorem 5.2.8.
6. Prove, without using the axiom of choice, that

$$(X \approx Y \;\&\; Y \subset X) \rightarrow (\exists z)(z \text{ is a denumerable } \& \; z \subseteq X)$$

   (Hint: See the proof of the Schröder–Bernstein theorem, 4.5.1).

*5.3. THE PRINCIPLE OF DEPENDENT CHOICES

There are occasions when the full strength of the axiom of choice is not needed. A weaker result will suffice. One such weaker proposition is called the *principle of dependent choices*. [It has been shown by S. Feferman (1964) that the principle of dependent choices does not imply the axiom of choice. See also A. Mostowski (1948). The formulation of the principle given here is due to A. Tarski (1948).]

PD:

$(\text{Rel}(R)\ \&\ R \neq \emptyset\ \&\ \mathfrak{D}(R) \subseteq \mathfrak{R}(R)\ \&\ (\forall u)(u \in \mathfrak{D}(R) \rightarrow S(R''\{u\})) \rightarrow$
$(\exists f)(\text{Func}(f)\ \&\ \mathfrak{D}(f) = \omega\ \&\ \mathfrak{R}(f) \subseteq \mathfrak{D}(R)\ \&\ (\forall n)(n \in \omega \rightarrow f(n)\, R\, f(n+1)).$

The name "principle of dependent choices" is used because PD enables us to choose a denumerable number of elements, $f(0), f(1), f(2), \ldots,$ and for each n, the choice of $f(n^+)$ depends upon the choice of $f(n)$. The non-constructive nature of PD is evident because there is no rule for constructing the function f. We shall use a form of the axiom of choice to "construct" the function f.

THEOREM 5.3.1. AC2 $\rightarrow$ PD.

Proof: Let R be a relation satisfying the hypothesis of PD. AC2 implies that there exists a function G such that $\mathfrak{D}(G) = \mathfrak{D}(R)$ and $G \subseteq R$. We can define the function f using the recursion theorem I. Let $u \in \mathfrak{D}(R)$, then we define

$$f(0) = u$$
$$f(n^+) = G(f(n)).$$

It follows easily from the definition of G that f is the required function. ■

Next, we shall show how PD could have been used to replace the axiom of choice in the proof of 5.2.17.

THEOREM 5.3.2. (PD)

$$(S(X)\ \&\ X \text{ is infinite}) \rightarrow (\exists Y)(Y \subseteq X\ \&\ Y \text{ is denumerable}).$$

Proof using PD: Let X be an infinite set and let Y be the class of all non-empty finite subsets of X. We define a relation R on Y as follows:

$$u\, R\, v \leftrightarrow (u,v \in Y\ \&\ u \subset v\ \&\ (\exists 1 w)(w \in v\ \&\ w \notin u)).$$

Thus, $u\, R\, v$ if and only if v has exactly one more element than u. R satisfies the hypothesis of PD; thus there exists a function f such that

$$\mathfrak{D}(f) = \omega,\ \mathfrak{R}(f) \subseteq Y$$

and

$$(\forall n)(n \in \omega \rightarrow f(n)\, R\, f(n^+)).$$

Therefore, for each $n \in \omega$ there is an element $y_n \in X$ such that $y_n \notin f(n)$ and

$$f(n^+) = f(n) \cup \{y_n\}.$$

Clearly, if $m < n$, then $f(m) \subset f(n)$. Thus, f is a 1–1 function mapping ω onto X. Consequently, $\mathfrak{R}(f)$ is a denumerable subset of X. ■

The principle of dependent choices can be used to replace the axiom of choice in the proofs of many theorems of analysis and topology which have non-constructive proofs. One well-known example is the proof of Urysohn's lemma—in a normal space, two closed sets can be separated by a continuous function. [See, for example, J. L. Kelly (1955).] Another example is the proof of the Baire Category theorem—a complete metric space is not the union of a countable collection of nowhere dense sets. [See Royden (1963).] Also, PD may be used to replace the axiom of choice in the proof of 5.2.8. This is true because PD implies the so-called *denumerable axiom of choice:* If x is a non-empty denumerable set of non-empty pairwise disjoint sets, then there exists a set c which consists of one and only one element from each set in x.

EXERCISE 5.3

1. Use the principle of dependent choices to prove the denumerable axiom of choice.

*5.4. THE AXIOM OF REGULARITY AGAIN

In this section we shall show that the axiom of regularity, A9, is equivalent to the statement: there does not exist a descending chain of sets.

THEOREM 5.4.1.

$$\text{A9} \rightarrow \neg(\exists f)[\text{Func}(f) \mathbin{\&} \mathfrak{D}(f) = \omega \mathbin{\&} (\forall n)(n \in \omega \rightarrow f(n^+) \in f(n))].$$

Proof: Suppose there is a function f such that $\mathfrak{D}(f) = \omega$ & for each $n \in \omega$, $f(n^+) \in f(n)$. Then, for each $n \in \omega$,

$$f(n^+) \in f(n) \text{ and } f(n^+) \in \mathfrak{R}(f).$$

Therefore, for each $n \in \omega$,

$$f(n) \cap \mathfrak{R}(f) \neq \emptyset.$$

This contradicts A9. ■

THEOREM 5.4.2.©

$$\neg\text{A9} \rightarrow (\exists f)[\text{Func}(f) \mathbin{\&} \mathfrak{D}(f) = \omega \mathbin{\&} (\forall n)(n \in \omega \rightarrow f(n^+) \in f(n))].$$

Proof: Suppose A9 is false. Then there exists a non-empty class of sets X such that for each $u \in X$, $u \cap X \neq \emptyset$. Let G be a choice function on the class $\{u \cap X : u \in X\}$. Then, for each $u \in X$, $G(u \cap X) \in u \cap X$. Using the recursion theorem I, define a function f as follows: let $u \in X$; then

$$f(0) = G(u \cap X)$$
$$f(n^+) = G(f(n) \cap X).$$

Clearly, $\mathfrak{D}(f) = \omega$ and for each $n \in \omega$, $f(n^+) \in f(n)$. ■

We shall also show that the axiom of regularity can be replaced by what is apparently a weaker axiom. In the case of the axiom of choice, it has been shown by Easton that the set form does not imply the class form. However, in the case of the axiom of regularity, we shall show that the set form does imply the class form.

a9: $[\mathrm{S}(X)\ \&\ X \neq \emptyset\ \&\ (\forall u)(u \in X \rightarrow \mathrm{S}(u))] \rightarrow (\exists u)(u \in X\ \&\ u \cap X = \emptyset).$

Clearly A9 implies a9 because every class is a set. But the converse is also true.

THEOREM 5.4.3. a9 $\rightarrow$ A9.

Proof: Suppose that X satisfies the hypothesis of A9. Let $u \in X$. If $u \cap X = \emptyset$, the theorem is true. Instead, suppose that

(1) $$u \cap X \neq \emptyset.$$

Let $T(u)$ be a set such that $u \subseteq T(u)$ and

(2) $$(\forall s)(\forall t)[(s \in t\ \&\ t \in T(u)) \rightarrow s \in T(u)].$$

[The existence of $T(u)$ follows from exercise 4.3.3.] Since $T(u)$ is a set, so is $T(u) \cap X$. And since $u \cap X \subseteq T(u) \cap X$, it follows from (1) that $T(u) \cap X \neq \emptyset$. Therefore, since X satisfies the hypothesis of A9, $T(u) \cap X$ satisfies the hypothesis of a9. Hence, there is an element $v \in T(u) \cap X$ such that

(3) $$v \cap (T(u) \cap X) = \emptyset.$$

Now we claim that $v \cap X = \emptyset$. For suppose that $w \in v \cap X$. Then

(4) $$w \in v$$

and

(5) $$w \in X.$$

But we have

(6) $$v \in T(u).$$

Since $T(u)$ satisfies (2), (4) and (6) imply

(7) $$w \in T(u).$$

Therefore, we have from (4), (5), and (7), $w \in v \cap (T(u) \cap X)$. This contradicts (3). Thus, $v \cap X = \emptyset$. ■

EXERCISE 5.4

1. Use PD instead of the axiom of choice to prove 5.4.2.

*Chapter 6: The Rational and the Real Numbers

6.1. INTRODUCTION

As an application of the set theoretical concepts developed, we shall indicate how the rational and real numbers can be defined. That is, we shall show how entities which have the well-known properties of the rational and real numbers can be defined using the tools of set theory.

Once the natural numbers have been defined, there are several alternative methods for constructing the rational and the real numbers:

(1) Define the integers (positive and negative), the rational numbers, and then the real numbers.

(2) Define the non-negative rational numbers, all rational numbers, and then all real numbers.

(3) Define the non-negative rational numbers, the non-negative real numbers, and then all real numbers.

(4) Define all the rational numbers and then all the real numbers.

Given the natural numbers, a non-negative integer could be defined as an ordered pair $\langle n,0\rangle$ and a non-positive integer as $\langle 0,n\rangle$ with $n \in \omega$. Then the desired properties could be postulated. Alternatively, an integer could be defined as an equivalence class of ordered pairs $[\langle n,m\rangle]_R$, $n,m \in \omega$, where intuitively $[\langle n,m\rangle]_R$, is the integer $n - m$. So we would define

$$\langle n,m\rangle \; R \; \langle l,k\rangle \leftrightarrow n + k = m + l.$$

Once the integers are defined, a rational number is defined as an equivalence class of ordered pairs of integers $[\langle u,v\rangle]_S$, $v \neq 0$. Intuitively, $[\langle u,v\rangle]_S = u/v$, therefore,

$$\langle u,v\rangle \; S \; \langle x,y\rangle \leftrightarrow uy = vx.$$

In the second and third alternatives, a non-negative rational number is defined to be an equivalence class of ordered pairs of natural numbers, $[\langle m,n\rangle]_S$, $n \neq 0$. So $[\langle m,n\rangle]_S$ represents the rational number m/n. In the fourth alternative, a rational number is defined to be an equivalence class of ordered triples of natural numbers $[\langle m,n,p\rangle]_T$, $p \neq 0$, where $[\langle m,n,p\rangle]_T$ represents the rational number $(m - n)/p$. We shall develop the first alternative in this text.

After the rational numbers have been constructed, there are several alternative methods for defining the real numbers. The two most common procedures are by *Dedekind cuts* and *Cauchy sequences.* [Dedekind cuts were discovered by the German mathematician Julius Wilhelm Richard Dedekind (1831–1916), and Cauchy sequences were named after the famous French mathematician Augustin Louis Cauchy (1789–1857). Cauchy gave a rigorous definition of the concepts of limits and continuity, thereby greatly increasing the understanding and development of analysis.] We shall sketch the Dedekind cut procedure here, and the Cauchy sequence procedure will be developed more completely later in the text.

A Dedekind cut is a partition of the set of rational numbers into two non-empty disjoint sets X and Y ($X \cap Y = \emptyset$ and $X \cup Y =$ set of rational numbers), such that for all $u \in X$ and $v \in Y$, $u < v$. X is called the *lower class* and Y, the *upper class*. Then a real number is defined as a Dedekind cut or, more simply, as the lower class (or upper class) of a Dedekind cut. This development is given in detail by Landau (1946).

The approach we shall give here is due to Cantor and is more analytic and less algebraic in character.

EXERCISES 6.1

1. Explain why it is necessary to define a rational number in alternatives (1)–(3) as an *equivalence class* of ordered pairs and in (4) as an *equivalence class* of ordered triplets, rather than as an ordered pair or an ordered triplet, respectively.
2. If a non-negative integer is defined as an ordered pair $\langle n,0\rangle$ and a non-positive integer as an ordered pair $\langle 0,n\rangle$ with $n \in \omega$, define the sum, difference and product of two integers in the natural way. Prove that addition and multiplication are commutative.

6.2. THE INTEGERS

Intuitively we can think of an integer u as the difference of two natural numbers m and n. So u is negative if $m < n$, u is zero if $m = n$, and u is positive if $m > n$. Therefore, it would be natural to define the integer u to be some function of the ordered pair $\langle m,n\rangle$. Why not the ordered pair itself? For the simple reason that two ordered pairs are equal if and only if they are identical, while two differences $m_1 - n_1$ and $m_2 - n_2$ are equal if and only if $m_1 + n_2 = m_2 + n_1$. Thus, for example,

$$4 - 2 = 6 - 4,$$

but

$$\langle 4,2\rangle \neq \langle 6,4\rangle.$$

Therefore, what we have to do is group together all ordered pairs which represent the same integer and we do this by forming equivalence classes of ordered pairs. There seems to be no reasonable way to avoid this complication.

DEFINITION 6.2.1.

$$m,n,p,q \in \omega \rightarrow (\langle m,n\rangle =_{\mathrm{i}} \langle p,q\rangle) =_{\mathrm{Df}} (m + q = p + n).$$

It is easy to prove,

THEOREM 6.2.2. $=_{\mathrm{i}}$ is an equivalence relation on $\omega \times \omega$.

Now we can define an integer as an equivalence class of ordered pairs of natural numbers.

DEFINITION 6.2.3. Integers

(a) $m,n \in \omega \rightarrow ([\langle m,n\rangle]_{\mathrm{i}} =_{\mathrm{Df}} \{\langle p,q\rangle : p,q \in \omega \;\&\; \langle p,q\rangle =_{\mathrm{i}} \langle m,n\rangle\})$.

(b) $u \in In =_{\mathrm{Df}} (\exists m)(\exists n)(m,n \in \omega \;\&\; u = [\langle m,n\rangle]_{\mathrm{i}})$.

Thus In is the class of all integers. Next, let us derive some properties of In. First, In is a set because $In \subseteq \mathcal{P}(\omega \times \omega)$.

THEOREM 6.2.4. $\mathrm{S}(In)$.

If $[\langle m,n\rangle]_{\mathrm{i}} \in In$, we should like to be able to say that $[\langle m,n\rangle]_{\mathrm{i}}$ is negative if $m < n$, zero if $m = n$, and positive if $m > n$. However, before saying this we have to be certain that these are properties which are possessed by all elements of the equivalence class. That is, if $m < n$ and $\langle p,q\rangle \in [\langle m,n\rangle]_{\mathrm{i}}$, then $p < q$. Similarly for the other properties. Thus, we have to prove

THEOREM 6.2.5. $(m,n,p,q \in \omega \;\&\; \langle m,n\rangle =_{\mathrm{i}} \langle p,q\rangle) \rightarrow$

(a) $m < n \leftrightarrow p < q$

(b) $m = n \leftrightarrow p = q$

(c) $m > n \leftrightarrow p > q$.

Proof: (a) If $\langle m,n\rangle =_{\mathrm{i}} \langle p,q\rangle$, then

(1) $$m + q = p + n.$$

Suppose $m < n$, then by 4.4.20(a)

(2) $$m + q < n + q.$$

Therefore, if $q \leqq p$,

(3) $$n + q \leqq n + p.$$

Then from (2) and (3) we obtain

(4) $$m + q < n + p$$

which contradicts (1). Thus $p < q$. By reason of symmetry this proves (a).

Part (b) follows from the cancellation law for addition of natural numbers 4.4.20(b), and (c) is analogous to (a). ■

Now we are ready to define negative, zero, and positive integers.

DEFINITION 6.2.6. $[\langle m,n\rangle]_{\text{i}} \in In \rightarrow$

(a) $[\langle m,n\rangle]_{\text{i}}$ is *negative* $=_{\text{Df}} m < n$

(b) $[\langle m,n\rangle]_{\text{i}}$ is *zero* $=_{\text{Df}} m = n$

(c) $[\langle m,n\rangle]_{\text{i}}$ is *positive* $=_{\text{Df}} m > n$.

Since $=_{\text{i}}$ is an equivalence relation on $\omega \times \omega$, its equivalence classes are pairwise disjoint and every element of $\omega \times \omega$ belongs to an equivalence class (3.2.9). Thus, for example, for each $n \in \omega$ the ordered pair $\langle n,0\rangle$ belongs to exactly one equivalence class, and similarly the ordered pair $\langle 0,n\rangle$ belongs to exactly one equivalence class. Moreover, we shall show that In is equipollent with the set of all elements of the form $\langle m,n\rangle$ such that either $m = 0$ or $n = 0$.

THEOREM 6.2.7. $[\langle m,n\rangle]_{\text{i}} \in In \rightarrow$

(a) $[\langle m,n\rangle]_{\text{i}}$ is negative $\rightarrow (\exists 1p)(p \in \omega \;\&\; p \neq 0 \;\&\; \langle 0,p\rangle =_{\text{i}} \langle m,n\rangle)$.

(b) $[\langle m,n\rangle]_{\text{i}}$ is zero $\rightarrow \langle 0,0\rangle =_{\text{i}} \langle m,n\rangle$.

(c) $[\langle m,n\rangle]_{\text{i}}$ is positive $\rightarrow (\exists 1p)(p \in \omega \;\&\; p \neq 0 \;\&\; \langle p,0\rangle =_{\text{i}} \langle m,n\rangle)$.

Proof:

(a) Suppose $[\langle m,n\rangle]_{\text{i}}$ is negative. Then by 6.2.6(a), $m < n$. Therefore, by 4.4.21 there is a unique $p \in \omega$ such that

$$m + p = n.$$

Since $m < n$, $p \neq 0$, and it follows from 6.2.1 that $\langle 0,p\rangle =_{\text{i}} \langle m,n\rangle$.

The proofs of (b) and (c) are left as exercises. ■

As immediate corollaries of 6.2.7 we have,

COROLLARY 6.2.8.

$$In \approx \{\langle m,n\rangle : m,n \in \omega \;\&\; (m = 0 \text{ or } n = 0)\}.$$

COROLLARY 6.2.9. *In* is denumerable.

Now, as is well known, if $m_1 - n_1$ and $m_2 - n_2$ are integers,

$$(m_1 - n_1) + (m_2 - n_2) = (m_1 + m_2) - (n_1 + n_2)$$
$$(m_1 - n_1) - (m_2 - n_2) = (m_1 + n_2) - (n_1 + m_2)$$
$$(m_1 - n_1)\cdot(m_2 - n_2) = (m_1m_2 + n_1n_2) - (m_1n_2 + n_1m_2).$$

This, then, gives us the motivation for the definition of addition, subtraction, and multiplication of integers. But first we give the preliminary theorem which tells us that these properties are independent of the particular choice of the element from the equivalence class.

THEOREM 6.2.10.

$$(m_1,n_1,p_1,q_1,m_2,n_2,p_2,q_2 \in In \;\&\; \langle m_1,n_1\rangle =_{\mathrm{i}} \langle m_2,n_2\rangle \;\&\; \langle p_1,q_1\rangle = \langle p_2,q_2\rangle) \rightarrow$$

(a) $\langle m_1 + p_1,\, n_1 + q_1\rangle =_{\mathrm{i}} \langle m_2 + p_2,\, n_2 + q_2\rangle$
(b) $\langle m_1 + q_1,\, n_1 + p_1\rangle =_{\mathrm{i}} \langle m_2 + q_2,\, n_2 + p_2\rangle$
(c) $\langle m_1p_1 + n_1q_1,\, m_1q_1 + n_1p_1\rangle =_{\mathrm{i}} \langle m_2p_2 + n_2q_2,\, m_2q_2 + n_2p_2\rangle$.

The proof is left as an exercise.

The operations on *In* are then defined as follows:

DEFINITION 6.2.11. Addition, Subtraction, and Multiplication

$$[\langle m,n\rangle]_{\mathrm{i}},\ [\langle p,q\rangle]_{\mathrm{i}} \in In \rightarrow$$

(a) $[\langle m,n\rangle]_{\mathrm{i}} +_{\mathrm{i}} [\langle p,q\rangle]_{\mathrm{i}} =_{\mathrm{Df}} [\langle m + p,\, n + q\rangle]_{\mathrm{i}}$
(b) $[\langle m,n\rangle]_{\mathrm{i}} -_{\mathrm{i}} [\langle p,q\rangle]_{\mathrm{i}} =_{\mathrm{Df}} [\langle m + q,\, n + p\rangle]_{\mathrm{i}}$
(c) $-_{\mathrm{i}}[\langle m,n\rangle]_{\mathrm{i}} =_{\mathrm{Df}} [\langle 0,0\rangle]_{\mathrm{i}} -_{\mathrm{i}} [\langle m,n\rangle]_{\mathrm{i}}$
(d) $[\langle m,n\rangle]_{\mathrm{i}} \cdot_{\mathrm{i}} [\langle p,q\rangle]_{\mathrm{i}} =_{\mathrm{Df}} [\langle mp + nq,\, mq + np\rangle]_{\mathrm{i}}$.

We shall leave for the reader the proof that the operations of addition and multiplication satisfy the commutative and associative laws, and that multiplication is distributive over addition. [See exercise 6.2.1(a)–(c). It is in proving theorems of this sort that the definition of the integers as equivalence classes of ordered pairs is far superior to the definition in which each integer is a specific ordered pair. (See section 6.1 and exercise 6.1.2.) For example, for the latter case, in the definition of addition alone there would be 4 different cases to consider—both numbers non-positive, both numbers non-negative, the first number non-negative and the second non-positive. Therefore, in any theorem about addition all these possibilities would have to be taken into account. Similarly for the other operations.]

Next we shall discuss inequality between integers. We have on hand the tools for making the definition.

DEFINITION 6.2.12. Inequality

$$[\langle m,n\rangle]_{\mathrm{i}},\ [\langle p,q\rangle]_{\mathrm{i}} \in In \rightarrow$$

(a) $[\langle m,n\rangle]_{\mathrm{i}} <_{\mathrm{i}} [\langle p,q\rangle]_{\mathrm{i}} =_{\mathrm{Df}} [\langle m,n\rangle]_{\mathrm{i}} -_{\mathrm{i}} [\langle p,q\rangle]_{\mathrm{i}}$ is negative
(b) $[\langle m,n\rangle]_{\mathrm{i}} >_{\mathrm{i}} [\langle p,q\rangle]_{\mathrm{i}} =_{\mathrm{Df}} [\langle p,q\rangle]_{\mathrm{i}} <_{\mathrm{i}} [\langle m,n\rangle]_{\mathrm{i}}$
(c) $[\langle m,n\rangle]_{\mathrm{i}} \leqq_{\mathrm{i}} [\langle p,q\rangle]_{\mathrm{i}} =_{\mathrm{Df}} ([\langle m,n\rangle]_{\mathrm{i}} <_{\mathrm{i}} [\langle p,q\rangle]_{\mathrm{i}}$ or $[\langle m,n\rangle]_{\mathrm{i}} = [\langle p,q\rangle]_{\mathrm{i}})$.
(d) $[\langle m,n\rangle]_{\mathrm{i}} \geqq_{\mathrm{i}} [\langle p,q\rangle]_{\mathrm{i}} =_{\mathrm{Df}} [\langle p,q\rangle]_{\mathrm{i}} \leqq_{\mathrm{i}} [\langle m,n\rangle]_{\mathrm{i}}$.

As a direct consequence of this definition, 6.2.11, and 6.2.6 we can prove

THEOREM 6.2.13. $[\langle m,n\rangle]_{\mathrm{i}}, [\langle p,q\rangle]_{\mathrm{i}} \in In \rightarrow$
(a) $[\langle m,n\rangle]_{\mathrm{i}} <_{\mathrm{i}} [\langle p,q\rangle]_{\mathrm{i}} \leftrightarrow m + q < n + p$
(b) $[\langle m,n\rangle]_{\mathrm{i}} \leqq_{\mathrm{i}} [\langle p,q\rangle]_{\mathrm{i}} \leftrightarrow m + q \leqq n + p$.

The proofs of the trichotomy, the monotonicity laws, and the cancellation laws are left for the reader [exercise 6.2.1(d)–(f)].

To conclude this section, we shall show that the natural numbers behave like the non-negative integers. It follows from 6.2.7 that if $[\langle m,n\rangle]_{\mathrm{i}} \in In$ and $[\langle m,n\rangle]_{\mathrm{i}}$ is non-negative, then there is a unique $p \in \omega$ such that $\langle m,n\rangle =_{\mathrm{i}} \langle p,0\rangle$. Moreover, for each $p \in \omega$ there is a unique element $u \in In$ such that $\langle p,0\rangle \in u$. Thus, there is a 1–1 function, ψ, mapping ω onto In. We have, if $p \in \omega$,

$$\psi(p) = [\langle p,0\rangle]_{\mathrm{i}}.$$

It is an easy matter to prove that ψ preserves all operations and relations. That is, $m,n \in \omega \rightarrow$

$$\begin{aligned} \psi(m + n) &= \psi(m) +_{\mathrm{i}} \psi(n) \\ \psi(m \cdot n) &= \psi(m) \cdot_{\mathrm{i}} \psi(n) \\ m < n &\leftrightarrow \psi(m) <_{\mathrm{i}} \psi(n), \end{aligned}$$

etc.

It is also easy to see that there is a 1–1 correspondence, ξ, between ω and the non-positive integers. Namely, for each $m \in \omega$,

$$\xi\,(m) = [\langle 0,m\rangle]_{\mathrm{i}}.$$

This function also preserves addition,

$$\xi(m + n) = \xi(m) +_{\mathrm{i}} \xi(n).$$

For multiplication we have,

$$\xi(m \cdot n) = -_{\mathrm{i}}\,(\xi(m) \cdot_{\mathrm{i}} \xi(n)).$$

And it reverses the inequality sign,

$$m < n \leftrightarrow \xi(n) <_{\mathrm{i}} \xi(m)$$

(see exercise 6.2.2).

In all future work we shall identify m and $\psi(m)$. That is, we shall identify ω with the set of non-negative integers and assume $\omega \subseteq In$. Moreover, we shall drop the subscript "i" from all the operation signs and relation signs on In.

EXERCISES 6.2

1. Prove each of the following: $u,v,w \in In \rightarrow$
   (a) $u + v = v + u \;\&\; u \cdot v = v \cdot u$ (Commutative laws)
   (b) $u + (v + w) = (u + v) + w \;\&\; u \cdot (v \cdot w) = (u \cdot v) \cdot w$ (Associative laws)
   (c) $u \cdot (v + w) = u \cdot v + u \cdot w$ (Distributive law)
   (d) $u < v$ or $u = v$ or $v < u$ (Trichotomy)
   (e) $u < v \rightarrow (u + w < v + w \;\&\; (w > 0 \rightarrow u \cdot w < v \cdot w) \;\&$
   $(w < 0 \rightarrow u \cdot w > v \cdot w))$ (Monotonicity laws)
   (f) $(u + w = v + w$ or $(w \neq 0 \;\&\; u \cdot w = v \cdot w)) \rightarrow u = v$ (Cancellation laws)
   (g) $u,v > 0 \rightarrow u \cdot v > 0$
   (h) $u,v < 0 \rightarrow u \cdot v > 0$
   (i) $(u > 0 \;\&\; v < 0) \rightarrow u \cdot v < 0$
   (j) $u \cdot v = 0 \leftrightarrow (u = 0$ or $v = 0)$
   (k) $u - v = w \leftrightarrow u = w + v.$
2. If for each $m \in \omega$

$$\begin{aligned} \psi(m) &= [\langle m,0\rangle]_i, \\ \xi(m) &= [\langle 0,m\rangle]_i, \\ In^+ &= \{u : u \in In \;\&\; u \geqq 0\}, \\ In^- &= \{u : u \in In \;\&\; u \leqq 0\}, \end{aligned}$$

   then prove each of the following:
   (a) $\psi : \omega \xrightarrow[\text{onto}]{1-1} In^+$
   (b) $\xi : \omega \xrightarrow[\text{onto}]{1-1} In^-$
   (c) $\psi(m + n) = \psi(m) + \psi(n)$
   (d) $\psi(m \cdot n) = \psi(m) \cdot \psi(n)$
   (e) $\xi(m + n) = \xi(m) + \xi(n)$
   (f) $\xi(m \cdot n) = -(\xi(m) \cdot \xi(n))$
   (g) $m < n \leftrightarrow \psi(m) < \psi(n)$
   (h) $m < n \leftrightarrow \xi(n) < \xi(m).$

6.3. THE RATIONAL NUMBERS

We think of a rational number as the ratio of two integers. However, because of the fact that

$$\frac{2}{4} = \frac{3}{6}$$

while

$$\langle 2,4\rangle \neq \langle 3,6\rangle,$$

we cannot define a rational number as an ordered pair of integers. Rather, we must again resort to equivalence classes and define a rational number as an equivalence class of ordered pairs. Thus, we make the following definition:

DEFINITION 6.3.1. $u,v,w,z \in In \rightarrow$

$$(\langle u,v\rangle =_{a} \langle w,z\rangle) =_{\mathrm{Df}} (uz = vw).$$

As a consequence of 6.3.1 we have

THEOREM 6.3.2.
$=_{a}$ is an equivalence relation on $In \times In$.

And we define *Ra*, the class of rational numbers as follows:

DEFINITION 6.3.3. Rational Numbers
(a) $u,v \in In \rightarrow ([\langle u,v\rangle]_{a} =_{\mathrm{Df}} \{\langle w,z\rangle : w,z \in In \;\&\; \langle w,z\rangle =_{a} \langle u,v\rangle\})$.
(b) $x \in Ra =_{\mathrm{Df}} (\exists u)(\exists v)(u,v \in In \;\&\; v \neq 0 \;\&\; x = [\langle u,v\rangle]_{a})$.

THEOREM 6.3.4. $\mathrm{S}(Ra)$

Proof: $Ra \subseteq \mathcal{P}(In \times In)$. ■

For rational numbers u/v and w/z we have

$$\begin{aligned} u/v + w/z &= (uz + vw)/vz \\ u/v - w/z &= (uz - vw)/vz \\ u/v \cdot w/z &= (uw/vz) \\ u/v \div w/z &= (uz/vw). \end{aligned}$$

Therefore, it will be a simple matter to define these operations between elements of *Ra*. But first the preliminary theorem.

THEOREM 6.3.5.

$$(u_1,v_1,w_1,z_1,u_2,v_2,w_2,z_2 \in In \;\&\; \langle u_1,v_1\rangle =_{a} \langle u_2,v_2\rangle \;\&\; \langle w_1,z_1\rangle =_{a} \langle w_2,z_2\rangle) \rightarrow$$

(a) $\langle u_1z_1 + v_1w_1,\ v_1z_1\rangle =_{a} \langle u_2z_2 + v_2w_2,\ v_2z_2\rangle$
(b) $\langle u_1z_1 - v_1w_1,\ v_1z_1\rangle =_{a} \langle u_2z_2 - v_2w_2,\ v_2z_2\rangle$
(c) $\langle u_1w_1,v_1z_1\rangle =_{a} \langle u_2w_2,v_2z_2\rangle$
(d) $\langle u_1z_1,v_1w_1\rangle =_{a} \langle u_2z_2,v_2w_2\rangle$
(e) $v_1,v_2 \neq 0 \rightarrow (u_1 = 0 \leftrightarrow u_2 = 0)$.

The proof is left as an exercise.

DEFINITION 6.3.6. Addition, Subtraction, Multiplication and Division. $[\langle u,v\rangle]_{a}, [\langle w,z\rangle]_{a} \in Ra \rightarrow$

(a) $[\langle u,v\rangle]_{a} +_{a} [\langle w,z\rangle]_{a} =_{\mathrm{Df}} [\langle uz + vw,\ vz\rangle]_{a}$
(b) $[\langle u,v\rangle]_{a} -_{a} [\langle w,z\rangle]_{a} =_{\mathrm{Df}} [\langle uz - vw,\ vz\rangle]_{a}$
(c) $[\langle u,v\rangle]_{a} \cdot_{a} [\langle w,z\rangle]_{a} =_{\mathrm{Df}} [\langle uw,vz\rangle]_{a}$
(d) $w \neq 0 \rightarrow ([\langle u,v\rangle]_{a} \div_{a} [\langle w,z\rangle]_{a} =_{\mathrm{Df}} [\langle uz,vw\rangle]_{a}$.

The proof that these operations satisfy all the well-known properties is left to the reader (see exercise 6.3.1).

A rational number u/v is positive if u and v have the same sign; zero if u is zero; and negative if u and v have opposite signs. Equivalently,

$$\begin{aligned} u/v > 0 &\leftrightarrow u\cdot v > 0 \\ u/v = 0 &\leftrightarrow u = 0 \\ u/v < 0 &\leftrightarrow u\cdot v < 0. \end{aligned}$$

This is the definition we shall use. However, the usual theorem precedes the definition.

THEOREM 6.3.7. $(u,v,w,z \in In \ \&\ v,z \neq 0 \ \&\ \langle u,v\rangle =_{\mathrm{a}} \langle w,z\rangle) \rightarrow$

(a) $u\cdot v > 0 \leftrightarrow w\cdot z > 0$
(b) $u = 0 \leftrightarrow w = 0$
(c) $u\cdot v < 0 \leftrightarrow w\cdot z < 0$.

The proof is left as an exercise.

DEFINITION 6.3.8. Positive, Negative, and Zero

$$[\langle u,v\rangle]_{\mathrm{a}} \in Ra \rightarrow$$

(a) $[\langle u,v\rangle]_{\mathrm{a}}$ is *positive* $=_{\mathrm{Df}} u\cdot v > 0$
(b) $[\langle u,v\rangle]_{\mathrm{a}}$ is *negative* $=_{\mathrm{Df}} u\cdot v < 0$
(c) $[\langle u,v\rangle]_{\mathrm{a}}$ is *zero* $=_{\mathrm{Df}} u = 0$.

Now the inequality relation on *Ra* can be defined similarly to the inequality relation on *In* (see 6.2.12).

DEFINITION 6.3.9. Inequality

$$[\langle u,v\rangle]_{\mathrm{a}}, [\langle w,z\rangle]_{\mathrm{a}} \in Ra \rightarrow$$

(a) $[\langle u,v\rangle]_{\mathrm{a}} <_{\mathrm{a}} [\langle w,z\rangle]_{\mathrm{a}} =_{\mathrm{Df}} ([\langle w,z\rangle]_{\mathrm{a}} -_{\mathrm{a}} [\langle u,v\rangle]_{\mathrm{a}}$ is positive$)$
(b) $[\langle u,v\rangle]_{\mathrm{a}} >_{\mathrm{a}} [\langle w,z\rangle]_{\mathrm{a}} =_{\mathrm{Df}} ([\langle w,z\rangle]_{\mathrm{a}} <_{\mathrm{a}} [\langle u,v\rangle]_{\mathrm{a}})$
(c) $[\langle u,v\rangle]_{\mathrm{a}} \leqq_{\mathrm{a}} [\langle w,z\rangle]_{\mathrm{a}} =_{\mathrm{Df}} ([\langle u,v\rangle]_{\mathrm{a}} < [\langle w,z\rangle]_{\mathrm{a}}$ or $[\langle u,v\rangle]_{\mathrm{a}} = [\langle w,z\rangle]_{\mathrm{a}})$
(d) $[\langle u,v\rangle]_{\mathrm{a}} \geqq_{\mathrm{a}} [\langle w,z\rangle]_{\mathrm{a}} =_{\mathrm{Df}} ([\langle w,z\rangle]_{\mathrm{a}} \leqq_{\mathrm{a}} [\langle u,v\rangle]_{\mathrm{a}})$.

The proof that the inequality relation behaves as it should is left as an exercise (see exercise 6.3.2).

There is a subset of *Ra* which behaves just like the integers. We shall designate this subset by *Rai*.

DEFINITION 6.3.10. Integral Rational Numbers

$$x \in Rai =_{\mathrm{Df}} x \in Ra \ \&\ (\forall u)(\forall v)(\langle u,v\rangle \in x \rightarrow (\exists w)(w \in In \ \&\ \langle u,v\rangle =_{\mathrm{a}} \langle w,1\rangle)).$$

We shall define a function ψ on *In* as follows: For each $u \in In$,

$$\psi(u) = [\langle u,1\rangle]_a.$$

It is easy to show that ψ is a 1–1 function mapping *In* onto *Rai*. Moreover, we have for all $u,v \in In$,

$$\begin{aligned} \psi(u + v) &= \psi(u) +_a \psi(v) \\ \psi(u - v) &= \psi(u) -_a \psi(v) \\ \psi(u \cdot v) &= \psi(u) \cdot_a \psi(v) \\ u < v &\leftrightarrow \psi(u) <_a \psi(v). \end{aligned}$$

Next, we shall sketch the proof that *Ra* is denumerable. It follows from the preceding remarks that $Rai \subseteq In$ and $Rai \approx In$. We have previously shown that $In \approx \omega$. Therefore,

$$\omega \lesssim Ra.$$

Let $[\langle u,v\rangle]_a \in Ra$. Define

$$x_{uv} = \{\langle w,z\rangle : \langle w,z\rangle \in [\langle u,v\rangle]_a \ \&\ z > 0\}.$$

The following two statements are easy to prove:

$$\begin{gathered} [\langle u,v\rangle]_a \in Ra \rightarrow x_{uv} \neq \emptyset \\ \langle w_1,z\rangle, \langle w_2,z\rangle \in [\langle u,v\rangle]_a \rightarrow w_1 = w_2. \end{gathered}$$

Let z_0 be the smallest natural number in the set,

$$\{z : (\exists w)(\langle w,z\rangle \in x_{uv}\}.$$

Then define

$$f([\langle u,v\rangle]_a) = \langle w,z_0\rangle.$$

Now, it is easy to show that f is a 1–1 function mapping *Ra* into $\omega \times In$. But $In \approx \omega$ and $\omega \times \omega \approx \omega$, therefore,

$$Ra \lesssim \omega.$$

Hence, we have shown

THEOREM 6.3.11. *Ra* is denumerable.

In what follows in the text we shall identify the integers with the integral rational numbers and assume $\omega \subseteq In \subseteq Ra$.

There is one additional function on *Ra* which will be useful in the following sections and that is the *absolute value*.

DEFINITION 6.3.12. Absolute Value $x \in Ra \rightarrow$

(a) $x \geqq_a 0 \rightarrow |x|_a =_{Df} x$

(b) $x <_a 0 \rightarrow |x|_a =_{Df} -_a x$.

("$-_a x$" is the abbreviation for "$0 -_a x$.")

Some properties of the absolute value are given in the following theorem:

THEOREM 6.3.13. $x,y \in Ra \rightarrow$

(a) $|x|_a \geqq_a 0$
(b) $|x|_a = 0 \leftrightarrow x = 0$
(c) $|x \cdot_a y|_a = |x|_a \cdot_a |y|_a$
(d) $y \neq 0 \rightarrow |x \div_a y|_a = |x|_a \div_a |y|_a$
(e) $|x +_a y|_a \leqq_a |x|_a +_a |y|_a$
(f) $|x|_a -_a |y|_a \leqq_a |x -_a y|_a$
(g) $|x -_a y|_a = |y -_a x|_a$.

The proof is left as an exercise.

In what follows in the text we shall assume that Ra has all its well-known arithmetic properties. We shall drop the subscript "a" from all the operation signs and relation signs on Ra and we shall often denote "$x \div y$" by "x/y."

EXERCISES 6.3

1. Prove each of the following: $x,y,z \in Ra \rightarrow$
   (a) $x + y = y + x$ & $x \cdot y = y \cdot x$ (Commutative laws)
   (b) $x + (y + z) = (x + y) + z$ & $x \cdot (y \cdot z) = (x \cdot y) \cdot z$ (Associative laws)
   (c) $x \cdot (y + z) = x \cdot y + x \cdot z$ (Distributive law).
2. Prove each of the following: $x,y,z \in Ra \rightarrow$
   (a) $x < y$ or $x = y$ or $y < x$ (Trichotomy)
   (b) $x < y \rightarrow (x + z < y + z$ & $(z > 0 \rightarrow x \cdot z < y \cdot z))$ & $(z < 0 \rightarrow x \cdot z > y \cdot z))$ (Monotonicity laws)
   (c) $(x + z = y + z \rightarrow x = y)$ & $((x \cdot z = y \cdot z$ & $z \neq 0) \rightarrow x = y)$ (Cancellation laws)
   (d) $x,y > 0 \rightarrow (x \cdot y > 0$ & $x/y > 0)$
   (e) $x,y < 0 \rightarrow (x \cdot y > 0$ & $x/y > 0)$
   (f) $((x < 0$ & $y > 0)$ or $(x > 0$ & $y < 0)) \rightarrow (x \cdot y < 0$ & $x/y < 0)$
   (g) $x \cdot y = 0 \leftrightarrow (x = 0$ or $y = 0)$
   (h) $x - y = z \leftrightarrow x = z + y$
   (i) $y \neq 0 \rightarrow (x/y = z \leftrightarrow x = z \cdot y)$
   (j) $(\exists u)(u \in In$ & $x < u)$.
3. Prove theorem 6.3.13.
4. Prove: $\psi = \{\langle u, [\langle u,1\rangle]_a\rangle : u \in In\} \rightarrow$
   (a) $\psi : In \xrightarrow[\text{onto}]{1-1} Rai$
   For all $u,v \in In$,
   (b) $\psi(u + v) = \psi(u) + \psi(v)$

(c) $\psi(u - v) = \psi(u) - \psi(v)$
(d) $\psi(u \cdot v) = \psi(u) \cdot \psi(v)$
(e) $u < v \leftrightarrow \psi(u) < \psi(v)$.

5. Prove $(x \subseteq Ra \ \& \ x$ is finite$) \rightarrow (\exists 1 f)(\exists 1 n)$

$$\left(f : x \xrightarrow[\text{onto}]{1-1} n \ \& \ (\forall u)(\forall v)(u,v \in x \rightarrow (u < v \leftrightarrow f(u) < f(v)))\right).$$

[If $x \neq 0$, then $n \neq 0$ and $f^{-1}(0)$ is the smallest element of x and $f^{-1}(n-1)$ is the largest element of x.]

6.4. CAUCHY SEQUENCES OF RATIONAL NUMBERS

In this section we shall lay the groundwork for the definition of real numbers.

DEFINITION 6.4.1. Sequences of Rational Numbers

$$u \subseteq \omega \rightarrow ((x \text{ is a } u\text{-sequence of rational numbers}) =_{\text{Df}} x \in (Ra)^u).$$

If $u \subseteq \omega$, then u and Ra are sets. Therefore, the class of all u-sequences of rational numbers is a set. For each $x \in (Ra)^u$, x is a function, $\mathfrak{D}(f) = u$ and $\mathfrak{R}(x) \subseteq Ra$. If $n \in u$ and $x \in (Ra)^u$ we shall usually denote "$x(n)$" by "x_n".

We shall define addition, subtraction, and multiplication of sequences in a natural manner. (Division will be defined later.)

DEFINITION 6.4.2. Addition, Subtraction, and Multiplication of Sequences. $(u \subseteq \omega \ \& \ x,y,z \in (Ra)^u \ \& \ (\forall n)(n \in u \rightarrow z_n = 0)) \rightarrow$

(a) $x +_s y =_{\text{Df}} \{\langle n, x_n + y_n \rangle : n \in u\}$
(b) $x -_s y =_{\text{Df}} \{\langle n, x_n - y_n \rangle : n \in u\}$
(c) $-_s x =_{\text{Df}} z -_s x$
(d) $x \cdot_s y =_{\text{Df}} \{\langle n, x_n \cdot y_n \rangle : n \in u\}$.

As an immediate consequence of definition 6.4.2 we have

THEOREM 6.4.3.

$$(u \subseteq \omega \ \& \ x,y \in (Ra)^u) \rightarrow x +_s y,\ x -_s y,\ -_s x,\ x \cdot_s y \in (Ra)^u.$$

The following theorem gives the commutative, associative, and distributive laws for sequences. Its proof follows easily from the corresponding properties of rational numbers.

THEOREM 6.4.4. $(u \subseteq \omega \ \& \ x,y,z \in (Ra)^u) \rightarrow$

(a) $x +_s y = y +_s x$
(b) $x \cdot_s y = y \cdot_s x$
(c) $x +_s (y +_s z) = (x +_s y) +_s z$
(d) $x \cdot_s (y \cdot_s z) = (x \cdot_s y) \cdot_s z$
(e) $x \cdot_s (y +_s z) = x \cdot_s y +_s x \cdot_s z$.

Next, we shall single out a special subset of $(Ra)^\omega$ called *Cauchy sequences*.

DEFINITION 6.4.5. Cauchy Sequences of Rational Numbers

$$x \in Ca =_{\mathrm{Df}} (x \in (Ra)^\omega \;\&\; (\forall\epsilon)((\epsilon \in Ra \;\&\; \epsilon > 0) \rightarrow (\exists N)(N \in \omega \;\&\; (\forall m)(\forall n)((n,m \in \omega \;\&\; n,m > N) \rightarrow |x_m - x_n| < \epsilon)))).$$

In other words, x is a Cauchy sequence of rational numbers if x is an ω-sequence of rational numbers, and for each positive rational number ϵ there is a natural number N such that for all natural numbers n and m, if $n,m > N$, then $|x_n - x_m| < \epsilon$. Intuitively, Cauchy sequences have the property that the further out the elements are in the tail of the sequence the closer together they are. It does not matter what happens in the beginning of the sequence. Several examples of Cauchy sequences follow.

(1) $$x_n = (-1)^n/2^n$$

(2) $$x_n = 1 + 1/n$$

(3) $$x_n = \begin{cases} 10^n, & \text{if } n \leqq 10^{10} \\ 1/10^n, & \text{if } n > 10^{10} \end{cases}$$

(4) $$x_0 = 0$$
$$x_{n+1} = x_n + 1/(n+1)!$$

$(0! = 1$ and $(n+1)! = (n+1)\cdot n!)$.

We shall prove (1) is a Cauchy sequence and leave the proof that the others are Cauchy sequences for the exercises.

Let ϵ be any positive rational number. We want to find a natural number N such that whenever $n,m > N$,

(5) $$|(-1)^n/2^n - (-1)^m/2^m| < \epsilon.$$

Suppose $n < m$, then

$$\begin{aligned} |(-1)^n/2^n - (-1)^m/2^m| &\leqq 1/2^m + 1/2^n \\ &< 2/2^n \\ &= 1/2^{n-1}, \end{aligned}$$

so we want

$$1/2^{n-1} < \epsilon$$

or

$$1/\epsilon < 2^{n-1}.$$

It is a simple matter to prove by induction that if $n > 2$, then $n < 2^{n-1}$. Therefore, if n is chosen larger than both 2 and $1/\epsilon$ and $m > n$, then (5) will hold. Hence N can be chosen to be any natural number which is larger than both 2 and $1/\epsilon$. This proves (1) is a Cauchy sequence.

On the other hand, it is easy to prove that none of the following sequences are Cauchy sequences.

(6) $$x_n = n$$

(7) $$x_n = 2^n$$

(8) $$x =_n \begin{cases} 1, & \text{if } n \text{ is even} \\ 0, & \text{if } n \text{ is odd} \end{cases}$$

(9) $$(a \in Ra \;\&\; a \neq 0) \rightarrow x_n = \begin{cases} a + 1/n, & \text{if } n \text{ is even} \\ -a - 1/n, & \text{if } n \text{ is odd.} \end{cases}$$

[Note that if $a = 0$, then (9) is a Cauchy sequence.]

The sum, difference, and product of two sequences was defined in 6.4.2. What we aim to do next is to show that the sum, difference, and product of two Cauchy sequences is a Cauchy sequence. The first theorem gives it for sum and difference.

THEOREM 6.4.6. $x,y \in Ca \rightarrow (x +_s y \in Ca \;\&\; x -_s y \in Ca)$.

Proof: Let $x,y \in Ca$ and let ϵ be any positive rational number. Then by 6.4.5, there exist natural numbers N and M such that for all natural numbers n and m,

$$n,m > N \rightarrow |x_n - x_m| < \epsilon/2$$
$$n,m > M \rightarrow |y_n - y_m| < \epsilon/2.$$

Let P be the maximum of N and M, $P = \text{Max}(M,N)$, and let $m,n > P$. Then,

$$\begin{aligned} |(x_n + y_n) - (x_m + y_m)| &= |(x_n - x_m) + (y_n - y_m)| \\ &\leqq |x_n - x_m| + |y_n - y_m| \\ &< \epsilon/2 + \epsilon/2 \\ &= \epsilon. \end{aligned}$$

Therefore, it follows from 6.4.5 and 6.4.2(a) that $x +_s y$ is a Cauchy sequence. There is an analogous proof for $x -_s y$. ■

Before proving that the product of two Cauchy sequences is a Cauchy sequence, we prove that every Cauchy sequence is bounded.

THEOREM 6.4.7. $x \in Ca \rightarrow (\exists N)(N \in Ra \;\&\; (\forall n)(n \in \omega \rightarrow |x_n| < N))$.

Proof: Suppose $x \in Ca$. Then, by 6.4.5, there is a natural number P such that for all $n,m \in \omega$,

$$n,m > P \rightarrow |x_n - x_m| < 1.$$

Let $M \in \omega$ and $M > P$. Then for all $n \in \omega$ and $n > M$ we have $|x_n - x_M| < 1$. Hence,

$$|x_n - x_M| \geqq |x_n| - |x_M|.$$

Therefore,

$$\begin{aligned} |x_n| &\leqq |x_M| + |x_n - x_M| \\ &< |x_M| + 1. \end{aligned}$$

Let Q be the largest (with respect to $<$) element in the set $\{|x_0|, |x_1|, \ldots, |x_M|\}$ (see exercise 6.3.5) and let $N = Q + 1$. Then we have for all $n \in \omega$, $|x_n| < N$. ■

Therefore, boundedness is a necessary condition for a sequence to be a Cauchy sequence, but it is not sufficient. The sequences given in examples (8) and (9) above are bounded, but they are not Cauchy sequences.

Now, we are ready to prove that the product of two Cauchy sequences is a Cauchy sequence.

THEOREM 6.4.8. $x,y \in Ca \rightarrow x \cdot_s y \in Ca$.

Proof: Let $x,y \in Ca$. Then by 6.4.7 there exist rational numbers M' and M'' such that for all $n \in \omega$,

$$|x_n| < M' \;\&\; |y_n| < M''.$$

Let $M = \max(M',M'')$. Let ϵ be any positive rational number. Since x and y are Cauchy sequences, there exist natural numbers N' and N'' such that for all $n,m \in \omega$,

$$\begin{aligned} n,m > N' &\rightarrow |x_n - x_m| < \epsilon/2M \\ n,m > N'' &\rightarrow |y_n - y_m| < \epsilon/2M. \end{aligned}$$

Let $N = \max(N',N'')$. Then, if $n,m \in \omega$ and $n,m > N$,

$$\begin{aligned} |x_n y_n - x_m y_m| &= |(x_n y_n - x_n y_m) + (x_n y_m - x_m y_m)| \\ &\leqq |x_n(y_n - y_m)| + |y_m(x_n - x_m)| \\ &= |x_n||y_n - y_m| + |y_m||x_n - x_m| \\ &< M\cdot\epsilon/2M + M\cdot\epsilon/2M \\ &= \epsilon. \end{aligned}$$

Consequently, $x \cdot_s y \in Ca$. ■

Next we shall define what it means for a sequence to have a *limit*.

DEFINITION 6.4.9. Limits

$$x \in (Ra)^\omega \rightarrow [(\lim x = L) =_{\mathrm{Df}} (L \in Ra \;\&\; (\forall\epsilon)[(\epsilon \in Ra \;\&\; \epsilon > 0) \rightarrow (\exists N)(N \in \omega \;\&\; (\forall n)((n \in \omega \;\&\; n > N) \rightarrow |x_n - L| < \epsilon))])].$$

If $\lim x = L$, L is called the *limit* of the sequence x and x is said to *converge* to the limit L. Examples of convergent sequences are (1), (2), and (3) above. The limit of sequences (1) and (3) is 0 and 1 is the limit of sequence (2). However, sequence (4), which is a Cauchy sequence, does not converge to a rational limit. [Sequence (4) actually converges to the irrational number e = 2.71828 . . . , the base of the natural logarithms. The proof that this sequence does not have a rational limit requires some number theory and is left to the student.]

The next theorem states that a sequence has at most one limit.

THEOREM 6.4.10.

$$(x \in (Ra)^{\omega} \ \& \ (\exists L)(L \in Ra \ \& \ \lim x = L) \rightarrow (\exists 1 L)(L \in Ra \ \& \ \lim x = L).$$

Proof: Suppose $x \in (Ra)^{\omega}$, $L, M \in Ra$, $L \neq M$,

$$\lim x = L, \text{ and } \lim x = M.$$

Let

$$\delta = |L - M|$$

and let

$$\epsilon = \delta/2.$$

By 6.4.9, there exist natural numbers N' and N'' such that for all $n \in \omega$,

$$\begin{aligned} n > N' &\rightarrow |x_n - L| < \epsilon/2, \\ N > N'' &\rightarrow |x_n - M| < \epsilon/2. \end{aligned}$$

Let $N = \max(N', N'')$. Then for all $n \in \omega$, $n > N \rightarrow$

$$\begin{aligned} \delta = |L - M| &= |(L - x_n) + (x_n - M)| \\ &\leqq |L - x_n| + |x_n - M| \\ &< \epsilon/2 + \epsilon/2 \\ &= \epsilon. \end{aligned}$$

This is a contradiction since we assumed $\epsilon < \delta$. Therefore, $L = M$. ■

Next, we shall show that if a sequence has a limit, then it is a Cauchy sequence.

THEOREM 6.4.11.

$$(x \in (Ra)^{\omega} \ \& \ (\exists L)(L \in Ra \ \& \ \lim x = L)) \rightarrow x \in Ca.$$

Proof: Suppose $x \in Ra^{\omega}$ and $\lim x = L$, $L \in Ra$. Then for each positive rational number ϵ there is a natural number N such that for all $n \in \omega$,

$$n > N \to |x_n - L| < \epsilon/2.$$

Suppose $m,n > N$. Then,

$$\begin{aligned} |x_n - x_m| &= |(x_n - L) + (L - x_m)| \\ &\leqq |x_n - L| + |L - x_m| \\ &< \epsilon/2 + \epsilon/2 \\ &= \epsilon. \end{aligned}$$

Hence $x \in Ca$. ■

The converse of 6.4.11 does not hold. There exist Cauchy sequences, like sequence (4) above, which have no rational limits.

Our plan now is to associate a real number with each Cauchy sequence. Intuitively, the real number is the "limit" of the sequence. As we saw above (following 6.4.9), different Cauchy sequences may converge to the same limit. Sequences (1) and (3) each converge to zero. Therefore, we shall group together all Cauchy sequences which have the same limit.

DEFINITION 6.4.12. Equivalent Cauchy Sequences

$$x,y \in Ca \to [(x =_c y) =_{\text{Df}} (\forall\epsilon)((\epsilon \in Ra \ \& \ \epsilon > 0) \to (\exists N)(N \in \omega \ \& \ (\forall n)((n \in \omega \ \& \ n > N) \to |x_n - y_n| < \epsilon)))].$$

In other words, two Cauchy sequences are equivalent if the corresponding elements in their tails are close together. Hence we have,

THEOREM 6.4.13.

$$x,y \in Ca \to [(x =_c y) \leftrightarrow \lim (x -_s y) = 0].$$

The proof is left to the reader.

It is also easy to prove that,

THEOREM 6.4.14. $=_c$ is an equivalence relation on Ca.

The following theorem states that if two Cauchy sequences have the same limit, then they are equivalent.

THEOREM 6.4.15.

$$(x,y \in Ca \ \& \ (\exists L)(L \in Ra \ \& \ \lim x = L \text{ and } \lim y = L)) \to x =_c y.$$

Proof: Suppose $x,y \in Ca$ and $\lim x = \lim y = L$. Then for each positive rational number ϵ, there exist natural numbers N' and N'' such that for all $n \in \omega$,

$$\begin{aligned} n > N' &\to |x_n - L| < \epsilon/2 \\ n > N'' &\to |y_n - L| < \epsilon/2. \end{aligned}$$

Let $N = \max(N',N'')$. Then for all $n \in \omega$, if $n > N$,

$$\begin{aligned}|x_n - y_n| &= |(x_n - L) + (L - y_n)|\\ &\leqq |x_n - L| + |L - y_n|\\ &< \epsilon/2 + \epsilon/2\\ &= \epsilon.\end{aligned}$$

Therefore, $x =_c y$. ■

We leave the proof of the converse of 6.4.15 as an exercise.

THEOREM 6.4.16.

$$[x, y \in (Ra)^\omega \ \& \ x =_c y \ \& \ (\exists L)(L \in Ra \ \& \ \lim x = L)] \rightarrow \lim y = L.$$

Division of sequences is more difficult to define than the other operations on sequences because we want to be able to divide in some cases when some of the terms in the divisor are zero. The procedure we shall use is to substitute ones for the zero terms in the divisor and then divide term by term.

DEFINITION 6.4.17. $x \in (Ra)^\omega \rightarrow$

$$x^* =_{\text{Df}} \{\langle n, x_n\rangle : n \in \omega \ \& \ x_n \neq 0\} \cup \{\langle n, 1\rangle : n \in \omega \ \& \ x_n = 0\}.$$

Clearly,

THEOREM 6.4.18. $x \in (Ra)^\omega \rightarrow x^* \in (Ra)^\omega$.

DEFINITION 6.4.19. Division of Sequences

$$x, y \in (Ra)^\omega \rightarrow x \div_s y = \{\langle n, x_n/y_n^*\rangle : n \in \omega\}.$$

It follows that

THEOREM 6.4.20. $x, y \in (Ra)^\omega \rightarrow x \div_s y \in (Ra)^\omega$.

There is, however, one source of trouble: The sum, difference, and product of two Cauchy sequences are Cauchy sequences, but this is not necessarily true for division. For example, if for all $n \in \omega$,

$$x_n = 1$$

and

$$y_n = 1/(n + 1),$$

then

$$(x \div_s y)(n) = n + 1.$$

Clearly, $x, y \in Ca$ but $x \div_s y \notin Ca$. In fact it could happen that $x \in Ca$ and $x^* \notin Ca$. For example, if for all $n \in \omega$

$$x_n = \begin{cases} 0, & \text{if } n \text{ is even} \\ 1/n, & \text{if } n \text{ is odd,} \end{cases}$$

then

$$x_n^* = \begin{cases} 1, & \text{if } n \text{ is even} \\ 1/n, & \text{if } n \text{ is odd.} \end{cases}$$

In this case $\lim x = 0$, so $x \in Ca$. But the terms of the sequence x^* alternate between 1's and terms which are close to zero, so $x^* \notin Ca$.

What can be done to patch up this difficulty? The trouble apparently lies with Cauchy sequences which converge to zero. We do not want to divide by zero, but what happens if we restrict the divisor to Cauchy sequences which do not converge to zero?

First, some properties of Cauchy sequences which do not converge to zero. The first theorem states that if a Cauchy sequence does not converge to zero, then its tail is bounded away from zero.

THEOREM 6.4.21.

$$(x \in Ca \;\&\; \lim x \neq 0) \rightarrow (\exists\delta)[\delta \in Ra \;\&\; \delta > 0 \;\&\; (\exists M)(M \in \omega \;\&\; (\forall n)((n \in \omega \;\&\; n > M) \rightarrow |x_n| > \delta))].$$

Proof: Suppose $x \in Ca$ and $\lim x \neq 0$. From the denial of theorem 6.4.9 with L replaced by 0, and ϵ replaced by 2δ, we obtain: There exists a positive rational number 2δ such that for all natural numbers N there is a natural number n such that $n > N$ and

(1) $$|x_n| > 2\delta.$$

Since x is a Cauchy sequence, there is a natural number M such that for all $n,m \in \omega$,

(2) $$n,m > M \rightarrow |x_n - x_m| < \delta.$$

Using the same argument we used to obtain (1), there exists a $p \in \omega$ such that $p > M$ and

(3) $$|x_p| > 2\delta.$$

Therefore, if $n \in \omega$ and $n > M$,

$$\begin{aligned} |x_n| &> |x_p| - \delta && (2) \\ &> 2\delta - \delta && (3) \\ &= \delta. \blacksquare \end{aligned}$$

As a corollary to 6.4.21 we have that if a Cauchy sequence does not converge to zero, then it contains at most a finite number of terms which are zero.

COROLLARY 6.4.22.

$$(x \in Ca \;\&\; \lim x \neq 0) \rightarrow \{n : n \in \omega \;\&\; x_n = 0\} \text{ is finite.}$$

The following two corollaries follow easily from 6.4.22.

COROLLARY 6.4.23. $(x \in Ca \ \&\ \lim x \neq 0) \rightarrow x^* \in Ca.$

COROLLARY 6.4.24. $(x \in Ca \ \&\ \lim x \neq 0) \rightarrow x =_c x^*.$

Now we are ready to prove the main result— The quotient of two Cauchy sequences is a Cauchy sequence as long as the divisor does not converge to zero.

THEOREM 6.4.25.

$$(x,y \in Ca \ \&\ \lim y \neq 0) \rightarrow x \div_s y \in Ca.$$

Proof: Suppose $x, y \in Ca$ and $\lim y \neq 0$. By 6.4.7, x is bounded. Therefore, there exists a rational number M such that for all $n \in \omega$,

$$(1) \qquad |x_n| < M.$$

Since y (and therefore y^*) does not converge to zero, it follows from 6.4.21 that there exist $\delta \in Ra$, $\delta > 0$, and $P \in \omega$ such that for all $n \in \omega$,

$$(2) \qquad n > P \rightarrow |y_n^*| > \delta.$$

Let ϵ be an arbitrary positive rational number. Since x and y^* are Cauchy sequences, there exist natural numbers N' and N'' such that for all $n,m \in \omega$,

$$(3) \qquad n,m > N' \rightarrow |x_n - x_m| < \delta\epsilon/2$$
$$(4) \qquad n,m > N'' \rightarrow |y_n^* - y_m^*| < \delta^2\epsilon/2M.$$

Let $N = \max(N', N'', P)$. For all $n,m \in \omega$, if $n,m > N$, then

$$\begin{aligned}
\left|\frac{x_n}{y_n^*} - \frac{x_m}{y_m^*}\right| &= \left|\frac{x_n y_m^* - x_m y_n^*}{y_n^* y_m^*}\right| \\
&= \left|\frac{(x_n y_m^* - x_n y_n^*) + (x_n y_n^* - x_m y_n^*)}{y_n^* y_m^*}\right| \\
&\leq \frac{|x_n||y_m^* - y_n^*|}{|y_n^*||y_m^*|} + \frac{|x_n - x_m|}{|y_m^*|} \\
&< \frac{M|y_m^* - y_n^*|}{|y_n^*||y_m^*|} + \frac{|x_n - x_m|}{|y_m^*|} && (1) \\
&< \frac{M|y_m^* - y_n^*|}{\delta^2} + \frac{|x_n - x_m|}{\delta} && (2) \\
&< \frac{M}{\delta^2} \cdot \frac{\delta^2\epsilon}{2M} + \frac{1}{\delta} \cdot \frac{\delta\epsilon}{2} && (3), (4) \\
&= \epsilon/2 + \epsilon/2 \\
&= \epsilon.
\end{aligned}$$

Consequently, $x \div_s y \in Ca$. ∎

We have now shown that if x and y are Cauchy sequences, then so is $x +_s y$, $x -_s y$, and $x \cdot_s y$, and if $\lim y \neq 0$, then so is $x \div_s y$.

DEFINITION 6.4.26. Inequality between Cauchy Sequences

$$x,y \in Ca \rightarrow$$

(a) $x <_c y =_{Df} (\exists\delta)(\exists N)(\delta \in Ra \ \& \ \delta > 0 \ \& \ N \in \omega \ \&$
$(\forall n)(n \in \omega \ \& \ n > N) \rightarrow y_n > x_n + \delta))$

(b) $x >_c y =_{Df} y <_c x$
(c) $x \leqq_c y =_{Df} (x <_c y \text{ or } x =_c y)$
(d) $x \geqq_c y =_{Df} y \leqq_c x$.

In other words, if $x,y \in Ca$, then $x <_c y$ if and only if $x_n < y_n$ for all n sufficiently large and $\lim(y -_s x) \neq 0$ $(x \neq_c y)$. It is easy to see that the relation $<_c$ is irreflexive, asymmetric, and transitive; $\leqq_c$ is reflexive and transitive; and if $x \leqq_c y$ and $y \leqq_c x$, then $x =_c y$.

The next theorem will eventually be used to prove the trichotomy for real numbers.

THEOREM 6.4.27. $x,y \in Ca \rightarrow (x <_c y \text{ or } x =_c y \text{ or } y <_c x)$.

Proof: Suppose $x,y \in Ca$ and $x \neq_c y$. Then from the denial of 6.4.12 with ϵ replaced by 2δ we obtain: There exists a positive rational number 2δ such that for all $N \in \omega$ there is an $n \in \omega$, $n > N$, such that

(1) $$|x_n - y_n| > 2\delta.$$

Since x and y are both Cauchy sequences, there is an $M \in \omega$ such that for all $n,m \in \omega$:

(2) $$n,m > M \rightarrow |x_n - x_m| < \delta/2$$
(3) $$n,m > M \rightarrow |y_n - y_m| < \delta/2.$$

Using the argument which was used to obtain (1), there is a natural number $p > M$ such that

(4) $$|x_p - y_p| > 2\delta.$$

Either $x_p < y_p$ or $y_p < x_p$. Suppose $x_p < y_p$, then from (4)

(5) $$y_p > x_p + 2\delta.$$

Moreover, for $n \in \omega$ and $n > p$, we obtain from (2) and (3)

(6) $$|x_n - x_p| < \delta/2$$
(7) $$|y_n - y_p| < \delta/2.$$

Hence, if $n > p > M$,

$$\begin{aligned} y_n &> y_p - \delta/2 && (7)\\ &> x_p + 3\delta/2 && (5)\\ &> x_n + \delta. && (6) \end{aligned}$$

Therefore, under the assumption that $x_p < y_p$ we obtain $x <_c y$. In an analogous way it can be shown that if $y_p < x_p$, then $y <_c x$. ∎

As a consequence of 6.4.27 we have that if $x, y \in Ca$ and $x_n \leqq y_n$ for all n sufficiently large, then $x \leqq_c y$.

COROLLARY 6.4.28.

$$(x,y \in Ca \;\&\; (\exists N)(N \in \omega \;\&\; (\forall n)(n \in \omega \;\&\; n > N) \rightarrow x_n \leqq y_n))) \rightarrow x \leqq_c y.$$

To conclude this section we shall summarize some further properties of Cauchy sequences.

THEOREM 6.4.29.

$$(x,y,u,v,z,w \in Ca \;\&\; \lim z = 0 \;\&\; \lim w = 1) \rightarrow$$

(a) $x +_s z =_c x$
(b) $x \cdot_s z =_c z$
(c) $x \cdot_s w =_c x$
(d) $x \cdot_s y =_c z \leftrightarrow (x =_c z \text{ or } y =_c z)$
(e) $x -_s x =_c z$
(f) $x \neq_c z \rightarrow x \div_s x =_c w$
(g) $x +_s u =_c y \leftrightarrow u =_c y -_s x$
(h) $x \neq_c z \rightarrow (x \cdot_s u =_c y \leftrightarrow u =_c y \div_s x)$
(i) $(x <_c y \;\&\; u \leqq_c v) \rightarrow x +_s u <_c y +_s v$
(j) $(x <_c y \;\&\; u >_c z) \rightarrow x \cdot_s u <_c y \cdot_s v$
(k) $(x <_c y \;\&\; u <_c z) \rightarrow y \cdot_s u <_c x \cdot_s u$
(l) $x +_s u =_c y +_s u \rightarrow x =_c y$
(m) $x +_s u <_c y +_s u \rightarrow x <_c y$
(n) $(u \neq_c z \;\&\; x \cdot_s u =_c y \cdot_s u) \rightarrow x =_c y$
(o) $(u >_c z \;\&\; x \cdot_s u <_c y \cdot_s u) \rightarrow x <_c y$
(p) $(u <_c z \;\&\; x \cdot_s u <_c y \cdot_s u) \rightarrow y <_c x$
(q) $x \leqq_c y \leftrightarrow (\exists u)(u \in Ca \;\&\; x +_s u =_c y)$
$(\exists L)(\exists M)(L, M \in Ra \;\&\; L = \lim x \;\&\; M = \lim y) \rightarrow$
(r) $\lim(x +_s y) = L + M$
(s) $\lim(x -_s y) = L - M$
(t) $\lim(x \cdot_s y) = L \cdot M$
(u) $M \neq 0 \rightarrow \lim(x \div_s y) = L/M$
(v) $x <_c y \leftrightarrow L < M$.

Definition 6.4.30. Absolute Value

$$x \in Ca \to |x|_c =_{\mathrm{Df}} \{\langle n, |x_n|\rangle : n \in \omega\}.$$

Theorem 6.4.31. $x \in Ca \to |x|_c \in Ca$

Theorem 6.4.32. $(x, y, z \in Ca \;\&\; \lim z = 0) \to$

(a) $x \geqq_c z \to |x|_c =_c x$
(b) $x <_c z \to |x|_c =_c -_s x$
(c) $|x|_c \geqq_c z$
(d) $|x|_c =_c z \leftrightarrow x =_c z$
(e) $|x \cdot_s y|_c =_c |x|_c \cdot_s |y|_c$
(f) $y \neq_c z \to |x \div_s y|_c = |x|_c \div_s |y|_c$
(g) $|x +_s y|_c \leqq |x|_c +_s |y|_c$
(h) $|x|_c -_s |y|_c \leqq_c |x -_s y|_c$
(i) $|x -_s y|_c =_c |y -_s x|_c$.

EXERCISES 6.4

1. Prove that sequences (2)–(4) (following 6.4.5) are Cauchy sequences.
2. Prove that sequences (6)–(9) (following 6.4.5) are not Cauchy sequences.
3. Give an example of two Cauchy sequences x and y such that
   (a) $x \neq y \;\&\; x =_c y$
   (b) $x <_c y$.
4. Prove corollary 6.4.28.
5. Prove theorem 6.4.29.
6. Prove theorem 6.4.31.
7. Prove theorem 6.4.32.

6.5. THE REAL NUMBERS

The equivalence relation $=_c$ between Cauchy sequences was defined in 6.4.12. A real number will now be defined as an equivalence class of Cauchy sequences.

Definition 6.5.1. Real Numbers

(a) $[x]_c =_{\mathrm{Df}} \{y : y \in Ca \;\&\; y =_c x\}$
(b) $u \in Re =_{\mathrm{Df}} (\exists x)(x \in Ca \;\&\; u = [x]_c)$.

Thus *Re* is the class of real numbers. We shall prove first that *Re* is a set.

Theorem 6.5.2. S(*Re*).

Proof: $Re \subseteq \mathcal{P}(Ca)$. ■

The operations of addition, subtraction, multiplication, and division of real numbers will be defined in the natural way. But first, the preliminary theorem.

THEOREM 6.5.3. $(x,y,u,v \in Ca \;\&\; x =_c u \;\&\; y =_c v) \rightarrow$

(a) $x +_s y =_c u +_s v$
(b) $x -_s y =_c u -_s v$
(c) $x \cdot_s y =_c u \cdot_s v$
(d) $\lim y \neq 0 \rightarrow x \div_s y =_c u \div_s v$.

DEFINITION 6.5.4. Addition, Subtraction, Multiplication, and Division. $x,y \in Ca \rightarrow$

(a) $[x]_c +_r [y]_c =_{Df} [x +_s y]_c$
(b) $[x]_c -_r [y]_c =_{Df} [x -_s y]_c$
(c) $[x]_c \cdot_r [y]_c =_{Df} [x \cdot_s y]_c$
(d) $\lim y \neq 0 \rightarrow ([x] \div_r [y]_c =_{Df} [x \div_s y]_c$.

Next, the inequality relation between real numbers.

THEOREM 6.5.5.

$$(x,y,u,v \in Ca \;\&\; x =_c u \;\&\; y =_c v) \rightarrow$$

(a) $x <_c y \leftrightarrow u <_c v$
(b) $x \leqq_c y \leftrightarrow u \leqq_c v$.

DEFINITION 6.5.6. Inequality

$$x,y \in Ca \rightarrow$$

(a) $[x]_c <_r [y]_c =_{Df} x <_c y$
(b) $[x]_c >_r [y]_c =_{Df} [y]_c <_r [x]_c$
(c) $[x]_c \leqq_r [y]_c =_{Df} x \leqq_c y$
(d) $[x]_c \geqq_r [y]_c =_{Df} [y]_c \leqq_r [x]_c$.

Finally, we define the absolute value of a real number.

THEOREM 6.5.7.

$$(x,y \in Ca \;\&\; x =_c y) \rightarrow |x|_c =_c |y|_c.$$

DEFINITION 6.5.8. Absolute Value

$$x \in Ca \rightarrow |[x]_c|_r =_{Df} [|x|_c]_c.$$

The proof that the real numbers satisfy all the expected arithmetic properties follows from 6.4.4, 6.4.27, 6.4.29, and 6.4.32. We shall assume that *Re* satisfies all these arithmetic properties. The remaining part of this section will be devoted to the analytic properties of the real numbers.

To each rational number we can associate a real number in a natural manner.

DEFINITION 6.5.9. Rational Real Numbers

$$x \in Rae =_{\mathrm{Df}} [x \in Re \ \&\ (\exists u)(u \in Ca \ \&\ (\exists y)(y \in Ra \ \&\ (\forall n)(n \in \omega \rightarrow u_n = y) \ \&\ x = [u]_c)))].$$

Clearly, for each $x \in Rae$ there exists a unique $y \in Ra$ such that $x = [u]_c$ and for all $n \in \omega$, $u_n = y$. And conversely, for each $y \in Ra$ there is a unique $x \in Rae$ such that $x = [u]_c$ and for all $n \in \omega$, $u_n = y$. Consequently, there is a 1–1 function mapping *Ra* onto *Rae*. Let us call this function ψ. Thus,

DEFINITION 6.5.10.

$$\psi = \{\langle x,[y]_c\rangle : x \in Ra \ \&\ y \in Ca \ \&\ (\forall n)(n \in \omega \rightarrow y_n = x)\}.$$

The proofs of the following two theorems are left as exercises.

THEOREM 6.5.11. $\psi : Ra \xrightarrow[\text{onto}]{1\text{–}1} Rae.$

THEOREM 6.5.12. $x,y \in Ra \rightarrow$

(a) $u \in \psi(x) \leftrightarrow \lim u = x$
(b) $\psi(x + y) = \psi(x) +_r \psi(y)$
(c) $\psi(x - y) = \psi(x) -_r \psi(y)$
(d) $\psi(x \cdot y) = \psi(x) \cdot_r \psi(y)$
(e) $y \neq 0 \rightarrow \psi(x \div y) = \psi(x) \div_r \psi(y)$
(f) $x < y \leftrightarrow \psi(x) <_r \psi(y)$
(g) $\psi(|x|) = |\psi(x)|_r$.

The rational real numbers also have the property that they are *dense* in the real numbers. That is,

THEOREM 6.5.13.

$$(x,y \in Re \ \&\ x <_r y) \rightarrow (\exists z)(z \in Rae \ \&\ x <_r z \ \&\ z <_r y).$$

Proof: Suppose $x,y \in Re$ and $x <_r y$. Let $u \in x$ and $v \in y$, then $u,v \in Ca$ and by 6.5.6(a),

(1) $$u <_c v.$$

Therefore, by 6.4.26(a) there exist $\delta \in Ra$, $\delta > 0$, and $N \in \omega$ such that for all $n \in \omega$

(2) $$n > N \rightarrow v_n > u_n + 4\delta$$

and by 6.4.5, for all $n,m \in \omega$

(3) $$n,m > N \rightarrow |u_n - u_m| < \delta$$

(4) $$n,m > N \rightarrow |v_n - v_m| < \delta.$$

Let

$$z = \psi(u_{N+1} + 2\delta).$$

Then, $z = [w]_c$, where for all $n \in \omega$

$$(5) \qquad w_n = u_{N+1} + 2\delta.$$

We shall show that z is the required rational real number. For all $n \in \omega$, if $n > N$, then

$$\begin{aligned} w_n &= u_{N+1} + 2\delta & (5)\\ &> u_n + \delta. & (3) \end{aligned}$$

Therefore, $x <_r z$. Also, for all $n \in \omega$, if $n > N$, then

$$\begin{aligned} v_n &> v_{N+1} - \delta & (4)\\ &> u_{N+1} + 3\delta & (2)\\ &= w_n + \delta. & (5) \end{aligned}$$

Hence $z <_r y$. ■

In the remaining part of the text, we shall drop the subscript "*r*" from the operation signs and relation signs between real numbers. If $x,y \in Re$, we shall often denote "$x \div y$" by "x/y." Moreover, for most intents and purposes it can be assumed that *Ra* and *Rae* are identical. Therefore, in the future, except where it might lead to confusion, we shall identify x with $\psi(x)$ and assume $\omega \subseteq In \subseteq Ra \subseteq Re$.

Sequences of real numbers, Cauchy sequences of real numbers and limits of sequences of real numbers are defined analogously to the corresponding definitions for rational numbers—6.4.1, 6.4.5, and 6.4.9.

Thus we have

Definition 6.5.14. Sequences of Real Numbers

$$u \subseteq \omega \rightarrow (x \text{ is a } u\text{-sequence of real numbers} =_{\mathrm{Df}} x \in (Re)^u).$$

Definition 6.5.15. Cauchy Sequences of Real Numbers

$$x \in Cr =_{\mathrm{Df}} [x \in (Re)^\omega \mathbin{\&} (\forall\epsilon)((\epsilon \in Re \mathbin{\&} \epsilon > 0) \rightarrow (\exists N)(N \in \omega \mathbin{\&} (\forall m)(\forall n)((n,m \in \omega \mathbin{\&} n,m > N) \rightarrow |x_m - x_n| < \epsilon)))].$$

Definition 6.5.16. Limits

$$x \in (Re)^\omega \rightarrow [(\lim x = L) =_{\mathrm{Df}} (L \in Re \mathbin{\&} (\forall\epsilon)((\epsilon \in Re \mathbin{\&} \epsilon > 0) \rightarrow (\exists N)[N \in \omega \mathbin{\&} (\forall n)(n \in \omega \mathbin{\&} n > N) \rightarrow |x_n - L| < \epsilon)]))].$$

The following two theorems about sequences of real numbers are analogous to the corresponding theorems about sequences of rational numbers.

THEOREM 6.5.17.

$$[x \in (Re)^\omega \; \& \; (\exists L)(L \in Re \; \& \; \lim x = L)] \rightarrow (\exists 1 L)(L \in Re \; \& \; \lim x = L).$$

Proof: See 6.4.10.

THEOREM 6.5.18.

$$(x \in (Re)^\omega \; \& \; (\exists L)(L \in Re \; \& \; \lim x = L)) \rightarrow x \in Cr.$$

Proof: See 6.4.11.

For sequences of rational numbers the converse of 6.5.18 does not hold. (See the remarks following 6.4.9.) However, one of the basic differences between the rational numbers and the real numbers is that the converse of 6.5.18 does hold for sequences of real numbers. This is the so-called "completeness" property of the set of real numbers.

THEOREM 6.5.19.

$$x \in Cr \rightarrow (\exists L)(L \in Re \; \& \; \lim x = L).$$

Proof: Suppose $x \in Cr$. Then by 6.5.15, for every real number $\epsilon > 0$ there exists a real number N' such that for all natural numbers n,m,

(1) $$n,m > N' \rightarrow |x_n - x_m| < \epsilon/3.$$

By theorem 6.5.13, there is a rational real number z such that

(2) $$x_n < z < x_n + 1/n.$$

Since $\omega \approx Rae$, there is a 1–1 function f mapping ω onto Rae. Let n' be the smallest natural number in the set

$$\{m : x_n < f(m) < x_n +_r 1/n\},$$

and let $y_n = f(n')$. Then we have for all $n \in \omega$, $y_n \in Rae$ and

(3) $$x_n < y_n < x_n + 1/n.$$

(Note we introduce the function f to avoid the necessity of using the axiom of choice to construct the sequence y.)

It follows from (3) that there exists a real number N'' such that for all natural numbers n,

(4) $$n > N'' \rightarrow |x_n - y_n| < 1/N'' < \epsilon/3.$$

Let $N = \max(N',N'')$. If $n,m \in \omega$ and $n,m > N$, then,

$$\begin{aligned} |y_n - y_m| &= |(y_n - x_n) + (x_n - x_m) + (x_m - y_m)| \\ &\leq |y_n - x_n| + |x_n - x_m| + |x_m - y_m| \\ &< |y_n - x_n| + \epsilon/3 + |x_m - y_m| && (1) \\ &< \epsilon/3 + \epsilon/3 + \epsilon/3 && (4) \\ &= \epsilon. \end{aligned}$$

Thus, y is a Cauchy sequence of real numbers. Since $y_n \in Rae$ for each $n \in \omega$, define

$$u_n = \psi^{-1}(y_n).$$

Then u_n is the rational number corresponding to y_n and since $y \in Cr$, we must have $u \in Ca$ (6.5.12(c)(f)(g)). Define

$$z = [u]_c.$$

Then $z \in Re$ and we claim

$$\text{(5)} \qquad \lim x = z.$$

To prove (5) we shall first prove

$$\text{(6)} \qquad \lim y = z.$$

By 6.5.8,

$$\text{(7)} \qquad |y_n - z|_r = [|v|_c]_c,$$

where

$$v \in y_n - z$$

and

$$v_m = u_m - u_n.$$

Let ϵ' be a rational real number such that $0 < \epsilon' < 2\epsilon/3$. Since $u \in Ca$, there is a natural number M such that for all $n,m \in \omega$,

$$n,m > M \rightarrow |u_n - u_m| < \psi^{-1}(\epsilon').$$

Therefore, by 6.4.28 and 6.5.6(c),

$$\text{(8)} \qquad n > M \rightarrow [|v|_c]_c \leqq \epsilon'.$$

Hence, from (7) and (8) we obtain

$$\text{(9)} \qquad n > M \rightarrow |y_n - z|_r \leqq \epsilon' < 2\epsilon/3.$$

This proves (6).

To prove (5), let $P = \max(N,M)$, then for all $n \in \omega$, if $n > P$,

$$\begin{aligned} |x_n - z|_r &= |(x_n - y_n) + (y_n - z)|_r \\ &\leqq |x_n - y_n|_r + |y_n - z|_r \\ &< \epsilon/3 + |y_n - z|_r && (4) \\ &< \epsilon/3 + 2\epsilon/3 && (9) \\ &= \epsilon. \blacksquare \end{aligned}$$

The next theorem deals with the limit of increasing and decreasing Cauchy sequences.

THEOREM 6.5.20. $x \in Cr \rightarrow$

(a) $(\forall n)(n \in \omega \rightarrow x_n \geqq x_{n+1}) \rightarrow (\forall n)(n \in \omega \rightarrow \lim x \leqq x_n)$

(b) $(\forall n)(n \in \omega \rightarrow x_n \leqq x_{n+1}) \rightarrow (\forall n)(n \in \omega \rightarrow \lim x \geqq x_n)$.

Proof: (a) Suppose $x \in Cr$ and $x_n \geqq x_{n+1}$ for all $n \in \omega$. Suppose the theorem is false, then there is an $n \in \omega$ such that $\lim x > x_n$. Choose an $\epsilon \in Re$ such that $0 < \epsilon < \lim x - x_n$. By hypothesis, for all $m \in \omega$ such that $m > n$, $x_n \geqq x_m$. Hence, for all $m > n$, $\lim x - x_m > \epsilon$, contradicting the definition of a limit, 6.5.12. Therefore, $\lim x \leqq x_n$ for all $n \in \omega$.

The proof of part (b) is analogous to that of (a). ■

To conclude this section, we shall give another characteristic property of the real numbers which is not possessed by the rational numbers. It can be stated as follows:

Every non-empty set of real numbers which has an upper bound has a least upper bound.

This is actually another form of 6.5.19. It is another form of the completeness property of the set of real numbers.

DEFINITION 6.5.21. Upper Bounds and Lower Bounds

$$x \subseteq Re \rightarrow$$

(a) u is an *upper bound* of $x =_{\mathrm{Df}} u \in Re \ \&\ (\forall v)(v \in x \rightarrow v \leqq u)$

(b) u is a *lower bound* of $x =_{\mathrm{Df}} u \in Re \ \&\ (\forall v)(v \in x \rightarrow v \geqq u)$

(c) u is a *least upper bound* of $x =_{\mathrm{Df}}$ (u is an upper bound of x & $(\forall v)$(v is an upper bound of $x \rightarrow u \leqq v$))

(d) u is a *greatest lower bound* of $x =_{\mathrm{Df}}$ (u is a lower bound of x & $(\forall v)$(v is a lower bound of $x \rightarrow u \geqq v$)).

The least upper bound is often called the *supremum* and the greatest lower bound, the *infinum*. The abbreviation $u =$ l.u.b. x or $u = \sup x$ is often used for the least upper bound, and $u =$ g.l.b. x or $u = \inf x$, for the greatest lower bound. It follows from the antisymmetry of "$\leqq$" that if the least upper bound or the greatest lower bound exists, then it is unique.

THEOREM 6.5.22.

$(x \subseteq Re \ \&\ x \neq \emptyset \ \&\ (\exists u)$($u$ is an upper bound of x)) $\rightarrow$ $(\exists v)$(v is the least upper bound of x).

Proof: Let x be a non-empty set of real numbers which has an upper bound. The idea of the proof is to construct a Cauchy sequence whose limit is the least upper bound of x. Let u_0 and v_0 be two real numbers such that $u_0 < v_0$, v_0 is an upper bound of x, u_0 is not an upper bound of x (that is, there is a $y \in x$ such that $u_0 < y$) and suppose $v_0 - u_0 = N$. Define u_n and v_n inductively as follows:

$$u_{n+1} = \begin{cases} (u_n + v_n)/2 & \text{if } (u_n + v_n)/2 \text{ is not an upper bound of } x \\ u_n & \text{if } (u_n + v_n)/2 \text{ is an upper bound of } x \end{cases}$$

$$v_{n+1} = \begin{cases} (u_n + v_n)/2 & \text{if } (u_n + v_n)/2 \text{ is an upper bound of } x \\ v_n & \text{if } (u_n + v_n)/2 \text{ is not an upper bound of } x \end{cases}$$

(see exercise 4.3.5). We shall show that v is a Cauchy sequence of real numbers and lim v = l.u.b. x. (The same is true for the sequence u, but we do not need it in the proof.)

Since $v_0 - u_0 = N$ and $v_{n+1} - u_{n+1} = (v_n - u_n)/2$, we easily infer, for all $n \in \omega$, that

(1) $$v_n - u_n = N/2^n.$$

Thus,

(2) $$u_n < v_n.$$

Also, either

$$v_n - v_{n+1} = 0$$

or

$$\begin{aligned} v_n - v_{n+1} &= v_n - ((u_n + v_n)/2) \\ &= (v_n - u_n)/2 \\ &= N/2^{n+1}. \end{aligned}$$

Hence, for all $n \in \omega$

(3) $$v_{n+1} \leqq v_n.$$

Similarly, we can show that for all $n \in \omega$

(4) $$u_n \leqq u_{n+1}.$$

Therefore, v is a non-increasing sequence and u is a non-decreasing sequence. If $m,n \in \omega$ and $m < n$, then

$$\begin{aligned} v_m - v_n &< v_m - u_n && (2) \\ &\leqq v_m - u_m && (4) \\ &= N/2^m. && (1) \end{aligned}$$

Thus, if m and n are large, the difference $v_m - v_n$ is small. Therefore, the sequence v is a Cauchy sequence, and by theorem 6.5.19 v has a limit. Let

$$w = \lim v.$$

We shall show w = l.u.b. x.

Suppose there is a $y \in x$ such that $w < y$. Choose a real number ϵ such that

(5) $$0 < \epsilon < y - w.$$

Since v_n is an upper bound of x for each $n \in \omega$, we have for all $n \in \omega$

(6) $$y \leqq v_n.$$

Therefore, from (5) and (6) we obtain for all $n \in \omega$

$$v_n - w > \epsilon,$$

which contradicts the fact that $w = \lim v$. Therefore, w is an upper bound of x.

Suppose y is an upper bound of x and $y < w$. By (1) there is an $n \in \omega$ such that

(7) $$v_n - u_n < w - y.$$

Since v is a non-decreasing sequence and $w = \lim v$, it follows from 6.5.20(a) that for all $n \in \omega$,

(8) $$w \leqq v_n.$$

Therefore, from (7) and (8) we obtain

$$w - u_n < w - y$$

or

$$y < u_n.$$

But u_n is not an upper bound of x and, therefore, neither is y. This is a contradiction. Consequently, $w = \text{l.u.b. } x$. ■

As an immediate corollary we have

COROLLARY 6.5.23.

$$(x \subseteq Re \ \& \ x \neq 0 \ \& \ (\exists u)(u \text{ is a lower bound of } x)) \rightarrow$$
$$(\exists v)(v \text{ is the greatest lower bound of } x).$$

EXERCISES 6.5

1. Prove theorem 6.5.3.
2. Prove theorem 6.5.5.
3. Prove theorem 6.5.7.
4. Prove theorem 6.5.11.
5. Prove theorem 6.5.12.
6. Prove each of the following: $x, y \in Re \rightarrow$
   (a) $x < y$ or $x = y$ or $y < x$

(b) $|x \cdot y| = |x| \cdot |y|$
(c) $y \neq 0 \rightarrow |x/y| = |x|/|y|$
(d) $|x + y| \leqq |x| + |y|$
(e) $|x| - |y| \leqq |x - y|$
(f) $|x - y| = |y - x|$.

7. Prove each of the following:
(a) "$\leqq$" is reflexive, antisymmetric, and transitive on *Re*
(b) "$<$" is irreflexive, asymmetric, and transitive on *Re*.

8. Let

$$x = \{y : y \in Rae \ \&\ y < \sqrt{2}\}.$$

Construct the sequences u and v, as in the proof of 6.5.22, up to $n = 7$.

6.6 DECIMAL REPRESENTATION

In the final section of this chapter we shall discuss the decimal representation of the real numbers and give Cantor's famous proof that the real numbers are not denumerable.

Let x be any real number. Let y_0 be the largest integer such that $y_0 \leqq x$. (The proof that y_0 exists is left as an exercise.) Then

$$x = y_0 + r_0, \text{ where } 0 \leqq r_0 < 1.$$

Let y_1 be the largest natural number such that $0 \leqq y_1 < 10$ and $y_1 \leqq 10r_0$. Then

$$r_0 = y_1/10 + r_1, \text{ where } 0 \leqq r_1 < 1/10.$$

Now continue this process. In general, y_n is the largest natural number such that $0 \leqq y_n < 10$ and $y_n \leqq 10^n r_{n-1}$, so

$$r_{n-1} = y_n/10^n + r_n, \text{ where } 0 \leqq r_n < 1/10^n$$

and

$$x = y_0 + y_1/10 + y_2/10^2 + \cdots + y_n/10^n + r_n.$$

(If x is negative, the construction given here does not lead to the usual decimal notation for x. For example, if $x = -7/5$, the usual decimal notation for x is $-1.4000\ldots$, while the preceding construction would give us $x = -2 + 6/10 + 0/10 + \cdots$. However, this is a minor difficulty and the advantages of this construction will save us a considerable amount of effort later.)

The existence of the sequences y and r follows from the recursion theorem. The number 10 is called the *base* of the number system, thus the term *decimal* system. The preceding result can be generalized to any base b as long as $b \in \omega$ and $b \geqq 2$. (If $b = 2$, it is called a *binary* system;

if $b = 3$, a *ternary* system; etc.) We state the general result as a theorem. [Note that condition (c) of theorem 6.6.1 guarantees that no representation will end with a sequence of $(b - 1)$'s. Thus, for example, in the decimal system the real number 3/2 is represented by the decimal 1.5000 . . . and not by 1.4999 . . . .]

THEOREM 6.6.1.

$$(x \in Re \;\&\; x \geqq 0 \;\&\; b \in \omega \;\&\; b \geqq 2) \rightarrow (\exists 1 y)[y \in (In)^{\omega} \;\&$$

$$\begin{aligned}
&\text{(a) } y_0 = \max\{u : u \in In \;\&\; u \leqq x\}\\
&\text{(b) } (\forall n)[(n \in \omega \;\&\; n > 0) \rightarrow (y_n \in \omega \;\&\; y_n < b)]\\
&\text{(c) } (\forall m)[m \in \omega \rightarrow (\exists n)(n \in \omega \;\&\; n > m \;\&\; y_n \neq b - 1)]\\
&\text{(d) } (\forall z)(z \in (Ra)^{\omega} \;\&\; z_0 = y_0 \;\&\; z_{n+1} = z_n + y_{n+1}/b^{n+1})] \rightarrow\\
&\qquad\qquad\qquad\qquad (z \in Cr \;\&\; \lim z = x)).
\end{aligned}$$

Proof: The existence of the sequence y follows from the remarks preceding the theorem.

To prove uniqueness, suppose y and u are both sequences satisfying the hypothesis. Then,

$$\begin{aligned} x &= y_0 + y_1/b + \cdots + y_n/b^n + r_n \\ &= u_0 + u_1/b + \cdots + u_n/b^n + s_n. \end{aligned} \tag{1}$$

It follows from (c) and (d) that

$$0 \leqq r_n,\, s_n < 1/b^n. \tag{2}$$

Thus,

$$|r_n - s_n| < 1/b^n. \tag{3}$$

Let n be the smallest natural number such that $y_n \neq u_n$. Then from (1) we get

$$0 = (y_n - u_n)/b^n + r_n - s_n. \tag{4}$$

Since y_n and u_n are integers and $y_n \neq u_n$, it follows that

$$|(y_n - u_n)/b^n| \geqq 1/b^n. \tag{5}$$

However, (3) and (5) contradict (4). Therefore, we must have $y_n = u_n$ for all $n \in \omega$ so $y = u$. ■

It is easy to see that the converse of theorem 6.6.1 also holds. That is,

THEOREM 6.6.2.

$$\begin{aligned}
&[b \in \omega \;\&\; b \geqq 2 \;\&\; y \in (In)^{\omega} \;\&\; (\forall n)((n \in \omega \;\&\; n > 0) \rightarrow\\
&\qquad (y_n \in \omega \;\&\; y_n < b))] \rightarrow (\exists 1 x)[x \in Re \;\&\; (\forall z)((z \in (Ra)^{\omega} \;\&\\
&\qquad\qquad z_0 = y_0 \;\&\; z_{n+1} = z_n + y_{n+1}/b^{n+1}) \rightarrow \lim z = x)].
\end{aligned}$$

Proof: The proof is left as an exercise.

If $x, y \in Re$ and $x < y$, let

$$\begin{aligned} Re[x,y] &= \{u : u \in Re \ \&\ x \leqq u \leqq y\}, \\ Re[x,y) &= \{u : u \in Re \ \&\ x \leqq u < y\}, \\ Re(x,y] &= \{u : u \in Re \ \&\ x < u \leqq y\}, \\ Re(x,y) &= \{u : u \in Re \ \&\ x < u < y\}. \end{aligned}$$

If the base of the number system is taken to be 2, then it follows from theorem 6.6.1 that $Re[0,1) \precsim 2^\omega$, and if the base is taken to be 3, it follows from 6.6.2 that $2^\omega \precsim Re[0,1)$. Consequently, the Schröder–Bernstein theorem implies,

THEOREM 6.6.3. $Re[0,1) \approx 2^\omega$.

It is not too difficult to prove that $Re[0,1) \approx Re(-1,1)$ (see exercises 6.6.2 and 6.6.3). Moreover, $Re(-1,1) \approx Re$, for if we define a function f as follows: For all $x \in Re(-1,1)$,

$$f(x) = x/(1 - |x|),$$

then it is easy to prove that f is a 1–1 function mapping $Re(-1,1)$ onto Re. [Note that

$$f^{-1}(x) = x/(1 + |x|).$$

Consequently, it can be shown that $Re[0,1) \approx Re$. Using this result and theorem 6.6.3, we obtain

THEOREM 6.6.4. $Re \approx 2^\omega$.

It follows from 3.5.23 that $2^\omega \approx \mathcal{P}(\omega)$ and from 3.4.3 that $\omega \prec \mathcal{P}(\omega)$. Consequently, by 6.6.4, Re is not denumerable. However, it is instructive to give Cantor's constructive proof of the non-denumerability of the real numbers using the well-known Cantor diagonal procedure.

THEOREM 6.6.5. $\omega \prec Re$.

Proof: Clearly $\omega \precsim Re$. Suppose $\omega \approx Re$. Let f be a 1–1 function mapping ω onto Re. We shall use the decimal representation for the real numbers (6.6.1). Then for each $n \in \omega$,

$$f(n) = y_0^{(n)} \cdot y_1^{(n)} y_2^{(n)} y_3^{(n)} \cdots,$$

where $y_0^{(n)} \in In$ and if $m > 0$, $y_m^{(n)} \in \omega$ and $0 \leqq y_m^{(n)} < 10$. Moreover, the sequence $y^{(n)}$ does not end with an infinite sequence of 9's. We shall construct a decimal z such that $z \notin \mathcal{R}(f)$, contradicting the fact that f maps ω onto Re.

Define

$$z_n = \begin{cases} 1 & \text{if } y_n^{(n)} \neq 1 \\ 2 & \text{if } y_n^{(n)} = 1. \end{cases}$$

Then,

$$z \neq f(0) \text{ because } z_0 \neq y_0^{(0)}$$
$$z \neq f(1) \text{ because } z_1 \neq y_0^{(1)}$$
$$z \neq f(2) \text{ because } z_2 \neq y_2^{(2)}$$

and in general

$$z \neq f(n) \text{ because } z_n \neq y_n^{(n)}.$$

Let us illustrate this procedure by an example. Suppose

$$f(0) = 10.66666\ldots$$
$$f(1) = 2.13979\ldots$$
$$f(2) = 1.21013\ldots$$
$$f(3) = 0.32622\ldots$$
$$f(4) = 62.71980\ldots$$

etc. Then

$$z_0 = 1,\ z_1 = 2,\ z_2 = 2,\ z_3 = 1,\ z_4 = 1, \text{ etc.,}$$

and

$$z = 1.211\ldots.$$

Thus, z is a decimal which is not an element of $\mathcal{R}(f)$. ■

EXERCISES 6.6

1. Prove theorem 6.6.2.
2. Prove $(x,y,u,v \in Re \ \&\ x < y \ \&\ u < v) \rightarrow Re[x,y] \approx Re[u,v]$.
3. Prove: $(x,y \in Re \ \&\ x < y) \rightarrow$
   (a) $Re[x,y] \approx Re[x,y)$
   (b) $Re[x,y] \approx Re(x,y]$
   (c) $Re[x,y) \approx Re(x,y)$.
4. Prove $Re[0,1) \times Re[0,1) \approx Re[0,1)$.

Chapter 7: Ordering Relations

7.1. PARTIAL ORDERING RELATIONS

A relation defined on a class superimposes an ordering on the elements of the class. It is the purpose of this chapter to study various types of relations which are commonly called *ordering* relations.

If X is a class and R a relation, we must be able to talk about the class X with the relation R defined on it, as distinguished from the class X alone. Normally this can be accomplished by forming the ordered pair $\langle X,R \rangle$. However, if X or R are proper classes, then the ordered pair $\langle X,R \rangle$ does not exist in our system. To avoid this difficulty we shall define a symbol, $\langle\langle X,R \rangle\rangle$, which has the same properties as the ordered pair, but is defined for all classes X and R.

DEFINITION 7.1.1. $(\mathrm{Cl}(X)\ \&\ \mathrm{Cl}(Y)\ \&\ \mathrm{Cl}(Z)) \rightarrow$

(a) $\langle\langle X,Y \rangle\rangle =_{\mathrm{Df}} (X \times \{0\}) \cup (Y \times \{1\})$

(b) $\langle\langle X,Y,Z \rangle\rangle =_{\mathrm{Df}} (X \times \{0\}) \cup (Y \times \{1\}) \cup (Z \times \{2\})$.

It is easily seen how this definition can be extended to any finite number of arguments, but we shall only use it for two and later for three arguments.

DEFINITION 7.1.2. Partial Ordering

(a) R is a *partial ordering (p.o.) relation* $=_{\mathrm{Df}}$ (Rel(R) & R is antisymmetric & transitive)

(b) $\langle\langle X,R \rangle\rangle$ is a *partially ordered (p.o.) class* $=_{\mathrm{Df}}$ (Cl(X) & $R|X$ is a partial ordering relation).

In some contexts, but not here, the requirement that a p.o. relation be antisymmetric is dropped. Then the term "p.o. relation" is used synonymously with "transitive relation." (However, linear orderings and well-orderings are almost always assumed to be antisymmetric. See definitions 7.2.2 and 7.2.4.) On occasion it is convenient for a p.o. relation to be reflexive, and on other occasions for it to be irreflexive. Most of the time it makes no difference if it is reflexive, irreflexive, or neither, so we have not imposed any conditions on the reflexivity of a p.o. relation.

Examples of p.o. relations are $\leqq$ and $<$ on any set of numbers, and $\langle\langle\omega, \leqq\rangle\rangle$ and $\langle\langle\omega, <\rangle\rangle$ are examples of p.o. classes.

If $\langle\langle X,R\rangle\rangle$ is a p.o. class and X is a set, we shall often call $\langle\langle X,R\rangle\rangle$ a p.o. *set*. Moreover, if X is a class which has a p.o. relation defined on it, then we shall sometimes call X itself a p.o. class as long as the p.o. relation is clearly understood. (Even though this latter notation is not strictly correct, it is in common usage. We shall use it on those occasions when it does not cause confusion.) Thus we might say "ω is a p.o. set" instead of "$\langle\langle\omega, \leqq\rangle\rangle$ is a p.o. set." Clearly, if $\langle\langle X,R\rangle\rangle$ is a p.o. class and $Y \subseteq X$ then $\langle\langle Y,R\rangle\rangle$ is a p.o. class, but if $S \subseteq R$, it does not follow that $\langle\langle X,S\rangle\rangle$ is a p.o. class.

There may be one element in a p.o. class which is "smaller" than all the other elements. For example, if X is a class of sets and $\emptyset \in X$, then $\emptyset$ is the smallest element of the p.o. class $\langle\langle X,R\rangle\rangle$, where $R = \{\langle u,v\rangle : u,v \in X \;\&\; u \subseteq v\}$, because $\emptyset \subseteq u$ for all $u \in X$. On the other hand, if $\emptyset \notin X$, then X may not have a smallest element but X may have an element which is smaller than all other elements to which it can be compared. For example, if

$$X = \{\{u\}, \{v\}, \{w\}, \{u,v\}, \{u,w\}, \{v,w\}, \{u,v,w\}\},$$
$$R = \{\langle x,y\rangle : x,y \in X \;\&\; x \subseteq y\},$$

then $\langle\langle X,R\rangle\rangle$ is a p.o. class. However, if the elements u,v, and w are distinct, X has no smallest element. There is no element in X which is a subset of every element of X. But the unit sets in X, $\{u\}$, $\{v\}$, and $\{w\}$, are subsets of each comparable set.

There are analogous considerations for the largest element of a set. These concepts are formally defined as follows:

DEFINITION 7.1.3. Smallest, Largest, Minimal, and Maximal Elements. $(\mathrm{Rel}(R) \;\&\; \mathrm{Cl}(X)) \rightarrow$

(a) u is an *R-first* element of $X =_{\mathrm{Df}}$
$$(u \in X \;\&\; (\forall v)((v \in X \;\&\; u \neq v) \rightarrow uRv)$$
(b) u is an *R-last* element of $X =_{\mathrm{Df}}$
$$(u \in X \;\&\; (\forall v)((v \in X \;\&\; u \neq v) \rightarrow vRu)$$
(c) u is an *R-minimal* element of $X =_{\mathrm{Df}}$
$$(u \in X \;\&\; (\forall v)((v \in X \;\&\; vRu) \rightarrow uRv))$$
(d) u is an *R-maximal* element of $X =_{\mathrm{Df}}$
$$(u \in X \;\&\; (\forall v)((v \in X \;\&\; uRv) \rightarrow vRu)).$$

The terms "R-smallest" and "R-largest" are sometimes used instead of "R-first" and "R-last", respectively. If R is a p.o. relation, or just antisymmetric, then there is at most one R-first element and at most one R-last element.

If $Y \subseteq X$, there may be an element in X which is smaller or larger than every element in Y.

DEFINITION 7.1.4. Lower and Upper Bounds

$$(\text{Rel}(R) \ \& \ \text{Cl}(X) \ \& \ Y \subseteq X) \rightarrow$$

(a) u is an *R-lower bound* of $Y =_{\text{Df}}$
$$(u \in X \ \& \ (\forall v)((v \in Y \ \& \ v \neq u) \rightarrow uRv))$$
(b) u is an *R-upper bound* of $Y =_{\text{Df}}$
$$(u \in X \ \& \ (\forall v)((v \in Y \ \& \ v \neq u) \rightarrow vRu)).$$

When the largest of the lower bounds and the smallest of the upper bounds exist they are given special names.

DEFINITION 7.1.5. Greatest Lower Bound and Least Upper Bound

$$(\text{Rel}(R) \ \& \ \text{Cl}(X) \ \& \ Y \subseteq X) \rightarrow$$

(a) u is an *R-greatest lower bound* (*R-g.l.b.*) of $Y =_{\text{Df}} (u$ is an R-lower bound of Y & $(\forall v)((v$ is an R-lower bound of Y & $v \neq u) \rightarrow vRu))$

(b) u is an *R-least upper bound* (*R-l.u.b.*) of $Y =_{\text{Df}} (u$ is an R-upper bound of Y & $(\forall v)((v$ is an R-upper bound of Y & $v \neq u) \rightarrow uRv))$.

A greatest lower bound is often called an *infimum* (inf.) and a least upper bound, a *supremum* (sup.). If R is antisymmetric, there can be at most one g.l.b. and at most one l.u.b.

Let us consider several examples from the set of rational numbers. Let X be the set of positive rational numbers, then $\langle\langle X, \leqq\rangle\rangle$ is a p.o. set. Let

$$X_1 = \{u : u \in \omega \ \& \ u > 0\} \subseteq X$$
$$X_2 = \{u : u \in X \ \& \ u > 1\} \subseteq X$$
$$X_3 = \{u : u \in X \ \& \ u > \sqrt{2}\} \subseteq X.$$

Neither X_1, X_2, nor X_3 have any $\leqq$-upper bounds but they each have an infinite number of $\leqq$-lower bounds. The set of $\leqq$-lower bounds for X_1 and X_2 is $\{u : u \in X \ \& \ 0 < u \leqq 1\}$; and for X_3, $\{u : u \in X \ \& \ 0 < u < \sqrt{2}\}$. The number 1 is the $\leqq$-g.l.b. of X_1 and X_2, ($1 \in X_1$ but $1 \notin X_2$). But X_3 has no $\leqq$-g.l.b.

EXERCISES 7.1

1. Determine which of the following relations are p.o. relations:
   (a) $\mathfrak{F}(R_1) = \omega = X_1 \ \& \ (nR_1m \leftrightarrow n < m + 1)$
   (b) $\mathfrak{F}(R_2) = \omega = X_2 \ \& \ (nR_2m \leftrightarrow n < m + 2)$
   (c) $\mathfrak{F}(R_3) = \omega \times \omega = X_3 \ \& \ (\langle n,m\rangle \ R_3 \ \langle p,q\rangle \leftrightarrow (n < p$ or $(n = p \ \& \ m < q)))$.
   (Lexiographic ordering.)

(d) $\mathfrak{F}(R_4) = \omega \times \omega = X_4$ & $(\langle n,m\rangle\ R_4\ \langle p,q\rangle \leftrightarrow (\max(n,m) < \max(p,q)$ or $(\max(n,m) = \max(p,q)$ & $n < p)$ or $(\max(n,m) = \max(p,q)$ & $n = p$ & $m \leqq q)))$

(e) $\mathfrak{F}(R_5) = \{\{n,m\} : n,m \in \omega\} = X_5$ & $(\{n,m\}\ R_5\ \{p,q\} \leftrightarrow (\max(n,m) < \max(p,q)$ or $(\max(n,m) = \max(p,q)$ & $\min(n,m) \leqq \min(p,q))))$

(f) $\mathfrak{F}(R_6) =$ set of integers $= X_6$ & $(xR_6y \leftrightarrow (|x| > |y|$ or $(|x| = |y|$ & $x \geqq y)))$

(g) $\mathfrak{F}(R_7) =$ set of rational numbers $= X_7$ & $(xR_7y \leftrightarrow (|x| < |y|$ or $(|x| = |y|$ & $x < y)))$.

2. Let $\mathfrak{F}(R) = \omega \times \omega = X$ & $(\langle m,n\rangle\ R\ \langle p,q\rangle \leftrightarrow (m < p$ or $(m = p$ & $n \leqq q)))$:
   (a) Show $\langle\langle X,R\rangle\rangle$ is a p.o. set
   (b) Find all R-minimal elements of X. Does X have an R-first element?
   (c) Let $Y = \{1,2\} \times \{1,2\}$. Find all R-upper bounds and R-lower bounds of Y in X. Does Y have an R-l.u.b? An R-g.l.b? Find all R-minimal and R-maximal elements of Y.
3. Let $\mathfrak{F}(R) = \omega \times \omega = X$ & $(\langle m,n\rangle\ R\ \langle p,q\rangle \leftrightarrow (m \leqq p$ & $n \leqq q)$:
   (a) Show $\langle\langle X,R\rangle\rangle$ is a p.o. set
   (b) Prove $(Y \subseteq X$ & $Y \neq \emptyset$ & Y has an R-upper bound$) \rightarrow Y$ has an R-l.u.b.
   (c) Prove $(Y \subseteq X$ & $Y \neq \emptyset) \rightarrow Y$ has an R-g.l.b.
   (d) Give an example of a non-empty set $Y \subseteq X$ which has an R-upper bound and an R-lower bound, but has no R-first element and no R-last element.

7.2. LINEAR AND WELL-ORDERING RELATION

The relation of $\leqq$ on ω has some other properties besides just being a p.o. relation. In this section we shall abstract some of these other properties.

DEFINITION 7.2.1. Connected Relation

R is *connected on* $X =_{\mathrm{Df}} (\forall u)(\forall v)(u,v \in X$ & $u \neq v) \rightarrow (uRv$ or $vRu))$.

DEFINITION 7.2.2. Linear Ordering

(a) R is a *linear ordering* (*l.o.*) *relation on* $X =_{\mathrm{Df}}$

$(R|X$ is a p.o. relation & R is connected on $X)$

(b) $\langle\langle X,R\rangle\rangle$ is a *linear ordered* (*l.o.*) *class* $=_{\mathrm{Df}}$

$(\mathrm{Cl}(X)$ & R is a linear ordering relation on $X)$.

A linear ordering is sometimes called a *complete* ordering, a *total* ordering, a *simple* ordering, or just an *ordering* and a linear ordered class is sometimes called a *chain*. If X is a set and $\langle\langle X,R\rangle\rangle$ is a l.o. class, we shall often call $\langle\langle X,R\rangle\rangle$ a l.o. set. Clearly, if $\langle\langle X,R\rangle\rangle$ is a l.o. class and $Y \subseteq X$, then $\langle\langle Y,R\rangle\rangle$ is a l.o. class.

For example, $\langle\langle \omega, \leqq\rangle\rangle$ is a l.o. set. However, if X is the class of all subsets of a class which has more than one element and $R = \{\langle u,v\rangle : u,v \in X$ & $u \subseteq v\}$, then $\langle\langle X,R\rangle\rangle$ is a p.o. class but not a l.o. class.

A l.o. class has at most one minimal element and at most one maximal element.

THEOREM 7.2.3. $\langle\langle X,R\rangle\rangle$ is a l.o. class $\rightarrow$
(a) u is an R-minimal element of $X \rightarrow u$ is the R-first element of X
(b) u is an R-maximal element of $X \rightarrow u$ is the R-last element of X.

Proof: (a) Suppose that $\langle\langle X,R\rangle\rangle$ is a l.o. class and u is an R-minimal element of X. Then, since R is connected, for all $v \in X$, $v \neq u$, either uRv or vRu. However, u is an R-minimal element of X, so vRu implies uRv. Therefore, for all $v \in X$, if $v \neq u$, then uRv. Consequently, u is the R-first element of X.

The proof of part (b) is similar. ∎

DEFINITION 7.2.4. Well-Ordering
(a) R is a *well-ordering* (*w.o.*) *relation on* $X =_{\mathrm{Df}}$
$$(\forall Y)((Y \subseteq X \ \&\ Y \neq \emptyset) \rightarrow (\exists 1 u)(u \text{ is an } R\text{-first element of } Y))$$
(b) $\langle\langle X,R\rangle\rangle$ is a *well-ordered* (*w.o.*) class $=_{\mathrm{Df}}$
$$(\mathrm{Cl}(X) \ \&\ R \text{ is a well-ordering relation on } X).$$

Just as is the case for p.o. and l.o. classes, if $\langle\langle X,R\rangle\rangle$ is a w.o. class and $Y \subseteq X$, then $\langle\langle Y,R\rangle\rangle$ is a w.o. class. Also if $\langle\langle X,R\rangle\rangle$ is a w.o. class and X is a set, then $\langle\langle X,R\rangle\rangle$ is called a w.o. set.

$\langle\langle \omega,<\rangle\rangle$ is a w.o. set. $\langle\langle \omega,>\rangle\rangle$ is a l.o. set, but not a w.o. set. If $X = \{u : u$ is a rational number $\&\ 0 \leqq u \leqq 1\}$, then $\langle\langle X,\leqq\rangle\rangle$ is a l.o. set, but not a w.o. set. Other examples of w.o. classes are given in the exercises.

At first glance, the definition of a w.o. relation looks very weak. It is not immediately obvious that a w.o. relation is a l.o. relation or even a p.o. relation. But this is indeed the case.

THEOREM 7.2.5.

$$R \text{ is a w.o. relation} \rightarrow R \text{ is a l.o. relation.}$$

Proof: Suppose R is a w.o. relation and $\mathfrak{F}(R) = X$. We shall show first that R is a p.o. relation. Suppose $u,v \in X$, uRv, and vRu. Then $\{u,v\}$, being a subset of X, has a unique R-first element. Therefore, uRv and vRu implies $u = v$. So R is antisymmetric.

To prove R is transitive, suppose $u,v,w \in X$, uRv, and vRw. Since $\{u,v,w\} \subseteq X$, $\{u,v,w\}$ has a unique R-first element. If u is the R-first element, then either uRw or $u = w$. If $u = w$, then it follows from the antisymmetry of R that $v = w$. Thus, uRv implies uRw. If v is the R-first element, then either $v = u$ or vRu. If vRu, it follows from the antisymmetry of R that $v = u$. Therefore, vRw implies uRw. Finally, if w is the R-first element, then by an argument similar to the one for v, we obtain uRw. Hence, we have shown that R is a p.o. relation.

To prove R is a l.o. relation it remains to be shown that R is connected. Suppose $u,v \in X$ and $u \neq v$. Then $\{u,v\} \subseteq X$, so $\{u,v\}$ has a unique R-first element. If u is the R-first element, then uRv and if v is the R-first element, then vRu. Thus R is connected. ∎

COROLLARY 7.2.6. $(\mathrm{Rel}(R)\ \&\ \mathrm{Cl}(X)) \rightarrow$

(a) $\langle\langle X,R\rangle\rangle$ is a w.o. class $\leftrightarrow$ ($R|X$ is antisymmetric & $(\forall Y)((Y \subseteq X\ \&\ Y \neq \emptyset) \rightarrow (\exists u)(u$ is an R-first element of $Y)))$

(b) $\langle\langle X,R\rangle\rangle$ is a w.o. class $\leftrightarrow$ (($\langle\langle X,R\rangle\rangle$ is a p.o. class & $(\forall Y)((Y \subseteq X\ \&\ Y \neq \emptyset) \rightarrow (\exists u)(u$ is an R-first element of $Y)))$

(c) $\langle\langle X,R\rangle\rangle$ is a w.o. class $\leftrightarrow$ (($\langle\langle X,R\rangle\rangle$ is a l.o. class & $(\forall Y)((Y \subseteq X\ \&\ Y \neq \emptyset) \rightarrow (\exists u)(u$ is an R-first element of $Y))$.

EXERCISES 7.2

1. Determine which of the relations given in Exercise 7.1.1 are l.o. relations and which are w.o. relations.
2. Define a relation which well-orders the set of integers.
3. Define a relation which well-orders the set of rational numbers.
4. Show that the relations defined in Exercises 7.1.2 and 7.1.3 are not l.o. relations.
5. A partial well-ordering (p.w.o) relation might be defined as follows:
   R is a *partial well-ordering (p.w.o.) relation on* $X =_{\mathrm{Df}} [R|X$ is antisymmetric & $(\forall Y)((Y \subseteq X\ \&\ Y \neq \emptyset) \rightarrow (\exists u)(u$ is an R-minimal element of $Y))]$.
   $\langle\langle X,R\rangle\rangle$ is a partial well-ordered (p.w.o) class $=_{\mathrm{Df}}$ (Cl(X) & R is a partial well-ordering relation on X):
   (a) Give an example of a p.w.o. relation which is not a w.o. relation
   (b) Prove that R is a p.w.o. relation on $X \rightarrow R$ is transitive on X.
6. Let $\langle\langle X,R\rangle\rangle$ be a p.o. class. Let $Y = \mathcal{P}(X)$. Define a relation S on Y as follows: $u,v \in Y \rightarrow (uSv \leftrightarrow u = v$ or $(\exists w)(w \in v\ \&\ u = \{s:s \in v\ \&\ sRw\}))$.
   Prove each of the following:
   (a) $\langle\langle Y,S\rangle\rangle$ is a p.o. class
   (b) $(y \subseteq Y\ \&\ \langle\langle y,S\rangle\rangle$ is a l.o. set$) \rightarrow (\bigcup y \in Y\ \&\ \bigcup y$ is the S-upper bound of $y)$.
7. Prove $\langle\langle x,R\rangle\rangle$ is a l.o. set $\rightarrow$ (($\langle\langle x,R\rangle\rangle$ is a w.o. set $\leftrightarrow (\forall u)(u \in x \rightarrow$ $\langle\langle \{v:v \in x\ \&\ vRu\},R\rangle\rangle$ is a w.o. set)).
   Does the same result hold if $\langle\langle x,R\rangle\rangle$ is a p.o. set?
8. Suppose $\langle\langle X,R_1\rangle\rangle$ and $\langle\langle Y,R_2\rangle\rangle$ are w.o. classes. Prove each of the following:
   (a) $(X \cap Y = \emptyset\ \&\ R = \{\langle u,v\rangle:(u,v \in X\ \&\ uR_1v)$ or $(u,v \in Y\ \&\ uR_2v)$ or $(u \in X\ \&\ v \in Y)\}) \rightarrow \langle\langle X \cup Y,R\rangle\rangle$ is a w.o. class
   (b) $S = \{\langle\langle s,t\rangle,\langle u,v\rangle\rangle:s,u \in X\ \&\ t,v \in Y\ \&\ ((tR_2v\ \&\ t \neq v)$ or $(t = v\ \&\ sR_1u))\} \rightarrow \langle\langle X \times Y, S\rangle\rangle$ is a w.o. class. (S is called a *reverse lexiographic* ordering.)
   (c) $T = \{\langle\langle s,t\rangle,\langle u,v\rangle\rangle:s,t,u,v \in X\ \&$
   $((\max(s,t)R_1\max(u,v)\ \&\ \max(s,t) \neq \max(u,v))$ or

(max(s,t) = max(u,v) & sR_1u & $s \neq u$) or
(max(s,t) = max(u,v) & $s = u$ & tR_1v))} $\rightarrow \langle\langle X \times X, T\rangle\rangle$ is a w.o. class.

9. Prove: X is finite $\rightarrow$
   (a) $(\exists R)(\langle\langle X,R\rangle\rangle$ & $\langle\langle X,R^{-1}\rangle\rangle$ are w.o. classes)
   (b) $\langle\langle X,R\rangle\rangle$ is a l.o. class $\rightarrow \langle\langle X,R\rangle\rangle$ is a w.o. class.
10. Prove $(\langle\langle X,R\rangle\rangle$ & $\langle\langle X,R^{-1}\rangle\rangle$ are w.o. classes) $\rightarrow X$ is finite.

7.3. TRANSFINITE INDUCTION

Transfinite induction on a w.o. class is a generalization of mathematical induction on ω. However, it is clear that the form of induction given in 4.1.8(d) does not hold for an arbitrary w.o. class. For example, let $X = \omega \cup \{\omega\}$. Define a relation R on X as follows:

$$n,m \in \omega \rightarrow (nRm \leftrightarrow n \leqq m)$$
$$(n \in \omega \text{ or } n = \omega) \rightarrow nR\omega.$$

Then $\langle\langle X,R\rangle\rangle$ is a w.o. set. Moreover, $0 \in \omega$ and if $n \in \omega$, then $n^+ \in \omega$, but $\omega \subset X$. The essential reason why mathematical induction fails for this set X is that ω has no immediate predecessor in X.

The form of mathematical induction which does work on any w.o. class is given in theorem 4.2.3. In this form, instead of passing to each element from its immediate predecessor, we pass to each element from the set of all its predecessors.

Before stating the principle of transfinite induction, we introduce some useful notation.

DEFINITION 7.3.1. Initial Segments

$$(\text{Rel}(R) \ \& \ \text{Cl}(X) \ \& \ u \in X) \rightarrow S_{XR}(u) =_{\text{Df}} \{v\!:\!v \in X \ \& \ vRu\} \sim \{u\}.$$

$S_{XR}(u)$ is called the *R-initial segment of X generated by u*. $S_{XR}(u)$ is the class of all elements in X which strictly precede u. For example, if $X = \omega$ and $R = \leqq$, then $S_{XR}(4) = \{0,1,2,3\}$.

LEMMA 7.3.2. $\langle\langle X,R\rangle\rangle$ is a p.o. class $\rightarrow$
(a) $u \in X \rightarrow S_{XR}(u) \subset X$
(b) $(Y \subseteq X \ \& \ u \in Y) \rightarrow S_{YR}(u) \subseteq S_{XR}(u)$
(c) $(u,v \in X \ \& \ uRv) \rightarrow S_{XR}(u) \subseteq S_{XR}(v)$
(d) $(u \in X \ \& \ Y = S_{XR}(u) \ \& \ v \in Y) \rightarrow S_{YR}(v) = S_{XR}(v)$.

The proof is left for the reader. [Actually (a) and (b) hold for all relations R, but we shall only use them when R is a p.o. relation.]

THEOREM 7.3.3. The Principle of Transfinite Induction

$$[\langle\langle X,R\rangle\rangle \text{ is a w.o. class } \& \ Y \subseteq X \ \& \ (\forall u)((u \in X \ \& \ S_{XR}(u) \subseteq Y) \rightarrow u \in Y)] \rightarrow Y = X.$$

[Note that if $X = \omega$ and $R = \leqq$, then $S_{XR}(n) = n$ for all $n \in \omega$. Consequently, 4.2.3 is a special case of 7.3.3.]

Proof: Suppose X, R, and Y satisfy the hypothesis. Also suppose $X \sim Y \neq \emptyset$. Since R is a w.o. relation, $X \sim Y$ must have a unique R-first element, say u. Therefore, all the elements in X which precede u must be in Y. That is, $S_{XR}(u) \subseteq Y$. But, by hypothesis, if $S_{XR}(u) \subseteq Y$, then $u \in Y$. This is a contradiction, therefore $X = Y$. ■

It is also true that if transfinite induction works on a l.o. class, then that class must necessarily be w.o.

THEOREM 7.3.4.

$$(\langle\langle X,R\rangle\rangle \text{ is a l.o. class } \& \ (\forall Y)(\forall u)((Y \subseteq X \ \& \ u \in X \ \& \ (S_{XR}(u) \subseteq Y \to u \in Y)) \to Y = X)) \to \langle\langle X,R\rangle\rangle \text{ is a w.o. class.}$$

The proof is similar to the proof of 4.2.2. We leave the details as an exercise.

EXERCISES 7.3

1. Prove lemma 7.3.2.
2. Prove theorem 7.3.4.
3. If X_i and R_i, $i = 1, 2, 3, \ldots, 7$, are the sets and relations defined in exercise 7.1.1, calculate each of the following initial segments.
   (a) $S_{X_1R_1}(7)$
   (b) $S_{X_2R_2}(7)$
   (c) $S_{X_3R_3}(\langle 1,1\rangle)$
   (d) $S_{X_4R_4}(\langle 1,1\rangle)$
   (e) $S_{X_5R_5}(\{1\})$
   (f) $S_{X_6R_6}(1)$
   (g) $S_{X_7R_7}(1)$.
4. Let $\langle\langle X,R_1\rangle\rangle$ and $\langle\langle Y,R_2\rangle\rangle$ be w.o. classes and let R, S, and T be the relations defined in exercise 7.2.8. Prove each of the following:
   (a) $X \cap Y = \emptyset \to$ (Z is an R-initial segment of $X \cup Y \leftrightarrow$ (Z is an R_1-initial segment of X or $(\exists Y_1)$(Y_1 is an R_2-initial segment of Y & $Z = X \cup Y_1$)))
   (b) Z is an S-initial segment of $X \times Y \leftrightarrow$ $(\exists X_1)(\exists Y_1)(\exists u)$($X_1$ is an R_1-initial segment of X & Y_1 is an R_2-initial segment of Y & u is the R_2-first element of $Y \sim Y_1$ & $Z = (X \times Y_1) \cup (X_1 \times \{u\})$)
   (c) Z is a T-initial segment of $X \times X \leftrightarrow$ ($(\exists X_1)(\exists X_2)(\exists u)$($X_1$ is an R_1-initial segment of X & X_2 is an R_1-initial segment of X & $X_2 \subseteq X_1$ & u is the R_1-first element of $X \sim X_1$ & ($Z = X_1 \times X_1$ or $Z = (X_1 \times X_1) \cup (X_2 \times \{u\})$ or $Z = (X_1 \times X_1) \cup (X_1 \times \{u\}) \cup (\{u\} \times X_2)$).
5. Prove that theorem 7.3.3 holds if $\langle\langle X,R\rangle\rangle$ is a partial well-ordered class. (See exercise 7.2.5.)

7.4. ISOMORPHISMS

If there exists a 1–1 function mapping one class onto another, the two classes are called equipollent. If, in addition, there are relations defined on both of the classes and the 1–1 function preserves the order, the two classes are called *isomorphic* or *similar*.

DEFINITION 7.4.1. Isomorphisms

(a) $F\colon X\ {}_{R}{\cong}_{S}\ Y =_{\text{Df}} [F\colon X \xrightarrow[\text{onto}]{1-1} Y \ \&\ (\forall u)(\forall v)(u,v \in X \rightarrow$
$(uRv \leftrightarrow F(u)S\,F(v)))]$

(b) $X\ {}_{R}{\cong}_{S}\ Y =_{\text{Df}} (\exists F)(F\colon X\ {}_{R}{\cong}_{S}\ Y)$

(c) $\langle\langle X,R\rangle\rangle \cong \langle\langle Y,S\rangle\rangle =_{\text{Df}} X\ {}_{R}{\cong}_{S}\ Y.$

The 1–1 function F which preserves order is called an *isomorphism* or a *similarity*. On occasion, when it will not lead to confusion, we shall omit the subscripts R and S from the symbol "${}_{R}{\cong}_{S}$."

The next two theorems follow immediately from 7.4.1.

THEOREM 7.4.2.

$$(\text{Cl}(X)\ \&\ \text{Cl}(Y)\ \&\ \text{Cl}(Z)\ \&\ \text{Rel}(R)\ \&\ \text{Rel}(S)\ \&\ \text{Rel}(T)) \rightarrow$$

(a) $X\ {}_{R}{\cong}_{R}\ X$

(b) $X\ {}_{R}{\cong}_{S}\ Y \rightarrow Y\ {}_{S}{\cong}_{R}\ X$

(c) $(X\ {}_{R}{\cong}_{S}\ Y\ \&\ Y\ {}_{S}{\cong}_{T}\ Z) \rightarrow X\ {}_{R}{\cong}_{T}\ Z.$

THEOREM 7.4.3.

$$(\text{Cl}(X)\ \&\ \text{Cl}(Y)\ \&\ \text{Rel}(R)\ \&\ \text{Rel}(S)\ \&\ X\ {}_{R}{\cong}_{S}\ Y) \rightarrow$$

(a) $\langle\langle X,R\rangle\rangle$ is a p.o. class $\leftrightarrow$ $\langle\langle Y,S\rangle\rangle$ is a p.o. class

(b) $\langle\langle X,R\rangle\rangle$ is a l.o. class $\leftrightarrow$ $\langle\langle Y,S\rangle\rangle$ is a l.o. class

(c) $\langle\langle X,R\rangle\rangle$ is a w.o. class $\leftrightarrow$ $\langle\langle Y,S\rangle\rangle$ is a w.o. class.

Essentially, it can be said that if two classes are isomorphic, the only difference between them is in the names of their elements. The two classes have the same number of elements and the same structure.

The remaining theorems in this section deal with w.o. classes. The first one states that if $\langle\langle X,R\rangle\rangle$ is a w.o. class and F is an isomorphism of X into itself, then for all $u \in X$, $u\,R\,F(u)$ or $u = F(u)$.

THEOREM 7.4.4.

$(\langle\langle X,R\rangle\rangle$ is a w.o. class $\&\ Y \subseteq X\ \&\ F\colon X\ {}_{R}{\cong}_{R}\ Y) \rightarrow$
$(\forall u)(u \in X \rightarrow (u\,R\,F(u)$ or $u = F(u))).$

Proof: Suppose the theorem is false. Let $\langle\langle X,R\rangle\rangle$ be a w.o. class and F an isomorphism of X into itself. Let

$$Z = \{u{:}u \in X \;\&\; R(u)\; R\; u \;\&\; u \neq F(u)\}.$$

If the theorem is false, then $Z \neq \emptyset$. Also, Z being a non-empty subclass of X, it has an R-first element, say s. Since $s \in Z$,

(1) $$F(s)\; R\; s \text{ and } s \neq F(s).$$

But since s is the R-first element of Z, it follows from (1) that $F(s) \notin Z$. Therefore,

(2) $$F(s)\; R\; F(F(s)).$$

However, F is an isomorphism, so (2) holds if and only if

(3) $$s\; R\; F(s).$$

(1) and (3) are contradictory. Hence, $Z = \emptyset$ and the theorem holds. ■

Theorem 7.4.4 will be used to prove the next two theorems. The first states that if $\langle\langle X,R\rangle\rangle$ and $\langle\langle Y,S\rangle\rangle$ are isomorphic w.o. classes, then there exists exactly one isomorphism mapping X onto Y.

THEOREM 7.4.5.

$$(\langle\langle X,R\rangle\rangle \;\&\; \langle\langle Y,S\rangle\rangle \text{ are w.o. classes } \&\; \langle\langle X,R\rangle\rangle \cong \langle\langle Y,S\rangle\rangle) \rightarrow (\exists 1 F)(F{:}X\; {}_R{\cong}_S\; Y).$$

Proof: Suppose $\langle\langle X,R\rangle\rangle$ and $\langle\langle Y,S\rangle\rangle$ satisfy the hypothesis and suppose F and G are both isomorphisms mapping X onto Y. Let

$$J = G^{-1} \circ F,$$

and

$$K = F^{-1} \circ G.$$

It is easy to see that both J and K are isomorphisms mapping X onto itself. Using 7.4.4,

(1) $$(\forall u)(u \in X \rightarrow (u\; R\; J(u) \text{ or } u = J(u))).$$

Since G is an isomorphism, (1) holds if and only if

(2) $$(\forall u)(u \in X \rightarrow (G(u)\; S\; F(u) \text{ or } G(u) = F(u))).$$

In an analogous way, using K instead of J, it follows that

(3) $$(\forall u)(u \in X \rightarrow (F(u)\; S\; G(u) \text{ or } F(u) = G(u))).$$

Since S is antisymmetric, (2) and (3) imply that $F(u) = G(u)$ for all $u \in X$. ■

Next we show that a w.o. class cannot be isomorphic to an initial segment of itself.

THEOREM 7.4.6.

$$\langle\langle X,R\rangle\rangle \text{ is a w.o. class} \to \neg(\exists u)(u \in X \;\&\; X\ {}_R{\cong}_R\ S_{XR}(u)).$$

Proof: Suppose $\langle\langle X,R\rangle\rangle$ is a w.o. class and there is a $u \in X$ such that $X\ {}_R{\cong}_R\ S_{XR}(u)$. Let F be the isomorphism which maps X onto $S_{XR}(u)$. Then $F(u) \in S_{XR}(u)$ which implies $F(u)\ R\ u$ and $F(u) \neq u$. But this contradicts theorem 7.4.4. ■

Now we come to the last, but by no means the least important result in this section. Namely, if two w.o. classes are not isomorphic, then one is isomorphic to an initial segment of the other—the trichotomy for w.o. classes.

THEOREM 7.4.7. [12]

$$[\langle\langle X,R\rangle\rangle \;\&\; \langle\langle Y,T\rangle\rangle \text{ are w.o. classes } \& \;((R|X \;\&\; T|Y \text{ are reflexive}) \text{ or } (R|X \;\&\; T|Y \text{ are irreflexive}))] \to$$

(a) $\langle\langle X,R\rangle\rangle \cong \langle\langle Y,T\rangle\rangle$ or
(b) $(\exists u)(u \in X \;\&\; \langle\langle S_{XR}(u),R\rangle\rangle \cong \langle\langle Y,T\rangle\rangle)$ or
(c) $(\exists v)(v \in Y \;\&\; \langle\langle X,R\rangle\rangle \cong \langle\langle S_{YS}(v),T\rangle\rangle)$.

Proof: Let $\langle\langle X,R\rangle\rangle$ and $\langle\langle Y,T\rangle\rangle$ be w.o. classes. Define

$$X_0 = \{u : u \in X \;\&\; (\exists v)(v \in Y \;\&\; S_{XR}(u)\ {}_R{\cong}_T\ S_{YT}(v))\}.$$

It can be readily seen that if $u \in X_0$, then there is exactly one $v \in Y$ such that $S_{XR}(u)\ {}_R{\cong}_T\ S_{YT}(v)$. For each $u \in X_0$, we shall call the unique $v \in Y$ which corresponds to it, $F(u)$. Then F is a 1–1 function mapping X_0 into Y. Let $Y_0 = \mathcal{R}(F)$. It is easy to prove that F is an isomorphism from X_0 onto Y_0, $\langle\langle X_0,R\rangle\rangle \cong \langle\langle Y_0,T\rangle\rangle$. We shall prove that either

$X_0 = X$ and $Y_0 = Y$, or
X_0 is an R-initial segment of X and $Y_0 = Y$, or
$X_0 = X$ and Y_0 is a T-initial segment of Y.

First we shall show that if $X_0 \subset X$, then X_0 is an R-initial segment of X. Let u be the R-first element of $X \sim X_0$. Suppose $v \in S_{XR}(u)$, then $v \in X$, vRu, and $v \neq u$. Since u is the R-first element of $X \sim X_0$, we must have $v \in X_0$. Conversely, suppose $v \in X_0$. Then $S_{XR}(v)\ {}_R{\cong}_T\ S_{YT}(F(v))$. Therefore, if uRv, then $u \in X_0 \subset X$. Since $u \notin X_0$, we must have vRu and

[12] If X and Y are both proper classes, then the predicate which defines X_0 in the proof may contain a bound class variable. See footnote 7 on page 31 and definition 7.4.1(a).

$v \neq u$. Consequently, since $v \in X_0 \subset X$, $v \in S_{XR}(u)$. Thus, we have shown $X_0 = S_{XR}(u)$.

In an analogous way it can be shown that if $Y_0 \subset Y$, then Y_0 is a T-initial segment of Y.

Finally, suppose $X_0 \neq X$ and $Y_0 \neq Y$. Let u be the R-first element of $X \sim X_0$ and v the T-first element of $Y \sim Y_0$. Then $X_0 = S_{XR}(u)$ and $Y_0 = S_{YT}(v)$. Therefore, $S_{XR}(u) \;{}_R{\cong}_T\; S_{YT}(v)$, but this implies $u \in X_0$ and $v \in Y_0$, contrary to the definition of u and v. Consequently, either $X_0 = X$ or $Y_0 = Y$. ■

COROLLARY 7.4.8.

$$\langle\langle X,R\rangle\rangle \text{ \& } \langle\langle Y,T\rangle\rangle \text{ are w.o. classes} \rightarrow (X \prec Y \text{ or } X \approx Y \text{ or } Y \prec X).$$

EXERCISES 7.4

1. Give an example to show that 7.4.4 is not a theorem if $\langle\langle X,R\rangle\rangle$ is a l.o. class.
2. Prove 7.4.4 using the form of transfinite induction given in 7.3.3.
3. Prove: $(\mathrm{Cl}(X) \text{ \& } \mathrm{Cl}(Y) \text{ \& } \mathrm{Rel}(R) \text{ \& } \mathrm{Rel}(T) \text{ \& } F{:}X \;{}_R{\cong}_T\; Y) \rightarrow$
   (a) $(\forall w)(w \in X \rightarrow S_{XR}(w) \;{}_R{\cong}_T\; S_{YT}(F(w))$
   (b) $(\forall Z)(Z \subseteq X \rightarrow (\forall w)(w$ is an R-upper bound of $Z \leftrightarrow F(w)$ is a T-upper bound of $F''Z))$
   (c) $(\forall Z)(Z \subseteq X \rightarrow (\forall w)(w$ is an R-l.u.b. of $Z \leftrightarrow F(w)$ is a T-l.u.b. of $F''Z)$.
4. Prove $((\langle\langle X,R\rangle\rangle \text{ \& } \langle\langle Y,S\rangle\rangle$ are w.o. classes$) \rightarrow$
   $(\exists X_1)(\exists Y_1)(\exists R_1)(\exists S_1)(X_1 \cap Y_1 = \emptyset \text{ \& } \langle\langle X_1,R_1\rangle\rangle \cong \langle\langle X,R\rangle\rangle \text{ \& } \langle\langle Y_1,S_1\rangle\rangle \cong \langle\langle Y,S\rangle\rangle)$.

*7.5. DENSE AND CONTINUOUS CLASSES

This section contains a description of the rational and real numbers as ordered by $\leqq$, but formally, no prior knowledge of either of these sets is necessary. However, we shall frequently refer to the rational and real numbers for examples and to motivate the development. Let

Ra = class of rational numbers, and
Re = class of real numbers.

A class is said to be *dense* if it has at least two elements, and if between each pair of distinct elements there is another element. Formally,

DEFINITION 7.5.1. Dense Classes

(a) X is R-*dense* $=_{\mathrm{Df}} [(\exists u)(\exists v)(u,v \in X \text{ \& } u \neq v) \text{ \& }$
$(\forall u)(\forall v)((u,v \in X \text{ \& } u \neq v) \rightarrow (\exists w)(w \neq u \text{ \& } w \neq v \text{ \& }$
$((uRw \text{ \& } wRv) \text{ or } (vRw \text{ \& } wRu)))]$

(b) $\langle\langle X,R\rangle\rangle$ is *dense* $=_{\mathrm{Df}}$ X is R-dense.

Both $\langle\langle Ra,\leqq\rangle\rangle$ and $\langle\langle Re,\leqq\rangle\rangle$ are examples of dense sets

It follows from the transitivity of a p.o. relation that if $\langle\langle X,R\rangle\rangle$ is a p.o., dense class, then it is a l.o. class.

THEOREM 7.5.2.

$$\langle\langle X,R\rangle\rangle \text{ is a p.o., dense class} \rightarrow \langle\langle X,R\rangle\rangle \text{ is a l.o. class.}$$

It follows simply from the definition of an isomorphism that

THEOREM 7.5.3.

$$X\ {}_R{\cong}_S\ Y \rightarrow (X \text{ is } R\text{-dense} \leftrightarrow Y \text{ is } S\text{-dense}).$$

The following theorem completely characterizes the p.o. class $\langle\langle Ra, \leqq\rangle\rangle$ up to isomorphisms. The proof is due to Cantor.

THEOREM 7.5.4.

(a) $[((\langle\langle X,R\rangle\rangle\ \&\ \langle\langle Y,S\rangle\rangle$ are p.o. dense classes) &
(R & S are reflexive)) &

(b) (X & Y are denumerable) &

(c) $\neg(\exists u)(u$ is the R-first element of X or u is the R-last element of X or u is the S-first element of Y or u is the S-last element of $Y)] \rightarrow$
$\langle\langle X,R\rangle\rangle \cong \langle\langle Y,S\rangle\rangle$.

Proof: We shall just indicate how the proof is to be carried out and let the reader fill in the details.

Let $\langle\langle X,R\rangle\rangle$ and $\langle\langle Y,S\rangle\rangle$ satisfy the hypothesis. Since both X and Y are denumerable, their elements can be represented in the following way,

$$X = \{x_n : n \in \omega\}$$
$$Y = \{y_n : n \in \omega\}.$$

It is not assumed that the labeling of the elements preserves order. (In fact the labeling cannot preserve order. Why?) We shall set up a 1–1 correspondence between X and Y in the following way. Let $u_0 = x_0$, $v_0 = y_0$, and $v_1 = y_1$. Let u_1 be the element in X with the smallest subscript which stands in the same relationship to u_1 as v_1 stands to v_0. For example, if v_0Sv_1 then u_1 is the element in X with the smallest subscript such that u_0Ru_1. Such an element exists because X has no R-first element.

Next let u_2 be the element in X with the smallest subscript which has not as yet been chosen. Then let v_2 be the element in Y with the smallest subscript which stands in the same relationship to v_0 and v_1 as u_2 does to u_0 and u_1. For example, if u_0Ru_2 and u_2Ru_1, then v_2 would be the element in Y with the smallest subcript such that v_0Sv_2 and v_2Sv_1. Such an element exists because $\langle\langle Y,S\rangle\rangle$ is dense.

Continuing this process of choosing elements alternating between sets we set up a 1–1 correspondence between X and Y which preserves order. ■

No form of the axiom of choice (or the principle of dependent choices) is needed in the proof of 7.5.4. (Why?)

A reflexive, p.o., dense, denumerable class with no first or last element is said to be of *type* η.

DEFINITION 7.5.5. Type η

$\langle\langle X,R\rangle\rangle$ is of *type* $\eta =_{\mathrm{Df}} [\langle\langle X,R\rangle\rangle$ is a p.o., dense class & X is denumerable & R is reflexive & $\neg(\exists u)(u$ is the R-first element of X or u is the R-last element of $X)]$.

Theorem 7.5.4 implies that all sets of type η are isomorphic. We shall prove that every reflexive, p.o., dense class contains a subset of type η. (The axiom of choice or the principle of dependent choices is used in the proof.)

THEOREM 7.5.6.©

$$(\langle\langle X,R\rangle\rangle \text{ is a p.o., dense class } \& \ R \text{ is reflexive}) \rightarrow (\exists Y)(Y \subseteq X \ \& \ \langle\langle Y,R\rangle\rangle \text{ is of type } \eta.$$

Proof: Suppose $\langle\langle Z,S\rangle\rangle$ is of type η. (We have shown in Chapter 6 that $\langle\langle Ra,\leqq\rangle\rangle$ is of type η. See 6.3.9, 6.3.11, and 6.5.13.) Let $\langle\langle X,R\rangle\rangle$ be an arbitrary p.o., dense class such that R is reflexive. We may assume, without loss of generality, that X has no R-first or R-last elements because if it does, they may be removed. Then the resulting class has no R-first or R-last elements. (Why?)

Since Z is denumerable, its elements may be expressed by a sequence, not necessarily preserving order. Let

$$Z = \{z_n : n \in \omega\}.$$

Now we construct a subset of X which is isomorphic to Z as follows. Let $x_0 \in X_1$. Let x_1 be any element of X, $x_1 \neq x_0$, which stands in the same relationship to x_0 as z_1 stands to z_0. Let x_2 be any element of X, different from x_0 and x_1, which stands in the same relationship to x_0 and x_1 as z_2 stands to z_0 and z_1, etc. This construction is possible because $\langle\langle X,R\rangle\rangle$ is dense and X has no R-first or R-last element. However, here, unlike the proof of theorem 7.5.4, the axiom of choice (or the principle of dependent choices) is needed to complete the proof. We leave the details for the reader. ■

Since $\langle\langle Ra,\leqq\rangle\rangle$ is of type η, it follows from 7.5.6 that every p.o., dense class has a subset isomorphic to $\langle\langle Ra,\leqq\rangle\rangle$.

In the remaining part of this section, we shall discuss classes which are isomorphic to $\langle\langle Re,\leqq\rangle\rangle$.

DEFINITION 7.5.7. Jumps, Cuts, and Gaps

$\langle\langle X,R\rangle\rangle$ is a p.o. class $\rightarrow$

(a) $\langle\langle X_0,X_1,R\rangle\rangle$ is an *ordered partition of* $X =_{\text{Df}}$
$[X_0,X_1 \subseteq X \;\&\; X_0,X_1 \neq \emptyset \;\&\; X_0 \cup X_1 = X \;\&\; X_0 \cap X_1 = \emptyset \;\&$
$(\forall u)(\forall v)((u \in X_0 \;\&\; v \in X_1) \rightarrow uRv)]$

(b) $\langle\langle X_0,X_1,R\rangle\rangle$ is a *jump in* $X =_{\text{Df}}$
$[\langle\langle X_0,X_1,R\rangle\rangle$ is an ordered partition of X &
$(\exists u)(\exists v)(u$ is an R-last element of X_0 & v is an R-first element of $X_1)]$

(c) $\langle\langle X_0,X_1,R\rangle\rangle$ is a *cut in* $X =_{\text{Df}}$
$[\langle\langle X_0,X_1,R\rangle\rangle$ is an ordered partition of X &
$[(\exists u)(u$ is an R-last element of $X_0)$ or $(\exists v)(v$ is an R-first element of $X_1)]$ & $\neg(\exists u)(\exists v)(u$ is an R-last element of X_0 & v is an R-first element of $X_1)]$

(d) $\langle\langle X_0,X_1,R\rangle\rangle$ is a *gap in* $X =_{\text{Df}}$
$[\langle\langle X_0,X_1,R\rangle\rangle$ is an ordered partition of X &
$\neg(\exists u)(u$ is an R-last element of X_0 or u is an R-first element of $X_1)]$.

For example, if

$$X_0 = \{n : n \in \omega \;\&\; n \leqq 5\}$$

and

$$X_1 = \omega \sim X_0,$$

then $\langle\langle X_0,X_1,\leqq\rangle\rangle$ is a jump in ω. Also, if

$$X_2 = \{u : u \in Ra \;\&\; u \leqq 5\}$$

and

$$X_3 = Ra \sim X_2,$$

then $\langle\langle X_2,X_3,\leqq\rangle\rangle$ is a cut in *Ra*. X_2 has a last element, but X_3 has no first element. Moreover, if

$$X_4 = \{u : u \in Ra \;\&\; u < \sqrt{2}\}$$

and

$$X_5 = Ra \sim X_4,$$

then $\langle\langle X_4,X_5,\leqq\rangle\rangle$ is a gap in *Ra*.

It is clear that jumps, cuts, and gaps are preserved under isomorphisms.

THEOREM 7.5.8.

$$(\langle\langle X,R\rangle\rangle \ \& \ \langle\langle Y,S\rangle\rangle \text{ are p.o. classes } \& \ F{:}X \ {}_R{\cong}_S \ Y) \rightarrow$$

(a) $\langle\langle X_0,X_1,R\rangle\rangle$ is a jump in $X \leftrightarrow \langle\langle F''X_0,F''X_1,S\rangle\rangle$ is a jump in Y
(b) $\langle\langle X_0,X_1,R\rangle\rangle$ is a cut in $X \leftrightarrow \langle\langle F''X_0,F''X_1,S\rangle\rangle$ is a cut in Y
(c) $\langle\langle X_0,X_1,R\rangle\rangle$ is a gap in $X \leftrightarrow \langle\langle F''X_0,F''X_1,S\rangle\rangle$ is a gap in Y.

Moreover, it follows directly from 7.5.1 that a p.o., dense class has no jumps.

THEOREM 7.5.9.

$$\langle\langle X,R\rangle\rangle \text{ is a p.o., dense class} \rightarrow \neg(\exists X_0)(\exists X_1)(\langle\langle X_0,X_1,R\rangle\rangle \text{ is a jump in } X).$$

A p.o. class is said to be *continuous* if it has no jumps or gaps.

DEFINITION 7.5.10. Continuous Classes

$$\langle\langle X,R\rangle\rangle \text{ is a p.o. class} \rightarrow [\langle\langle X,R\rangle\rangle \text{ is } continuous =_{\mathrm{Df}} \neg(\exists X_0)(\exists X_1)(\langle\langle X_0,X_1,R\rangle\rangle \text{ is a jump or a gap in } X)].$$

Continuity is the property which distinguishes the real numbers from the rational numbers. $\langle\langle Re,\leqq\rangle\rangle$ is continuous while $\langle\langle Ra,\leqq\rangle\rangle$ is not.

The following two theorems follow immediately from 7.5.1 and 7.5.10.

THEOREM 7.5.11.

$$\langle\langle X,R\rangle\rangle \text{ is a p.o. continuous class} \rightarrow \langle\langle X,R\rangle\rangle \text{ is dense.}$$

THEOREM 7.5.12.

$$[\langle\langle X,R\rangle\rangle \text{ is a p.o., dense class } \& \ \neg(\exists X_0)(\exists X_1)(\langle\langle X_0,X_1,R\rangle\rangle \text{ is a gap in } X)] \rightarrow \langle\langle X,R\rangle\rangle \text{ is continuous.}$$

Next we shall prove that every p.o., dense, denumerable set has a gap.

THEOREM 7.5.13.

$$(\langle\langle X,R\rangle\rangle \text{ is a p.o., dense class } \& \ X \text{ is denumerable}) \rightarrow (\exists X_0)(\exists X_1)(\langle\langle X_0,X_1,R\rangle\rangle \text{ is a gap in } X).$$

Proof: Let $\langle\langle X,R\rangle\rangle$ be a p.o., dense, denumerable set and let

$$X = \{x_n{:}n \in \omega\}.$$

Suppose x_0Rx_1 and $x_0 \neq x_1$. Let $u_0 = x_0$ and $v_0 = x_1$. We construct sequences u and v as follows: u_1 is the element of X with the smallest subscript which has not been chosen and is between u_0 and v_0; v_1 is the element of X with the smallest subscript which has not been chosen and is between u_1 and v_0; u_2 is the element of X with smallest subscript which has not been chosen and is between u_1 and v_1; v_2 is the element of X with smallest subscript which has not been chosen and is between u_2 and v_1; etc. By this method we can construct two sequences u and v such that for all $n,m \in \omega$,

$$u_n \; R \; u_{n+1}$$
$$v_{n+1} \; R \; v_n$$
$$u_n \; R \; v_m.$$

Now let

$$X_0 = \{x : x \in X \;\&\; (\exists n)(n \in \omega \;\&\; x \; R \; u_n)\}$$

and

$$X_1 = \{x : x \in X \;\&\; (\exists n)(n \in \omega \;\&\; v_n \; R \; x)\}.$$

Since u is an increasing sequence, X_0 has no R-last element. And since v is a decreasing sequence, X_1 has no R-first element. Moreover, since $u_m \; R \; v_n$ and $u_m \neq v_n$ for all $m,n \in \omega$, then each element of X_0 precedes each element of X_1. Therefore, it remains only to be shown that $X_0 \cup X_1 = X$.

If $X_0 \cup X_1 \neq X$, then there must be elements of X between X_0 and X_1. For each $n \in \omega$, define

$$Y_n = \{m : (\forall j)((j \in \omega \;\&\; j < n) \rightarrow (u_j \; R \; x_m \;\&\; u_j \neq x_m \;\&\; x_m \; R \; v_j \;\&\; x_m \neq v_j))\}.$$

In other words, Y_n is the set of all subscripts m such that x_m is between u_j and v_j for all $j < n$. Let

$$s(n) = \text{smallest element of } Y_n.$$

It follows from the definition of u and v that $x_{s(n)} = u_n$, therefore, $s(n+1) > s(n)$. Clearly, $s(0) \geqq 0$. Hence, it follows by induction that $s(n) \geqq n$ for all $n \in \omega$. Thus, $s(n+1) > n$, and this implies $n \notin Y_{n+1}$. Consequently, it follows from the definition of Y_{n+1} that

$$(\exists j)(j \in \omega \;\&\; j < n+1 \;\&\; (x_n \; R \; u_j \text{ or } u_j = x_n \text{ or } v_j \; R \; x_n \text{ or } x_n = v_j)).$$

And this implies that for each $n \in \omega$, $x_n \in X_0$ or $x_n \in X_1$. ■

Since a continuous class has no gaps (7.5.10), as an immediate consequence of theorem 7.5.13 we have,

COROLLARY 7.5.14.

$$(\langle\langle X,R \rangle\rangle \text{ is a p.o., dense class } \& \; X \text{ is denumerable}) \rightarrow \neg(\langle\langle X,R \rangle\rangle \text{ is continuous}).$$

In particular, $\langle\langle Ra, \leqq \rangle\rangle$ is not continuous.

DEFINITION 7.5.15. Denseness

Y is *R-dense in* $X =_{\mathrm{Df}} [Y \subseteq X \;\&\; (\forall u)(\forall v)((u,v \in X \;\&\; u \neq v) \rightarrow (\exists w)[w \in Y \;\&\; w \neq u \;\&\; w \neq v \;\&\; ((uRw \;\&\; wRv) \text{ or } (vRw \;\&\; wRu))])]$.

In other words, Y is R-dense in X if there is an element of Y between each pair of distinct elements of X. It follows immediately from 7.5.15 and 7.5.1, that

THEOREM 7.5.16. $(\exists X)(Y \text{ is } R\text{-dense in } X) \rightarrow Y$ is R-dense.

Moreover, it is also easy to prove,

THEOREM 7.5.17.

$$(\langle\langle X,R\rangle\rangle \text{ is a p.o. class } \& \;(\exists Y)(Y \text{ is } R\text{-dense in } X)) \rightarrow \langle\langle X,R\rangle\rangle \text{ is a l.o. class.}$$

Now we are ready to characterize $\langle\langle Re, \leq\rangle\rangle$.

THEOREM 7.5.18.

(a) $[((\langle\langle X,R\rangle\rangle \;\&\; \langle\langle Y,S\rangle\rangle$ are p.o., continuous classes) & (R & S are reflexive)) &

(b) $\neg(\exists u)(u$ is the R-first element of X or u is the R-last element of X or u is the S-first element of Y or u is the S-last element of Y) &

(c) $(\exists X_0)(\exists Y_0)(X_0$ is denumerable & Y_0 is denumerable & X_0 is R-dense in X & Y_0 is S-dense in $Y)] \rightarrow$

$$\langle\langle X,R\rangle\rangle \cong \langle\langle Y,S\rangle\rangle.$$

Proof: Suppose $\langle\langle X,R\rangle\rangle$ and $\langle\langle Y,S\rangle\rangle$ satisfy the hypothesis and X_0 and Y_0 are denumerable subsets of X and Y, which are dense in X and Y, respectively. First we note that neither X_0 nor Y_0 have first or last elements. For suppose u is the R-first element of X_0. Then since X has no R-first element, there is a $v \in X$ such that $v \neq u$ and $v \, R \, u$. But remember X_0 is R-dense in X_1 so there is a $w \in X_0$, $w \neq u$ and $w \, R \, u$. This contradicts the fact that u is the R-first element of X_0. The proof is similar for the R-last element of X_0 and the R-first and R-last elements of Y_0. Thus, $\langle\langle X_0,R\rangle\rangle$ and $\langle\langle Y_0,S\rangle\rangle$ are p.o., dense denumerable sets without first or last elements, and R and S are reflexive. Therefore, by 7.5.4,

$$\langle\langle X_0,R\rangle\rangle \cong \langle\langle Y_0,S\rangle\rangle.$$

By 7.5.14, $\langle\langle X_0,R\rangle\rangle$ is not continuous, but by hypothesis $\langle\langle X,R\rangle\rangle$ is continuous. Therefore $X_0 \neq X$. Let $x \in X \sim X_0$. We shall partition X_0 as follows:

$$X_{01} = \{u : u \in X_0 \;\&\; u \, R \, x\}$$
$$X_{02} = X_0 \sim X_{01}.$$

$\langle\langle X_{01},X_{02},R\rangle\rangle$ must be a gap in X_0. (Why?) Moreover, since X_0 is dense in X, there is exactly one element of X (namely x) between X_{01} and X_{02}. Consequently, each element of $X \sim X_0$ is uniquely determined by a gap in $\langle\langle X_0,R\rangle\rangle$.

Conversely, each gap in $\langle\langle X_0,R\rangle\rangle$ uniquely determines an element of $X \sim X_0$. For suppose the partition of X_0 into X_{01} and X_{02} is a gap and there is no element of X between X_{01} and X_{02}. Let

$$X_1 = \{u{:}u \in X \;\&\; (\exists v)(v \in X_{01} \;\&\; u \; R \; v\}$$
$$X_2 = X \sim X_1.$$

Then the partition of X into X_1 and X_2 is a gap (why?) contradicting the fact that $\langle\langle X,R\rangle\rangle$ is continuous.

Since gaps are preserved under isomorphisms, the isomorphism between $\langle\langle X_0,R\rangle\rangle$ and $\langle\langle Y_0,S\rangle\rangle$ can easily be extended to an isomorphism between $\langle\langle X,R\rangle\rangle$ and $\langle\langle Y,S\rangle\rangle$. ∎

A p.o. class which satisfies (a)–(c) of 7.5.18 is said to be of *type* λ.

DEFINITION 7.5.19. Type λ

$\langle\langle X,R\rangle\rangle$ is of *type* $\lambda =_{\mathrm{Df}} [\langle\langle X,R\rangle\rangle$ is a p.o., continuous class & R is reflexive & $\neg(\exists u)(u$ is the R-first element of X or u is the R-last element of $X)$ & $(\exists X_0)(X_0$ is denumerable & X_0 is R-dense in $X)]$.

The final result of this section is similar to 7.5.6 for classes of type λ.

THEOREM 7.5.20.©

$$(\langle\langle X,R\rangle\rangle \text{ is a p.o., continuous class } \& \; R \text{ is reflexive}) \rightarrow (\exists Y)(Y \subseteq X \;\&\; \langle\langle Y,R\rangle\rangle \text{ is of type } \lambda).$$

Proof: Let $\langle\langle X,R\rangle\rangle$ be a p.o., continuous class and suppose R is reflexive. By 7.5.11, $\langle\langle X,R\rangle\rangle$ is dense; by 7.5.6, there is a $Y \subseteq X$ such that $\langle\langle Y,R\rangle\rangle$ is of type η; and by 7.5.13, there is a partition of Y into Y_0 and Y_1 which is a gap. There must be an element of X between Y_0 and Y_1. To show this, let us suppose otherwise

$$X_0 = \{u{:}u \in X \;\&\; (\exists v)(v \in Y_0 \;\&\; v \; R \; u)\}$$
$$X_1 = \{u{:}u \in X \;\&\; (\exists v)(v \in Y_1 \;\&\; u \; R \; v)\}.$$

Then the decomposition of X into X_0 and X_1 is a partition which is a gap. (Why?) This contradicts the fact that $\langle\langle X,R\rangle\rangle$ is continuous.

For each gap in $\langle\langle Y,R\rangle\rangle$, choose an element of X which is between the two classes in the partition. (Use the axiom of choice.) Let Z be the class of all these elements and let $W = Y \cup Z$. It is easy to see that $\langle\langle W,R\rangle\rangle$ is of type λ since by construction all the gaps of $\langle\langle Y,R\rangle\rangle$ have been filled. ∎

EXERCISES 7.5

1. Give an example of a p.o. class which contains jumps, cuts, and gaps.
2. Prove $\langle\langle X,R\rangle\rangle$ is a w.o. class $\rightarrow \neg(\langle\langle X,R\rangle\rangle$ is dense).
3. Prove theorem 7.5.3.
4. Prove theorem 7.5.8.
5. Prove theorem 7.5.9.
6. Prove $[\langle\langle X,R\rangle\rangle$ is a l.o. class & $(\exists u)(\exists v)(u,v \in X \;\&\; u \neq v)] \rightarrow$
   $(\langle\langle X,R\rangle\rangle$ is dense $\leftrightarrow \neg(\exists X_0)(\exists X_1)(\langle\langle X_0,X_1,R\rangle\rangle$ is a jump in $X))]$.
7. Prove theorem 7.5.11.
8. Prove theorem 7.5.12.
9. Prove theorem 7.5.16.
10. Prove theorem 7.5.17.
11. Prove
    $(\langle\langle X,R\rangle\rangle$ is continuous & $Y = \{u:u \in Re \;\&\; 0 \leqq u \leqq 1\}$ & $Z = X \times Y$ &
    $S = \{\langle\langle u,v\rangle,\langle s,t\rangle\rangle : u,s \in X \;\&\; v,t \in Y \;\&\; (uRs \;\&\; u \neq s)$ or $(u = s \;\&\; v \leqq t)\}) \rightarrow$
    (a) $\langle\langle Z,S\rangle\rangle$ is continuous
    (b) $\neg(\exists W)(W \subseteq Z \;\&\; W$ is S-dense in Z & W is denumerable).

Chapter 8: Ordinal Numbers

8.1. INTRODUCTION

Let us count—0, 1, 2, 3, 4, ... The natural or counting numbers start with 0, the empty set, and continue with

$$\begin{aligned} 1 &= 0^+, \\ 2 &= 1^+, \\ 3 &= 2^+, \end{aligned}$$

etc. [If x is a set, the successor of x, $x^+ = x \cup \{x\}$ (see 4.1.1).] It turns out that it is quite useful to continue the counting procedure beyond the natural numbers. Therefore, start with ω and define

$$\begin{aligned} \omega + 1 &= \omega^+, \\ \omega + 2 &= (\omega + 1)^+, \\ \omega + 3 &= (\omega + 2)^+, \end{aligned}$$

etc. Let

$$x = \{\omega + n : n \in \omega\}.$$

The existence of x follows from the recursion theorem, and x is a set because $x \approx \omega$. Define,

$$\omega \cdot 2 = \omega + \omega = x \cup \omega = \bigcup x.$$

Now that we have extended the natural numbers somewhat, it is easy to go on to $\omega \cdot 2 + 1$, $\omega \cdot 2 + 2$, . . . , $\omega \cdot 3$, . . . , $\omega \cdot 4$, . . . , $\omega \cdot \omega = \omega^2$; and then start over again with $\omega^2 + 1$, $\omega^2 + 2$, . . . , $\omega^2 + \omega$, $\omega^2 + \omega + 1$, $\omega^2 + \omega + 2$, . . . , $\omega^2 + \omega \cdot 2$, . . . , $\omega^2 + \omega \cdot 3$, . . . , $\omega^2 \cdot 2$, . . . , $\omega^2 \cdot 3$, . . . , ω^3, . . . , ω^4, . . . , ω^ω, etc.

These numbers are called *ordinal numbers*. The natural numbers are called *finite ordinal numbers* and the new ones, *infinite ordinal numbers*.

It is clear from the preceding discussion that the class of ordinal numbers, On, is intended to be a successor class (4.1.4). That is,

(1) $$0 \in On$$

(2) $$x \in On \rightarrow x^+ \in On.$$

Moreover, it also has the property that

(3) $$x \subseteq On \rightarrow \bigcup x \in On.$$

Then, as in the case of the natural numbers, we could postulate the existence of a class which satisfies (1)–(3) and define the class of ordinal numbers to be the smallest such class. It turns out that not only would this definition require the postulation of another axiom, but also it would be quite cumbersome to work with. Thus in the next section we shall give an alternative definition of an ordinal number, without adding another axiom, but still preserving the properties described above.

8.2. ORDINALS

The definition of an ordinal which is given here is due to J. von Neumann (1928) and K. Gödel (1940). Like Gödel, we shall first define an ordinal and then define an ordinal number to be an ordinal which is a set.

An ordinal is a class which is well-ordered (w.o.) by the element relation, $\in$. However, $\in$ is not a relation in our system. It is not a class of ordered pairs. In fact, sets and atoms can be elements of proper classes. Thus, $\in$ is a metamathematical relation, and in order to work with it in our system of set theory we must redefine it as a class of ordered pairs. Consequently, we make the following definition:

DEFINITION 8.2.1. $E =_{\text{Df}} \{\langle u,v\rangle : u \in v\}$.

In the future, the symbol "E" will be reserved for this relation.

DEFINITION 8.2.2. Ordinals

(a) X is an *ordinal* $=_{\text{Df}}$

$(\langle\langle X,E\rangle\rangle$ is a w.o. class & $E|X$ is irreflexive & X is transitive)

(b) X is an *ordinal number* $=_{\text{Df}}$ (X is an ordinal & $S(X)$)

(c) $On =_{\text{Df}} \{u : u$ is an ordinal number$\}$.

[Recall that a class is transitive if every element is a subset (theorem 4.1.14).]

We shall prove later that On is an ordinal and is a proper class. Since ordinal numbers play such an important role in set theory we shall use special symbols for them. The lower case Greek letters, α, β, γ, . . . , and these letters with subscripts will denote variables each of whose range is On.

The next thing to do is to show that definition 8.2.2 is adequate. That is to prove that every natural number is an ordinal number (8.2.5a), every finite ordinal number is a natural number, (8.2.7) and that On satisfies conditions (1)–(3) of section 8.1 (8.2.4 and 8.2.15). But first a preliminary result.

THEOREM 8.2.3

(a) $\alpha \notin \alpha$

(b) $\alpha \notin \beta$ or $\beta \notin \alpha$.

Proof:

(a) $\alpha \in \alpha$ contradicts the irreflexivity of $E|\alpha$.

(b) Suppose $\alpha \in \beta$ and $\beta \in \alpha$. Since α and β are transitive, this implies $\alpha \subseteq \beta$ and $\beta \subseteq \alpha$, which, in turn, implies $\alpha = \beta$. This again contradicts the irreflexivity of $E|\alpha$. ■

THEOREM 8.2.4.

(a) $0 \in On$

(b) $\alpha \in On \to \alpha^+ \in On$.

Proof:

(a) 0 is an ordinal because it has no elements so all the conditions of 8.2.2(a) are satisfied vacuously. Moreover, 0 is a set by 4.1.3.

(b) Suppose $\alpha \in On$. Then α is a set and since $\alpha^+ = \alpha \cup \{\alpha\}$, so is α^+. For all $\beta \in \alpha^+$ such that $\beta \neq \alpha$, $\beta \in \alpha$. Moreover, it follows from 8.2.3(b) that if $\beta \in \alpha$, then $\alpha \notin \beta$. Therefore, α is the E-last element of α^+. Hence, since $\langle\langle \alpha, E\rangle\rangle$ is a w.o. set, so is $\langle\langle \alpha^+, E\rangle\rangle$. Also, since $E|\alpha$ is irreflexive, $\alpha \notin \alpha$. Therefore, $E|\alpha^+$ is irreflexive. Finally, to show α^+ is transitive, suppose $u \in \alpha^+$. Then $u = \alpha$ or $u \in \alpha$. If $u = \alpha$, then clearly $u \subseteq \alpha^+$. If $u \in \alpha$, then $u \subseteq \alpha$ since α is transitive. But $\alpha \subseteq \alpha^+$, therefore, $u \subseteq \alpha^+$. Consequently, α^+ is transitive. ■

We shall prove next that every natural number is an ordinal number, and also that ω is an ordinal number.

THEOREM 8.2.5.

(a) $\omega \subseteq On$

(b) $\omega \in On$.

Proof:

(a) It follows from 8.2.4 that On is a successor class. Therefore, since ω is the smallest successor class (4.1.6), we obtain $\omega \subseteq On$.

(b) By 4.1.7, ω is a set and by 4.1.13, ω is transitive. Every non-empty subset of ω has an E-first element by 4.2.2, and the uniqueness of the E-first element follows from 4.1.15. Therefore, it follows from 7.2.4 that $\langle\langle \omega, E\rangle\rangle$ is a w.o. class. Finally, the irreflexivity of $E|\omega$ follows from 4.1.14. ■

The next theorem states that if two ordinals are isomorphic, then they must be identical.

THEOREM 8.2.6.

$$(X \,\&\, Y \text{ are ordinals} \,\&\, \langle\langle X,E\rangle\rangle \cong \langle\langle Y,E\rangle\rangle) \to X = Y$$

Proof: The proof is by transfinite induction. Suppose X and Y satisfy the hypothesis. Let F be an isomorphism mapping X onto Y and let

$$Z = \{u : u \in X \,\&\, F(u) = u\}.$$

We shall prove $Z = X$.

Suppose $Z \subset X$. Let v be the E-first element of $X \sim Z$. Therefore,

$$(1) \qquad (\forall u)(u \in v \to F(u) = u).$$

We shall now derive a contradiction by proving $v = F(v)$.

Suppose $u \in v$. Then since F is an isomorphism, $F(u) \in F(v)$. By (1), $F(u) = u$, so $u \in F(v)$. Conversely, suppose $u \in F(v)$. Then $u \in Y$, so there is a $w \in X$ such that $F(w) = u$. But since F is an isomorphism, $F(w) \in F(v)$ implies $w \in v$. From (1), $w \in v$ implies $F(w) = w$. Thus, $u = w$ and $u \in v$. Hence, we have shown $v = F(v)$, contradicting the definition of v. Consequently, $Z = X$. ■

Now we will show that every finite ordinal is a natural number. (A finite ordinal is a set and is, therefore, an ordinal number.)

THEOREM 8.2.7. $\qquad \alpha$ is finite $\to \alpha \in \omega$.

Proof: Suppose α is a finite ordinal. Then there is a natural number n such that $\alpha \approx n$. Theorem 8.2.4 implies that $n \in On$. $\langle\langle \alpha,E\rangle\rangle$ and $\langle\langle n,E\rangle\rangle$ are both w.o. sets, therefore by 7.4.7 either they are isomorphic or one is isomorphic to an initial segment of the other. If the latter alternative holds, then since $\alpha \approx n$, one of α or n is equipollent to an initial segment of itself. This contradicts 5.1.7. Consequently, $\langle\langle \alpha,E\rangle\rangle \cong \langle\langle n,E\rangle\rangle$ and by 8.2.6, $\alpha = n$. ■

Now, to complete the proof of the adequacy of the definition of an ordinal, we must show that the union of each set of ordinal numbers is an ordinal number [condition (3) of Section 8.1]. In the process of proving this we shall show that On itself is an ordinal.

THEOREM 8.2.8. $\qquad (X \text{ is an ordinal} \,\&\, u \in X) \to$

(a) $u \in On$

(b) $u = \mathrm{S}_{XE}(u)$.

Proof:

(a) Suppose X is an ordinal and $u \in X$. Thus, the transitivity of X implies $u \subseteq X$. Consequently, since u is an element and a class, u is a set. Moreover, since $\langle\langle X,E\rangle\rangle$ is a w.o. class and $E|X$ is irreflexive, $u \subseteq X$ implies $\langle\langle u,E\rangle\rangle$ is a w.o. class and $u|E$ is irreflexive. Therefore, it remains to be shown that u is transitive.

Suppose $v \in u$ and $w \in v$. Since $u \in X$ and X is transitive, $v,w \in X$. But $E|X$ is transitive. Hence $w \in v$ and $v \in u$ implies $w \in u$. This proves $v \subseteq u$, so u is transitive.

(b) Again suppose X is an ordinal and $u \in X$. If $v \in u$, then since X is transitive, $v \in X$. Thus, $v \in u$ implies $v \in X$ and $v \mathrel{E} u$. Therefore, the irreflexivity of $E|X$ implies $v \in S_{XE}(u)$. Conversely, it is clear that if $v \in S_{XE}(u)$, then $v \in u$. ■

As an immediate consequence of 8.2.8(a) we obtain,

Corollary 8.2.9. *On* is transitive.

Proof: Suppose $\alpha \in On$. Then α is an ordinal, so it follows from 8.2.8(a) that if $u \in \alpha$, then $u \in On$. Thus, $\alpha \subseteq On$. ■

It is also easy to prove that $E|On$ is irreflexive.

Theorem 8.2.10. $E|On$ is irreflexive.

Proof: Suppose $\alpha \in On$. Then by 8.2.3(b) $\alpha^+ \in On$. Therefore, $E|\alpha^+$ is irreflexive. But $\alpha \in \alpha^+$. Consequently, $\alpha \notin \alpha$. ■

To prove that *On* is an ordinal, it remains to be shown that

Theorem 8.2.11. $\langle\langle On,E\rangle\rangle$ is a w.o. class.

Proof: First we shall show that $E|On$ is antisymmetric. Suppose $\alpha \in \beta$ and $\beta \in \alpha$. Since α and β are transitive, it follows from the irreflexivity of $E|On$ that

(1) $$\alpha \in \beta \rightarrow \alpha \subset \beta$$

and

(2) $$\beta \in \alpha \rightarrow \beta \subset \alpha.$$

Therefore, from (1) we have

(3) $$\alpha \in \beta \rightarrow (\forall\gamma)(\gamma \in \alpha \rightarrow \gamma \in \beta),$$

and from (2),

(4) $$\beta \in \alpha \rightarrow (\exists\gamma)(\gamma \in \alpha \;\&\; \gamma \notin \beta).$$

Consequently, if $\alpha \in \beta$ and $\beta \in \alpha$, we obtain a contradiction. Hence, $E|On$ is antisymmetric.

Now, because of 7.2.6(a), it remains to be shown that every nonempty subclass of *On* has an *E*-first element. Suppose $X \subseteq On$ and $X \neq \emptyset$. Then there is an ordinal number $\alpha \in X$. If α is the *E*-first element of X, then we are all through. So suppose α is not the E-first element of X Then there is a $\beta \in X$ such that $\beta \in \alpha$. Consequently, $\alpha \cap X = \emptyset$. Since $\alpha \cap X \subseteq \alpha$, $\alpha \cap X \neq \emptyset$, and E w.o. α, $\alpha \cap X$ has an E-first element, say γ. Now we claim γ is an E-first element of X. For suppose it is not; suppose there is a $\beta \in X$ such that $\beta \in \gamma$. Since $\gamma \in \alpha$ and On is transitive, $\beta \in \alpha$. But then $\beta \in X$ and $\beta \in \alpha$, so $\beta \in \alpha \cap X$. Therefore, $\beta \in \gamma$ contradicts the fact that γ is the E-first element of $\alpha \cap X$. ■

Therefore, it follows from 8.2.9, 8.2.10, and 8.2.11 that

THEOREM 8.2.12. On is an ordinal.

The trichotomy for ordinal numbers follows immediately because E is connected on On.

COROLLARY 8.2.13. $\alpha \in \beta$ or $\alpha = \beta$ or $\beta \in \alpha$.

Also, as another corollary we have

COROLLARY 8.2.14. $x \subseteq On \rightarrow (x \in On \leftrightarrow x$ is transitive$)$.

Now we can easily prove that the union of each subset of On is an element of On.

THEOREM 8.2.15. $x \subseteq On \rightarrow \bigcup x \in On$.

Proof: Suppose $x \subseteq On$. Then x is a set so $\bigcup x$ is a set also. Now suppose $u \in \bigcup x$. Then there is an $\alpha \in x$ such that $u \in \alpha$. Since On is transitive, $u \in On$. Thus $\bigcup x \subseteq On$. Therefore, by 8.2.14, to prove $\bigcup x$ is an ordinal number it is sufficient to prove $\bigcup x$ is transitive.

Suppose $\alpha \in \bigcup x$. Then there is a $\gamma \in x$ such that $\alpha \in \gamma$. Suppose $\beta \in \alpha$. Since On is transitive, $\beta \in \alpha$ and $\alpha \in \gamma$ implies $\beta \in \gamma$. Therefore, $\beta \in \bigcup x$. This implies $\alpha \subseteq \bigcup x$. ■

If On is a set, then it follows from 8.2.12 that On is an ordinal number. Thus, if On is a set, then $On \in On$, but this contradicts the irreflexivity of $E|On$ (theorem 8.2.10). Before the advent of axiomatic set theory and before there was any distinction made between sets and classes, it was assumed that On was a set. Hence, this led to one of the paradoxes of set theory. It was published in 1897 by C. Burali-Forti and was later called the Burali-Forti paradox.

In our system of set theory, the fact that On is an ordinal does not lead to a contradiction. We merely infer that On is a proper class.

THEOREM 8.2.16. $\Pr(On)$.

However, it follows from 8.2.12 and 8.2.8(b) that every E-initial segment of On is a set.

THEOREM 8.2.17. $S(S_{On,E}(\alpha))$.

And now it is easy to prove

THEOREM 8.2.18. $S_{On,E}(\alpha) = \alpha$.

Moreover, it follows from 7.4.7 that *On* is the smallest w.o. proper class.

THEOREM 8.2.19.[13]

$$(\langle\langle X,R\rangle\rangle \text{ is a w.o. class } \& \ \Pr(X)) \rightarrow On \lesssim X.$$

Proof: Suppose $\langle\langle X,R\rangle\rangle$ is a w.o. class. Define a relation S on X as follows:

$$u,v \in X \ \& \ u \neq v \rightarrow (uSv \leftrightarrow uRv) \ \& \ (u \in X \rightarrow \neg uSu).$$

Then $\langle\langle X,S\rangle\rangle$ is a w.o. class & $S|X$ is irreflexive. Therefore, by 7.4.7, if $On \not\lesssim X$, then $\langle\langle X,S\rangle\rangle$ is isomorphic to an E-initial segment of On. But, by 8.2.17, every E-initial segment of On is a set. This contradicts the fact that X is a proper class. ∎

Also we can show that each w.o. proper class in which each initial segment is a set is isomorphic to *On*.

THEOREM 8.2.20

$$[\langle\langle X,R\rangle\rangle \text{ is a w.o. class } \& \ \Pr(X) \ \& \ R|X \text{ is irreflexive } \& \ (\forall u)(u \in X \rightarrow S(S_{XR}(u)))] \rightarrow X \ {}_R{\cong}_E \ On.$$

Proof: Suppose $\langle\langle X,R\rangle\rangle$ satisfies the hypothesis but X is not isomorphic to On. Then by 7.4.7, either X is isomorphic to an E-initial segment of On or On is isomorphic to an R-initial segment of X. The first alternative implies that X is a set and the second that On is a set. However, this is a contradiction, so $X \ {}_R{\cong}_E \ On$. ∎

Because of the definition of an ordinal number which is given here, we are able to prove

$$(\forall\alpha)(\alpha \notin \alpha)$$

and

$$(\forall\alpha)(\forall\beta)(\alpha \notin \beta \text{ or } \beta \notin \alpha)$$

without using the axiom of regularity, A9. However, it turns out that by using the axiom of regularity, the definition of an ordinal can be weakened.

[13] The proofs of both 8.2.19 and 8.2.20 require the strong form of 7.4.7 See footnote 12 page 165. We shall prove in the next section that both of these theorems can be proved without using such a strong result. See 8.3.5 and 8.3.6.

Hence, we can prove the following theorem which is due to R. M. Robinson (1937).

THEOREM 8.2.21.®

X is an ordinal $\leftrightarrow$ (Cl(X) & E is connected on X & X is transitive).

Proof: It is clear that it follows from 8.2.2(a) without any use of the axiom of regularity that if X is an ordinal, then X is a class, E is connected on X and X is transitive.

Conversely, suppose X is a class, E is connected on X, and X is transitive. It follows from the axiom of regularity (3.6.7) that if $u \in X$, then $u \notin u$. Therefore, $E|X$ is irreflexive. Suppose $u,v \in X$, then by 3.6.8, it is impossible for $u \in v$ and $v \in u$. Thus, $E|X$ is antisymmetric. Finally, suppose $Y \subseteq X$ and $Y \neq \emptyset$. By A9, there is a $u \in Y$ such that $u \cap Y = \emptyset$. We claim u is an E-first element of Y. For suppose $w \in Y$ and $w \neq u$. Since E is connected on Y either $w \in u$ or $u \in w$. If $w \in u$, since $w \in Y$, then $w \in u \cap Y$. But $u \cap Y = \emptyset$, so $w \in u$ is impossible. Thus we must have $u \in w$, proving w is an E-first element of Y.

Now it follows from 7.2.6(a) that $\langle\langle X,E\rangle\rangle$ is a w.o. class. Since we already have that $E|X$ is irreflexive and X is transitive, it follows from 8.2.2(a) that X is an ordinal. ■

Next, we shall discuss two types of ordinal numbers—*limit ordinal numbers*, ordinal numbers which have no immediate predecessor, like ω for example, and *non-limit ordinal numbers*, ordinal numbers which have an immediate predecessor, like ω^+.

DEFINITION 8.2.22. Limit Ordinals

(a) α is a *limit ordinal* $=_{\mathrm{Df}} (\alpha \neq 0 \ \& \ \neg(\exists\beta)(\beta^+ = \alpha))$

(b) α is a *non-limit ordinal* $=_{\mathrm{Df}} (\alpha = 0$ or $(\exists\beta)(\beta^+ = \alpha))$.

Before stating properties of limit and non-limit ordinals, we state a lemma which holds for all ordinal numbers.

LEMMA 8.2.23. $\alpha \in \beta \rightarrow (\alpha^+ \in \beta$ or $\alpha^+ = \beta)$.

The proof is left as an exercise.

The next theorem gives a necessary and sufficient condition for an ordinal number to be a limit ordinal number.

THEOREM 8.2.24.

α is a limit ordinal $\leftrightarrow (\alpha \neq 0 \ \& \ (\forall\beta)(\beta \in \alpha \rightarrow \beta^+ \in \alpha))$.

Proof: Suppose α is a limit ordinal. Then $\alpha \neq 0$. By 8.2.23, for all α, if $\beta \in \alpha$, then either $\beta^+ \in \alpha$ or $\beta^+ = \alpha$. But if α is a limit ordinal, $\beta^+ \neq \alpha$.

Conversely, suppose $\alpha \neq 0$ and for all β, if $\beta \in \alpha$, then $\beta^+ \in \alpha$. If α is not a limit ordinal number, then since $\alpha \neq 0$, there is a γ such that $\gamma^+ = \alpha$. Consequently, $\gamma \in \alpha$ but $\gamma^+ \notin \alpha$. This is a contradiction, so α must be a limit ordinal number. ■

The proofs of the following two theorems will be left as exercises.

THEOREM 8.2.25. $\alpha \neq 0 \rightarrow (\alpha \text{ is a limit ordinal} \leftrightarrow \bigcup \alpha = \alpha)$.

THEOREM 8.2.26. $\alpha \neq 0 \rightarrow (\alpha \text{ is a non-limit ordinal} \leftrightarrow (\bigcup \alpha)^+ = \alpha)$.

The final theorem of this section gives the relationship between ordinal numbers and w.o. sets. It is because of this theorem that we can speak of *the ordinal number of a w.o. set*.

THEOREM 8.2.27.

$$(\langle\langle x,R\rangle\rangle \text{ is a w.o. set } \& \ R|x \text{ is irreflexive}) \rightarrow (\exists 1\alpha)(\langle\langle \alpha,E\rangle\rangle \cong \langle\langle x,R\rangle\rangle).$$

Proof: Uniqueness follows from 8.2.6. To prove existence, let $\langle\langle x,R\rangle\rangle$ be a w.o. set such that $R|x$ is irreflexive. Then by 7.4.7 either

(1) $\langle\langle x,R\rangle\rangle \cong \langle\langle On,E\rangle\rangle$, or
(2) $\langle\langle On,E\rangle\rangle \cong R$-initial segment of $\langle\langle x,R\rangle\rangle$, or
(3) $\langle\langle x,R\rangle\rangle \cong R$-initial segment of $\langle\langle On,E\rangle\rangle$.

(1) and (2) are impossible since they imply On is a set, and, by 8.2.18, (3) implies that x is isomorphic to an ordinal number. ■

If $\langle\langle x,R\rangle\rangle$ is a w.o. set and $R|x$ is irreflexive, then the unique ordinal number α such that $\langle\langle x,R\rangle\rangle \cong \langle\langle \alpha,E\rangle\rangle$ is called the *ordinal number of* $\langle\langle x,R\rangle\rangle$, symbolically, $\alpha = \overline{\langle\langle x,R\rangle\rangle}$. If $R|X$ is not irreflexive, then we shall define $\overline{\langle\langle x,R\rangle\rangle} = \overline{\langle\langle x,R \sim I\rangle\rangle}$, for $R \sim I$ is always irreflexive. (I is the identity relation.)

DEFINITION 8.2.28. Ordinal Number of a W.O. Set

$$(\langle\langle x,R\rangle\rangle \text{ is a w.o. set } \& \ \langle\langle x,R \sim I\rangle\rangle \cong \langle\langle \alpha,E\rangle\rangle) \rightarrow \overline{\langle\langle x,R\rangle\rangle} =_{\mathrm{Df}} \alpha.$$

Often this notation is abbreviated by replacing "$\overline{\langle\langle x,R\rangle\rangle}$" by "$\overline{x}$." However, it must be remembered that if $\langle\langle x,R\rangle\rangle$ and $\langle\langle x,S\rangle\rangle$ are both w.o. sets, it is not necessarily true that $\overline{\langle\langle x,R\rangle\rangle} = \overline{\langle\langle x,S\rangle\rangle}$. For example, if $x = \omega$, $R = <$, and S is defined as follows:

$$(\forall m)(\forall n)(m,n \in \omega \sim \{0\} \rightarrow (mSn \leftrightarrow m < n)) \ \& \\ (\forall m)(m \in \omega \sim \{0\} \rightarrow mS0) \ \& \ \neg 0S0,$$

then

$$\overline{\langle\langle x,R\rangle\rangle} = \omega,$$

but

$$\overline{\langle\langle x, S\rangle\rangle} = \omega^+.$$

Consequently, the abbreviated notation should only be used if the relation is clearly understood.

As an immediate consequence of 8.2.28 we have

THEOREM 8.2.29. $\overline{\langle\langle \alpha, E\rangle\rangle} = \alpha.$

EXERCISES 8.2

1. Prove corollary 8.2.14.
2. Prove theorem 8.2.18.
3. Prove lemma 8.2.23.
4. Prove each of the following:
   (a) $(\forall\alpha)(0 \in \alpha \text{ or } 0 = \alpha)$
   (b) $\alpha \in \beta \leftrightarrow \alpha \subset \beta$
   (c) $\alpha^+ = \beta^+ \rightarrow \alpha = \beta$
   (d) $\alpha \in \beta \rightarrow \alpha = S_{\beta E}(\alpha)$
   (e) $[x, y \subseteq On \;\&\; (\forall\alpha)(\alpha \in x \rightarrow (\exists\beta)(\beta \in y \;\&\; \alpha \in \beta))] \rightarrow$ $(\bigcup x \in \bigcup y \text{ or } \bigcup x = \bigcup y)$
   (f) $x \subseteq On \rightarrow \bigcup x$ is the E-l.u.b. of x in On
   (g) $(X \subseteq On \;\&\; \Pr(X)) \rightarrow \bigcup X = On.$
5. Prove theorem 8.2.25.
6. Prove theorem 8.2.26.
7. Prove $(\langle\langle x, R\rangle\rangle$ is a w.o. set & $\overline{x} = \alpha) \rightarrow$ (α is a limit ordinal $\leftrightarrow \neg$(x has an R-last element)).
8. Prove $[\alpha$ is a limit ordinal & $x \subseteq \alpha \;\&\; (\forall\beta)(\beta \in \alpha \rightarrow (\exists\gamma)(\gamma \in x \;\&\; \beta \in \gamma))] \rightarrow$ $\alpha = \bigcup x.$

8.3. TRANSFINITE RECURSION THEOREM

In section 4.3 a recursion theorem was derived by using the principle of mathematical induction. It was shown that if a function is defined at 0, and whenever the function is defined at n, its value at $n + 1$ can be determined, then the function exists for all $n \in \omega$. Alternatively, whenever the function is defined for all values less than n, its value at n can be determined, then the function exists for all $n \in \omega$. In this section we shall extend this result to On by using the principle of transfinite induction. We shall state four forms of the transfinite recursion theorem and show that they are all equivalent.

THEOREM 8.3.1. Transfinite Recursion Theorem I

$$(\text{Func}(F_1) \ \& \ \mathfrak{D}(F_1) = V \ \& \ u_1 \in V) \rightarrow (\exists 1 G_1)$$

(a) $\text{Func}(G_1)$
(b) $\mathfrak{D}(G_1) = On$
(c) $G_1(0) = u_1$
(d) $(\forall\alpha)(G_1(\alpha^+) = F_1(G_1(\alpha)))$
(e) $(\forall\alpha)(\alpha$ is a limit ordinal $\rightarrow G_1(\alpha) = \bigcup G_1''\alpha)$.

THEOREM 8.3.2. Transfinite Recursion Theorem II

$$(\text{Func}(F_2) \ \& \ \text{Func}(G_2) \ \& \ \mathfrak{D}(F_2) = V \ \& \ \mathfrak{D}(G_2) = V \ \& \ u_2 \in V) \rightarrow (\exists 1 H_2)$$

(a) $\text{Func}(H_2)$
(b) $\mathfrak{D}(H_2) = On$
(c) $H_2(0) = u_2$
(d) $(\forall\alpha)(H_2(\alpha^+) = F_2(H_2(\alpha)))$
(e) $(\forall\alpha)(\alpha$ is a limit ordinal $\rightarrow H_2(\alpha) = G_2(H_2|\alpha))$.

THEOREM 8.3.3. Transfinite Recursion Theorem III

$$(\text{Func}(F_3) \ \& \ \mathfrak{D}(F_3) = V) \rightarrow (\exists 1 G_3)$$

(a) $\text{Func}(G_3)$
(b) $\mathfrak{D}(G_3) = On$
(c) $(\forall\alpha)(G_3(\alpha) = F_3(G_3|\alpha))$.

THEOREM 8.3.4. Transfinite Recursion Theorem IV

$$(\text{Func}(F_4) \ \& \ \mathfrak{D}(F_4) = V) \rightarrow (\exists 1 G_4)$$

(a) $\text{Func}(G_4)$
(b) $\mathfrak{D}(G_4) = On$
(c) $(\forall\alpha)(G_4(\alpha) = F_4(G_4''\alpha))$.

Theorems 8.3.1 and 8.3.2 are generalizations of 4.3.1. In these theorems, limit ordinals have to be treated separately because they have no immediate predecessors. Theorems 8.3.3 and 8.3.4 are obtained from 4.3.2 and 4.3.3, respectively, by changing ω to *On*. Here, as in Section 4.3, it is not necessary to take the domains of the functions in the hypotheses to be V. The domains must be large enough for the functions in the conclusions to be defined.

We shall just sketch the proofs of these theorems because they follow the same lines as the proofs of the corresponding theorems in Section 4.3.

Proof of 8.3.1: First, to prove uniqueness, suppose G_1 and H_1 both satisfy (a)–(e). Let α be the E-first ordinal number such that $G_1(\alpha) \neq H_1(\alpha)$.

It follows from (c) that $\alpha \neq 0$. Suppose α is a non-limit ordinal. Then there is a β such that $\beta^+ = \alpha$. Since α is the E-first ordinal number such that $G_1(\alpha) \neq H_1(\alpha)$, $G_1(\beta) = H_1(\beta)$. By (d),

$$G_1(\beta^+) = F_1(G_1(\beta)) = F_1(H_1(\beta)) = H_1(\beta^+).$$

Therefore, $G_1(\alpha) = H_1(\alpha)$, which is a contradiction.

Suppose α is a limit ordinal. By the definition of α, $G_1''\alpha = H_1''\alpha$. Therefore, by (e)

$$G_1(\alpha) = \bigcup G_1''\alpha = \bigcup H_1''\alpha = H_1(\alpha).$$

Again we have a contradiction. Hence, $G_1 = H_1$.

To prove existence, define

$$\begin{aligned} H = \{h\colon & \mathrm{Func}(h) \ \&\ (\exists\alpha)[\alpha \neq 0 \ \&\ \mathfrak{D}(h) = \alpha \ \&\ h(0) = u_1 \ \& \\ & (\forall\beta)(\beta^+ \in \alpha \rightarrow h(\beta^+) = F_1(h(\beta))) \ \& \\ & \qquad (\forall\beta)((\beta \in \alpha \ \&\ \beta \text{ is a limit ordinal}) \rightarrow h(\beta) = \textstyle\bigcup h''\beta)]\}. \end{aligned}$$

Then it is easy to show that $G_1 = \bigcup H$ is the required function. (See the proof of 4.3.1.) ■

To prove the equivalence of these four theorems we shall prove

$$8.3.1 \rightarrow 8.3.3 \rightarrow 8.3.4 \rightarrow 8.3.2 \rightarrow 8.3.1.$$

Clearly 8.3.2 → 8.3.1, for take

$$G_2(H_2|\alpha) = \bigcup \mathfrak{R}(H_2|\alpha).$$

It is also clear that 8.3.3 → 8.3.4, for take

$$F_3(G_3|\alpha) = F_4(\mathfrak{R}(G_3|\alpha)).$$

(See the proof that 4.3.2 → 4.3.3.)

Proof that 8.3.1 → 8.3.3: (See the proof that 4.3.1 → 4.3.2.) Let F_3 satisfy the hypothesis of 8.3.3. Theorem 8.3.1 implies that there is a unique G such that

$$\begin{gathered} \mathrm{Func}(G) \\ \mathfrak{D}(G) = On \\ G(0) = 0 \\ (\forall\alpha)(G(\alpha^+) = G(\alpha) \cup \{\langle\alpha, F_3(G(\alpha))\rangle\} \\ (\forall\alpha)(\alpha \text{ is a limit ordinal} \rightarrow G(\alpha) = \bigcup G''\alpha). \end{gathered}$$

Then it is easy to show that $G_3 = \bigcup_{\alpha \in On} G(\alpha)$ is the required function. Uniqueness follows by transfinite induction. ■

Proof that 8.3.4 → 8.3.2: (See the proof that 4.3.3 → 4.3.1.) Let F_2 and G_2 satisfy the hypothesis of 8.3.2. Then we shall construct a function F_4 such that $H_2|\alpha = G_4''\alpha$. Define F_4 as follows:

$$\begin{aligned}&(\text{Func}(x) \;\&\; \mathfrak{D}(x) = 0) \rightarrow F_4(x) = \langle 0,u_2\rangle\\ &(\text{Func}(x) \;\&\; \mathfrak{D}(x) = \alpha^+) \rightarrow F_4(x) = \langle \alpha^+,F_2(x(\alpha))\rangle\\ &(\text{Func}(x) \;\&\; \mathfrak{D}(x) = \alpha \;\&\; \alpha \text{ is a limit ordinal}) \rightarrow\\ &\qquad\qquad F_4(x) = \langle \alpha,G_2(x)\rangle.\end{aligned}$$

Then, by 8.3.4, there exists a G_4 such that

$$\begin{gathered}\text{Func}(G_4)\\ \mathfrak{D}(G_4) = On\\ (\forall\alpha)(G_4(\alpha) = F_4(G_4''\alpha).\end{gathered}$$

Now define $H_2 = \bigcup_{\alpha\in On} G_4''\alpha$. Then it is easy to show that H_2 is the required function. Uniqueness again follows by transfinite induction. ■

These proofs of equivalence give an insight into the use of the transfinite recursion theorem. As another example of its use we shall give an alternative proof of 8.2.20.

THEOREM 8.3.5.

$$[\langle\langle X,R\rangle\rangle \text{ is a w.o. class} \;\&\; \Pr(X) \;\&\; R|X \text{ is irreflexive} \;\&\; (\forall u)(u \in X \rightarrow \text{S}(\text{S}_{XR}(u))] \rightarrow X \;{}_R{\cong}_E\; On.$$

Proof: Suppose $\langle\langle X,R\rangle\rangle$ satisfies the hypothesis. We shall define a function G on On as follows: for each $\alpha \in On$

$$G(\alpha) = R\text{-first element of } X \sim \mathfrak{R}(G|\alpha).$$

That is, $G(\alpha)$ is the R-first element of X which has not as yet occurred as a value of G. To prove that G exists, using 8.3.3, we must prove that there is a function F such that $G(\alpha) = F(G|\alpha)$. Take

$$F = \{\langle u,v\rangle : v = R\text{-first element of } X \sim \mathfrak{R}(u)\}.$$

For any set u, $\mathfrak{R}(u)$ is a set. Therefore, since X is a proper class, $X \sim \mathfrak{R}(u) \neq \emptyset$. Thus, since $\langle\langle X,R\rangle\rangle$ is a w.o. class, every set $u \in \mathfrak{D}(F)$. It follows from 8.3.3 that there is a unique G such that

$$\begin{aligned}&\text{Func}(G)\\ &\mathfrak{D}(G) = On\\ &(\forall\alpha)(G(\alpha) = R\text{-first element of } X \sim \mathfrak{R}(G|\alpha)).\end{aligned}$$

We shall show $G : On \;{}_E{\cong}_R\; X$. Clearly, $\mathfrak{R}(G) \subseteq X$. Moreover, $G(\alpha)\; R\; G(\alpha^+)$ for all $\alpha \in On$ because $G(\alpha) \notin X \sim \mathfrak{R}(G|\alpha^+)$ and $(X \sim \mathfrak{R}(G|\alpha^+)) \subseteq (X \sim \mathfrak{R}(G|\alpha))$. Therefore, G is 1–1 and G is an isomorphism.

Suppose $\mathcal{R}(G) \subset X$. Let u be the R-first element of $X \sim \mathcal{R}(G)$. Then we would have $On\ {}_E{\cong}_R\ \mathrm{S}_{XR}(u)$. However, by hypothesis, $\mathrm{S}_{XR}(u)$ is a set. This contradicts the fact that On is a proper class. Consequently, we must have $\mathcal{R}(G) = X$. ■

COROLLARY 8.3.6.

$$(\langle\langle X,R\rangle\rangle \text{ is a w.o. class } \& \Pr(X)) \to On \precsim X.$$

Proof: Suppose X is a proper class. Define a relation S on X such that $\langle\langle X,S\rangle\rangle$ is a w.o. class and $S|X$ is irreflexive (see the proof of 8.2.19). The only part of the proof of 8.3.5 which we cannot carry through is the last paragraph. Consequently, we can infer $On \precsim X$. ■

Thus, we can prove 8.2.19 and 8.2.20 without using the strong form of 7.4.7. (See footnote 12.)

EXERCISES 8.3

1. Give a direct proof of theorem 8.3.3.
2. Prove directly that 8.3.4 → 8.3.3.
3. Prove: $[\langle\langle Z,R\rangle\rangle$ is a p.w.o. class & $(\forall u)(u \in Z \to \mathrm{S}(\mathrm{S}_{ZR}(u)))$ & $\mathrm{Func}(F)$ & $\mathcal{D}(F) = V] \to (\exists 1 G)$
   (a) $\mathrm{Func}(G)$
   (b) $\mathcal{D}(G) = Z$
   (c) $(\forall u)(u \in Z \to G(u) = F(G''\mathrm{S}_{ZR}(u))$.
   (See exercises 7.2.5 and 7.3.5. Also, in the other transfinite recursion theorems, On can be replaced by a partially well-ordered class as long as every initial segment of the class is a set.)

*8.4. ADDITION AND SUBTRACTION

The definition of addition of ordinal numbers is an application of the transfinite recursion theorem I, 8.3.1. For any ordinal number α we shall define the function $\alpha\,+$.

DEFINITION 8.4.1. Addition

(a) $\alpha + 0 =_{\mathrm{Df}} \alpha$
(b) $(\forall\beta)(\alpha + \beta^+ =_{\mathrm{Df}} (\alpha + \beta)^+)$
(c) $(\forall\beta)(\beta$ is a limit ordinal $\to \alpha + \beta =_{\mathrm{Df}} \bigcup(\alpha +'' \beta))$.

Note that

$$\alpha +'' \beta = \{\alpha + \gamma : \gamma \in \beta\}.$$

Definition 8.4.1 is a generalization of the definition of addition for natural numbers, 4.4.1. Here we shall dispense with the symbol "s_α" and use the usual notation immediately. Of course, for natural numbers, (c) does not apply because no natural number is a limit ordinal. To give an example of how (c) is used, let us calculate $1 + \omega$.

$$1 + \omega = \bigcup\{1 + n : n \in \omega\}.$$

Clearly,

$$\{1 + n : n \in \omega\} = \omega \sim \{0\},$$

and it is easy to prove that

$$\bigcup(\omega \sim \{0\}) = \omega.$$

Thus, we have shown that

$$1 + \omega = \omega.$$

The next theorem states that *On* is closed with respect to addition.

THEOREM 8.4.2. $\alpha + \beta \in On.$

Proof: The proof is by transfinite induction on β. Suppose $\alpha \in On$. Let

$$X = \{\beta : \alpha + \beta \in On\}.$$

Suppose $X \subset On$. Let γ be the E-first element of $On \sim X$. It follows from 8.4.1(a) that $\gamma \neq 0$.

Suppose $\gamma = \delta^+$. Then $\delta \in X$, so $\alpha + \delta \in On$. By 8.4.1(b)

$$\alpha + \gamma = (\alpha + \delta)^+.$$

But $\alpha + \delta$ is an ordinal number and, by 8.2.4(b), the successor of an ordinal number is an ordinal number. This implies that $\gamma \in X$ which is a contradiction.

Finally, suppose γ is a limit ordinal. Then by 8.4.1(c)

$$\alpha + \gamma = \bigcup\{\alpha + \delta : \delta \in \gamma\}.$$

Thus, $\alpha + \gamma$ is the union of a set of ordinal numbers. Therefore, by 8.2.15, $\alpha + \gamma$ is an ordinal number. This again is a contradiction. Hence, $\alpha + \beta \in On$ for all α and β. ■

The arithmetic of ordinal numbers is a bit more difficult than the arithmetic of natural numbers. One reason for this is that the commutative law does not hold. For example, we saw above that

$$1 + \omega = \omega.$$

But

$$\omega + 1 = (\omega + 0)^+ = \omega^+.$$

Clearly, $\omega \neq \omega^+$.

In order to gain more of an insight into ordinal arithmetic, we believe it will be instructive to examine the operations in a more set theoretical manner. It follows from the transfinite recursion theorem IV, 8.3.4, that for each α there exists a unique function F_α such that $\mathfrak{D}(F_\alpha) = On$ and for each β,

$$F_\alpha(\beta) = \alpha \cup F_\alpha''\beta.$$

We claim that $F_\alpha(\beta) = \alpha + \beta$.

THEOREM 8.4.3. $\alpha + \beta = \alpha \cup \{\alpha + \gamma : \gamma \in \beta\}$.

Proof: The proof is by transfinite induction on β. Suppose the theorem is true for all $\gamma \in \beta$.

Case 1. $\beta = 0$. Then by 8.4.1(a), $\alpha + \beta = \alpha$. Also, if $\beta = 0$, $\{\alpha + \gamma : \gamma \in \beta\} = \emptyset$. Therefore, $\alpha \cup \{\alpha + \gamma : \gamma \in \beta\} = \alpha$.

Case 2. $\beta = \gamma^+$. Then

$$\begin{aligned}
\alpha + \beta &= (\alpha + \gamma)^+ && \text{(8.4.1b)}\\
&= (\alpha \cup \{\alpha + \delta : \delta \in \gamma\})^+ && \text{(induction hypothesis)}\\
&= (\alpha \cup \{\alpha + \delta : \delta \in \gamma\} \cup \{\alpha \cup \{\alpha + \delta : \delta \in \gamma\}\}) && \text{(4.1.1)}\\
&= (\alpha \cup \{\alpha + \delta : \delta \in \gamma\}) \cup \{\alpha + \gamma\} && \text{(induction hypothesis)}\\
&= \alpha \cup \{\alpha + \delta : \delta \in \beta\}. && \text{(4.1.1)}
\end{aligned}$$

Case 3. β is a limit ordinal. Then, by 8.4.1(c),

$$\alpha + \beta = \bigcup \{\alpha + \delta : \delta \in \beta\}. \tag{1}$$

Therefore,

$$\gamma \in \alpha + \beta \leftrightarrow (\exists \delta)(\delta \in \beta \ \&\ \gamma \in \alpha + \delta).$$

However, by the induction hypothesis, if $\delta \in \beta$,

$$\gamma \in \alpha + \delta \leftrightarrow (\gamma \in \alpha \text{ or } (\exists \delta_1)(\delta_1 \in \delta \ \&\ \gamma = \alpha + \delta_1)).$$

But since β is transitive, if $\delta_1 \in \delta$ and $\delta \in \beta$, then $\delta_1 \in \beta$. Consequently,

$$\alpha + \beta \subseteq \alpha \cup \{\alpha + \gamma : \gamma \in \beta\}.$$

On the other hand, if $\gamma \in \alpha$, then by (1), $\gamma \in \alpha + \beta$. Or if $\gamma = \alpha + \delta$ for some $\delta \in \beta$, then since β is a limit ordinal $\delta^+ \in \beta$. By 8.4.1(b) $\alpha + \delta^+ = (\alpha + \delta)^+$, so $\gamma \in \alpha + \delta^+$. Therefore, it follows from (1) that $\gamma \in \alpha + \beta$. Hence,

$$\alpha \cup \{\alpha + \gamma : \gamma \in \beta\} \subseteq \alpha + \beta. \ \blacksquare$$

Theorem 8.4.3 can be stated in terms of w.o. sets. We shall prove this after we state a preliminary lemma.

LEMMA 8.4.4.

$[\langle\langle X,R\rangle\rangle$ & $\langle\langle Y,S\rangle\rangle$ are w.o. classes & $X \cap Y = \emptyset$ & $T = \{\langle u,v\rangle$: $(u,v \in X$ & $u\,R\,v)$ or $(u,v \in Y$ & $u\,S\,v)$ or $(u \in X$ & $v \in Y)\}] \rightarrow$

(a) $\langle\langle X \cup Y,T\rangle\rangle$ is a w.o. class

(b) Z is a T-initial segment of $X \cup Y \leftrightarrow$ ((Z is an R-initial segment of X) or ($Z = X \cup Y_1$ & Y_1 is an S-initial segment of Y)).

Proof: See exercises 7.2.8(a) and 7.3.4(a).

It follows directly from exercise 7.4.4 that for each pair of ordinal numbers α and β, there exist sets x and y and relations R and S such that $x \cap y = \emptyset$, $\overline{\langle\langle x,R\rangle\rangle} = \alpha$, and $\overline{\langle\langle y,S\rangle\rangle} = \beta$. [For example, take $x = \alpha \times \{1\}$, and define R and S as follows:

$$\gamma,\delta \in \alpha \rightarrow (\langle\gamma,0\rangle\, R\, \langle\delta,0\rangle \leftrightarrow \gamma \in \delta)$$
$$\gamma,\delta \in \beta \rightarrow (\langle\gamma,1\rangle\, S\, \langle\delta,1\rangle \leftrightarrow \gamma \in \delta).$$

Then it is clear that $\overline{\langle\langle x,R\rangle\rangle} = \alpha$ and $\overline{\langle\langle y,S\rangle\rangle} = \beta$.] Now we can state a theorem which gives a relationship between addition of ordinal numbers and w.o. sets.

THEOREM 8.4.5.

$(\langle\langle x,R\rangle\rangle$ & $\langle\langle y,S\rangle\rangle$ are w.o. sets & $x \cap y = \emptyset$ & $\overline{\langle\langle x,R\rangle\rangle} = \alpha$ & $\overline{\langle\langle y,S\rangle\rangle} = \beta) \rightarrow \overline{\langle\langle x \cup y,T\rangle\rangle} = \alpha + \beta$. ($T$ is the relation defined in 8.4.4.)

Proof: Let $\langle\langle x,R\rangle\rangle$ and $\langle\langle y,S\rangle\rangle$ be w.o. sets satisfying the hypothesis. Then clearly

$$\langle\langle x,R\rangle\rangle \cong \langle\langle \alpha,E\rangle\rangle$$

and

$$\langle\langle y,S\rangle\rangle \cong \langle\langle \{\alpha + \gamma : \gamma \in \beta\},E\rangle\rangle.$$

Moreover,

$$\alpha \cap \{\alpha + \gamma : \gamma \in \beta\} = \emptyset$$

and

$$\langle\langle x \cup y,T\rangle\rangle \cong \langle\langle \alpha \cup \{\alpha + \gamma : \gamma \in \beta\},E\rangle\rangle.$$

By 8.4.3,

$$\alpha \cup \{\alpha + \gamma : \gamma \in \beta\} = \alpha + \beta.$$

Hence, it follows from 8.2.29 that

$$\overline{\langle\langle x \cup y,T\rangle\rangle} = \alpha + \beta. \blacksquare$$

Applying 8.4.5, we see that $\omega + 1$ is the ordinal number of a denumerable set which has one element tacked on at the end, while $1 + \omega$ is the ordinal number of a denumerable set which has one element tacked on at the beginning. Thus, we see again that $\omega + 1 = \omega^+$ and $1 + \omega = \omega$.

Even though the commutative law for addition of ordinal numbers does not hold, the associative law does hold. This is easy to prove using 8.4.3.

THEOREM 8.4.6. $(\alpha + \beta) + \gamma = \alpha + (\beta + \gamma)$.

Proof: Use 8.4.3 and the associative law for union. We leave the details for the reader. ■

Further elementary properties of addition of ordinal numbers are exhibited in the following theorems. It is shown in the proof of many of these theorems how 8.4.3 and 8.4.5 can be used to great advantage.

THEOREM 8.4.7.
(a) $\alpha + 0 = \alpha$
(b) $0 + \alpha = \alpha$.

Proof: Part (a) follows immediately from 8.4.1(a). Let R be any relation and let $\langle\langle y,S\rangle\rangle$ be a w.o. set such that $\overline{\langle\langle y,S\rangle\rangle} = \alpha$. Then $\overline{\langle\langle \emptyset \cup y,T\rangle\rangle} = 0 + \alpha$ where T is the relation defined in 8.4.4. Clearly,

$$\langle\langle \emptyset \cup y,T\rangle\rangle = \langle\langle y,S\rangle\rangle.$$

Therefore, it follows from 8.4.5 that $0 + \alpha = \alpha$. ■

THEOREM 8.4.8. $\alpha + 1 = \alpha^+$.

Proof: Definition 8.4.1(b). ■

THEOREM 8.4.9.

$$\beta \text{ is a limit ordinal} \rightarrow (\forall\alpha)(\alpha + \beta \text{ is a limit ordinal}).$$

Proof: Suppose $\gamma \in \alpha + \beta$. Then by 8.4.3 either $\gamma \in \alpha$ or there is a $\delta \in \beta$ such that $\gamma = \alpha + \delta$. Then either $\gamma^+ \in \alpha$ or $\gamma^+ = \alpha$ or $\gamma^+ = (\alpha + \delta)^+ = \alpha + \delta^+$ where $\delta \in \beta$. Since β is a limit ordinal, $\delta \in \beta$ implies $\delta^+ \in \beta$. Hence it follows from 8.4.3 that $\gamma^+ \in \alpha + \beta$. ■

THEOREM 8.4.10.

$$\beta \text{ is a limit ordinal} \rightarrow \bigcup\{\alpha + \gamma : \gamma \in \beta\} = \bigcup\{\gamma : \gamma \in \alpha + \beta\}.$$

Proof: Theorems 8.4.9 and 8.2.25, and definition 8.4.1(c). ■

There are occasions when it seems a little unnatural, and sometimes even awkward, to use the symbol "$\in$" for inequality between ordinal numbers. For example, when we want to say $\alpha \in \beta$ or $\alpha = \beta$. In the case of the natural numbers, we introduced the symbols "$<$" and "$\leqq$" for inequality and we shall do the same thing here.

DEFINITION 8.4.11. Inequality

(a) $\alpha < \beta =_{\mathrm{Df}} \alpha \in \beta$

(b) $\alpha > \beta =_{\mathrm{Df}} \beta < \alpha$

(c) $\alpha \leqq \beta =_{\mathrm{Df}} (\alpha \in \beta \text{ or } \alpha = \beta)$

(d) $\alpha \geqq \beta =_{\mathrm{Df}} \beta \leqq \alpha$.

In the case that α and β are natural numbers, 8.4.11 coincides with 4.4.19. The reader may wonder why the symbol "$<$" was not used instead of "E" in 8.2.1. There is no good answer to this question except that it is traditional to reserve the symbol "$<$" for a relationship between numbers.

Now we shall prove some more properties of ordinal numbers, using our new inequality symbol when appropriate. We shall show first that a right monotonicity law holds for ordinal numbers.

THEOREM 8.4.12. $\beta < \gamma \rightarrow \alpha + \beta < \alpha + \gamma$.

Proof: By theorem 8.4.3 $\alpha + \gamma = \alpha \cup \{\alpha + \delta : \delta \in \gamma\}$. Therefore, if $\beta < \gamma$, then $\alpha + \beta < \alpha + \gamma$. ∎

However, the left monotonicity law does not hold—$0 \in 1$ but $0 + \omega = 1 + \omega$.

Using theorem 8.4.12 we can derive a left cancellation law.

THEOREM 8.4.13. $\alpha + \beta = \alpha + \gamma \rightarrow \beta = \gamma$.

Proof: Suppose $\alpha + \beta = \alpha + \gamma$ but $\beta \neq \gamma$. Then we may suppose $\beta < \gamma$. Therefore, 8.4.12 implies $\alpha + \beta < \alpha + \gamma$ which is a contradiction. ∎

On the other hand, the right cancellation law does not hold—$1 + \omega = 0 + \omega$ but $1 \neq 0$.

Even though the left monotonicity law does not hold, we can prove a weaker version of it.

THEOREM 8.4.14. $\alpha < \beta \rightarrow \alpha + \gamma \leqq \beta + \gamma$.

Proof: The proof is by transfinite induction on γ. Suppose the theorem is true for all $\delta \in \gamma$ and assume $\alpha < \beta$. By 8.4.3,

$$\xi \in \alpha + \gamma \leftrightarrow (\xi \in \alpha \text{ or } (\exists \delta)(\delta \in \gamma \;\&\; \xi = \alpha + \delta)).$$

But $\alpha < \beta$, therefore it follows from the transitivity of β that $\xi \in \alpha$ implies $\xi \in \beta$. If $\xi = \alpha + \delta$ where $\delta \in \gamma$ then by the induction hypothesis $\xi \leqq \beta + \delta$. Hence, it follows from 8.4.3 that if $\xi \in \alpha + \gamma$, then $\xi \in \beta + \gamma$. This implies that $\alpha + \gamma \subseteq \beta + \gamma$. But for ordinal numbers $\subseteq$ and $\leqq$ coincide (see exercise 8.2.4b). Therefore, we have $\alpha < \beta$ implies $\alpha + \gamma \leqq \beta + \gamma$. ∎

It follows from the next theorem that subtraction of ordinal numbers is possible.

THEOREM 8.4.15. $\alpha \leqq \beta \rightarrow (\exists 1\gamma)(\alpha + \gamma = \beta)$.

Proof: Uniqueness; this follows from the left cancellation law, theorem 8.4.13.

If $\alpha = \beta$, then take $\gamma = 0$. Suppose $\alpha < \beta$. Let $\langle\langle x,R\rangle\rangle$ and $\langle\langle y,S\rangle\rangle$ be w.o. sets such that $\overline{\langle\langle x,R\rangle\rangle} = \alpha$ and $\overline{\langle\langle y,S\rangle\rangle} = \beta$. Since $\alpha \in \beta$, we may assume that x is an S-initial segment of y and that $R|x = S|x$. Let $z = y \sim x$. Then $\langle\langle z,S\rangle\rangle$ is a w.o. set, and thus there is an ordinal number γ such that $\overline{\langle\langle z,S\rangle\rangle} = \gamma$. It follows from 8.4.5 that $\alpha + \gamma = \beta$. ∎

Now subtraction can be defined as follows:

DEFINITION 8.4.16. Subtraction

$$\alpha \leqq \beta \rightarrow ((\beta - \alpha = \gamma) =_{\text{Df}} (\alpha + \gamma = \beta)).$$

We leave the proof of the next theorem as an exercise.

THEOREM 8.4.17. $\alpha \leqq \beta \rightarrow$

(a) $\alpha - 0 = \alpha$
(b) $\alpha - \alpha = 0$
(c) $\alpha^+ - \alpha = 1$
(d) $\alpha + (\beta - \alpha) = \beta$
(e) $\beta - \alpha \leqq \beta$.

Note that if $\alpha \leqq \beta$, it does not follow that there is a γ such that $\gamma + \alpha = \beta$ [see exercise 8.4.1(f)]. Moreover, if such a γ exists, there is no guarantee that it is unique.

Now we know how to add two ordinal numbers together and it is easy to see how to extend this definition to any finite number of ordinal numbers. The next definition extends 8.4.1 to the sum of an infinite number of ordinal numbers.

DEFINITION 8.4.18. Infinite Sums

$$(\text{Func}(F) \;\&\; \mathfrak{D}(F) = On \;\&\; \mathfrak{R}(F) \subseteq On) \rightarrow$$

(a) $\Sigma_F(0) =_{\text{Df}} 0$
(b) $(\forall\alpha)(\Sigma_F(\alpha^+) =_{\text{Df}} \Sigma_F(\alpha) + F(\alpha))$
(c) $(\forall\alpha)(\alpha \text{ is a limit ordinal} \rightarrow \Sigma_F(\alpha) =_{\text{Df}} \bigcup \Sigma_F{}''\alpha)$.

The existence and uniqueness of the function Σ_F follows from the transfinite recursion theorem I, 8.3.1. Moreover, it is easy to prove using transfinite induction that

THEOREM 8.4.19.

$$(\mathrm{Func}(F)\ \&\ \alpha \subseteq \mathfrak{D}(F)\ \&\ \mathfrak{R}(F) \subseteq On) \rightarrow \Sigma_F(\alpha) \in On.$$

$\Sigma_F(\alpha)$ is just $\Sigma_{\beta\in\alpha}F(\beta)$, and from here on we shall use the standard notation.

DEFINITION 8.4.20.

$$(\mathrm{Func}(F)\ \&\ \alpha \subseteq \mathfrak{D}(F)\ \&\ \mathfrak{R}(F) \subseteq On) \rightarrow \Sigma_{\beta\in\alpha}F(B) =_{\mathrm{Df}} \Sigma_F(\alpha).$$

Definition 8.4.20 makes it clear that the "β" in "$\Sigma_{\beta\in\alpha}F(\beta)$" is just a dummy variable. That is,

$$\Sigma_{\beta\in\alpha}F(\beta) = \Sigma_{\gamma\in\alpha}F(\gamma).$$

Let us take several examples of the infinite sum.

$$\begin{aligned}\Sigma_{n\in\omega}n &= 0 + 1 + 2 + 3 + \cdots \\ &= \bigcup_{n\in\omega}\Sigma_{m\in n}m \\ &= \bigcup_{n\in\omega}\frac{(n-1)(n)}{2} \\ &= \omega.\end{aligned}$$

Suppose that for each $n \in \omega$, a function f_n is defined as follows:

$$\begin{aligned}\mathfrak{D}(f_n) &= \omega + 1 \\ (\forall m)(m \in \omega\ \&\ m \neq n \rightarrow f_n(m) &= m) \\ f_n(n) &= \omega \\ f_n(\omega) &= n.\end{aligned}$$

Then

$$\begin{aligned}\Sigma_{\alpha\in\omega+1}f_n(\alpha) &= 0 + 1 + 2 + \cdots + (n-1) + \omega + (n+1) + \cdots + n \\ &= \bigcup_{\alpha\in\omega}\Sigma_{m\in\alpha}f_n(m) + n \\ &= \omega + \omega + n.\end{aligned}$$

It is easy to prove that 8.4.18 is a generalization of 8.4.1. That is,

THEOREM 8.4.21.

$$(\mathrm{Func}(F)\ \&\ 2 \subseteq \mathfrak{D}(F)\ \&\ \mathfrak{R}(F) \subseteq On) \rightarrow \Sigma_{\beta\in 2}F(\beta) = F(0) + F(1).$$

The following theorem gives two monotonicity laws for the infinite sum.

THEOREM 8.4.22.

$$(\mathrm{Func}(F)\ \&\ \mathrm{Func}(G)\ \&\ \alpha \subseteq \mathfrak{D}(F)\ \&\ \alpha \subseteq \mathfrak{D}(G)\ \&\ \mathfrak{R}(F) \subseteq On\ \&$$
$$\mathfrak{R}(G) \subseteq On) \rightarrow$$

(a) $\beta < \alpha \rightarrow \Sigma_{\gamma \in \beta} F(\gamma) \leqq \Sigma_{\gamma \in \alpha} F(\gamma)$
(b) $(\forall \beta)(\beta < \alpha \rightarrow F(\beta) \leqq G(\beta)) \rightarrow \Sigma_{\beta \in \alpha} F(\beta) \leqq \Sigma_{\beta \in \alpha} G(\beta)$.

The proof is left as an exercise. It so happens that even if the symbol "$\leqq$" in the hypothesis of (b) is replaced by "$<$", the conclusion remains the same. For example, if $\alpha = \omega$ and for all $n < \omega$

$$F(n) = n \quad \text{and} \quad G(n) = n + 1,$$

then for all $n \in \omega$,

$$F(n) < G(n),$$

but

$$\Sigma_{n \in \omega} F(n) = \omega = \Sigma_{n \in \omega} G(n).$$

However, it can be shown that if we add the condition

$$(\forall \gamma)(\gamma \in \alpha \rightarrow F(\gamma) \neq 0),$$

then the symbol "$\leqq$" in the conclusion of (a) can be replaced by "$<$."

Theorem 8.4.5 can be generalized to the infinite sum. We shall just sketch the ideas and leave the details to the reader.

Let F be a function mapping an ordinal number α into *On*. For each $\beta \in \alpha$ choose a set $G(\beta)$ and a relation R_β such that

$$\langle\langle G(\beta), R_\beta \rangle\rangle \cong \langle\langle F(\beta), E \rangle\rangle$$

and for all $\beta, \gamma, \in \alpha$,

$$G(\beta) \cap G(\gamma) = \emptyset.$$

(For example, let $G(\beta) = F(\beta) \times \{\beta\}$.)

Now define a relation S as follows:

$$S = \{\langle u,v \rangle : (\exists \beta)(\exists \gamma)(\beta, \gamma \in \alpha \,\&\, \beta \in \gamma) \,\&\, u \in G(\beta) \,\&\, v \in G(\gamma)) \text{ or } (\exists \beta)(\beta \in \alpha \,\&\, u,v \in G(\beta) \,\&\, u \, R_\beta \, v)\}.$$

It is easy to prove that $\langle\langle \bigcup_{\beta \in \alpha} G(\beta), S \rangle\rangle$ is a w.o. set and that

$$\Sigma_{\beta \in \alpha} F(\beta) = \overline{\langle\langle \bigcup_{\beta \in \alpha} G(\beta), S \rangle\rangle}.$$

EXERCISES 8.4

1. Prove each of the following:
   (a) $n \in \omega \rightarrow n + \omega = \omega$
   (b) $(n \in \omega \,\&\, \alpha \geqq \omega) \rightarrow n + \alpha = \alpha$
   (c) $\alpha + \beta < \alpha + \gamma \rightarrow \beta < \gamma$
   (d) $\alpha + \gamma < \beta + \gamma \rightarrow \alpha < \beta$
   (e) $\alpha + \beta = \gamma \rightarrow (\alpha \leqq \gamma \,\&\, \beta \leqq \gamma)$

(f) $\neg(\exists\alpha)(\alpha + \omega = \omega^+)$
(g) $(\exists\alpha)(\alpha + \beta$ is a limit ordinal$) \rightarrow (\beta$ is a limit ordinal or $\beta = 0)$.

2. Prove theorem 8.4.17.
3. Prove theorem 8.4.19.
4. Prove theorem 8.4.21.
5. Prove theorem 8.4.22.
6. Prove: $\text{Func}(F)$ & $\mathfrak{D}(F) = \omega$ &
   (a) $(\forall n)(n \in \omega \rightarrow F(n) = n^2) \rightarrow \Sigma_{n\in\omega}F(n) = \omega$
   (b) $(\forall m)(\forall n)(m,n \in \omega \rightarrow F(n) = n + m) \rightarrow \Sigma_{n\in\omega}F(n) = \omega$
   (c) $(\forall m)(\forall n)((m,n \in \omega$ & $m \neq 0) \rightarrow F(n) = m) \rightarrow \Sigma_{n\in\omega}F(n) = \omega$.

*8.5. MULTIPLICATION AND EXPONENTIATION

We can think of multiplication as repeated addition. The product $\alpha\cdot\beta$ is α added to itself β times. Thus, we can define multiplication in terms of the infinite sum.

DEFINITION 8.5.1. Multiplication

$$\alpha\cdot\beta =_{\text{Df}} \Sigma_{\gamma\in\beta}I(\alpha).$$

(I is the identity function.) Thus, according to this definition,

$$\begin{aligned}\alpha\cdot 0 &= 0,\\ \alpha\cdot 1 &= \alpha,\\ \alpha\cdot 2 &= \alpha + \alpha,\\ \alpha\cdot 3 &= \alpha + \alpha + \alpha, \text{ etc.}\end{aligned}$$

It follows immediately from 8.4.19 that

THEOREM 8.5.2. $\alpha\cdot\beta \in On$.

We shall often omit the dot and replace the symbol "$\alpha\cdot\beta$" by "$\alpha\beta$."

Now we can prove as a theorem that multiplication of natural numbers is a special case of multiplication of ordinal numbers (see 4.4.11).

THEOREM 8.5.3.
(a) $\alpha 0 = 0$
(b) $(\forall\beta)(\alpha\beta^+ = \alpha\beta + \alpha)$
(c) $(\forall\beta)(\beta$ is a limit ordinal $\rightarrow \alpha\beta = \bigcup\{\alpha\delta : \delta \in \beta\})$.

Proof:
(a) By 8.5.1,

$$\begin{aligned}\alpha 0 &= \Sigma_{\gamma\in 0}I(\alpha)\\ &= 0. && (8.4.17a)\end{aligned}$$

(b)
$$\begin{aligned}\alpha\beta^+ &= \Sigma_{\gamma\in\beta^+}I(\alpha) && (8.5.1)\\ &= \Sigma_{\gamma\in\beta}I(\alpha) + I(\alpha) && (8.4.18b)\\ &= \alpha\beta + \alpha. && (8.5.1)\end{aligned}$$

(c) Suppose β is a limit ordinal.

$$\begin{aligned} \alpha\beta &= \Sigma_{\gamma\in\beta} I(\alpha) && (8.5.1)\\ &= \bigcup\{\Sigma_{\gamma\in\delta} I(\alpha) : \delta \in \beta\} && (8.4.18c)\\ &= \bigcup\{\alpha\delta : \delta \in \beta\}. && (8.5.1) \blacksquare \end{aligned}$$

It follows from the transfinite recursion theorem I, 8.3.1, that there is exactly one function $\alpha\cdot$ which satisfies conditions (a)–(c) of 8.5.3. Thus, 8.5.3 could have been used as the definition of multiplication.

Just as in the case of addition, it is useful to describe multiplication of ordinal numbers in terms of w.o. sets. But first, two lemmas.

LEMMA 8.5.4.

$(\langle\langle X,R\rangle\rangle$ & $\langle\langle Y,S\rangle\rangle$ are w.o. classes &
$T = \{\langle\langle s,t\rangle,\langle u,v\rangle\rangle : s,u \in X$ &
$t,v \in Y$ & $((t\ S\ v$ & $t \neq v)$ or $(t = v$ & $s\ R\ u))\}) \rightarrow$

(a) $\langle\langle X \times Y,T\rangle\rangle$ is a w.o. class

(b) Z is a T-initial segment of $X \times Y \leftrightarrow$
$(\exists X_1)(\exists Y_1)(\exists u)(X_1$ is an R-initial segment of X & Y_1 is an S-initial segment of Y & u is the S-first element of $Y \sim Y_1$ &
$Z = (X \times Y_1) \cup (X_1 \times \{u\}))$.

(T is called the *reverse lexiographic* ordering of $X \times Y$.)

Proof: See exercises 7.2.8(b) and 7.3.4(b). ■

As an example, if $2 \times \omega$ were ordered by the reverse lexiographic ordering, its elements would be ordered as follows: $\langle 0,0\rangle$, $\langle 1,0\rangle$, $\langle 0,1\rangle$, $\langle 1,1\rangle$, $\langle 0,2\rangle$, $\langle 1,2\rangle$, $\langle 2,2\rangle$, $\langle 0,3\rangle$, $\langle 1,3\rangle$, ... On the other hand, if $\omega \times 2$ were ordered by the reverse lexiographic ordering, its elements would have the following ordering: $\langle 0,0\rangle$, $\langle 1,0\rangle$, $\langle 2,0\rangle$, $\langle 3,0\rangle$, . . . , $\langle 0,1\rangle$, $\langle 1,1\rangle$, $\langle 2,1\rangle$, $\langle 3,1\rangle$, ... Therefore, if T_1 is the reverse lexiographic ordering on $2 \times \omega$,

$$\overline{\langle\langle 2 \times \omega, T_1\rangle\rangle} = \omega.$$

But if T_2 is the reverse lexiographic ordering on $\omega \times 2$,

$$\overline{\langle\langle \omega \times 2, T_2\rangle\rangle} = \omega + \omega.$$

LEMMA 8.5.5.

$[\langle\langle X,R\rangle\rangle$ & $\langle\langle Y,S\rangle\rangle$ are w.o. classes & T is the reverse lexiographic ordering on $X \times Y$ & $(\neg(\exists u)(u$ is the R-last element of $X)$ or $\neg(\exists v)(v$ is the S-last element of $Y))] \rightarrow \neg(\exists w)(w$ is the T-last element of $X \times Y)$.

Proof: Suppose $\langle u,v\rangle$ is the T-last element of $X \times Y$. Then for all $s \in X$ and $t \in Y$, $\langle s,t\rangle\ T\ \langle u,v\rangle$ or $\langle s,t\rangle = \langle u,v\rangle$. Since T is the reverse lexiographic ordering, this implies $t\ S\ v$ or $t = v$. Therefore, v is the S-last element of Y.

Suppose there is an $s \in X$ such that $u\ R\ s$. Then, by the definition of T, $\langle u,v\rangle\ T\ \langle s,v\rangle$ or $u = s$. But since $\langle u,v\rangle$ is the T-last element of $X \times Y$, $\langle u,v\rangle\ T\ \langle s,v\rangle$ implies $u = s$. Thus, u is the R-last element of X. ■

Now we are ready to give the relationship between multiplication and w.o. sets.

THEOREM 8.5.6.
$(\langle\langle x,R\rangle\rangle\ \&\ \langle\langle y,S\rangle\rangle$ are w.o. sets $\&\ \overline{\overline{\langle\langle x,R\rangle\rangle}} = \alpha\ \&\ \overline{\overline{\langle\langle y,S\rangle\rangle}} = \beta\ \&\ T$ is the reverse lexiographic ordering on $x \times y) \rightarrow \overline{\overline{\langle\langle x \times y, T\rangle\rangle}} = \alpha\beta$.

Proof: The proof is by transfinite induction on β. Suppose the theorem is true for all $\gamma \in \beta$.

Case 1. $\beta = 0$. Then $y = \emptyset$. Therefore, $x \times y = \emptyset$, so $\overline{\overline{\langle\langle x \times y,T\rangle\rangle}} = 0$.

Case 2. $\beta = \gamma^+$. Then, it follows from exercise 8.2.7 that y has an S-last element, say u. Let $z = y \sim \{u\}$. Then $\overline{\overline{\langle\langle z,S\rangle\rangle}} = \gamma$, so by the induction hypothesis

$$\overline{\overline{\langle\langle x \times y,T\rangle\rangle}} = \alpha\gamma.$$

We have

$$\begin{aligned} x \times y &= x \times (z \cup \{u\}) \\ &= (x \times z) \cup (x \times \{u\}). \end{aligned}$$

Therefore, by 8.4.5 and the definition of T,

$$\begin{aligned} \overline{\overline{\langle\langle x \times y,T\rangle\rangle}} &= \alpha\gamma + \alpha \\ &= \alpha\beta. && \text{(8.5.3b)} \end{aligned}$$

Case 3. β is a limit ordinal. For each $\gamma \in \beta$ there is one and only one z such that z is an S-initial segment of y and $\overline{\overline{\langle\langle z,S\rangle\rangle}} = \gamma$. Also, it follows from 8.5.4(b) that $x \times z$ is a T-initial segment of $x \times y$. Therefore, by the induction hypothesis,

(1) $$\overline{\overline{\langle\langle x \times y,T\rangle\rangle}} = \alpha\gamma.$$

Moreover, since y has no S-last element, $x \times y$ has no T-last element (8.5.5). Therefore, $\overline{\overline{\langle\langle x \times y,T\rangle\rangle}}$ is a limit ordinal. Hence, by 8.2.25,

$$\overline{\overline{\langle\langle x \times y,T\rangle\rangle}} = \bigcup\{\overline{\overline{\langle\langle z,T\rangle\rangle}} : z \text{ is a } T\text{-initial segment of } x \times y\}.$$

From 8.5.4(b) it follows that for every z which is a T-initial segment of $x \times y$, there is a w such that w is an S-initial segment of y, $x \times w$ is a T-initial segment of $x \times y$, and $z \subseteq x \times w$. Hence,

$$\begin{aligned} \overline{\overline{\langle\langle x \times y,T\rangle\rangle}} &= \bigcup\{\overline{\overline{\langle\langle x \times w,T\rangle\rangle}} : w \text{ is an } S\text{-initial segment of } y\} \\ &= \bigcup\{\alpha\gamma : \gamma \in \beta\gamma\} && \text{(1)} \\ &= \alpha\beta. && \text{(8.5.3c)} \end{aligned}$$ ■

If $\alpha\beta$ had been defined as the sum of β added to itself α times, then in 8.5.6, T would have been the lexiographic ordering instead of the reverse lexiographic ordering. But it is customary to define $\alpha\beta$ as the sum of α added to itself β times, so we must use the reverse lexiographic ordering in 8.5.6.

It follows from the discussion following lemma 8.5.4 that

$$2\cdot\omega = \omega$$

and

$$\omega\cdot 2 = \omega + \omega.$$

Thus we see that multiplication of ordinal numbers is not commutative. Some other properties of multiplication are given in the following theorems.

THEOREM 8.5.7.
(a) $0\cdot\alpha = \alpha$
(b) $\alpha\cdot 1 = \alpha$
(c) $1\cdot\alpha = \alpha$.

Proof: Parts (a) and (c) follow from 8.5.6, and (b), from 8.5.3(b). ∎

THEOREM 8.5.8. $(\alpha\beta)\gamma = \alpha(\beta\gamma)$.

Proof: Use 8.5.6 and exercise 3.4.3(b). ∎

THEOREM 8.5.9.

$[(\alpha \neq 0$ & β is a limit ordinal) or ($\beta \neq 0$ & α is a limit ordinal)$] \rightarrow \alpha\beta$ is a limit ordinal.

Proof: Use theorems 8.5.5 and 8.5.6. ∎

The converse of 8.5.9 is also true. See exercise 8.5.2(e).

THEOREM 8.5.10.

(β is a limit ordinal & $\alpha \neq 0$) $\rightarrow \bigcup\{\alpha\gamma : \gamma \in \beta\} = \bigcup\{\gamma : \gamma \in \alpha\beta\}$.

Proof: Use theorems 8.5.9, 8.5.3(c), and 8.2.25. ∎

The monotonicity and cancellation laws for multiplication are analogous to those of addition.

THEOREM 8.5.11. ($\alpha \neq 0$ & $\beta < \gamma$) $\rightarrow \alpha\beta < \alpha\gamma$.

Proof: It follows from 8.5.4(b) and 8.5.5 that if $\alpha \neq 0$ and β is an initial segment of γ then $\alpha\beta$ is an initial segment of $\alpha\gamma$. ∎

THEOREM 8.5.12. ($\alpha \neq 0$ & $\alpha\beta = \alpha\gamma$) $\rightarrow \beta = \gamma$.

Proof: Use theorem 8.5.11 and corollary 8.2.13. ∎

Theorem 8.5.12 gives the left cancellation law. The right cancellation law does not hold, since

$$1\cdot\omega = \omega = 2\cdot\omega,$$

but $1 \neq 2$. Moreover, this same example demonstrates that the left monotonicity law does not hold—$1 \in 2$ but $1\cdot\omega = 2\cdot\omega$. However, we can prove

THEOREM 8.5.13. $\alpha < \beta \rightarrow \alpha\gamma \leqq \beta\gamma$.

Proof: The proof is by transfinite induction on γ. Suppose the theorem is true for all $\delta \in \gamma$ and suppose

(1) $$\alpha < \beta.$$

Case 1. $\gamma = 0$. In this case $\alpha\gamma = \beta\gamma = 0$ by 8.5.3(a).

Case 2. $\gamma = \delta^+$. Then by the induction hypothesis

(2) $$\alpha\delta \leqq \beta\delta.$$

Moreover, by 8.5.3(b),

$$\begin{aligned} \alpha\gamma &= \alpha\delta + \alpha \\ &\leqq \beta\delta + \alpha && [(2)\ \&\ 8.4.14] \\ &< \beta\delta + \beta && [(1)\ \&\ 8.4.12] \\ &= \beta\gamma. && (8.5.3b) \end{aligned}$$

Case 3. γ is a limit ordinal. If $\alpha = 0$, then $\alpha\gamma = 0$, so $\alpha\gamma \leqq \beta\gamma$. Suppose $\alpha \neq 0$. Then by 8.5.9 and (1), $\alpha\gamma$ and $\beta\gamma$ are both limit ordinals. Therefore, by 8.5.3(c)

$$\begin{aligned} \alpha\gamma &= \bigcup\{\alpha\delta : \delta \in \gamma\} \\ &\leqq \bigcup\{\beta\delta : \delta \in \gamma\} && [(2)\ \&\ \text{exercise } 8.2.4e] \\ &= \beta\gamma. && (8.5.3c) \end{aligned}$$ ∎

Next we shall show that multiplication is distributive from the left with respect to addition. However, it is not distributive from the right, as the following simple example illustrates.

$$\begin{aligned} (1+1)\omega &= 2\omega = \omega \\ 1\omega + 1\omega &= \omega + \omega \neq \omega. \end{aligned}$$

THEOREM 8.5.14. $\alpha(\beta + \gamma) = \alpha\beta + \alpha\gamma$.

Proof: Let $\langle\langle x,R_1\rangle\rangle$, $\langle\langle y,R_2\rangle\rangle$, and $\langle\langle z,R_3\rangle\rangle$ be w.o. sets such that $y \cap z = \emptyset$, $\overline{\langle\langle x,R_1\rangle\rangle} = \alpha$, $\overline{\langle\langle y,R_2\rangle\rangle} = \beta$, and $\overline{\langle\langle z,R_3\rangle\rangle} = \gamma$. Let S_1 be the ordering on $y \cup z$ as given in 8.4.4, and let T_1 be the reverse lexiographic ordering on $x \times (y \cup z)$. Then

(1) $$\overline{\langle\langle x \times (y \cup z),T_1\rangle\rangle} = \alpha(\beta + \gamma).$$

Let S_2 and S_3 be the reverse lexiographic ordering on $x \times y$ and $x \times z$, respectively, and let T_2 be the ordering on $(x \times y) \cup (x \times z)$ as given in 8.4.4. Then

(2) $$\overline{\langle\langle (x \times y) \cup (x \times z), T_2 \rangle\rangle} = \alpha\beta + \alpha\gamma.$$

By 3.1.23(a), $x \times (y \cup z) = (x \times y) \cup (x \times z)$. Moreover, it is not difficult to prove that $T_1 = T_2$. (The details are left as an exercise.) Then it follows from (1) and (2) that

$$\alpha(\beta + \gamma) = \alpha\beta + \alpha\gamma. \blacksquare$$

The final topic of this section is ordinal exponentiation. Exponentiation stands in the same relationship to multiplication as multiplication stands in relation to addition. We considered $\alpha\beta$ to mean α added to itself β times and we consider α^β to mean α multiplied by itself β times. The first step is to define an infinite product.

DEFINITION 8.5.15. Infinite Product

$$(\text{Func}(F) \,\&\, \mathfrak{D}(F) = On \,\&\, \mathfrak{R}(F) \subseteq On) \rightarrow$$

(a) $\Pi_F(0) =_{\text{Df}} 1$
(b) $(\forall\alpha)(\Pi_F(\alpha^+) =_{\text{Df}} \Pi_F(\alpha) \cdot F(\alpha))$
(c) $(\forall\alpha)[(\alpha \text{ is a limit ordinal } \& \, (\exists\beta)(\beta \in \alpha \,\&\, F(\beta) = 0)) \rightarrow \Pi_F(\alpha) =_{\text{Df}} 0]$
(d) $(\forall\alpha)[(\alpha \text{ is a limit ordinal } \& \, (\forall\beta)(\beta \in \alpha \rightarrow F(\beta) \neq 0)) \rightarrow \Pi_F(\alpha) =_{\text{Df}} \bigcup \Pi_F''\alpha]$.

The existence and uniqueness of the function Π_F follows from the transfinite recursion theorem I. Moreover, using transfinite induction, it is easy to prove that

THEOREM 8.5.16. $(\text{Func}(F) \,\&\, \alpha \subseteq \mathfrak{D}(F) \,\&\, \mathfrak{R}(F) \subseteq On) \rightarrow$
(a) $\Pi_F(\alpha) \in On$
(b) $\Pi_F(\alpha) = 0 \leftrightarrow (\exists\beta)(\beta \in \alpha \,\&\, F(\beta) = 0)$.

Just as for the infinite sum, we shall use the standard notation for the infinite product.

DEFINITION 8.5.17.

$$(\text{Func}(F) \,\&\, \alpha \subseteq \mathfrak{D}(F) \,\&\, \mathfrak{R}(F) \subseteq On) \rightarrow \Pi_{\beta\in\alpha}F(\beta) =_{\text{Df}} \Pi_F(\alpha).$$

Let us apply 8.5.15 to several examples.

$$\begin{aligned}\Pi_{n\in\omega}(n+1) &= 1 \cdot 2 \cdot 3 \cdot 4 \cdots. \\ &= \textstyle\bigcup_{n\in\omega} \Pi_{m\in n}(m+1) \\ &\leq \textstyle\bigcup_{n\in\omega}(n+1)^n \\ &= \omega.\end{aligned}$$

But clearly, $\Pi_{n\in\omega}(n+1) \geqq \omega$. Thus, we have

$$\Pi_{n\in\omega}(n+1) = \omega.$$

For each $n \in \omega$, define f_n as follows.

$$\begin{aligned} \mathfrak{D}(f_n) &= \omega + 1 \\ (\forall m)((m \in \omega \;\&\; m \neq n) \rightarrow f_n(m) &= m + 1) \\ f_n(n) &= \omega \\ f_n(\omega) &= n + 1. \end{aligned}$$

Then

$$\begin{aligned} \Pi_{\alpha\in\omega+1} f_n(\alpha) &= 1\cdot 2\cdots n\cdot\omega\cdot(n+2)\cdots(n+1) \\ &= (\textstyle\bigcup_{\alpha\in\omega}\Pi_{m\in\alpha} f_n(\alpha))(n+1) \\ &= \omega\cdot\omega\cdot(n+1). \end{aligned}$$

We also have theorems analogous to 8.4.21 and 8.4.22 for the infinite product. We leave their proofs as an exercise.

THEOREM 8.5.18.

$$(\mathrm{Func}(F) \;\&\; 2 \subseteq \mathfrak{D}(F) \;\&\; \mathfrak{R}(F) \subseteq On) \rightarrow \Pi_{\beta\in 2}F(\beta) = F(0)\cdot F(1).$$

THEOREM 8.5.19.

$$\begin{aligned} &(\mathrm{Func}(F) \;\&\; \mathrm{Func}(G) \;\&\; \alpha \subseteq \mathfrak{D}(F) \;\&\; \alpha \subseteq \mathfrak{D}(G) \;\&\; \mathfrak{R}(F) \subseteq On \;\& \\ &\qquad\qquad \mathfrak{R}(G) \subseteq On \;\&\; (\forall\gamma)(\gamma \in \alpha \rightarrow F(\gamma) \neq 0)) \rightarrow \end{aligned}$$

(a) $\beta < \alpha \rightarrow \Pi_{\gamma\in\beta}F(\gamma) \leqq \Pi_{\gamma\in\alpha}F(\gamma)$
(b) $(\forall\beta)(\beta < \alpha \rightarrow F(\beta) \leqq G(\beta)) \rightarrow \Pi_{\beta\in\alpha}F(\beta) \leqq \Pi_{\beta\in\alpha}G(\beta)$.

In this theorem, just as in theorem 8.4.22, if the symbol "$\leqq$" in the hypothesis of (b) is replaced by "$<$," the conclusion remains the same. To see this consider the following example. For all $n \in \omega$,

$$F(n) = n + 1 \;\&\; G(n) = n + 2.$$

Then, for all $n \in \omega$,

$$F(n) < G(n),$$

but it is easy to show that

$$\Pi_{n\in\omega}F(n) = \omega = \Pi_{n\in\omega}G(n).$$

Also, if we add the condition

$$(\forall\gamma)(\gamma \in \alpha \rightarrow F(\gamma) \neq 1),$$

the symbol "$\leqq$" in the conclusion of (a) can be replaced by "$<$".

Now we are ready to define exponentiation.

DEFINITION 8.5.20. Exponentiation

$$\alpha^{\beta} =_{\mathrm{Df}} \Pi_{\gamma \in \beta} I(\alpha).$$

In other words, α^{β} is the product of α multiplied by itself β times. Unfortunately, ordinal exponentiation as defined in 8.5.20 is not the same as set exponentiation as defined in 3.5.17, even though the same symbol is used in both cases. However, when α and β are ordinal numbers, the symbol "α^{β}" will always stand for ordinal exponentiation as defined in 8.5.20, and when x and y are arbitrary sets the symbol "x^{y}" will stand for set exponentiation as defined in 3.5.17.

As a direct consequence of 8.5.20 and 8.5.16(a) we have

THEOREM 8.5.21. $\alpha^{\beta} \in On.$

The next theorem suggests an alternative definition of exponentiation.

THEOREM 8.5.22.

(a) $\alpha^0 = 1$

(b) $(\forall\beta)(\alpha^{\beta^+} = \alpha^{\beta}\cdot\alpha)$

(c) $(\forall\beta)(\beta$ is a limit ordinal $\rightarrow 0^{\beta} = 0)$

(d) $(\forall\beta)((\beta$ is a limit ordinal $\& \alpha \neq 0) \rightarrow \alpha^{\beta} = \bigcup\{\alpha^{\delta}:\delta \in \beta\})$.

Proof:

(a) $\alpha^0 = \Pi_{\gamma\in 0} I(\alpha) = 1$ (8.5.15a).

(b) $\alpha^{\beta^+} = \Pi_{\gamma\in\beta^+} I(\alpha)$ (8.5.20)

$= (\Pi_{\gamma\in\beta} I(\alpha))\cdot\alpha$ (8.5.15b)

$= \alpha^{\beta}\cdot\alpha.$ (8.5.20)

(c) If β is a limit ordinal, then

$$0^{\beta} = \Pi_{\gamma\in\beta} I(0) \quad (8.5.20)$$
$$= 0. \quad (8.5.15c)$$

(d) If β is a limit ordinal and $\alpha \neq 0$,

$$\alpha^{\beta} = \Pi_{\gamma\in\beta} I(\alpha) \quad (8.5.20)$$
$$= \bigcup\{\Pi_{\gamma\in\delta} I(\alpha):\delta \in \beta\} \quad (8.5.15d)$$
$$= \bigcup\{\alpha^{\delta}:\delta \in \beta\}. \quad (8.5.20)$$ ∎

It follows from the transfinite recursion theorem I that the function which satisfies (a)–(d) of 8.5.22 exists and is unique.

As an immediate consequence of 8.5.20 and 8.5.22, we have,

THEOREM 8.5.23.

(a) $0^0 = 1$

(b) $\beta \neq 0 \rightarrow 0^{\beta} = 0$

(c) $\alpha^1 = \alpha$

(d) $\alpha^2 = \alpha\cdot\alpha.$

Next we shall describe a relationship between exponentiation and w.o. sets.

DEFINITION 8.5.24.

(a) $Z(\alpha,\beta) =_{\mathrm{Df}} \{f\colon \mathrm{Func}(f) \;\&\; \mathfrak{D}(f) = \beta \;\&\; \mathfrak{R}(f) \subseteq \alpha \;\&$
$\{\gamma\colon \gamma \in \beta \;\&\; f(\gamma) \neq 0\}$ is finite$\}$

(b) $W_{\alpha\beta} =_{\mathrm{Df}} \{\langle f,g\rangle\colon f,g \in Z(\alpha,\beta) \;\&\; f \neq g \;\&\; (\forall\delta)(\delta$ is the E-last element of $\{\gamma\colon \gamma \in \beta \;\&\; f(\gamma) \neq g(\gamma)\} \rightarrow f(\delta) < g(\delta))\}$.

Therefore, if $f \in Z(\alpha,\beta)$, $f\colon \beta \rightarrow \alpha$ and there are at most a finite number of $\gamma \in \beta$ such that $f(\gamma) \neq 0$. Consequently, if $f,g \in Z(\alpha,\beta)$, $\{\gamma\colon \gamma \in \beta \;\&\; f(\gamma) \neq g(\gamma)\}$ is finite and therefore has an E-last element. Since E is connected on On, this implies

THEOREM 8.5.25. $W_{\alpha\beta}$ is connected on $Z(\alpha,\beta)$.

Our intention is to prove

$$\overline{\langle\langle Z(\alpha,\beta), W_{\alpha\beta}\rangle\rangle} = \alpha^{\beta}.$$

But first we must derive some preliminary results.

LEMMA 8.5.26.

$T_{\alpha\gamma}$ is the reverse lexiographic ordering on $Z(\alpha,\gamma) \times Z(\alpha,1) \rightarrow$
$\langle\langle Z(\alpha,\gamma^+), W_{\alpha\gamma^+}\rangle\rangle \cong \langle\langle Z(\alpha,\gamma) \times Z(\alpha,1), T_{\alpha\gamma}\rangle\rangle$.

Proof: By hypothesis,

$$\langle f_1,g_1\rangle T_{\alpha\gamma} \langle f_2,g_2\rangle \leftrightarrow [f_1,f_2 \in Z(\alpha,\gamma) \;\&\; g_1,g_2 \in Z(\alpha,1) \;\&\; (g_1 W_{\alpha 1} g_2 \text{ or } (g_1 = g_2 \;\&\; f_1 W_{\alpha\gamma} f_2))].$$

Define a function F on $Z(\alpha,\gamma^+)$ as follows: For each $f \in Z(\alpha,\gamma^+)$, $F(f) = \langle f|\gamma,g\rangle$, where g is the function such that $\mathfrak{D}(g) = 1$ and $g(0) = f(\gamma)$. It is easy to prove that F is the required isomorphism. We leave the details as an exercise. ■

Next we shall show that $W_{\alpha\beta}$ is transitive.

THEOREM 8.5.27. $W_{\alpha\beta}$ is transitive.

Proof: Suppose $f,g,h \in Z(\alpha,\beta)$, $f\, W_{\alpha\beta}\, g$, and $g\, W_{\alpha\beta}\, h$. Let

$$\delta_1 = E\text{-last element of } \{\gamma\colon \gamma \in \beta \;\&\; f(\gamma) \neq g(\gamma)\}$$
$$\delta_2 = E\text{-last element of } \{\gamma\colon \gamma \in \beta \;\&\; g(\gamma) \neq h(\gamma)\}.$$

We have

(1) $\quad f(\delta_1) < g(\delta_1) \;\&\; (\forall\gamma)((\gamma \in \beta \;\&\; \delta_1 \in \gamma) \rightarrow f(\gamma) = g(\gamma))$

and

(2) $\quad g(\delta_2) < h(\delta_2) \;\&\; (\forall\gamma)((\gamma \in \beta \;\&\; \delta_2 \in \gamma) \rightarrow g(\gamma) = h(\gamma))$.

Suppose $f = h$. If $\delta_1 \in \delta_2$, then it follows from (1) that $f(\delta_2) = g(\delta_2)$. Therefore, from (2), $f(\delta_2) < h(\delta_2) = f(\delta_2)$. This is a contradiction. Similarly, if $\delta_2 \in \delta_1$, we obtain a contradiction. And if $\delta_1 = \delta_2$, then (1) and (2) contradict the asymmetry of E. Therefore, $f \neq h$. Let

$$\delta_3 = E\text{-last element of } \{\gamma : \gamma \in \beta \,\&\, f(\gamma) \neq h(\gamma)\}.$$

If $\delta_1 = \delta_2$, then by (1) and (2), for all $\gamma \in \beta$ such that $\delta_1 \in \gamma$, we have

$$f(\gamma) = g(\gamma) = h(\gamma).$$

Therefore, $\delta_3 = \delta_1$, and it follows from (1), (2), and the transitivity of E, that $f(\delta_3) < h(\delta_3)$.

If $\delta_1 < \delta_2$, then, from (1), for all $\gamma \in \beta$ such that $\delta_1 \in \gamma$, $f(\gamma) = g(\gamma)$. Consequently, it follows from (2) that $\delta_3 = \delta_2$. Moreover, since $\delta_1 \in \delta_2$, $f(\delta_2) = g(\delta_2)$. Therefore, from (2) we get $f(\delta_3) < h(\delta_3)$.

Finally, if $\delta_2 \in \delta_1$, then from (2), for all $\gamma \in \beta$ such that $\delta_2 \in \gamma$, $g(\gamma) = h(\gamma)$. Therefore, it follows from (1) that $\delta_3 = \delta_1$. Since, $g(\delta_1) = h(\delta_1)$, it follows from (1) that $f(\delta_3) < h(\delta_3)$.

Thus, it follows from the definition of $W_{\alpha\beta}$ that $f \, W_{\alpha\beta} \, h$. ■

THEOREM 8.5.28.

$\langle\langle Z(\alpha,\beta), W_{\alpha\beta}\rangle\rangle$ is a w.o. set and $W_{\alpha\beta}$ is irreflexive.

Proof: $Z(\alpha,\beta)$ is a set because

$$Z(\alpha,\beta) \subseteq \times_{\gamma\in\beta} I(\alpha).$$

Moreover, it follows directly from the definition of $W_{\alpha\beta}$ that $W_{\alpha\beta}$ is irreflexive and asymmetric. Asymmetry implies antisymmetry. Thus, to prove the theorem it remains to be shown that every non-empty subset of $Z(\alpha,\beta)$ has a $W_{\alpha\beta}$-first element. We shall prove this by transfinite induction on β. Suppose the theorem is true for all $\gamma \in \beta$.

Case 1. $\beta = 0$. Then $Z(\alpha,\beta) = \{\emptyset\}$ and the theorem is clearly true.

Case 2. $\beta = \gamma^+$. If $T_{\alpha\gamma}$ is the reverse lexiographic ordering on $Z(\alpha,\gamma) \times Z(\alpha,1)$, then it follows from 8.5.26 that

(1) $$\langle\langle Z(\alpha,\gamma^+), W_{\alpha\gamma^+}\rangle\rangle \cong \langle\langle Z(\alpha,\gamma) \times Z(\alpha,1), T_{\alpha\gamma}\rangle\rangle.$$

By the induction hypothesis $\langle\langle Z(\alpha,\gamma), W_{\alpha\gamma}\rangle\rangle$ is a w.o. set. Clearly, $\langle\langle Z(\alpha,1), W_{\alpha 1}\rangle\rangle$ is a w.o. set because it is isomorphic to $\langle\langle \alpha, E\rangle\rangle$. Consequently, it follows from 8.5.4(a) that $\langle\langle Z(\alpha,\gamma) \times Z(\alpha,1), T_{\alpha\gamma}\rangle\rangle$ is a w.o. set. Therefore, the theorem follows from (1).

Case 3. β is a limit ordinal. Suppose $X \subseteq Z(\alpha,\beta)$ and $X \neq \emptyset$. Let $\in X$. There are at most a finite number of ordinal numbers $\gamma \in \beta$ such that $f(\gamma) \neq 0$. If $f(\gamma) = 0$ for all $\gamma \in \beta$, then f would be the $W_{\alpha\beta}$-first element of X. Suppose there is a $\gamma \in \beta$ such that $f(\gamma) \neq 0$. Let δ be the largest ordinal number in the set $\{\gamma : \gamma \in \beta \,\&\, f(\gamma) \neq 0\}$. Then it follows from the definition of $W_{\alpha\beta}$ that if $g \in Z(\alpha,\beta)$ and $g \; W_{\alpha\beta} \; f$, then $g(\delta) \leqq f(\delta)$, and for all $\gamma \in \beta$ such that $\delta \in \gamma$, $g(\gamma) = 0$. Thus, to all intents and purposes, $g \in Z(\alpha,\delta^+)$. But β is a limit ordinal, and so $\delta \in \beta$ implies $\delta^+ \in \beta$. Consequently, it follows from the induction hypothesis that if $Y = \{g : g \in X \,\&\, g \; W_{\alpha\beta} \; f\} \neq \emptyset$, it has a $W_{\alpha\beta}$-first element, h. Since $W_{\alpha\beta}$ is transitive and connected on $Z(\alpha,\beta)$, it follows that h is the $W_{\alpha\beta}$-first element of X. If $Y = \emptyset$, then f is the $W_{\alpha\beta}$-first element of X. ■

Now we are finally ready to prove the main theorem.

THEOREM 8.5.29. $\overline{\langle\langle Z(\alpha,\beta), W_{\alpha\beta}\rangle\rangle} = \alpha^\beta$.

Proof: It follows from 8.5.28 that $\overline{\langle\langle Z(\alpha,\beta), W_{\alpha\beta}\rangle\rangle}$ is an ordinal number. We shall prove by transfinite induction that it satisfies conditions (a)–(d) of 8.5.22, then the theorem follows from the transfinite recursion theorem I. Suppose the theorem is true for all $\gamma \in \beta$.

Case 1. $\beta = 0$. Then $Z(\alpha,\beta) = \{\emptyset\}$, so $\overline{\langle\langle \{\emptyset\}, W_{\alpha 0}\rangle\rangle} = 1$. This proves (a).

Case 2. $\beta = \gamma^+$. If $T_{\alpha\gamma}$ is the reverse lexiographic ordering on $Z(\alpha,\gamma) \times Z(\alpha,1)$, then by 8.5.26,

$$\langle\langle Z(\alpha,\beta), W_{\alpha\beta}\rangle\rangle \cong \langle\langle Z(\alpha,\gamma) \times Z(\alpha,1), T_{\alpha\gamma}\rangle\rangle.$$

By the induction hypothesis,

$$\overline{\langle\langle Z(\alpha,\gamma), W_{\alpha\gamma}\rangle\rangle} = \alpha^\gamma$$

and it is clear that

$$\overline{\langle\langle Z(\alpha,1), W_{\alpha 1}\rangle\rangle} = \alpha.$$

Therefore, it follows from 8.5.6 that

$$\overline{\langle\langle Z(\alpha,\beta), W_{\alpha\beta}\rangle\rangle} = \alpha^\gamma \cdot \alpha.$$

This proves (b).

Case 3. β is a limit ordinal. If $\alpha = 0$, then $Z(\alpha,\beta) = \emptyset$ and $\overline{\langle\langle \emptyset, W_{\alpha,\beta}\rangle\rangle} = 0$. If $\alpha \neq 0$, then $Z(\alpha,\beta) \neq \emptyset$. Since β is a limit ordinal, it is easy to see that $Z(\alpha,\beta)$ has no $W_{\alpha\beta}$-last element. Thus, $\overline{\langle\langle Z(\alpha,\beta), W_{\alpha\beta}\rangle\rangle}$ is a limit ordinal. Therefore, it follows from 8.2.25 that

$$\overline{\langle\langle Z(\alpha,\beta), W_{\alpha\beta}\rangle\rangle} = \bigcup \{\overline{\langle\langle z, W_{\alpha\beta}\rangle\rangle} : z \text{ is an } W_{\alpha\beta}\text{-initial segment of } Z(\alpha,\beta)\}.$$

Let us see what the $W_{\alpha\beta}$-initial segments of $Z(\alpha,\beta)$ look like. Let $f \in Z(\alpha,\beta)$ and let z be the $W_{\alpha\beta}$-initial segment of $Z(\alpha,\beta)$ generated by f. If $f(\gamma) = 0$ for all $\gamma \in \beta$, then $z = \emptyset$. Suppose there is a $\gamma \in \beta$ such that $f(\gamma) \neq 0$.

Let δ be the largest element of the set $\{\gamma : \gamma \in \beta \,\&\, f(\gamma) \neq 0\}$. Then, if $g \in z$, we must have that $g(\delta) < f(\delta)$ and for all $\gamma \in \beta$ such that $\delta \in \gamma$, $g(\gamma) = 0$. Let

$$z_1 = \{g|\delta^+ : g \in z\}.$$

Clearly, z_1 is a $W_{\alpha\delta^+}$-initial segment of $Z(\alpha,\delta^+)$, and it is easy to see that

$$\langle\langle z, W_{\alpha\beta}\rangle\rangle \cong \langle\langle z_1, W_{\alpha\delta^+}\rangle\rangle.$$

Therefore,

$$\overline{\langle\langle Z(\alpha,\beta), W_{\alpha\beta}\rangle\rangle} = \bigcup\{\overline{\langle\langle Z(\alpha,\gamma), W(\alpha,\gamma)\rangle\rangle} : \gamma \in \beta\}.$$

Thus, it follows from the induction hypothesis that

$$\overline{\langle\langle Z(\alpha,\beta), W_{\alpha\beta}\rangle\rangle} = \bigcup\{\alpha^\gamma : \gamma \in \beta\}. \ \blacksquare$$

Now, we may use 8.5.20, 8.5.22, and 8.5.29 interchangeably to prove properties about the exponential function.

THEOREM 8.5.30.

(β is a limit ordinal & $\alpha > 1$) $\rightarrow$ α^β is a limit ordinal.

Proof: Clearly, if β is a limit ordinal and $\alpha > 1$, then $Z(\alpha,\beta)$ has no $W_{\alpha\beta}$-last element. ■

THEOREM 8.5.31.

(α is a limit ordinal & $\beta \neq 0$) $\rightarrow$ α^β is a limit ordinal.

The proof is by transfinite induction on β. The details are left as an exercise.

THEOREM 8.5.32.

(β is a limit ordinal & $\alpha \neq 0$) $\rightarrow \bigcup\{\alpha^\gamma : \gamma \in \beta\} = \bigcup\{\gamma : \gamma \in \alpha^\beta\}$.

Proof: Use theorems 8.5.30, 8.5.22(d), and 8.2.25. ■

THEOREM 8.5.33. $\alpha^{\beta+\gamma} = \alpha^\beta \cdot \alpha^\gamma$.

Proof: By 8.5.29,

$$\alpha^{\beta+\gamma} = \overline{\langle\langle Z(\alpha,\beta+\gamma), W_{\alpha,\beta+\gamma}\rangle\rangle},$$

and by 8.5.29 and 8.5.6

$$\alpha^\beta \cdot \alpha^\gamma = \overline{\langle\langle Z(\alpha,\beta) \times Z(\alpha,\gamma), T\rangle\rangle},$$

where T is the reverse lexiographic ordering on $Z(\alpha,\beta) \times Z(\alpha,\gamma)$. We shall construct a function F from $Z(\alpha,\beta+\gamma)$ to $Z(\alpha,\beta) \times Z(\alpha,\gamma)$ as follows. For each $f \in Z(\alpha,\beta+\gamma)$,

$$F(f) = \langle f|\beta, g\rangle,$$

where $g \in Z(\alpha,\gamma)$, and for each $\delta \in \gamma$,

$$g(\delta) = f(\beta + \delta).$$

It is easy to prove, using 8.4.3, that F is a 1–1 function mapping $Z(\alpha,\beta + \gamma)$ onto $Z(\alpha,\beta) \times Z(\alpha,\gamma)$.

Suppose that $f_1, f_2 \in Z(\alpha,\beta + \gamma)$ and

$$F(f_1) = \langle f_1|\beta, g_1\rangle,$$
$$F(f_2) = \langle f_2|\beta, g_2\rangle.$$

By 8.5.24(b)

$$f_1\, W_{\alpha,\beta+\gamma}\, f_2 \leftrightarrow [f_1 \neq f_2 \;\&\; (\forall\delta)(\delta \text{ is the } E\text{-last element of } \{\xi : \xi \in \beta + \gamma \;\&\; f_1(\xi) \neq f_2(\xi)\} \to f_1(\delta) < f_2(\delta))].$$

By 5.4.3, either $\delta \in \beta$ or $\delta = \beta + \eta$, where $\eta \in \gamma$. If $\delta \in \beta$, then $g_1 = g_2$, so

$$\begin{aligned} f_1\, W_{\alpha,\beta+\gamma}\, f_2 &\leftrightarrow f_1|\beta\, W_{\alpha\beta}\, f_2|\beta \\ &\leftrightarrow F(f_1)\, T\, F(f_2). \end{aligned}$$

If $\delta = \beta + \eta$ where $\eta \in \gamma$, then $g_1 \neq g_2$, so

$$\begin{aligned} f_1\, W_{\alpha,\beta+\gamma}\, f_2 &\leftrightarrow g_1\, W_{\alpha\gamma}\, g_2 \\ &\leftrightarrow F(f_1)\, T\, F(f_2). \end{aligned}$$

Hence, we have shown F is an isomorphism mapping $Z(\alpha,\beta + \gamma)$ onto $Z(\alpha,\beta) \times Z(\alpha,\gamma)$. ∎

THEOREM 8.5.34. $(\alpha^\beta)^\gamma = \alpha^{\beta\gamma}$.

The proof is by transfinite induction on γ and is left as an exercise.

Because multiplication of ordinal numbers is not commutative, it is not true that $(\alpha\beta)^\gamma = \alpha^\gamma\beta^\gamma$ for all ordinal numbers α,β, and γ. To see this, let $\alpha = \omega$ and $\beta = \gamma = 2$. Then

$$\begin{aligned} (\omega\cdot 2)^2 &= (\omega\cdot 2)(\omega\cdot 2) \\ &= \omega\cdot\omega\cdot 2 \\ &= \omega^2\cdot 2, \\ \omega^2\cdot 2^2 &= \omega^2\cdot 4. \end{aligned}$$

However, $\omega^2\cdot 2 \neq \omega^2\cdot 4$.

EXERCISES 8.5

1. Prove each of the following:
   (a) $(n \in \omega \;\&\; n \neq 0) \to n\omega = \omega$
   (b) $(\alpha \neq 0 \;\&\; \beta \neq 0) \to \alpha\omega^\beta = \alpha^+\omega^\beta$
   (c) $\alpha\beta < \alpha\gamma \to \beta < \gamma$

(d) $\alpha\gamma < \beta\gamma \rightarrow \alpha < \beta$
(e) $\alpha\beta = 0 \leftrightarrow (\alpha = 0$ or $\beta = 0)$
(f) $(\alpha < \beta$ & γ is a non-limit ordinal & $\gamma \neq 0) \rightarrow \alpha\gamma < \beta\gamma$
(g) (α is infinite & $\beta \neq 0$ & β is a non-limit ordinal) $\rightarrow (\alpha + 1)\beta = \alpha\beta + 1$
(h) $(1 < \alpha$ & $1 < \beta) \rightarrow \alpha + \beta \leq \alpha\beta$.

2. Prove each of the following:
(a) $\alpha < \beta\gamma \rightarrow (\exists 1\beta_1)(\exists 1\gamma_1)(\beta_1 < \beta$ & $\gamma_1 < \gamma$ & $\alpha = \beta\gamma_1 + \beta_1)$
(b) $\alpha \neq 0 \rightarrow (\forall\beta)(\exists 1\gamma)(\exists 1\delta)(\delta < \alpha$ & $\beta = \alpha\gamma + \delta)$
(c) α is a limit ordinal $\rightarrow (\exists 1\beta)(\alpha = \omega\beta)$
(d) α is a non-limit ordinal $\rightarrow (\exists 1\beta)(\exists 1n)(n \in \omega$ & $n \neq 0$ & $\alpha = \omega\beta + n)$
(e) $\alpha\beta$ is a limit ordinal $\rightarrow$
(($\alpha \neq 0$ & β is a limit ordinal) or ($\beta \neq 0$ & α is a limit ordinal)).

3. Prove theorem 8.5.16.
4. Prove theorem 8.5.18.
5. Prove theorem 8.5.19.
6. Prove theorem 8.5.31.
7. Prove theorem 8.5.34.
8. Prove each of the following:
(a) $(1 < \alpha$ & $\beta < \gamma) \rightarrow \alpha^\beta < \alpha^\gamma$
(b) $\alpha < \beta \rightarrow \alpha^\gamma \leqq \beta^\gamma$
(c) $\alpha^\beta < \alpha^\gamma \rightarrow \beta < \gamma$
(d) $\alpha^\gamma < \beta^\gamma \rightarrow \alpha < \beta$
(e) $(\alpha > 1$ & $\beta > 0) \rightarrow \alpha\beta \leqq \alpha^\beta$
(f) $(\alpha > 0$ & $\beta > 1) \rightarrow \alpha \leqq \beta^\alpha$
(g) $\alpha,\beta < \omega^\delta \rightarrow \alpha + \beta < \omega^\delta$
(h) $\alpha,\beta < \omega^{\omega^\delta} \rightarrow \alpha\beta < \omega^{\omega^\delta}$
(i) $(n \in \omega$ & $n \neq 0$ & $\alpha \neq 0) \rightarrow n\omega^\alpha = \omega^\alpha$.

9. Calculate each of the following sums and products:
(a) $\Sigma_{\alpha \in \omega} 2^\omega$
(b) $\Sigma_{\alpha \in \omega 2} \alpha^2$
(c) $\Sigma_{n \in \omega} \omega n$
(d) $\Sigma_{n \in \omega} \omega^n$
(e) $\Pi_{\alpha \in \omega 2} (\alpha + 1)$
(f) $\Pi_{n \in \omega} \omega^n$
(g) $\Pi_{n \in \omega} (\omega + n)$
(h) $\omega \cdot 1 + \omega \cdot 2 + \omega \cdot 3 + \cdots + 1 + 2 + 3 + \cdots$
(i) $\omega \cdot \omega^2 \cdot \omega^3 \cdots 1 \cdot 2 \cdot 3 \cdots$
(j) $\omega \cdot \omega^2 \cdot \omega^3 \cdots \omega^{n-1} \cdot \omega^{n+1} \cdots \omega^n \cdot 2 \cdot 3 \cdots$.

10. Express each of the following ordinal numbers in the form

$$\omega^{\alpha_n} \cdot a_n + \omega^{\alpha_{n-1}} \cdot a_{n-1} + \cdots + \omega^{\alpha_1} \cdot a_1 + a_0$$

where $\alpha_1 \in \alpha_2 \in \cdots \in \alpha_{n-1} \in \alpha_n$, and $a_i \in \omega$, $a_i \neq 0$, $i = 0, 1, 2, \ldots, n$:
(a) $3 \cdot \omega$
(b) $(\omega + 1)^2$
(c) $\omega \cdot 2 \cdot (\omega + 1)$
(d) $(\omega + 1)2$
(e) $(\omega^2 \cdot 2 + \omega \cdot 4 + 3)5$
(f) $2 + \omega \cdot 2 + \omega^2$
(g) $(\omega^2 \cdot 3 + \omega \cdot 2)(\omega^3 \cdot 2 + \omega \cdot 4 + 2)$.

*8.6. RANK

The notion of rank was originally defined by Mirimanoff (1917) and later expanded upon by Tarski. Rank is a function which we shall designate by the symbol "ρ." For each $x \in \mathfrak{D}(\rho)$, $\rho(x) \in On$. If we assume the axiom of regularity, we can prove that every element in the universe has a rank. That is, every element in the universe belongs to the domain of ρ. Moreover, if we assume that the class of atoms is a set, then we can prove that the class of all elements which have a given rank is a set and, therefore, the universe can be partitioned into a class of sets such that two elements belong to the same set in the partition if and only if they have the same rank.

Before defining rank we shall define some auxiliary concepts. The *ancestral* of an element was defined in exercise 4.3.3. Thus, if f is a function such that $\mathfrak{D}(f) = \omega$, $f(0) = x$, and for all $n \in \omega$, $f(n^+) = \bigcup f(n)$, then

$$N(x) = \bigcup_{n \in \omega} f(n).$$

In other words, if x is a set, then

$$N(x) = x \cup \bigcup x \cup \bigcup\bigcup x \cup \bigcup\bigcup\bigcup x \cup \cdots$$

and if x is an atom, $N(x) = \emptyset$.

A class was defined to be transitive if every element is a subset (4.1.14). Since $N(x)$ may contain atoms as elements it may not be transitive. However, $N(x)$ does have a property which is closely related to transitivity.

Definition 8.6.1. Weakly Transitive
X is *weakly transitive* $=_{\text{Df}} (\forall u)(\forall v)((u \in X \;\&\; v \in u) \rightarrow v \in X)$.

Now we can prove that, if x is a set, then $N(x)$ is the smallest weakly transitive set which contains x as a subset.

Theorem 8.6.2.
(a) $\mathrm{S}(N(x))$
(b) $\mathrm{S}(x) \rightarrow x \subseteq N(x)$
(c) $N(x)$ is weakly transitive
(d) $(\forall Y)((x \subseteq Y \;\&\; Y$ is weakly transitive$) \rightarrow N(x) \subseteq Y)$
(e) $\mathrm{A}(x) \rightarrow N(x) = \emptyset$
(f) $u \in N(x) \leftrightarrow (u \in x$ or $(\exists v)(v \in x \;\&\; u \in N(v)))$.

The proof is left as an exercise.

A class is called *regular* if it satisfies the axiom of regularity.

DEFINITION 8.6.3. Regular

X is *regular* $=_{\text{Df}}$ [A(X) or $X = \emptyset$ or $(\exists u)(\text{A}(u)\ \&\ u \in X)$ or $(\exists u)(u \in X\ \&\ u \cap X = \emptyset)$].

Now, using the concepts of ancestral and regular, we define *Cantorian.*

DEFINITION 8.6.4. Cantorian

(a) x is *Cantorian* $=_{\text{Df}} (\forall y)(y \subseteq N(x) \rightarrow y$ is regular)

(b) $C =_{\text{Df}} \{x : x$ is Cantorian$\}$.

Thus, x is Cantorian if every subset of the ancestral of x is regular. It is easy to prove that every atom is Cantorian, $\emptyset$ is Cantorian, and C is weakly transitive.

THEOREM 8.6.5.

(a) $\text{A}(x) \rightarrow x \in C$

(b) $\emptyset \in C$

(c) C is weakly transitive.

It is also clear that if the axiom of regularity holds, then every element is Cantorian.

THEOREM 8.6.6.® $C = V$.

Next, we shall define a relation E^* as follows:

DEFINITION 8.6.7. $E^* =_{\text{Df}} \{\langle x,y\rangle : x \in N(y)\}$.

THEOREM 8.6.8. E^* is transitive.

Proof: Suppose that

$$x\ E^*\ y\ \&\ y\ E^*\ z.$$

Then

$$x \in N(y)\ \&\ y \in N(z).$$

Since $N(z)$ is weakly transitive $y \in N(z)$ implies $y \subseteq N(z)$ or y is an atom. However, since $x \in N(y)$, it follows from 8.6.2(e) that y is not an atom. Therefore, $y \subseteq N(z)$. But $N(y)$ is the smallest weakly transitive set which contains y as a subset. Therefore, $y \subseteq N(z)$ implies $N(y) \subseteq N(z)$. Consequently, $x \in N(y)$ implies $x \in N(z)$. Thus, $x\ E^*\ z$. ■

In fact, E^* is the smallest transitive relation which contains E as a subclass. The relation E^* is often called the *transitive closure* of E.

The notion of a p.w.o. relation was defined in exercise 7.2.5. $\langle\langle X,R\rangle\rangle$ is a p.w.o. class if $\langle\langle X,R\rangle\rangle$ is a p.o. class and every non-empty subclass of X has an R-minimal element.

THEOREM 8.6.9. $\langle\langle C, E^*\rangle\rangle$ is a p.w.o. class.

Proof: It follows from 8.6.8 that $E^*|C$ is transitive. To prove that $E^*|C$ is antisymmetric we shall prove it is irreflexive. A transitive, irreflexive relation is automatically antisymmetric.

Suppose that $E^*|C$ is not irreflexive. Then there is an $x \in C$ such that $x\ E^*\ x$. Let

$$z = \{y : y \in C \ \&\ y\ E^*\ x \ \&\ x\ E^*\ y\}.$$

Then $x \in z$ and $z \subseteq N(x)$. Therefore, since x is Cantorian, there is a $y \in z$ such that

(1) $$y \cap z = \emptyset.$$

Since $y \in z$, then $x \in N(y)$. Hence, by 8.6.2(f), either

(2) $$x \in y$$

or

(3) $$(\exists u)(u \in y \ \&\ x \in N(u)).$$

If (2) holds, then, since $x \in z$, we would have $x \in y \cap z$, contradicting (1). Suppose (3) holds. Since $N(x)$ is weakly transitive if $u \in y$ and $y \in N(x)$, then $u \in N(x)$. Therefore, if $x \in N(u)$, we would have $u \in z$. But it is also true that $u \in y$. Thus, $u \in y \cap z$, which contradicts (1).

To complete the proof we must show that every non-empty subclass of C has an E^*-minimal element. Suppose that $X \subseteq C$ and $X \neq \emptyset$. Also suppose that $u \in X$. If u is an E^*-minimal element of X, then the theorem is true. If not, then there is a $v \in X$ such that $v \in N(u)$. Let

$$y = \{v : v \in N(u) \ \&\ N(v) \cap X \neq \emptyset\}.$$

If $y = \emptyset$, then for all $v \in N(u)$, $N(v) \cap X = \emptyset$. This implies that every element of $N(u)$ is an E^*-minimal element of X.

Suppose then that $y \neq \emptyset$. Since u is Cantorian and $y \subseteq N(u)$, there is a $v \in y$ such that

(4) $$v \cap y = \emptyset.$$

$N(v) \cap X \neq \emptyset$ because $v \in y$. Suppose $w \in N(v) \cap X$. If $w \notin v$, then, by 8.6.2(f), there is a $t \in v$ such that $w \in N(t)$. Hence, $N(t) \cap X \neq \emptyset$ because $w \in N(t) \cap X$, therefore $t \in v \cap y$. This contradicts (4). Consequently, $w \in v$. If $N(w) \cap X \neq \emptyset$, then, since $N(u)$ is weakly transitive, $w \in v \cap y$, again contradicting (4). Thus, we must have $N(w) \cap X = \emptyset$ and this implies that w is an E^*-minimal element of X. ■

THEOREM 8.6.10. $x \in C \rightarrow \mathrm{S}(\mathrm{S}_{CE^*}(x))$.

Proof: Suppose that $x \in C$. Then

$$\mathrm{S}_{CE^*}(x) = \{y : y \in C \;\&\; y \in N(x)\} \subseteq N(x).$$

Therefore, it follows from 8.6.2(a) that $\mathrm{S}_{CE^*}(x)$ is a set (see exercise 8.6.8). ■

It follows from 8.6.9, 8.6.10, and exercise 8.3.3 that

THEOREM 8.6.11.

$$(\exists 1\rho)[\mathrm{Func}(\rho) \;\&\; \mathfrak{D}(\rho) = C \;\&\; (\forall x)(x \in C \rightarrow \rho(x) = \rho''\mathrm{S}_{CE^*}(x))].$$

Consequently, we make the following definition.

DEFINITION 8.6.12. Rank

(a) $\mathrm{Func}(\rho)$
(b) $\mathfrak{D}(\rho) = C$
(c) $(\forall x)(x \in C \rightarrow \rho(x) =_{\mathrm{Df}} \rho''\mathrm{S}_{CE^*}(X))$.

$\rho(x)$ is called the *rank* of x. It follows from 8.6.12(c) that for all $x \in C$,

$$\rho(x) = \{\rho(u) : u \in C \;\&\; u\, E^*\, x\}.$$

If we assume the axiom of regularity, it follows from 8.6.4 and 8.6.6 that every element has a rank.

THEOREM 8.6.13.® $\mathfrak{D}(\rho) = V$.

We shall prove next that $\mathfrak{R}(\rho) \subseteq On$.

THEOREM 8.6.14. $\mathfrak{R}(\rho) \subseteq On$.

Proof: Suppose that $\mathfrak{R}(\rho) \nsubseteq On$. Then

$$Z = \{y : y \in C \;\&\; \rho(y) \notin On\} \neq \emptyset.$$

Let x be an E^*-minimal element of Z. Then, for all $y \in C$ if $y\, E^*\, x$, then $\rho(y) \in On$. Since $\rho(x) = \{\rho(y) : y \in C \;\&\; y\, E^*\, x\}$, $\rho(x)$ is a set of ordinal numbers. Suppose $\alpha \in \rho(x)$. Then $\alpha = \rho(y)$ for some $y \in C$ such that $y\, E^*\, x$. If $\beta \in \alpha$, then $\beta = \rho(z)$ for some $z \in C$ such that $z\, E^*\, y$. But since E^* is transitive, $z\, E^*\, y$ and $y\, E^*\, x$ imply $z\, E^*\, x$. Therefore, if $\beta \in \alpha$, then $\beta \in \rho(x)$. Consequently, $\rho(x)$ is a transitive set of ordinal numbers and is therefore an ordinal number (8.2.14). This contradicts the definition of x. ■

We leave the proof of the following theorem as an exercise.

THEOREM 8.6.15.

(a) $On \subseteq \mathfrak{D}(\rho)$
(b) $(\forall \alpha)(\rho(\alpha) = \alpha)$
(c) $\mathfrak{R}(\rho) = On$.

Next we shall prove that the rank of x is the smallest ordinal number α such that $\rho(u) < \alpha$ for all $u \in x$.

THEOREM 8.6.16.

$$x \in C \rightarrow \rho(x) = E\text{-first element of } \{\beta : (\forall u)(u \in x \rightarrow \rho(u) < \beta)\}.$$

Proof: We shall sketch the proof and leave the details for the reader. Suppose that $x \in C$. Let

$$Y = \{\beta : (\forall u)(u \in x \rightarrow \rho(u) < \beta)\}$$
$$Z = \{\beta : (\forall u)(u\ E^*\ x \rightarrow \rho(u) < \beta)\}.$$

First prove that $\rho(x)$ is the E-first element of Z. Then prove that $\rho(x)$ is the E-first element of Y by proving that $Z \subseteq Y$ and for each $\beta \in Y$. There is an $\alpha \in Z$ such that $\alpha \leqq \beta$. ■

COROLLARY 8.6.17. $\rho(x) = 0 \leftrightarrow (\mathrm{A}(x) \text{ or } x = \emptyset)$.

Next, we shall study the notion of rank from a slightly different angle.

DEFINITION 8.6.18. $\tau(\alpha) =_{\mathrm{Df}} \{x : \rho(x) \leqq \alpha\}$.

Note that τ is not necessarily a function because $\tau(\alpha)$ may be a proper class.

For convenience we shall denote the class of all atoms by "$\mathcal{A}$."

DEFINITION 8.6.19. Class of Atoms

$$\mathcal{A} =_{\mathrm{Df}} \{x : \mathrm{A}(x)\}.$$

A union of proper classes was defined in 3.5.4. Thus, we have the following theorem:

THEOREM 8.6.20. $\tau(\alpha) = \mathcal{A} \cup \mathcal{P}(\bigcup_{\beta<\alpha} \tau(\beta))$.

Proof: Suppose that $x \in \tau(\alpha)$ and $x \notin \mathcal{A}$. Then

$$u \in x \rightarrow \rho(u) < \rho(x) \leqq \alpha.$$

Consequently, $u \in \tau(\beta)$ for some $\beta < \alpha$. Therefore, $x \subseteq \bigcup_{\beta<\alpha} \tau(\beta)$ or $x \in \mathcal{P}(\bigcup_{\beta<\alpha} \tau(\beta))$.

Conversely, suppose $x \in \mathcal{A} \cup \mathcal{P}(\bigcup_{\beta<\alpha} \tau(\beta))$. If $x \in \mathcal{A}$, then by 8.6.17, $\rho(x) = 0$, so $x \in \tau(\alpha)$. If $x \in \mathcal{P}(\bigcup_{\beta<\alpha} \tau(\beta))$, then $x \subseteq \bigcup_{\beta<\alpha} \tau(\beta)$. Consequently, for all $u \in x$, there is a $\beta < \alpha$ such that $u \in \tau(\beta)$. This implies that

$$(\forall u)(u \in x \rightarrow (\exists \beta)(\beta < \alpha \ \&\ \rho(u) \leqq \beta)).$$

Therefore, by theorem 8.6.16, $\rho(x) \leqq \alpha$, so $x \in \tau(\alpha)$. ■

Let us calculate $\tau(\alpha)$ for several value of α.

$$\begin{aligned}\tau(0) &= \mathcal{A} \cup \mathcal{P}(\textstyle\bigcup_{\beta<0} \tau(\beta))\\ &= \mathcal{A} \cup \mathcal{P}(\emptyset)\\ &= \mathcal{A} \cup \{\emptyset\}.\end{aligned}$$

Of course, this result also follows from 8.6.17 and 8.6.18.

$$\begin{aligned}\tau(1) &= \mathcal{A} \cup \mathcal{P}(\textstyle\bigcup_{\beta<1} \tau(\beta))\\ &= \mathcal{A} \cup \mathcal{P}(\tau(0))\\ &= \mathcal{A} \cup \mathcal{P}(\mathcal{A} \cup \{\emptyset\}).\end{aligned}$$

Therefore, $\rho(x) = 1$ if and only if $x \neq \emptyset$ and $x \subseteq \mathcal{A} \cup \{\emptyset\}$. Now, how to continue is clear:

$$\tau(2) = \mathcal{A} \cup \mathcal{P}(\mathcal{A} \cup \{\emptyset\} \cup \mathcal{P}(\mathcal{A} \cup \{\emptyset\})).$$

Thus, $\rho(x) = 2$ if and only if $x \neq \emptyset$, $x \not\subseteq \mathcal{A} \cup \{\emptyset\}$ and $x \subseteq \mathcal{A} \cup \{\emptyset\} \cup \mathcal{P}(\mathcal{A} \cup \{\emptyset\})$. Intuitively, $\rho(x) = 0$ if x can be defined without using braces, $\{\ \ \}$; $\rho(x) = 1$ if x can be defined using one level of braces; $\rho(x) = 2$ if x can be defined using two levels of braces; etc.

Now, it can easily be shown using transfinite induction that if $\mathcal{A}$ is a set, then so is $\tau(\alpha)$ for each $\alpha \in On$. Then it easily follows from 8.6.18 that if $\mathcal{A}$ is a set, then for each $\alpha \in On$, $\{x : \rho(x) = \alpha\}$ is a set. Thus, we leave the proof of the following theorem as an exercise.

THEOREM 8.6.21. $\quad S(\mathcal{A}) \rightarrow$
(a) $(\forall\alpha)(S(\tau(\alpha)))$
(b) $(\forall\alpha)(S(\{x : \rho(x) = \alpha\}))$.

The only part the axiom of regularity played in the preceding discussion was in the proof that $\mathfrak{D}(\rho) = V$. Without this axiom we can only prove that $\mathfrak{D}(\rho) = C$. In the following discussion we shall assume $\mathfrak{D}(\rho) = V$ and also that $\mathcal{A}$ is a set. The notion of rank will then be applied to solve some problems which arose earlier in the text.

THEOREM 8.6.22.

$$(\mathfrak{D}(\rho) = V \,\&\, S(\mathcal{A})) \rightarrow [\mathrm{Rel}(R) \rightarrow (\exists T)(\mathrm{Rel}(T) \,\&\, \mathfrak{D}(T) = \mathfrak{D}(R) \,\&\, T \subseteq R \,\&\, (\forall u)(u \in \mathfrak{D}(R) \rightarrow S(T''\{u\}))].$$

Proof: Suppose R is a relation. We define a relation T as follows:

$$T = \{\langle u,v\rangle : \langle u,v\rangle \in R \,\&\, (\forall w)(\langle u,w\rangle \in R \rightarrow \rho(v) \leqq \rho(w))\}.$$

Then, assuming $\mathfrak{D}(\rho) = V$, it follows that $\mathfrak{D}(T) = \mathfrak{D}(R)$ and $T \subseteq R$. It follows from the definition of T that $T''\{u\}$ is the class of all elements of smallest rank which belong to $R''\{u\}$. Thus, if $\mathcal{A}$ is a set, it follows from 8.6.21(b), that $T''\{u\}$ is a set. ∎

There were two formulations of the axiom of choice in Section 3.6, namely AC2 and AC3, in which it was specified in the hypothesis that certain classes be sets. If we assume that $\mathfrak{D}(\rho) = V$ and that $\mathfrak{A}$ is a set, then it follows easily from 8.6.22 that these conditions can be omitted and that AC2 and AC3 are equivalent, respectively, to the following two propositions.

AC2S: $\quad \text{Rel}(R) \rightarrow (\exists F)(\text{Func}(F) \,\&\, \mathfrak{D}(F) = \mathfrak{D}(R) \,\&\, F \subseteq R).$

AC3S: $\quad \text{Func}(F) \rightarrow (\exists G)(\text{Func}(G) \,\&\, \mathfrak{D}(G) = \mathfrak{R}(F) \,\&\, G \subseteq F^{-1}).$

Moreover, in Section 5.3 in the formulation of the principle of dependent choices, PD, it is also assumed that a certain class is a set. If $\mathfrak{D}(\rho) = V$ and $\mathfrak{A}$ is a set, it follows from 8.6.22 that this condition can also be omitted in this case and that PD is equivalent to the following statement:

PDS: $\quad (\text{Rel}(R) \,\&\, R \neq \emptyset \,\&\, \mathfrak{D}(R) \subseteq \mathfrak{R}(R)) \rightarrow (\exists f)[\text{Func}(f) \,\&$
$\qquad \mathfrak{D}(f) = \omega \,\&\, \mathfrak{R}(f) \subseteq \mathfrak{D}(R) \,\&\, (\forall n)(n \in \omega \rightarrow f(n)\, R\, f(n+1))].$

EXERCISES 8.6

1. Prove theorem 8.6.2.
2. Prove theorem 8.6.5.
3. Prove theorem 8.6.15.
4. Complete the proof of theorem 8.6.16.
5. Prove corollary 8.6.17.
6. Prove theorem 8.6.21.
7. Prove:
   (a) $\alpha < \beta \rightarrow \tau(\alpha) \in \tau(\beta)$
   (b) $\alpha < \beta \rightarrow \tau(\alpha) \subset \tau(\beta)$.
8. Prove $x \in C \rightarrow \text{S}_{CE^*}(x) = N(x)$.
9. Let us construct a model M^* for set theory as follows:

$$\begin{aligned} V^* &=_{\text{Df}} C \\ \text{A}^*(X) &=_{\text{Df}} \text{A}(X) \\ \text{Cl}^*(X) &=_{\text{Df}} X \subseteq V^* \\ x \in^* Y &=_{\text{Df}} (x \in Y \,\&\, x \in V^* \,\&\, Y \subseteq V^*). \end{aligned}$$

   Prove that axioms A1–A10 are all satisfied in M^* if A1–A8, and A10 are satisfied in the original system, thereby proving that A9, the axiom of regularity, is consistent with the other axioms. (Model M3 of Section 2.4 is a model for set theory in which all the axioms except A9 are satisfied. See exercise 3.6.6. Thus, the axiom of regularity is both consistent with and independent of the other axioms.)
10. Prove that each of the following two models satisfy all the axioms of set theory if all the axioms are satisfied in the original system.

M1:

$$
\begin{aligned}
&V_1 =_{\mathrm{Df}} \{x : \neg \mathrm{A}(x)\ \&\ \mathfrak{a} \cap N(x) = \emptyset\} \\
&\neg \mathrm{A}_1(x) \\
&\mathrm{Cl}_1(X) =_{\mathrm{Df}} X \subseteq V_1 \\
&x \in_1 Y =_{\mathrm{Df}} (x \in Y\ \&\ x \in V_1\ \&\ Y \subseteq V_1).
\end{aligned}
$$

M2: Let $W \subseteq V$ such that

$$(W \times W) \cap E^* = \emptyset\ \&\ u \in W.$$

Then define

$$
\begin{aligned}
V_2 &=_{\mathrm{Df}} \{x : x \cap \textstyle\bigcup_{v \in W} N(v) = \emptyset\} \\
\mathrm{A}_2(X) &=_{\mathrm{Df}} (X \in W\ \&\ X \neq u) \\
\mathrm{Cl}_2(X) &=_{\mathrm{Df}} X \subseteq V_2 \\
x \in_2 Y &=_{\mathrm{Df}} (x \in Y\ \&\ x \in V_2\ \&\ Y \subseteq V_2).
\end{aligned}
$$

(The element u is the empty set.)

Note that in M1 there are no atoms and in M2 there are atoms. The fact that all the axioms of set theory are satisfied in both these models implies that both the existence of atoms and the non-existence of atoms is consistent with the other axioms.

11. Use AC2S to prove

$$(\mathrm{Cl}(X)\ \&\ X \text{ is infinite}) \rightarrow (\exists Y)(Y \subseteq X\ \&\ Y \text{ is denumerable})$$

(see 5.2.16).

Chapter 9: Ordinal Number Theory

9.1. NORMAL FORM

It is easily shown in elementary number theory that if n is any natural number, then there exists a natural number m and natural numbers $a_i < 10$, $i = 0, 1, \ldots, m$, such that

$$n = a_m \cdot 10^m + a_{m-1} \cdot 10^{m-1} + \cdots + a_1 \cdot 10 + a_0$$

and the representation is unique. In fact, it can be shown that 10 can be replaced by any natural number $b > 1$, in which case the condition for the coefficients a_i, $i = 0, 1, \ldots, m$, is that they be natural numbers less than b.

We shall prove a similar theorem for ordinal numbers, taking $b = \omega$, but any other ordinal number larger than 1 would serve as well. First, we shall prove a preliminary lemma.

LEMMA 9.1.1. $[n \in \omega \ \& \ (\forall m)(m \leqq n \rightarrow$
(a) $a_m \in \omega \ \& \ a_m \neq 0 \ \&$
(b) $m + 1 \leqq n \rightarrow \alpha_m < \alpha_{m+1} \ \&$
(c) $\alpha = \omega^{\alpha_n} a_n + \omega^{\alpha_{n-1}} a_{n-1} + \cdots + \omega^{\alpha_0} a_0)] \rightarrow$

$$\alpha < \omega^{\alpha_n{}^+}.$$

Proof: By (c),

$$\begin{aligned} \alpha &= \omega^{\alpha_n} a_n + \omega^{\alpha_{n-1}} a_{n-1} + \cdots + \omega^{\alpha_0} a_0 \\ &\leqq \omega^{\alpha_n} a_n + \omega^{\alpha_n} a_{n-1} + \cdots + \omega^{\alpha_n} a_0 && \text{(b)} \\ &= \omega^{\alpha_n}(a_n + a_{n-1} + \cdots + a_0) && \text{(8.5.14)} \\ &< \omega^{\alpha_n}\omega && \text{(a, 8.5.11)} \\ &= \omega^{\alpha_n{}^+}. && \text{(8.5.22b)} \ \blacksquare \end{aligned}$$

THEOREM 9.1.2.

$$\alpha \neq 0 \rightarrow (\exists 1 n)[n \in \omega \ \& \ (\forall m)(m \leqq n \rightarrow (\exists 1 a_m)(\exists 1 \alpha_m)(a_m < \omega \ \& \ a_m \neq 0 \ \& \ (m + 1 \leq n \rightarrow \alpha_m < \alpha_{m+1}) \ \& \ \alpha = \omega^{\alpha_n} a_n + \omega^{\alpha_{n-1}} a_{n-1} + \cdots + \omega^{\alpha_0} a_0))].$$

Proof: The proof of existence is by transfinite induction. Suppose that the theorem is true for all $\beta < \alpha$. It follows from exercise 8.5.8(f) that $\alpha \leqq \omega^\alpha$. Therefore, it follows from 8.5.22(b) and the monotonicity laws, 8.5.11 and 8.5.13, that $\alpha < \omega^{\alpha^+}$. Let

$$\delta = E\text{-first element of } \{\gamma : \alpha < \omega^\gamma\}.$$

Then

$$\alpha < \omega^\delta$$

and

$$(\forall\gamma)(\gamma < \delta \to \omega^\gamma \leqq \alpha).$$

If δ is a limit ordinal, then

$$\omega^\delta = \bigcup\{\omega^\gamma : \gamma < \delta\}.$$

Therefore, $\alpha < \omega^\delta$ implies there is a $\gamma < \delta$ such that $\alpha < \omega^\gamma$. This contradicts the definition of δ. Moreover, $\delta \neq 0$ because $\alpha \neq 0$. Therefore, there exists an ordinal number η such that $\delta = \eta^+$ and we have

$$\omega^\eta \leqq \alpha$$

and

$$(\forall\gamma)(\gamma > \eta \to \alpha < \omega^\gamma).$$

By exercise 8.5.2(b), there exist unique ordinal numbers b and β such that $\beta < \omega^\eta$ and

$$\alpha = \omega^\eta b + \beta. \tag{1}$$

If $\omega \leqq b$, then there is a γ such that $b = \omega + \gamma$. Then,

$$\begin{aligned} \alpha &= \omega^\eta(\omega + \gamma) + \beta \\ &= \omega^{\eta+1} + \omega^\eta\gamma + \beta. \end{aligned}$$

But this implies that $\omega^\delta = \omega^{\eta+1} \leqq \alpha$ which contradicts the definition of δ. Therefore, $b \in \omega$. Moreover, since $\beta < \omega^\eta$ and $\omega^\eta \leqq \alpha$, then $\beta < \alpha$. Consequently, by the induction hypothesis, the theorem holds for β. Therefore, there is a natural number m, natural numbers a_k, $a_k \neq 0$, $k = 0, 1, \ldots, m$ and ordinal numbers α_k, $k = 0, 1, \ldots, m$ such that if $k + 1 \leqq m$, then $\alpha_k < \alpha_{k+1}$ and

$$\beta = \omega^{\alpha_m}a_m + \omega^{\alpha_{m-1}}a_{m-1} + \cdots + \omega^{\alpha_0}a_0.$$

Since $\beta < \omega^\eta$, then $\alpha_m \leqq \eta$. Suppose that $\alpha_m = \eta$. Then

$$\begin{aligned} \alpha &= \omega^\eta b + \omega^\eta a_m + \omega^{\alpha_{m-1}}a_{m-1} + \cdots + \omega^{\alpha_0}a_0 \\ &= \omega^\eta(b + a_m) + \omega^{\alpha_{m-1}}a_{m-1} + \cdots + \omega^{\alpha_0}a_0. \end{aligned}$$

But this contradicts the uniqueness of b and β in (1). Therefore, $\alpha_m < \eta$. This completes the proof of existence.

To prove uniqueness we argue as follows. Suppose that

$$\begin{aligned}\alpha &= \omega^{\alpha_n}a_n + \omega^{\alpha_{n-1}}a_{n-1} + \cdots + \omega^{\alpha_0}a_0 \\ &= \omega^{\beta_m}b_m + \omega^{\beta_{m-1}}b_{m-1} + \cdots + \omega^{\beta_0}b_0\end{aligned} \tag{2}$$

where n, m, the α's, β's, a's, and b's all satisfy the hypothesis. If $\alpha_n < \beta_m$, then

$$\omega^{\alpha_n^+} \leqq \omega^{\beta_m} \leqq \alpha. \tag{3}$$

But from 9.1.1 we obtain

$$\alpha < \omega^{\alpha_n^+}. \tag{4}$$

This contradicts (3). Because of symmetry, we arrive at a contradiction in an analogous way if $\beta_m < \alpha_n$. Therefore, we must have $\alpha_n = \beta_m$.

Let

$$\gamma = \omega^{\alpha_{n-1}}a_{n-1} + \cdots + \omega^{\alpha_0}a_0$$

and

$$\delta = \omega^{\beta_{m-1}}b_{m-1} + \cdots + \omega^{\beta_0}b_0.$$

Then

$$\alpha = \omega^{\alpha_n}a_n + \gamma \tag{5}$$

and

$$\alpha = \omega^{\alpha_n}b_m + \delta. \tag{6}$$

Since $\alpha_{n-1} < \alpha_n$ and $\beta_{m-1} < \beta_m$, it follows from 9.1.1 that

$$\gamma < \omega^{\alpha_{n-1}^+} \leqq \omega^{\alpha_n} \tag{7}$$

and

$$\beta < \omega^{\beta_{m-1}^+} \leqq \omega^{\alpha_n}.$$

Suppose that $a_n < b_m$. Then there exists a natural number $c \neq 0$ such that

$$b_m = a_n + c.$$

Therefore, from (5) and (6) we obtain

$$\begin{aligned}\omega^{\alpha_n}a_n + \gamma &= \omega^{\alpha_n}b_m + \delta \\ &= \omega^{\alpha_n}(a_n + c) + \delta \\ &= \omega^{\alpha_n}a_n + \omega^{\alpha_n}c + \delta.\end{aligned}$$

Applying the left cancellation law we obtain

$$\gamma = \omega^{\alpha_n}c + \delta.$$

But this contradicts (7). By an analogous argument, we can show that $b_m \nless a_n$. Thus $a_n = b_m$ and $\gamma = \delta$. By continuing this argument for γ and δ, we can prove that the representation of α given in (2) is unique. ∎

If $\alpha \neq 0$, the representation

$$\alpha = \omega^{\alpha_n}a_n + \omega^{\alpha_{n-1}}a_{n-1} + \cdots + \omega^{\alpha_0}a_0$$

where $\alpha_n > \alpha_{n-1} > \cdots > \alpha_0$, $a_n, a_{n-1}, \ldots, a_0 \in \omega$, and $a_n, a_{n-1}, \ldots, a_0 \neq 0$ is called the *normal form* of α. It follows from theorem 9.1.2 that every non-zero ordinal number has a unique normal form.

It is clear from the proof of 9.1.2 that any ordinal number $\beta > 1$ could have been chosen instead of ω. Therefore, the following more general theorem holds.

THEOREM 9.1.3.

$$(\alpha \neq 0 \;\&\; \beta > 1) \rightarrow (\exists 1 n)[n \in \omega \;\&\; (\forall m)(m \leqq n \rightarrow (\exists 1 a_m)(\exists 1 \alpha_m)(a_m < \beta \;\&\; a_m \neq 0 \;\&\; (m + 1 \leqq n \rightarrow \alpha_m < \alpha_{m+1}) \;\&\; \alpha = \beta^{\alpha_n}a_n + \beta^{\alpha_{n-1}}a_{n-1} + \cdots + \beta^{\alpha_0}a_0))].$$

Suppose that $\alpha \neq 0$ and that α is in normal form. If $\alpha_0 \neq 0$, then

$$\alpha = \omega(\omega^{\alpha_n - 1}a_n + \omega^{\alpha_{n-1}-1}a_{n-1} + \cdots + \omega^{\alpha_0 - 1}a_0).$$

Therefore, since ω is a limit ordinal, it follows from theorem 8.5.9 that α is a limit ordinal. On the other hand, if $\alpha_0 = 0$ then, since $a_0 \neq 0$, there is a b_0 such that $a_0 = b_0^+$. Thus,

$$\begin{aligned}\alpha &= \omega^{\alpha_n}a_n + \omega^{\alpha_{n-1}}a_{n-1} + \cdots + \omega^{\alpha_1}a_1 + b_0^+\\ &= (\omega^{\alpha_n}a_n + \omega^{\alpha_{n-1}}a_{n-1} + \cdots + \omega^{\alpha_1}a_1 + b_0)^+.\end{aligned}$$

Therefore, in this case α is a non-limit ordinal. Consequently, we have the following theorem.

THEOREM 9.1.4.

$$(\alpha \neq 0 \;\&\; \alpha = \omega^{\alpha_n}a_n + \omega^{\alpha_{n-1}}a_{n-1} + \cdots + \omega^{\alpha_0}a_0 \text{ is the normal form of } \alpha) \rightarrow (\alpha \text{ is a limit ordinal} \leftrightarrow \alpha_0 \neq 0).$$

Hence, the ordinal number

$$\omega^5 2 + \omega^2 + \omega^3$$

is a limit ordinal, but

$$\omega^\omega 7 + \omega^5 9 + \omega 4 + 7$$

is not.

The remaining part of this section is devoted to calculating the normal form of $\alpha + \beta$, $\alpha\beta$, and α^β.

THEOREM 9.1.5. $(a,b \in \omega \;\&\; a,b \neq 0) \rightarrow$
(a) $\omega^\alpha a + \omega^\alpha b = \omega^\alpha(a + b)$
(b) $\alpha < \beta \rightarrow \omega^\alpha a + \omega^\beta b = \omega^\beta b$.

Proof: Part (a) is true because multiplication from the left is distributive over addition (8.5.14).

To prove (b) we note that if $\alpha < \beta$, then there exists a $\gamma \neq 0$ such that $\beta = \alpha + \gamma$. Thus

$$\begin{aligned} \omega^\alpha a + \omega^\beta b &= \omega^\alpha a + \omega^{\alpha+\gamma} b \\ &= \omega^\alpha a + \omega^\alpha \omega^\gamma b && (8.5.33) \\ &= \omega^\alpha(a + \omega^\gamma b) && (8.5.14) \\ &= \omega^\alpha \omega^\gamma b && (\text{ex. } 8.4.1\text{b}) \\ &= \omega^{\alpha+\gamma} b && (8.5.33) \\ &= \omega^\beta b. \blacksquare \end{aligned}$$

If α and β are given in normal form, we can calculate the normal form of $\alpha + \beta$ using 9.1.5. For example, if

$$\alpha = \omega^\omega 2 + \omega^3 4 + \omega^2$$

and

$$\beta = \omega^3 3 + \omega^2 2 + 1,$$

then

$$\begin{aligned} \alpha + \beta &= \omega^\omega 2 + \omega^3 4 + \omega^2 + \omega^3 3 + \omega^2 2 + 1 \\ &= \omega^\omega 2 + \omega^3 4 + \omega^3 3 + \omega^2 2 + 1 && (9.1.4\text{b}) \\ &= \omega^\omega 2 + \omega^3 7 + \omega^2 2 + 1. && (9.1.4\text{a}) \end{aligned}$$

If

$$\alpha = \omega^6 3 + \omega^2 4 + 2$$

and

$$\beta = \omega^4 5 + \omega^2,$$

then it follows from 9.1.4(b) that

$$\alpha + \beta = \omega^6 3 + \omega^4 5 + \omega^2.$$

If the largest exponent in α is smaller than the largest exponent in β, then $\alpha + \beta = \beta$. Thus, if

$$\alpha = \omega^\omega 4 + \omega^{10} 5 + \omega^3$$

and

$$\beta = \omega^{\omega+1} 3 + \omega 2 + 5,$$

then it follows from 9.1.4(b) that

$$\alpha + \beta = \omega^{\omega+1}3 + \omega 2 + 5.$$

Since multiplication is distributive from the left over addition, if α and β are in normal form, then

$$\alpha\beta = \alpha\omega^{\beta_m}b_m + \alpha\omega^{\beta_{n-1}}b_{m-1} + \cdots + \alpha\omega^{\beta_0}b_0.$$

Consequently, to calculate the product $\alpha\beta$ it is sufficient to calculate a term of the form $\alpha\omega^{\gamma}b$. This is the purpose of the next theorem.

THEOREM 9.1.6.

$(\alpha \neq 0 \;\&\; \alpha = \omega^{\alpha_n}a_n + \gamma$ is the normal form of $\alpha \;\&\; b \in \omega \;\&\; b \neq 0) \rightarrow$

(a) $\alpha b = \omega^{\alpha_n}a_n b + \gamma$
(b) $\beta \neq 0 \rightarrow \alpha\omega^{\beta} = \omega^{\alpha_n+\beta}$
(c) β is a limit ordinal $\rightarrow \alpha(\beta + b) = \omega^{\alpha_n}\beta + \omega^{\alpha_n}a_n b + \gamma$.

Proof: Suppose that $\alpha \neq 0$ and that

(1) $$\alpha = \omega^{\alpha_n}a_n + \gamma$$

is the normal form of α. Then it follows from 9.1.1 that

(2) $$\gamma < \omega^{\alpha_n}.$$

(a) We shall prove (a) by induction on b. If $b = 1$, then (a) is true. Suppose that if $b \in \omega \;\&\; b \neq 0$, then

(3) $$\alpha b = \omega^{\alpha_n}a_n b + \gamma.$$

Now αb^{+} can be calculated as follows:

αb^{+}	$= \alpha b + \alpha$	(8.5.3b)
	$= \omega^{\alpha_n}a_n b + \gamma + \omega^{\alpha_n}a_n + \gamma$	(1,3)
	$= \omega^{\alpha_n}a_n b + \omega^{\alpha_n}a_n + \gamma$	(2,9.1.5a)
	$= \omega^{\alpha_n}a_n b^{+} + \gamma.$	(8.5.3b)

(b) We shall prove (b) by transfinite induction on β. Suppose that (b) holds for all $\gamma < \beta$.

Case 1: $\beta = 1$.

$\alpha\omega$	$= \bigcup_{b<\omega} \alpha b$	(8.5.3c)
	$= \bigcup_{b<\omega}(\omega^{\alpha_n}a_n b + \gamma)$	(a)
	$\leqq \bigcup_{b<\omega} \omega^{\alpha_n}a_n b^{+}$	(2,8.4.12,8.5.3b)
	$= \omega^{\alpha_n}a_n\omega$	(8.5.3c)
	$= \omega^{\alpha_n}\omega$	(Ex. 8.5.1a)
	$= \omega^{\alpha_n^{+}}.$	(8.5.22b)

On the other hand,

$$\begin{aligned} \omega^{\alpha_n^+} &= \omega^{\alpha_n}\omega && \text{(8.5.22b)} \\ &\leqq \alpha\omega && \text{(8.5.13).} \end{aligned}$$

Case 2: $\beta = \gamma^+$.

$$\begin{aligned} \alpha\omega^{\gamma^+} &= \alpha\omega^{\gamma}\omega && \text{(8.5.22b)} \\ &= \omega^{\alpha_n+\gamma}\omega && \text{(induction hypothesis)} \\ &= \omega^{\alpha_n+\gamma^+} && \text{(8.5.22b).} \end{aligned}$$

Case 3: β is a limit ordinal.

$$\begin{aligned} \alpha\omega^{\beta} &= \textstyle\bigcup_{\gamma<\beta} \alpha\omega^{\gamma} && \text{(8.5.3c, 8.5.22c)} \\ &= \textstyle\bigcup_{\gamma<\beta} \omega^{\alpha_n+\gamma} && \text{(induction hypothesis)} \\ &= \omega^{\alpha_n+\beta}. && \text{(8.4.1c, 8.5.22c)} \end{aligned}$$

(c) The proof follows immediately from (a), (b), and the distributive law, 8.5.14. ∎

Now we may use 9.1.6 to calculate the product of two ordinal numbers. For example, if

$$\begin{aligned} \alpha &= \omega^{10}3 + \omega^{2}7 + 3 \\ \beta_1 &= \omega^{5}4 + \omega^{4}9 \\ \beta_2 &= \omega^{5}4 + 9, \end{aligned}$$

then

$$\begin{aligned} \alpha\beta_1 &= \alpha\omega^{5}4 + \alpha\omega^{4}9 && \text{(8.5.14)} \\ &= \omega^{10+5}4 + \omega^{10+4}9 && \text{(9.1.6b)} \\ &= \omega^{15}4 + \omega^{14}9 && \text{(8.5.33)} \end{aligned}$$

and

$$\begin{aligned} \alpha\beta_2 &= \alpha\omega^{5}4 + \alpha 9 && \text{(8.5.14)} \\ &= \omega^{15}4 + \alpha 9 && \text{(9.1.6b, 8.5.33)} \\ &= \omega^{15} + \omega^{10}(27) + \omega^{2}7 + 3. && \text{(9.1.6a)} \end{aligned}$$

The next problem concerns the normal form of α^{β} when both α and β are in normal form. Since $\alpha^{\beta+\gamma} = \alpha^{\beta}\alpha^{\gamma}$, it is sufficient to consider exponents which are of the form $\omega^{\delta}d$, where $d \in \omega$ and $d \neq 0$. We shall consider two cases, $\delta = 0$ and $\delta \neq 0$. Clearly, if both α and β are finite, then α^{β} is finite and is in normal form. Also, if $\beta \leqq 1$ and α is in normal form, then α^{β} is in normal form. Thus, the first case we shall consider assumes that α is infinite and $1 \leqq \beta < \omega$.

THEOREM 9.1.7.

$(\alpha \geqq \omega \;\&\; \alpha = \omega^{\alpha_n}a_n + \omega^{\alpha_{n-1}}a_{n-1} + \cdots + \omega^{\alpha_0}a_0$ is the normal form of α & $\beta \neq 0 \;\&\; \beta < \omega) \rightarrow$

(a) α is a limit ordinal $\rightarrow$

$$\alpha^\beta = \omega^{\alpha_n\beta}a_n + \omega^{\alpha_n(\beta-1)}(\omega^{\alpha_{n-1}}a_{n-1} + \cdots + \omega^{\alpha_0}a_0)$$

(b) α is a non-limit ordinal $\rightarrow$

$$\alpha^\beta = (\omega^{\alpha_n}a_n + \cdots + \omega^{\alpha_1}a_1)^\beta + \alpha^{\beta-1}a_0$$
$$[= (\alpha - a_0)^\beta + (\alpha - a_0)^{\beta-1}a_0 + \cdots + (\alpha - a_0)a_0 + a_0].$$

Proof:

(a) Suppose that α and β satisfy the hypothesis. Then by 9.1.4, $\alpha_0 \neq 0$. The proof is by induction on β. The theorem is obviously true if $\beta = 1$. Suppose the theorem is true for some natural number $m \geqq 1$. Then

(1) $$\alpha^m = \omega^{\alpha_n m}a_n + \omega^{\alpha_n(m-1)}(\omega^{\alpha_{n-1}}a_{n-1} + \cdots + \omega^{\alpha_0}a_0).$$

Let us calculate α^{m^+}.

$$\begin{aligned}
\alpha^{m^+} &= \alpha^m\alpha && (8.5.22b)\\
&= (\omega^{\alpha_n m}a_n + \omega^{\alpha_n(m-1)}(\omega^{\alpha_{n-1}}a_{n-1} + \cdots + \omega^{\alpha_0}a_0))\alpha && (1)\\
&= \omega^{\alpha_n m+\alpha_n}a_n + \omega^{\alpha_n m+\alpha_{n-1}}a_{n-1} + \cdots + \omega^{\alpha_n m+\alpha_0}a_0 && (8.5.14,\ 9.1.6a)\\
&= \omega^{\alpha_n m^+}a_n + \omega^{\alpha_n m}(\omega^{\alpha_{n-1}}a_{n-1} + \cdots + \omega^{\alpha_0}a_0). && (8.5.22a,\ 8.5.33)
\end{aligned}$$

We have proved the theorem for m^+.

(b) The proof is again by induction on β. Again suppose that α and β satisfy the hypothesis. In this case it follows from 9.1.4 that $\alpha_0 = 0$. The theorem is true if $\beta = 1$. Suppose the theorem is true for $m \geqq 1$. Then

(2) $$\alpha^m = (\omega^{\alpha_n}a_n + \cdots + \omega^{\alpha_1}a_1)^m + \alpha^{m-1}a_0.$$

Calculating α^{m^+} we get

$$\begin{aligned}
\alpha^{m^+} &= \alpha^m\alpha && (8.5.22b)\\
&= [(\omega^{\alpha_n}a_n + \cdots + \omega^{\alpha_1}a_1)^m + \alpha^{m-1}a_0]\alpha && (2)\\
&= [\omega^{\alpha_n m}a_n + \omega^{\alpha_n(m-1)}(\omega^{\alpha_{n-1}}a_{n-1} + \cdots + \omega^{\alpha_1}a_1)\\
&\quad + \alpha^{m-1}a_0]\alpha && (1)\\
&= \omega^{\alpha_n m+\alpha_n}a_n + \omega^{\alpha_n m+\alpha_{n-1}}a_{n-1} + \cdots + \omega^{\alpha_n m+\alpha_1}a_1\\
&\quad + [\omega^{\alpha_n m}a_n + \omega^{\alpha_n(m-1)}(\omega^{\alpha_{n-1}}a_{n-1} + \cdots + \omega^{\alpha_1}a_1)\\
&\quad + \alpha^{m-1}a_0]a_0 && (8.5.14,\ 9.1.6a)\\
&= \omega^{\alpha_n m^+}a_n + \omega^{\alpha_n m}(\omega^{\alpha_{n-1}}a_{n-1} + \cdots + \omega^{\alpha_1}a_1)\\
&\quad + [\omega^{\alpha_n m}a_n + \omega^{\alpha_n(m-1)}(\omega^{\alpha_{n-1}}a_{n-1} + \cdots + \omega^{\alpha_1}a_0)\\
&\quad + \alpha^{m-1}a_0]a_0 && (8.5.22b,\ 8.5.33)
\end{aligned}$$

$$= (\omega^{\alpha_n}a_n + \omega^{\alpha_{n-1}}a_{n-1} + \cdots + \omega^{\alpha_1}a_1)^{m^+}$$
$$+ [(\omega^{\alpha_n}a_n + \cdots + \omega^{\alpha_1}a_1)^m + \alpha^{m-1}a_0]a_0 \quad (1)$$
$$= (\omega^{\alpha_n}a_n + \omega^{\alpha_{n-1}}a_{n-1} + \cdots + \omega^{\alpha_1}a_1)^{m^+} + \alpha^m a_0. \quad (2)$$

Thus the theorem is true for m^+. ■

Let us consider two examples which demonstrate the application of 9.1.7.

$$(\omega^2 3 + \omega 2)^4 = \omega^8 3 + \omega^6 \omega 2 \qquad (9.1.7a)$$
$$= \omega^8 3 + \omega^7 2.$$

$$(\omega^2 3 + 2)^4 = (\omega^2 3)^4 + (\omega^2 3 + 2)^3 2 \qquad (9.1.7b)$$
$$= \omega^8 3 + [(\omega^2 3)^3 + (\omega^2 3 + 2)^2 2]2$$
$$= \omega^8 3 + \omega^6 6 + [(\omega^2 \cdot 3)^2 + (\omega^2 3 + 2)2]2$$
$$= \omega^8 3 + \omega^6 6 + \omega^4 6 + \omega^2 6 + 2.$$

The next theorem accounts for the remaining case, $\alpha^{\omega^\beta b}$, where $b \neq 0$ and $\beta \geqq 1$.

THEOREM 9.1.8.

$(\alpha > 1 \;\&\; \alpha = \omega^{\alpha_n}a_n + \omega^{\alpha_{n-1}}a_{n-1} + \cdots + \omega^{\alpha_0}a_0$ is the normal form of α & $b \in \omega \;\&\; b \neq 0 \;\&\; \beta \geqq 1) \rightarrow$

(a) $\alpha \geqq \omega \rightarrow \alpha^{\omega^\beta b} = \omega^{\alpha_n \omega^\beta b}$

(b) $\alpha < \omega \rightarrow$

(i) $(\beta < \omega \;\&\; \gamma^+ = \beta) \rightarrow \alpha^{\omega^\beta b} = \omega^{\omega^\gamma b}$

(ii) $\beta \geqq \omega \rightarrow \alpha^{\omega^\beta b} = \omega^{\omega^\beta b}$.

Proof:

(a) Suppose that α, β, and b satisfy the hypothesis. Since $\alpha \geqq \omega$, we must have $\alpha_n \neq 0$. Thus, by hypothesis and 9.1.1

$$\omega^{\alpha_n} \leqq \alpha < \omega^{\alpha_n^+}.$$

Therefore, by exercise 8.5.8(b),

$$(\omega^{\alpha_n})^{\omega^\beta} \leqq \alpha^{\omega^\beta} \leqq (\omega^{\alpha_n^+})^{\omega^\beta}.$$

Consequently, by 8.5.34,

(1) $$\omega^{\alpha_n \omega^\beta} \leqq \alpha^{\omega^\beta} \leqq \omega^{\alpha_n^+ \omega^\beta}.$$

But, by 9.1.6(b), $\alpha_n \omega^\beta = \alpha_n^+ \omega^\beta$. Hence, from (1) we obtain

(2) $$\omega^{\alpha^\beta} = \omega^{\alpha_n \omega^\beta}.$$

Part (a) follows from (2).

(b) Suppose that $1 < \alpha < \omega$. We shall first consider the case in which $b = 1$.

Suppose that $1 \leqq \beta < \omega$. First we shall calculate α^ω.

$$\text{(3)} \qquad \begin{aligned} \alpha^\omega &= \textstyle\bigcup_{m \in \omega} \alpha^m && \text{(8.5.22d)} \\ &= \omega. \end{aligned}$$

Now suppose that $\beta = \gamma^{++}$ and

$$\text{(4)} \qquad \alpha^{\omega^{\gamma^+}} = \omega^{\omega^\gamma}.$$

Then

$$\begin{aligned} \alpha^{\omega^{\gamma^{++}}} &= \alpha^{\omega^{\gamma^+}\cdot\omega} && \text{(8.5.22b)} \\ &= (\alpha^{\omega^{\gamma^+}})^\omega && \text{(8.5.34)} \\ &= (\omega^{\omega^\gamma})^\omega && \text{(4)} \\ &= \omega^{\omega^{\gamma^+}}. && \text{(8.5.22b)} \end{aligned}$$

Therefore, by mathematical induction, it follows that

$$\text{(5)} \qquad \beta < \omega \;\&\; \gamma^+ = \beta \rightarrow \alpha^{\omega^\beta} = \omega^{\omega^\gamma}.$$

Now suppose that $\beta \geqq \omega$. Then

$$\begin{aligned} \alpha^{\omega^\beta} &= \alpha^{\omega^{1+\beta}} && \text{(ex. 8.1.1b)} \\ &= \alpha^{\omega\omega^\beta} && \text{(8.5.33)} \\ &= (\alpha^\omega)^{\omega^\beta} && \text{(8.5.34)} \\ &= \omega^{\omega^\beta}. && \text{(3)} \end{aligned}$$

Therefore, if $\beta \geqq \omega$ then

$$\text{(6)} \qquad \alpha^{\omega^\beta} = \omega^{\omega^\beta}.$$

Hence, we have proved (i) and (ii) for the case $b = 1$.

To complete the proof of the theorem for an arbitrary b such that $1 \leqq b < \omega$, use (5), (6), and (8.5.34). ∎

It follows immediately from 9.1.8(a) and 8.5.33 that

THEOREM 9.1.9.

$(\alpha \geqq \omega \;\&\; \alpha = \omega^{\alpha_n}a_n + \cdots + \omega^{\alpha_0}a_0$ is the normal form of α & β is a limit ordinal$) \rightarrow$

$$\alpha^\beta = \omega^{\alpha_n\beta}.$$

We shall demonstrate the preceding theorems with several examples.

$$\begin{aligned} 2^{\omega^\omega} + \omega^3 4 + 7 &= 2^{\omega^\omega} 2^{\omega^3 4} 2^7 && \text{(8.5.33)} \\ &= \omega^{\omega^\omega} \omega^{\omega^2 4} 2^7 && \text{(9.1.8b)} \\ &= \omega^{\omega^\omega} + \omega^{\omega^2 4} 2^7 && \text{(8.5.33)} \end{aligned}$$

$$
\begin{aligned}
(\omega^{\omega}3 + \omega^{3}2 + \omega)^{\omega^{2}4+\omega} &= \omega^{\omega(\omega^{2}4+\omega)} && (9.1.9)\\
&= \omega^{\omega^{3}4+\omega^{2}} && (8.5.14)
\end{aligned}
$$

$$
\begin{aligned}
(\omega^{\omega}3 + \omega)^{\omega^{2}4+\omega2+5} &= (\omega^{\omega}3 + \omega)^{\omega^{2}4+\omega2}(\omega^{\omega}3 + \omega)^{5} && (8.5.33)\\
&= \omega^{\omega(\omega^{2}4+\omega2)}(\omega^{\omega}3 + \omega)^{5} && (9.1.9)\\
&= \omega^{\omega(\omega^{2}4+\omega2)}(\omega^{\omega5}3 + \omega^{\omega4}\omega) && (9.1.7a)\\
&= \omega^{\omega^{3}4+\omega^{2}2+\omega^{5}}3 + \omega^{\omega^{3}4+\omega^{2}2+\omega4+1}
\end{aligned}
$$

$$
\begin{aligned}
(\omega^{5}4 + 3)^{\omega^{2}4+\omega2+2} &= (\omega^{5}4 + 3)^{\omega^{2}4+\omega2}(\omega^{5}4 + 3)^{2} && (8.5.33)\\
&= \omega^{5(\omega^{2}4+\omega2)}(\omega^{5}4 + 3)^{2} && (9.1.9)\\
&= \omega^{\omega^{2}4+\omega2}(\omega^{5}4 + 3)^{2} && (\text{ex. } 8.5.1\text{b})\\
&= \omega^{\omega^{2}4+\omega2}[(\omega^{5}4)^{2} + (\omega^{5}4 + 3)3] && (9.1.7\text{b})\\
&= \omega^{\omega^{2}4+\omega2}[\omega^{10}4 + (\omega^{5}4 + 3)3] && (9.1.7\text{a})\\
&= \omega^{\omega^{2}4+\omega2}(\omega^{10}4 + \omega^{5}12 + 3). && (9.1.6\text{b})
\end{aligned}
$$

EXERCISES 9.1

1. Express each of the following ordinal numbers in normal form:
   (a) $\omega^{3}2 + \omega + 7 + \omega^{\omega} + 4$
   (b) $2(\omega + 1)3(\omega + 2)$
   (c) $(\omega^{2} + \omega)(\omega^{2} + \omega + 1)$
   (d) $(\omega^{2}2 + \omega3 + 4)^{\omega}$
   (e) $\omega^{\omega}2 + \omega^{4}3 + \omega^{7} + \omega^{4}2 + \omega^{2}5 + 7$
   (f) $(\omega^{2}2 + \omega3)(\omega^{\omega}5 + \omega^{2}3 + 4)$
   (g) $(\omega^{2}2 + 3)^{\omega^{2}2+3}$
   (h) $(\omega^{\omega^{\omega}}2 + \omega^{\omega}3 + \omega4)^{\omega^{\omega}2+\omega3}$
   (i) $(\omega^{\omega}4 + \omega3 + 2)^{\omega^{4}4+2}$
   (j) $2^{\omega^{\omega}}$
   (k) $(10)^{\omega^{3}3+\omega2+1}$.
2. Determine which of the ordinal numbers in exercise 1 are limit ordinals.
3. Prove:
   (a) $\alpha,\beta \geqq \omega \rightarrow \alpha^{\beta}$ is a limit ordinal
   (b) (α is a limit ordinal & $\beta > 0$) $\rightarrow \alpha^{\beta}$ is a limit ordinal
   (c) (β is a limit ordinal & $\alpha > 1$) $\rightarrow \alpha^{\beta}$ is a limit ordinal.
4. Use theorem 9.1.3 with $\beta = 2$ to express each of the following ordinal numbers as a sum of powers of 2.
   (a) ω
   (b) ω^{2}
   (c) ω^{ω}
   (d) $\omega^{\omega}7 + \omega^{2}3 + 5$.

9.2. PRIMES

Just as in elementary number theory, an ordinal number is a *prime* if it is not the product of two smaller ordinal numbers.

DEFINITION 9.2.1. Primes

$$\alpha > 1 \rightarrow [\ \alpha \text{ is a } prime =_{\text{Df}} \neg(\exists\beta)(\exists\gamma)(1 < \beta,\gamma < \alpha \ \&\ \alpha = \beta\gamma)].$$

Thus, the finite primes are 2, 3, 5, 7, 11, 13, ... Examples of infinite primes are ω, $\omega + 1$, $\omega^2 + 1$, $\omega^3 + 1$, ω^ω, ...

We shall prove that every ordinal number greater than 1, whether it is finite or infinite, can be expressed as a product of a finite number of primes.

THEOREM 9.2.2.

$$\alpha > 1 \rightarrow (\exists n)[n \in \omega \ \&\ (\forall m)(m < n \rightarrow (\exists \alpha_m)(\alpha_m \text{ is a prime } \&\ \alpha = \Pi_{m<n}\, \alpha_m))].$$

Proof: Suppose that $\alpha > 1$. We shall prove the theorem by transfinite induction. Suppose the theorem is true for all δ such that $1 < \delta < \alpha$. If α is a prime, then the theorem is also true for α. If α is not a prime, then by 9.2.1 there exist ordinal numbers β,γ such that $1 < \beta,\gamma < \alpha$ and $\alpha = \beta\gamma$. By the induction hypothesis, the theorem is true for β and γ. Therefore, since $\alpha = \beta\gamma$ the theorem must be true for α. ∎

It can be shown that each natural number can be uniquely represented as a product of primes. That is, if $n \in \omega$ and

$$\begin{aligned} n &= p_1p_2 \cdots p_m, & p_1 \leqq p_2 \leqq \cdots \leqq p_m \\ &= q_1q_2 \cdots q_s, & q_1 \leqq q_2 \leqq \cdots \leqq q_s, \end{aligned}$$

then $m = s$ and $p_i = q_i$, $i = 1, 2, \ldots, m$. However, in the infinite case the representation is not necessarily unique. For example,

$$\begin{aligned} \omega^2 &= \omega\,\omega \\ &= (\omega + 1)\omega. \end{aligned}$$

This is unfortunate since many of the theorems of elementary number theory depend upon the uniqueness of the representation.

However, there is one advantage in ordinal number theory—the infinite primes can be completely categorized. There is an explicit representation for each infinite prime. (This has not been done for the finite primes.) We shall show that a limit ordinal is a prime, if and only if it has the form ω^{ω^α}, and that a non-limit ordinal is a prime, if and only if it has the form $\omega^\beta + 1$ where $\beta > 0$.

THEOREM 9.2.3.

$$\alpha \text{ is a limit ordinal} \rightarrow [\alpha \text{ is a prime} \leftrightarrow (\exists\delta)(\alpha = \omega^{\omega^\delta})].$$

Proof: First we shall prove that ω^{ω^δ} is a prime. If $\delta = 0$ then $\omega^{\omega^\delta} = \omega$, which is a prime since the product of 2 natural numbers is a natural number. Suppose that $\delta > 0$, then by 8.5.31, ω^δ is a limit ordinal. Suppose there exist β and γ such that $1 < \beta,\gamma < \omega^{\omega^\delta}$ and

$$(1) \qquad \alpha = \omega^{\omega^\delta} = \beta\gamma.$$

Since ω^δ is a limit ordinal,

$$\alpha = \bigcup_{\xi < \omega^\delta} \omega^\xi.$$

Therefore, $\beta,\gamma < \alpha$ implies that there exist $\xi_1,\xi_2 < \omega^\delta$ such that

$$\beta < \omega^{\xi_1} \;\&\; \gamma < \omega^{\xi_2}.$$

Hence,

$$(2) \qquad \beta\gamma < \omega^{\xi_1}\omega^{\xi_2} = \omega^{\xi_1+\xi_2}.$$

Since $\xi_1,\xi_2 < \omega^\delta$, it follows from exercise 8.5.8(i) that $\xi_1 + \xi_2 < \omega^\delta$. Therefore,

$$(3) \qquad \omega^{\xi_1+\xi_2} < \omega^{\omega^\delta}. \qquad \text{(ex. 8.5.8a)}$$

But (2) and (3) contradict (1); thus ω^{ω^δ} is a prime.

Conversely, suppose that α is a limit ordinal and is also a prime. Then it follows from exercise 8.5.2(c) that there exists a $\beta > 0$ and γ such that γ is a non-limit ordinal and

$$\alpha = \omega^\beta\gamma.$$

Since α is a prime, either $\gamma = 1$ or $\gamma = \alpha$. The latter alternative is impossible since α is a limit ordinal and γ is not; therefore $\gamma = 1$ and

$$(4) \qquad \alpha = \omega^\beta.$$

If β is a non-limit ordinal and $\beta > 1$, then there is a $\gamma > 0$ such that $\beta = \gamma^+$. Then

$$\alpha = \omega^{\gamma^+} = \omega^\gamma\omega.$$

But this is impossible since α is a prime. Therefore, either $\beta = 1$, in which case the theorem is true, or β is a limit ordinal. If β is a limit ordinal, then it follows from exercise 8.5.2(c) that there is a $\delta \geqq 1$ and a ξ, which is a non-limit ordinal, such that

$$(5) \qquad \beta = \omega^\delta\xi.$$

Clearly, $\xi \leqq \beta$. But since β is a limit ordinal and ξ is not, we must have $\xi < \beta$. We want to prove that $\xi = 1$. Suppose that $\xi > 1$. Then since ξ is a non-limit ordinal, there is an $\eta > 0$ such that

$$\xi = \eta + 1.$$

Therefore, from (5),

$$\begin{aligned}\beta &= \omega^{\delta}(\eta + 1) \\ &= \omega^{\delta}\eta + \omega^{\delta}.\end{aligned}$$

Hence, substituting in (4), we obtain

$$\begin{aligned}\alpha &= \omega^{\omega^{\delta}\eta + \omega^{\delta}} \\ &= \omega^{\omega^{\delta}\eta}\,\omega^{\omega^{\delta}}.\end{aligned}$$

But if $\eta > 0$, this contradicts the fact that α is a prime. Consequently, $\eta = 0$ and $\xi = 1$. Hence, it follows from (4) and (5) that

$$\alpha = \omega^{\omega^{\delta}}. \blacksquare$$

THEOREM 9.2.4.

$(\alpha$ is a non-limit ordinal & $\alpha > \omega) \rightarrow$
$[\alpha$ is a prime $\leftrightarrow (\exists\delta)(\delta > 0$ & $\alpha = \omega^{\delta} + 1)]$.

Proof: We shall prove first that if $\delta > 0$ then $\omega^{\delta} + 1$ is a prime. For suppose that this is not the case. Suppose there exist ordinal numbers β and γ such that

(1) $$1 < \beta,\gamma < \omega^{\delta} + 1$$

and

(2) $$\omega^{\delta} + 1 = \beta\gamma.$$

Since $\omega^{\delta} + 1$ is not a limit ordinal, neither β nor γ are limit ordinals (8.5.9). Therefore, there exist ordinal numbers β_1 and γ_1 such that

$$\beta = \beta_1 + 1, \gamma = \gamma_1 + 1.$$

Thus,

$$\begin{aligned}\omega^{\delta} + 1 &= (\beta_1 + 1)(\gamma_1 + 1) \\ &= (\beta_1 + 1)\gamma_1 + \beta_1 + 1.\end{aligned}$$

Hence, by exercise 8.2.4(c),

(3) $$\omega^{\delta} = (\beta_1 + 1)\gamma_1 + \beta_1.$$

It follows from (3) and exercise 8.5.8(g) that either $\beta_1 = \omega^{\delta}$ or $(\beta_1 + 1)\gamma_1 = \omega^{\delta}$. The first alternative contradicts (1) and the second alternative implies $\beta_1 = 0$ which also contradicts (1). Hence (2) is impossible, and thus $\omega^{\delta} + 1$ is a prime.

Conversely, suppose that α is a non-limit ordinal and a prime. Then it follows from exercises 8.5.2 (c) and (d) that there exist ordinal numbers

n, β, and δ such that $n \in \omega$, $n \neq 0$, $\beta < \alpha$, β is a non-limit ordinal, and

(4) $$\alpha = \omega^{\delta}\beta + n.$$

From (4), exercise 8.5.8(i), and the distributive law it follows that

$$\alpha = n(\omega^{\delta}\beta + 1).$$

Since α is a prime, $n = 1$. Hence,

$$\begin{aligned} \alpha &= \omega^{\delta}\beta + 1 \\ &= (\omega^{\delta} + 1)\beta. \qquad \text{(ex. 8.5.1g)} \end{aligned}$$

But α is a prime; therefore, either $\beta = \alpha$ or $\beta = 1$. The first alternative is impossible since we found above that $\beta < \alpha$. Consequently,

$$\alpha = \omega^{\delta} + 1. \blacksquare$$

Let us consider a few examples of factoring ordinal numbers into prime factors:

$$\begin{aligned} \omega^2 + \omega + 1 &= (\omega + 1)(\omega + 1) \\ \omega^2 3 + 1 &= (\omega^2 + 1)3 \\ \omega^2 + 2 &= 2(\omega^2 + 1) \\ \omega^3 7 + \omega^2 5 + 3 &= 3(\omega^3 7 + \omega^2 5 + 1) \\ &= 3(\omega^3 + \omega^2 5 + 1)7 \\ &= 3(\omega^2 5 + 1)(\omega + 1)7 \\ &= 3(\omega^2 + 1)5(\omega + 1)7 \\ \omega^{\omega} + \omega + 1 &= (\omega + 1)(\omega^{\omega} + 1) \\ \omega^{\omega+1} + \omega^{\omega} + \omega^4 + \omega^2 &= \omega^2(\omega^{\omega+1} + \omega^{\omega} + \omega^2 + 1) \\ &= \omega^2(\omega^2 + 1)(\omega^{\omega+1} + \omega^{\omega} + 1) \\ &= \omega^2(\omega^2 + 1)(\omega^{\omega} + 1)(\omega + 1) \\ &= \omega\omega(\omega^2 + 1)(\omega^{\omega} + 1)(\omega + 1). \end{aligned}$$

EXERCISES 9.2

1. Express each of the following ordinal numbers as a product of primes:
   (a) $\omega^4 + 24$
   (b) $\omega 2 + 1$
   (c) $\omega^2 + \omega 2 + 1$
   (d) $\omega^3 3 + \omega^2 7 + 6$
   (e) $\omega^{\omega} + \omega^3 + \omega^2$
   (f) $\omega^{\omega+1} 2 + \omega^{\omega} 3 + 2$
   (g) $\omega^6 2 + \omega^5 5 + \omega^3 + \omega^2 7$
   (h) $\omega^{\omega 2} 6 + \omega^{\omega+5} 3 + \omega^{\omega+1} 2 + \omega^{\omega} 4.$

9.3. SEQUENCES AND LIMITS

A sequence of ordinal numbers is a function whose domain is an ordinal number and whose range is a subset of *On*. If the domain of the function is α, we shall call it a *sequence of type* α.

DEFINITION 9.3.1. Sequence of Type α

f is a *sequence (of ordinal numbers) of type* $\alpha =_{\mathrm{Df}} f \in (On)^{\alpha}$.

The limit of a sequence of ordinal numbers can be defined in a similar way to the limit of a sequence of real numbers.

DEFINITION 9.3.2. Limit

$$(f \in (On)^{\alpha} \;\&\; \alpha \text{ is a limit ordinal}) \rightarrow$$
$$\lambda = \lim_{\beta<\alpha} f(\beta) =_{\mathrm{Df}} (\forall\mu)[\mu < \lambda \rightarrow (\exists\gamma)(\gamma < \alpha \;\&\; (\forall\delta)(\gamma < \delta < \alpha \rightarrow \mu < f(\delta) \leqq \lambda))].$$

Notice that a sequence of ordinal numbers cannot approach a limit from above. There does not exist an infinite descending sequence of ordinal numbers. Thus, in the definition of limit, we require that all ordinal numbers in the tail of the sequence—that is, all $f(\delta)$'s such that $\gamma < \delta < \alpha$—are close to the limit but are less than or equal to the limit. Therefore, if λ is the limit of the sequence f, for all δ such that $\gamma < \delta < \alpha$,

$$\mu < f(\delta) \leqq \lambda.$$

We find, for example, that

$$\begin{aligned} \omega &= \lim_{n<\omega} n \\ &= \lim_{n<\omega} n^2 \\ &= \lim_{n<\omega} 2^n. \end{aligned}$$

The proof of the following theorem is left as an exercise.

THEOREM 9.3.3.

$$f \in (On)^{\alpha} \;\&\; \alpha \text{ is a limit ordinal} \;\&\; (\exists\lambda)(\lambda = \lim_{\beta<\alpha} f(\beta)) \rightarrow$$

(a) $(\exists 1\lambda)(\lambda = \lim_{\beta<\alpha} f(\beta))$
(b) $(\forall\gamma)(\gamma < \alpha \rightarrow \lim_{\gamma<\beta<\alpha} f(\beta) = \lim_{\beta<\alpha} f(\beta))$.

What sort of sequences have limits? If $f \in (On)^{\omega}$ and

$$f(n) = n \text{ if } n \text{ is odd,}$$

and

$$f(n) = \omega + n \text{ if } n \text{ is even,}$$

then f has no limit. However, if $f \in (On)^\omega$ and for all $n \in \omega$,

$$f(n) = \omega^n,$$

then f does have a limit, $\lim_{n<\omega} f(n) = \omega^\omega$. In general, we can prove that if f is a monotonically increasing sequence, then f has a limit.

DEFINITION 9.3.4. Monotonically Increasing Sequences

(a) f is a *monotonically increasing sequence* of type $\alpha =_{\text{Df}}$
$$[f \in (On)^\alpha \ \&\ (\forall\beta)(\forall\gamma)(\beta < \gamma < \alpha \rightarrow f(\beta) \leqq f(\gamma))]$$

(b) f is a *strictly monotonically increasing sequence* of type $\alpha =_{\text{Df}}$
$$[f \in (On)^\alpha \ \&\ (\forall\beta)(\forall\gamma)(\beta < \gamma < \alpha \rightarrow f(\beta) < f(\gamma))].$$

THEOREM 9.3.5.

$$(f \text{ is a monotonically increasing sequence of type } \alpha \ \&\ \alpha \text{ is a limit ordinal}) \rightarrow (\exists\lambda)(\lambda = \lim_{\beta<\alpha} f(\beta)).$$

Proof: Suppose that f and α satisfy the hypothesis. Let

(1) $$\lambda = \cup_{\beta<\alpha} f(\beta).$$

We shall show that

$$\lambda = \lim_{\beta<\alpha} f(\beta).$$

For suppose that this is not the case. Then by 9.3.2, there is a $\mu < \lambda$ such that for all $\gamma < \alpha$ there is a δ such that $\gamma < \delta < \alpha$ and either

$$\lambda < f(\delta) \text{ or } f(\delta) \leqq \mu.$$

The first alternative contradicts (1). If the second alternative holds, it follows from the fact that f is monotonically increasing that $f(\beta) \leqq \mu$ for all $\beta < \alpha$ and this also contradicts (1). ■

COROLLARY 9.3.6.

$$(f \text{ is a monotonically increasing sequence of type } \alpha \ \&\ \alpha \text{ is a limit ordinal}) \rightarrow \lim_{\beta<\alpha} f(\beta) = \cup_{\beta<\alpha} f(\beta).$$

In particular, if f is any monotonically increasing sequence of natural numbers of type ω, then $\lim_{n\in\omega} f(n) = \omega$. Also, if α is any limit ordinal, then $\lim_{\beta<\alpha} \beta = \alpha$ and thus the name *limit ordinal.*

Of course there are sequences besides monotonically increasing sequences which have limits. For example, if $f \in (On)^\omega$ and

$$f(n) = n \text{ if } n \text{ is odd,}$$
$$f(n) = \omega \text{ if } n \text{ is even,}$$

then $\lim_{n<\omega} f(n) = \omega$, but f is clearly not a monotonically increasing sequence. Not much can be said in general about such sequences.

THEOREM 9.3.7.

$[f,g \in (On)^\alpha$ & α is a limit ordinal & $(\forall\beta)(f(\beta) \leqq g(\beta))$ &
$(\exists\lambda)(\lambda = \lim_{\beta<\alpha} f(\beta))$ & $(\exists\mu)(\mu = \lim_{\beta<\alpha} g(\beta))] \rightarrow \lambda \leqq \mu$.

Proof: Suppose that f,g, and α satisfy the hypothesis and suppose that $\xi < \lambda$. Then, since $\lambda = \lim_{\beta<\alpha} f(\beta)$, there is a $\gamma < \alpha$ such that

(1) $$\xi < f(\beta) \leqq \lambda$$

for all β such that $\gamma < \beta < \alpha$. By hypothesis,

(2) $$f(\beta) \leqq g(\beta)$$

for all $\beta < \alpha$. Since $\mu = \lim_{\beta<\alpha} g(\beta)$, there must be at least one β, say β_1, such that $\gamma < \beta_1 < \alpha$ and

(3) $$g(\beta_1) \leqq \mu.$$

Now, it follows from (1), (2), and (3) that $\xi < \mu$. ∎

A simple example shows that equality of the limits is possible even when $f(\beta) < g(\beta)$ for all $\beta < \alpha$. Let $f,g \in (On)^\omega$ and for all $n \in \omega$

$$f(n) = n,\ g(n) = n + 1.$$

Then $f(n) \in g(n)$ for all $n \in \omega$, but

$$\lim_{n\in\omega} f(n) = \lim_{n\in\omega} g(n) = \omega.$$

If $f \in (On)^\alpha$, we can obtain a *subsequence* by omitting some of the terms from the sequence f.

DEFINITION 9.3.8. Subsequences

$f \in (On)^\alpha \rightarrow [g$ is a β-*subsequence* of $f =_{\mathrm{Df}} (g \in (On)^\beta$ &
$(\exists h)(h \in (On)^\beta$ & h is strictly monotonically increasing &
$\lim_{\gamma<\beta} h(\gamma) = \alpha$ & $g = f \circ h))]$.

Thus for example if $f \in (On)^{\omega 2}$ and for all $\alpha < \omega 2$, $f(\alpha) = \omega^\alpha$, and if $g(\alpha) = \omega^{\omega+\alpha}$ for all $\alpha \in \omega$, then $g \in (On)^\omega$ and g is an ω-subsequence of f.

THEOREM 9.3.9.

$[\alpha$ is a limit ordinal & $f \in (On)^\alpha$ & $(\exists\beta)(g$ is a β-subsequence of $f)$ &
$(\exists\lambda)(\lambda = \lim_{\gamma<\beta} f(\gamma))] \rightarrow \lim_{\gamma<\alpha} f(\gamma) = \lim_{\gamma<\beta} g(\gamma)$.

Proof: Suppose that f and g satisfy the hypothesis and let

(1) $$\lambda = \lim_{\gamma<\alpha} f(\gamma).$$

Suppose that $\delta < \lambda$. Then by (1) there is a $\xi < \alpha$ such that

(2) $$(\forall\gamma)(\xi < \gamma < \alpha \rightarrow \delta < f(\gamma) \leqq \lambda).$$

Since g is a β-subsequence of f for some β, there is an $h \in (On)^{\beta}$ such that

(3) h is strictly monotonically increasing,

(4) $$\lim_{\gamma<\beta} h(\gamma) = \alpha,$$

(5) $$g = f \circ h.$$

By (4) and (3) there is an $\eta < \beta$ such that

$$(\forall\gamma)(\eta < \gamma < \beta \rightarrow \xi < h(\gamma) < \alpha).$$

Therefore, by (2) and (5),

$$(\forall\gamma)(\eta < \gamma < \beta \rightarrow \delta < g(\gamma) \leqq \lambda).$$

Thus, $\lambda = \lim_{\gamma<\beta} g(\gamma)$. ■

EXERCISES 9.3

1. Prove theorem 9.3.3.
2. Calculate each of the following limits:
   (a) $\lim_{n<\omega}(2^n + n)$
   (b) $\lim_{n<\omega} n\omega$
   (c) $\lim_{n<\omega} \omega n$
   (d) $\lim_{\beta<\omega^2} \beta\omega$
   (e) $\lim_{\beta<\omega 2} 2^{\beta}$
   (f) $\lim_{\beta<\omega 2} \beta^2$.
3. Prove $[(f,g \in (On)^{\omega} \;\&\; (\exists\psi)(\psi : f \xrightarrow[\text{onto}]{1-1} g) \;\&\; (\exists\lambda)(\lambda = \lim_{n<\omega} f(n))] \rightarrow$
   $\lim_{n<\omega} f(n) = \lim_{n<\omega} g(n).$
   (In other words, if the terms of a sequence of type ω are rearranged, the limit is not changed.)
4. Prove [α is a limit ordinal & $f \in (On)^{\alpha}$ &
   f is strictly monotonically increasing] $\rightarrow \lim_{\beta<\alpha} f(\beta)$ is a limit ordinal.

9.4. CONTINUOUS FUNCTIONS

If $F \in (On)^{\alpha}$ and α is a limit ordinal, then F is said to be *continuous at* α if $\lim_{\beta<\alpha} F(\beta) = F(\alpha)$.

DEFINITION 9.4.1. Continuous Functions

(a) $F \in (On)^{\beta} \rightarrow [F$ is *continuous* at $\alpha =_{\text{Df}}$
$[\alpha < \beta$ & α is a limit ordinal & $\lim_{\beta<\alpha} F(\beta) = F(\alpha))]$.

(b) $F \in (On)^{On} \rightarrow [F$ is *continuous* $=_{\text{Df}}$
$(\forall\alpha)(\alpha$ is a limit ordinal $\rightarrow \lim_{\beta<\alpha} F(\beta) = F(\alpha))]$.

The following functions are examples of continuous functions.

$$F_1(\beta) = \gamma, \qquad \text{for all } \beta \in On,$$
$$F_2(\beta) = \beta, \qquad \text{for all } \beta \in On.$$

We find that if α is a limit ordinal,

$$\lim_{\beta<\alpha} F_1(\beta) = \gamma = F_1(\alpha),$$
$$\lim_{\beta<\alpha} F_2(\beta) = \alpha = F_2(\alpha).$$

The next theorem provides more examples of continuous functions.

THEOREM 9.4.2.
(a) $(F \in (On)^{On}$ & $F(\beta) = \gamma + \beta) \to F$ is continuous
(b) $(G \in (On)^{On}$ & $G(\beta) = \gamma\beta) \to G$ is continuous
(c) $(H \in (On)^{On}$ & $H(\beta) = \gamma^{\beta}) \to H$ is continuous.

Proof: To prove part (a) we must show that if α is a limit ordinal, then

$$\lim_{\beta<\alpha} F(\beta) = \gamma + \alpha.$$

It follows from 8.4.12 that F is a monotonically increasing function; thus, we have

$$\begin{aligned} F(\alpha) &= \gamma + \alpha \\ &= \bigcup_{\beta<\alpha} (\gamma + \beta) && (8.4.1c) \\ &= \lim_{\beta<\alpha} (\gamma + \beta) && (9.3.6) \\ &= \lim_{\beta<\alpha} F(\beta). \end{aligned}$$

The proofs of (b) and (c) are analogous. Use 8.5.3(c), 8.5.22(c), (d), and the monotonicity laws for multiplication and exponentiation, 8.5.11 and exercise 8.5.8(a). ∎

Strangely enough, if the order of the operations is reversed in 9.4.2, the functions may no longer be continuous. For example, if $F_1, G_1, H_1 \in (On)^{On}$ &

$$F_1(\beta) = \beta + \omega$$
$$G_1(\beta) = \beta\omega$$
$$H_1(\beta) = \beta^{\omega},$$

then

$$\lim_{\beta<\omega} F_1(\beta) = \omega \text{ but } F_1(\omega) = \omega 2$$
$$\lim_{\beta<\omega} G_1(\beta) = \omega \text{ but } G_1(\omega) = \omega^2$$
$$\lim_{\beta<\omega} H_1(\beta) = \omega \text{ but } H_1(\omega) = \omega^{\omega}.$$

Moreover, the preceding examples show that if two functions are continuous neither the sum, product, nor powers of the two functions need be continuous. If

$$K_1(\beta) = \beta \text{ and } K_2(\beta) = \omega,$$

then K_1 and K_2 are both continuous, but

$$\begin{aligned} F_1(\beta) &= K_1(\beta) + K_2(\beta) \\ G_1(\beta) &= K_1(\beta) \cdot K_2(\beta) \\ H_1(\beta) &= (K_1(\beta))^{K_2(\beta)}. \end{aligned}$$

We saw above that neither F_1, G_1, nor H_1 are continuous.

Infinite sums of ordinal numbers were defined in 8.4.18. The definition specifies that if α is a limit ordinal and f is a sequence of type α, then

$$\Sigma_{\beta<\alpha} f(\beta) = \bigcup_{\beta<\alpha} \Sigma_{\gamma<\beta} f(\gamma).$$

Let

$$g(\beta) = \Sigma_{\gamma<\beta} f(\gamma).$$

Then g is a sequence of type α. Moreover, it follows from 8.4.22 that g is a monotonically increasing sequence. Consequently, by 9.3.6, the sequence g has a limit and

$$\begin{aligned} \lim_{\beta<\alpha} g(\beta) &= \bigcup_{\beta<\alpha} g(\beta) \\ &= \Sigma_{\beta<\alpha} f(\beta). \end{aligned}$$

In other words,

THEOREM 9.4.3.

$$(\alpha \text{ is a limit ordinal } \& f \in (On)^{\alpha}) \rightarrow \Sigma_{\beta<\alpha} f(\beta) = \lim_{\beta<\alpha} \Sigma_{\beta<\alpha} f(\gamma).$$

Thus, the infinite sum is a continuous function.

There is a similar result for the infinite product.

THEOREM 9.4.4.

$$[\alpha \text{ is a limit ordinal } \& f \in (On)^{\alpha} \ \& \ (\forall\beta)(\beta < \alpha \rightarrow f(\beta) \neq 0] \rightarrow \Pi_{\beta<\alpha} f(\beta) = \lim_{\beta<\alpha} \Pi_{\gamma<\beta} f(\gamma).$$

The proof is left as an exercise.

In the last theorem of this section, we prove that the limit of an infinite monotonically increasing sequence of monotonically increasing continuous functions is continuous.

THEOREM 9.4.5.

(a) [α & β are limit ordinals & $\beta < \gamma$ &

(b) $(\forall\delta)(\delta < \alpha \rightarrow f_\delta \in (On)^\gamma)$ &

(c) $(\forall\xi)(\forall\delta_1)(\forall\delta_2)(\xi < \gamma \;\&\; \delta_1 < \delta_2 < \alpha) \rightarrow f_{\delta_1}(\xi) \leqq f_{\delta_2}(\xi))$ &

(d) $(\forall\delta)(\forall\xi_1)(\forall\xi_2)((\delta < \alpha \;\&\; \xi_1 < \xi_2 < \gamma) \rightarrow f_\delta(\xi_1) \leqq f_\delta(\xi_2))$ &

(e) $(\forall\delta)(\delta < \alpha \rightarrow f_\delta$ is continuous at $\beta)$ &

(f) $(\forall\xi)(\xi < \gamma \rightarrow \lim_{\delta<\alpha} f_\delta(\xi) = f(\xi))] \rightarrow$

$(f \in (On)^\gamma$ & f is continuous at $\beta)$.

Proof: Let us assume that (a)–(f) hold. It follows from (c), (f), and 9.3.5 that $f(\xi)$ exists for each $\xi < \gamma$. Therefore, $f \in (On)^\gamma$. Moreover, it follows from (d), (f), and 9.3.7 that

(1) $$(\forall\xi_1)(\forall\xi_2)(\xi_1 < \xi_2 < \gamma \rightarrow f(\xi_1) \leqq f(\xi_2)).$$

Thus, f is a monotonically increasing function. To prove f is continuous at β we must show that

$$\lim_{\delta<\beta} f(\delta) = f(\beta).$$

It follows from (1) and 9.3.5 that $\lim_{\delta<\beta} f(\delta)$ exists. Let

$$\lambda = \lim_{\delta<\beta} f(\delta).$$

Suppose that $\mu \in \lambda$. Then by 9.3.2, there is a $\xi < \beta$ such that if $\xi < \delta < \beta$, then $\mu \in f(\delta)$. Therefore, it follows from (1) that $\mu \in f(\beta)$.

Conversely, suppose that $\mu \in f(\beta)$. Then it follows from (f) and 9.3.2 that there is a $\xi < \alpha$ such that

(2) $$(\forall\delta)(\xi < \delta < \alpha \rightarrow \mu \in f_\delta(\beta)).$$

By (e), if $\delta < \alpha$ then f_δ is continuous at β. Therefore, by 9.4.1,

$$f_\delta(\beta) = \lim_{\eta<\beta} f_\delta(\eta).$$

Thus, by 9.3.2, there is a $\eta_1 < \beta$ such that

(3) $$(\forall\eta)(\eta_1 < \eta < \beta \rightarrow \mu \in f_\delta(\eta)).$$

Now we can infer from (2) and (3) that for some $\delta < \alpha$, say δ_1, and some $\xi < \beta$, say ξ_1, $\mu \in f_{\delta_1}(\xi_1)$.

Consequently, by (c) and (f), $\mu \in f(\xi_1)$. Thus it follows from (1) that $\mu \in \lambda$. Hence, we have shown that $\lambda = f(\beta)$. ■

The conclusion of 9.4.5 may not be true if either (c) or (d) of the hypothesis is false. For example, let $\alpha = \beta = \omega$ and $\gamma = \omega + 1$. For each $n < \omega$ and $\xi < \omega + 1$, define

$$f_n(\xi) = \begin{cases} 1, & \text{if } \xi \leqq n \\ \omega, & \text{if } \xi > n. \end{cases}$$

Then

$$f(\xi) = \lim_{n<\omega} f_n(\xi) = \begin{cases} 1, & \text{if } \xi < \omega \\ \omega, & \text{if } \xi = \omega. \end{cases}$$

It is easy to see that (a), (b), (d), (e), and (f) of the hypothesis of 9.4.5 are satisfied. But (c) is not true since $f_1(2) = \omega$ and $f_2(2) = 1$. Moreover, f is not continuous at ω.

$$f(\omega) = \omega$$
$$\lim_{\xi<\omega} f(\xi) = 1.$$

Similarly, the following example shows that if (d) is not true, then the theorem is false. Again assume that $\alpha = \beta = \omega$ and $\gamma = \omega + 1$. For each $n < \omega$ and $\xi < \omega + 1$, let

$$f_n(\xi) = \begin{cases} \omega, & \text{if } \xi \leqq n \\ 1, & \text{if } \xi > n. \end{cases}$$

Then

$$f(\xi) = \lim_{n<\omega} f_n(\xi) = \begin{cases} \omega, & \text{if } \xi < \omega \\ 1, & \text{if } \xi \geqq \omega. \end{cases}$$

In this case, the whole hypothesis of 9.4.5 is satisfied except for (d)–$f_2(2) = \omega$ and $f_2(3) = 1$. Further, f is not continuous at ω since

$$f(\omega) = 1$$
$$\lim_{\xi<\omega} f(\xi) = \omega.$$

EXERCISES 9.4

1. Prove theorem 9.4.4.
2. Determine which of the following functions are continuous: for each $\alpha \in On$:
   (a) $F(\alpha) = \alpha + 1$
   (b) $F(\alpha) = \alpha^2$
   (c) $F(\alpha) = \alpha 2$
   (d) $F(\alpha) = \omega^\alpha + \alpha$
   (e) $F(\alpha) = \begin{cases} \alpha, & \text{if } \alpha < \omega \\ \omega, & \text{if } \alpha \geqq \omega \end{cases}$
   (f) $F(\alpha) = \begin{cases} \alpha + 1, & \text{if } \alpha \text{ is a non-limit ordinal} \\ \alpha, & \text{if } \alpha \text{ is a limit ordinal.} \end{cases}$
3. Prove: ($f, g \in (On)^\alpha$ & α is a limit ordinal) $\rightarrow$
   (a) $\lim_{\beta<\alpha}(f(\beta) + g(\beta)) \leqq \lim_{\beta<\alpha} f(\beta) + \lim_{\beta<\alpha} g(\beta)$
   (b) $\lim_{\beta<\alpha}(f(\beta) \cdot g(\beta)) \leqq (\lim_{\beta<\alpha} f(\beta))(\lim_{\beta<\alpha} g(\beta))$.
4. Prove [α is a limit ordinal & $f \in (On)^\alpha$ & $(\forall\beta)(\beta < \alpha \rightarrow f(\beta) \neq 0)$] $\rightarrow$ $\Sigma_{\beta<\alpha} f(\beta)$ is a limit ordinal.
5. Prove [α is a limit ordinal & $f \in (On)^\alpha$ & $(\forall\beta)(\beta < \alpha \rightarrow f(\beta) > 1)$] $\rightarrow$ $\Pi_{\beta<\alpha} f(\beta)$ is a limit ordinal.

6. Prove ($f \in (On)^\omega$ & f is monotonically increasing) $\rightarrow$
$\Sigma_{n<\omega} f(n) = \lim_{n<\omega}(f(n)\cdot\omega)$.
7. Prove $n \in \omega \rightarrow \Sigma_{\alpha<\omega^n}\alpha = \omega^{2n-1}$.
8. If $\alpha! = \Pi_{1\leqq\beta\leqq\alpha}\beta$, calculate each of the following:
   (a) $\omega!$ (c) $(\omega!)!$
   (b) $(\omega\cdot 2)!$ (d) $(\omega^\omega)!$
9. Prove $(\forall\alpha)(f(\alpha) = \alpha!) \rightarrow f$ is not continuous at ω.
10. Prove ($F \in (On)^{On}$ & F is a continuous, strictly monotonically increasing function) $\rightarrow (\exists\alpha)(F(\alpha) = \alpha)$.

9.5. EPSILON NUMBERS

In this section we shall discuss some of the properties of a certain class of limit ordinals which Cantor has called *epsilon numbers.*

DEFINITION 9.5.1. Epsilon Numbers

$$\alpha \text{ is an } \textit{epsilon number} =_{\text{Df}} \alpha = \omega^\alpha.$$

The ordinal number ω^α is a limit ordinal if $\alpha \neq 0$; therefore, every epsilon number is a limit ordinal. But not every limit ordinal is an epsilon number. For example, ω is a limit ordinal but $\omega \neq \omega^\omega$. Epsilon numbers do exist, however. Suppose that

$$\alpha = 1 + \omega + \omega^\omega + \omega^{\omega^\omega} + \cdots.$$

In other words,

$$\alpha = \Sigma_{n<\omega} f(n)$$

where

$$f(0) = 1$$
$$f(n^+) = \omega^{f(n)}.$$

Let

$$\sigma_n = \Sigma_{m\leqq n} f(m).$$

Then, by 9.4.3,

$$\alpha = \lim_{n<\omega}\sigma_n.$$

It follows from the definition of f and from 9.1.5(b) that

$$f(n) + f(n^+) = f(n^+).$$

Therefore,

$$\sigma_n = f(n).$$

Since f is a strictly monotonically increasing function, it follows from exercise 9.3.4 that α is a limit ordinal. Since the exponential function is a continuous function of its exponent,

$$\begin{aligned} \omega^\alpha &= \lim_{n<\omega} \omega^{f(n)} \\ &= \lim_{n<\omega} f(n^+) \\ &= \alpha. \end{aligned}$$

Thus, α is an epsilon number and will be denoted hereafter by ϵ_0. Therefore,

$$\epsilon_0 = 1 + \omega + \omega^\omega + \omega^{\omega^\omega} + \cdots.$$

In fact, ϵ_0 is the smallest epsilon number. For suppose that β is an epsilon number. We shall show that $f(n) < \beta$ for each $n \in \omega$. Since $f(0) = 1$ and β is infinite, $f(0) \in \beta$. Suppose that $f(n) \in \beta$. Then

$$\begin{aligned} f(n^+) &= \omega^{f(n)} \\ &< \omega^\beta \\ &= \beta. \end{aligned}$$

Consequently, it follows by mathematical induction that $f(n) \in \beta$ for all $n \in \omega$. Therefore,

$$\epsilon_0 = \lim_{n<\omega} f(n) \leqq \beta.$$

Thus, we have shown

THEOREM 9.5.2.

ϵ_0 is the smallest epsilon number.

DEFINITION 9.5.3.

$$E(\alpha) =_{\mathrm{Df}} (\alpha + 1) + \omega^{\alpha+1} + \omega^{\omega^{\alpha+1}} + \omega^{\omega^{\omega^{\alpha+1}}} + \cdots.$$

THEOREM 9.5.4.

$E(\alpha)$ is an epsilon number & $\alpha < E(\alpha)$ &
$\neg(\exists\beta)(\beta$ is an epsilon number & $\alpha < \beta < E(\alpha))$.

The proof is similar to the proof of 9.5.2 and is left as an exercise.

COROLLARY 9.5.5.

$[\alpha < \beta$ & $\neg(\exists\gamma)(\gamma$ is an epsilon number & $\alpha < \gamma \leqq \beta)] \rightarrow E(\alpha) = E(\beta)$.

Thus ϵ_0 is the smallest epsilon number; $\epsilon_1 = E(\epsilon_0)$ is next; $\epsilon_2 = E(\epsilon_1)$ is third; and in general $\epsilon_{\alpha^+} = E(\epsilon_\alpha)$ for each $\alpha \in \mathrm{On}$.

Suppose that α is a limit ordinal and that

$$\gamma = \lim_{\beta<\alpha} \epsilon_\beta.$$

Then

$$\begin{aligned}\omega^{\gamma} &= \lim_{\beta<\alpha} \omega^{\epsilon_\beta} \\ &= \lim_{\beta<\alpha} \epsilon_\beta \\ &= \gamma.\end{aligned}$$

Therefore, γ is an epsilon number. Moreover, γ is the smallest epsilon number which is larger than ϵ_β for all $\beta < \alpha$. Hence, we define,

$$\epsilon_\alpha = \lim_{\beta<\alpha} \epsilon_\beta.$$

Formally, we make the following definition:

DEFINITION 9.5.6.
(a) $\epsilon_0 =_{\text{Df}} E(0)$
(b) $(\forall\alpha)(\epsilon_{\alpha^+} =_{\text{Df}} E(\epsilon_\alpha))$
(c) $(\forall\alpha)(\alpha$ is a limit ordinal $\rightarrow \epsilon_\alpha =_{\text{Df}} \lim_{\beta<\alpha} \epsilon_\beta)$.

It follows from the transfinite recursion theorem that there exists a unique function ϵ on *On* satisfying (a)–(c) of 9.5.6. Moreover, we have

THEOREM 9.5.7.
(a) $(\forall\alpha)(\epsilon_\alpha$ is an epsilon number)
(b) $(\forall\beta)(\beta$ is an epsilon number $\rightarrow (\exists\alpha)(\beta = \epsilon_\alpha))$.

Some additional properties of epsilon numbers are given in the following theorems.

THEOREM 9.5.8.

$$\beta \text{ is an epsilon number} \rightarrow$$

(a) $(\forall\alpha)(\alpha < \beta \rightarrow \alpha + \beta = \beta)$
(b) $(\forall\alpha)(1 \leqq \alpha < \beta \rightarrow \alpha\beta = \beta)$
(c) $(\forall\alpha)(2 \leqq \alpha < \beta \rightarrow \alpha^\beta = \beta)$.

Proof: Suppose the normal form of α is given by the following formula:

$$\alpha = \omega^{\alpha_n}a_n + \omega^{\alpha_{n-1}}a_{n-1} + \cdots + \omega^{\alpha_0}a_0.$$

Suppose that β is an epsilon number. Then $\beta = \omega^\beta$. If $\alpha < \beta$ then $\alpha < \omega^\beta$, and thus $\alpha_n < \beta$. Therefore, by 9.1.5(b), $\alpha + \beta = \beta$, which proves (a).

By 9.1.6(a), if $\alpha \neq 0$ then $\alpha\beta = \omega^{\alpha_n+\beta}$. But if $\alpha < \beta$ then $\alpha_n < \beta$, and thus by (a), $\alpha_n + \beta = \beta$. Therefore, $\alpha\beta = \omega^\beta = \beta$.

Finally, to prove (c), suppose that $2 \leqq \alpha < \beta$. Then

$$\alpha^\beta = \alpha^{\omega\beta} = \begin{cases} \omega^{\omega^\beta}, & \text{if } \alpha < \omega \\ \omega^{\alpha_n\omega\beta}, & \text{if } \alpha \geqq \omega. \end{cases} \tag{9.1.8}$$

Since $\omega^\beta = \beta$ and $1 \leqq \alpha_n < \beta$, it follows from part (b) that $\alpha_n\omega^\beta = \beta$. Therefore, $\alpha^\beta = \omega^\beta = \beta$. ∎

It is clear that neither the converse of 9.5.8(a) or (b) is true. For example,

$$\omega + \omega^\omega = \omega^\omega$$

and

$$\omega \cdot \omega^\omega = \omega^\omega,$$

but ω^ω is not an epsilon number. Moreover, the converse of (c) is not true either because if $n \in \omega$, then $n^\omega = \omega$ and ω is not an epsilon number. However, we can prove a partial converse of (c).

THEOREM 9.5.9.

$(\exists\alpha)(\alpha \geqq \omega \ \&\ \alpha^\beta = \beta) \rightarrow \beta$ is an epsilon number.

Proof: Suppose that $\alpha \geqq \omega$ and $\alpha^\beta = \beta$. Then

$$\beta = \alpha^\beta \geqq \omega^\beta \geqq \beta.$$

Therefore, $\beta = \omega^\beta$, and thus β is an epsilon number. ∎

The final theorem in this section gives another necessary and sufficient condition for an ordinal number to be an epsilon number.

THEOREM 9.5.10.

γ is an epsilon number $\leftrightarrow [\gamma > \omega \ \&\ (\forall\alpha)(\forall\beta)(\alpha,\beta < \gamma \rightarrow \alpha^\beta < \gamma)]$.

Proof: Suppose that γ is an epsilon number. Then $\gamma > \omega$. Suppose that $\alpha,\beta < \gamma$. If $\alpha = 0$ or $\alpha = 1$, then $\alpha^\beta = 0$ or $\alpha^\beta = 1$ respectively, so that $\alpha^\beta < \gamma$. If $2 \leqq \alpha < \gamma$ and $\beta < \gamma$, then by exercise 8.5.8(a) and 9.5.8(c),

$$\alpha^\beta < \alpha^\gamma = \gamma.$$

Conversely, suppose that $\gamma > \omega$ and for all $\alpha,\beta < \gamma$, $\alpha^\beta < \gamma$. First we shall show that γ must be a limit ordinal. For suppose that $\gamma = \delta^+$ and $\delta \geqq \omega$. Then by hypothesis, since $\delta < \gamma$, $\delta^\delta < \gamma$ or $\delta^\delta \leqq \delta$. But this is impossible if $\delta > 1$. Therefore, γ is a limit ordinal and

$$\gamma = \lim_{\xi<\gamma} \xi.$$

Since $\omega < \gamma$, $\omega^\xi < \gamma$ for all $\xi < \gamma$. Therefore,

$$\omega^\gamma = \lim_{\xi<\gamma} \omega^\xi \leqq \gamma.$$

But, it is always true that

$$\gamma \leqq \omega^\gamma.$$

Consequently, $\gamma = \omega^\gamma$, so γ must be an epsilon number. ∎

See exercise 9.5.6 for an alternative development of the epsilon numbers. Additional results in ordinal number theory can be found in Sierpinski (1960) Chapter XIV.

EXERCISES 9.5

1. Prove theorem 9.5.4.
2. Prove α is an epsilon number $\leftrightarrow (\alpha > \omega \,\&\, 2^\alpha = \alpha)$.
3. Prove:
   (a) $\alpha^\beta = \beta \rightarrow \alpha\beta = \beta$
   (b) $\alpha\beta = \beta \rightarrow \alpha + \beta = \beta$.
4. Prove β is an epsilon number $\rightarrow (\forall\alpha)(\alpha^{\omega^\beta} = (\alpha^\omega)^\beta)$.
5. Prove $(\alpha < \beta \,\&\, \alpha$ is a limit ordinal $\&\, \beta$ is an epsilon number$) \rightarrow \alpha^{\beta\alpha} = (\beta\alpha)^\alpha$.
6. Let $F = \{\langle\alpha,\omega^\alpha\rangle : \alpha \in On\}$.
   Prove:
   (a) F is a continuous, strictly monotonically increasing function.
   (b) $\{\alpha : F(\alpha) = \alpha\} \approx On$.
   (The fixed points of F are the epsilon numbers.)

Chapter 10: Propositions Equivalent to the Axiom of Choice

10.1. THE WELL-ORDERING THEOREM

In 1904 E. Zermelo published his proof that the axiom of choice implies the well-ordering theorem. Previously the well-ordering theorem was considered self-evident and was used without hesitation when needed by Cantor and others.

The set form of the well-ordering theorem states that *every set can be well-ordered.* However, this statement tends to be misleading. It should be understood to mean that given any set x, then there *exists* a relation R which well-orders x. The relation R may have no relationship whatever with any previously defined ordering on x. Moreover, there are well-known sets for which no well-ordering has ever been found—the set of real numbers for example. In fact, there are sets commonly used in mathematics for which no linear ordering has ever been found—for example, the set of all real functions of a real variable. Consequently, the statement that every set can be well-ordered is quite a strong statement to make. However, we shall prove that it is equivalent to the axiom of choice. (Just as is the case for the axiom of choice, there are class forms and set forms of the well-ordering theorem. We shall discuss the set forms first. The class forms may be omitted in a short course.)

w1: $\quad S(x) \rightarrow (\exists R)(\mathrm{Rel}(R) \;\&\; \langle\langle x, R\rangle\rangle \text{ is a w.o. set}).$

w2: $\quad S(x) \rightarrow (\exists \alpha)(\alpha \in On \;\&\; x \approx \alpha).$

Since each ordinal number is a w.o. set, then w2 implies w1. It follows from theorem 8.2.27, that w1 implies w2. Thus we have,

THEOREM 10.1.1. $\quad$ w1 $\leftrightarrow$ w2.

It is also easy to prove that the well-ordering theorem implies the axiom of choice.

THEOREM 10.1.2. w1 → a8.

Proof: Let x be a non-empty set of non-empty pairwise disjoint sets. Let R be a w.o. relation on $\bigcup x$. We can choose an element from each set $u \in x$ by choosing the R-first element of $u \subseteq \bigcup x$. Therefore, a choice set

$$c = \{v:(\exists u)(u \in x \;\&\; v \text{ is the } R\text{-first element of } u)\}. \blacksquare$$

The proof that the axiom of choice implies the well-ordering theorem is not quite so easy. The proof given here is essentially the same as Zermelo's original proof (1904). The intuitive approach is as follows. Let x be a non-empty set and let f be a choice function on the non-empty subsets of x. Now, let $f(x) = a$ be the first element of x; $f(x \sim \{a\}) = b$, the second element; $f(x \sim \{a,b\})$, the third element; etc. Thus, we can see intuitively that we can use a choice function to well-order x. The formal proof follows.

THEOREM 10.1.3. ac1 → w2.

Proof: Let x be a non-empty set and let f be a choice function on $\mathcal{P}(x) \sim \{\emptyset\}$. Define $f(\emptyset) = u$, where u is some element which does not belong to x. Now, define a function G on On as follows: for each $\alpha \in On$,

$$G(\alpha) = f(x \sim G''\alpha).$$

We have, for example,

$$G(0) = f(x \sim G''0) = f(x)$$
$$G(1) = f(x \sim G''1) = f(x \sim \{f(x)\}), \text{ etc.}$$

It is easy to see, using the transfinite recursion theorem IV, 8.3.4, and the definition of f that the function G exists and is unique and $\mathcal{R}(G) \subseteq x$.

Suppose that $G(\alpha) = u$ for some $\alpha \in On$. That is, $x \sim G''\alpha = \emptyset$ for some $\alpha \in On$. Then $G(\beta) = u$ for all $\beta > \alpha$, because if $\alpha < \beta$, then $G''\alpha \subseteq G''\beta$. Let

$$Y = \{\alpha : G(\alpha) \neq u\}.$$

Then Y is either an ordinal number or On.

We shall show that $G|Y$ is 1–1. Suppose $\alpha,\beta \in Y$ and $\alpha < \beta$. Then

$$G(\beta) = f(x \sim G''\beta) \in x \sim G''\beta.$$

But, if $\alpha < \beta$ then $G(\alpha) \in G''\beta$, so

$$G(\alpha) \notin x \sim G''\beta.$$

Therefore, $G(\alpha) \neq G(\beta)$.

Suppose $Y = On$. Then G would be a 1–1 function mapping On

into x. This is impossible since On is a proper class and x is a set. Thus, $Y \in On$. Suppose $G''Y \subset x$. Then

$$G(Y) = f(x \sim G''Y) \neq u$$

which implies $Y \in Y$. But this is impossible because Y is an ordinal number. Consequently, G is a 1–1 function mapping Y onto x, and since Y is an ordinal number, this proves w2. ∎

We shall discuss three class forms of the well-ordering theorem in this section. The first is obtained from w1 by changing the order of the quantifiers.

W1: $(\exists R)[\mathrm{Rel}(R) \ \& \ (\forall x)(\mathrm{S}(x) \rightarrow \langle\langle x,R\rangle\rangle$ is a w.o. set$)]$.

The next form is obtained from w1 by changing the word "set" to "class."

W2: $\mathrm{Cl}(X) \rightarrow (\exists R)(\mathrm{Rel}(R) \ \& \ \langle\langle X,R\rangle\rangle$ is a w.o. class$)$.

The last form is a strong form of w2.

W3: $\mathrm{Pr}(X) \rightarrow X \approx On$.

We shall prove that these three forms are equivalent by proving

$$\mathrm{W3} \rightarrow \mathrm{W2} \rightarrow \mathrm{W1} \rightarrow \mathrm{W3}.$$

THEOREM 10.1.4. W3 → W2.

Proof: By W3, $V \approx On$. Let X be any class, then $X \subseteq V$. Therefore, $X \lesssim On$, so X can be well-ordered. ∎

THEOREM 10.1.5. W2 → W1.

Proof: It follows from W2 that there is a relation R such that $\langle\langle V,R\rangle\rangle$ is a w.o. class. For any set x, $x \subset V$; thus, x is w.o. by R. ∎

To prove W1 → W3 we assume that $\mathfrak{A}$, the class of atoms, is a set and we also use the notion of rank (see section 8.6).

THEOREM 10.1.6.® $\mathrm{S}(\mathfrak{A}) \rightarrow (\mathrm{W1} \rightarrow \mathrm{W3})$.

Proof: Suppose that $\mathfrak{A}$ is a set and R is a relation which w.o. each set. Let X be a proper class. It follows from 8.6.13 that for each $u \in X$, the rank of u, $\rho(u)$, exists, and from 8.6.21 that $\{v : \rho(v) = \rho(u)\}$ is a set. Now we can w.o. X as follows. Define a relation T such that for all $u,v \in X$,

$$u \ T \ v \leftrightarrow [\rho(u) < \rho(v) \text{ or } (\rho(u) = \rho(v) \ \& \ u \ R \ v)].$$

It is easy to see that $\langle\langle X,T\rangle\rangle$ is a w.o. class. Moreover, for each $u \in X$,

$$S_{XT}(u) \subseteq \{v : \rho(v) \leqq \rho(u)\}.$$

Thus, it follows from 8.6.21 that each T-initial segment of X is a set. Therefore, by 8.2.20, $X \approx On$. ∎

To conclude this section we shall show that the class form of the well-ordering theorem is equivalent to the class form of the axiom of choice.

THEOREM 10.1.7. W2 $\rightarrow$ A8.

The proof is the same as the proof of 10.1.2.

In order to prove the converse we first prove a preliminary lemma.

LEMMA 10.1.8.

$$\text{AC1} \rightarrow (\exists F)[\text{Func}(F)\ \&\ (\forall x)(\text{S}(x) \rightarrow \langle\langle x,F(x)\rangle\rangle \text{ is a w.o. set})].$$

Proof: Let x be a set and let

$$T_x = \{R : R \subseteq x \times x\ \&\ \langle\langle x,R\rangle\rangle \text{ is a w.o. set}\}.$$

Now if $R \in T_x$, then R is a w.o. relation on x. By 3.6.4(b) and 10.1.3, we have

$$\text{AC1} \rightarrow \text{ac1} \rightarrow \text{w2}$$

and

$$\text{w2} \rightarrow (\forall x)(\text{S}(x) \rightarrow T_x \neq \emptyset).$$

Therefore, AC1 implies that there exists a choice function G on $\{T_x : \text{S}(x)\}$. Define

$$F(x) = G(T_x).$$

Then for each set x, $F(x)$ w.o. x. ∎

Now, assuming $\mathfrak{a}$ is a set and the axiom of regularity, we can prove the converse of 10.1.7.

THEOREM 10.1.9.® $\text{S}(\mathfrak{a}) \rightarrow (\text{AC1} \rightarrow \text{W2})$

Proof: Suppose AC1 holds. Apply 10.1.8, and suppose F is a function such that for every set x, $\langle\langle x,F(x)\rangle\rangle$ is a w.o. set. Now let X be any class. X can be w.o. as follows. Suppose $u,v \in X$. Let

$$x_u = \{w : \rho(w) = \rho(u)\}.$$

Then, if $\mathfrak{a}$ is a set, it follows from 8.6.21 that x_u is a set. Define

$$u\ R\ v \leftrightarrow [\rho(u) < \rho(v) \text{ or } (\rho(u) = \rho(v)\ \&\ u\ F(x_u)\ v)].$$

It is now simple to prove that $\langle\langle X,R\rangle\rangle$ is a w.o. class. ∎

EXERCISES 10.1

1. Use the well-ordering theorem to prove:
   $\langle\langle X,R\rangle\rangle$ is a p.o. class $\rightarrow (\exists S)(\mathrm{Rel}(S)\ \&\ R \subseteq S\ \&\ \langle\langle X,S\rangle\rangle$ is a l.o. class).
2. Use the principle of dependent choices (section 5.3) to prove W1 $\rightarrow$ W2.
3. Under the assumption that $\mathfrak{a}$ is a set give a proof that AC1 $\rightarrow$ W3 which is similar to the proof of 10.1.3. (The axiom of regularity is used in the proof.)

10.2. THE TRICHOTOMY

The proof that the trichotomy implies the well-ordering theorem was given by Hartogs (1915). The trichotomy for sets is as follows.

t: $\quad (\mathrm{S}(x)\ \&\ \mathrm{S}(y)) \rightarrow (x \lesssim y$ or $y \lesssim x)$.

In other words, each pair of sets is comparable. It is easy to prove that the well-ordering theorem implies the trichotomy.

THEOREM 10.2.1. $\quad$ w2 $\rightarrow$ t.

Proof: Let x and y be any two sets. By w2, there exist ordinal numbers α and β such that

$$x \approx \alpha\ \&\ y \approx \beta.$$

Now the trichotomy for ordinal numbers, 8.2.13, implies t. ■

Before proving the converse of 10.2.1, we shall need some preliminary material.

LEMMA 10.2.2. $\quad \mathrm{S}(x) \rightarrow \mathrm{S}(\{\alpha : \alpha \lesssim x\})$.

Proof: Let x be a set and let

$$Y = \{R : R \subseteq x \times x\ \&\ \langle\langle \mathfrak{D}(R),R\rangle\rangle \text{ is a w.o. set}\}.$$

Y is a set because $Y \subseteq \mathcal{P}(x \times x)$. Moreover, for each $R \in Y$ there exists a unique ordinal number α such that $\overline{\langle\langle \mathfrak{D}(R),R\rangle\rangle} = \alpha$ (8.2.27, 8.2.28). Define

$$F(R) = \alpha.$$

Then F is a mapping from Y into $\{\alpha : \alpha \lesssim x\}$.

We shall show F is onto. Suppose $\beta \lesssim x$. Then there is a $y \subseteq x$ such that $y \approx \beta$. Let g be a 1–1 function mapping y onto β. Define a relation R as follows:

$$R = \{\langle u,v\rangle : u,v \in y\ \&\ g(u) \leqq g(v)\}$$

Then, clearly, $\mathfrak{D}(R) = y$, $\langle\langle y,R\rangle\rangle$ is a w.o. set and

$$\overline{\overline{\langle\langle y,R\rangle\rangle}} = \beta.$$

Thus, $F(R) = \beta$.

Consequently, F is a function which maps Y onto $\{\alpha : \alpha \precsim x\}$. Therefore, since Y is a set, it follows from A6 that $\{\alpha : \alpha \precsim x\}$ is a set. ■

We shall next define a function Γ which is commonly called *Hartogs' function.*

DEFINITION 10.2.3. Hartogs' Function

$$S(x) \rightarrow \Gamma(x) =_{Df} \{\alpha : \alpha \precsim x\}.$$

It follows from 10.2.2 and 10.2.3 that for each set x, $\Gamma(x)$ is a set of ordinal numbers. We shall prove that $\Gamma(x)$ is actually an ordinal number.

THEOREM 10.2.4. $S(x) \rightarrow \Gamma(x) \in On.$

Proof: Suppose x is a set. Since $\Gamma(x)$ is a set of ordinal numbers, to prove that it is an ordinal number it is sufficient to prove that it is transitive (8.2.14). Suppose $\alpha \in \Gamma(x)$ and $\beta \in \alpha$. Then $\alpha \precsim x$ and $\beta \subset \alpha$. Therefore, $\beta \precsim x$, so $\beta \in \Gamma(x)$. ■

Now we are prepared to show that the trichotomy implies the well-ordering theorem.

THEOREM 10.2.5. $t \rightarrow w2.$

Proof: By t, for any set x either

$$x \precsim \Gamma(x) \text{ or } \Gamma(x) \precsim x.$$

Since $\Gamma(x)$ is an ordinal number, if $\Gamma(x) \precsim x$, then $\Gamma(x) \in \Gamma(x)$, which is impossible. Therefore we must have $x \precsim \Gamma(x)$ and this clearly implies w2 because $\Gamma(x)$ is an ordinal number. ■

EXERCISES 10.2

1. Prove $S(x) \rightarrow \mathcal{P}(\Gamma(x)) \precsim \mathcal{P}(\mathcal{P}(x \times x))$. (See 10.2.2 and exercise 3.4.4.)
2. Prove $\alpha \prec \Gamma(\alpha)$ & $(\forall\beta)(\alpha \prec \beta \rightarrow \Gamma(\alpha) \precsim \beta)$.
3. Prove that the following statement is equivalent to the set form of the axiom of choice:

   t′: $(S(x) \,\&\, S(y) \,\&\, x,y \neq \emptyset) \rightarrow (\exists f)(f : x \xrightarrow{\text{onto}} y \text{ or } f : y \xrightarrow{\text{onto}} x)$

   (t′ was stated by Lindenbaum [in Lindenbaum and Tarski (1926)] and later proved by Sierpinski (1948). Hint: To prove t′ → w2, compare x and $\Gamma(\mathcal{P}(x))$ and use exercise 3.4.4.)

10.3. MAXIMAL PRINCIPLES

Maximal principles appeared in the literature as early as 1914. F. Hausdorf (1914) derived m2 (below) from the well-ordering theorem. C. Kuratowski (1922) derived a proposition similar to m1 from the well-ordering theorem. M. Zorn (1935) was the first one to state that a maximal principle implies the axiom of choice, but he gave no proof in his paper. (Later Bourbaki in 1939 and Tukey in 1940 referred to a maximal principle as *Zorn's lemma*, and this partial misnomer has stuck.) The form m3, below, was given independently by O. Teichmuller (1939) and J. Tukey (1940) and m1 was also given by Tukey.

The first maximal principle, m1, states that if x is a non-empty set such that $\langle\langle x,R\rangle\rangle$ is a p.o. set and every subset of x which is l.o. by R has an R-upper bound, then x has an R-maximal element.

m1: $[x \neq \emptyset$ & $\langle\langle x,R\rangle\rangle$ is a p.o. set &
$(\forall y)((y \subseteq x$ & $\langle\langle y,R\rangle\rangle$ is a l.o. set$) \rightarrow$
$(\exists u)(u \in x$ & u is an R-upper bound of $y))] \rightarrow$
$(\exists u)(u \in x$ & u is an R-maximal element of $x)$.

The R-maximal element of x may not be unique.

The second maximal principle given here states that, if $\langle\langle x,R\rangle\rangle$ is a p.o. set, then there exists a $\subseteq$-maximal R-linearly ordered subset of x.

m2: $\langle\langle x,R\rangle\rangle$ is a p.o. set $\rightarrow$
$(\exists y)[y \subseteq x$ & $\langle\langle y,R\rangle\rangle$ is a l.o. set &
$(\forall z)((z \subseteq x$ & $\langle\langle z,R\rangle\rangle$ is a l.o. set$) \rightarrow y \not\subset z)]$.

The third and last maximal principle to be discussed here involves a concept which has not as yet been defined. To define this concept we use a *meta-definition* or *definition schema*—a rule for producing definitions.

DEFINITION 10.3.1. Finite Character

For each wff $\mathbf{P}(X)$ in which X is a free variable, the following definition is introduced:

P is a property of finite character $=_{\mathrm{Df}}$

$$(\forall X)(\mathbf{P}(X) \leftrightarrow (\forall Y)[(Y \subseteq X \;\&\; Y \text{ is finite}) \rightarrow \mathbf{P}(Y)].$$

For example, if $\mathbf{P}(X)$ stands for any one of the following four statements, then **P** is a property of finite character.

(1) $\langle\langle X,R\rangle\rangle$ is a p.o. class.
(2) $\langle\langle X,R\rangle\rangle$ is a l.o. class.
(3) $u \notin X$.
(4) Pr Dis (X). (The elements of X are pairwise disjoint.)

To prove that (1) is a property of finite character it must be shown that,

$$\langle\langle X,R\rangle\rangle \text{ is a p.o. class} \leftrightarrow (\forall Y)[(Y \subseteq X \ \&\ Y \text{ is finite}) \rightarrow \langle\langle Y,R\rangle\rangle \text{ is a p.o. class}].$$

The proof of this is trivial, as is the proof that (2), (3), and (4) are properties of finite character. (Note: We shall often say that "**P**(X) is a property of finite character" when we mean "**P** is a property of finite character.)

On the other hand, if **P**(X) stands for

(5) X is infinite,

then **P** is clearly not a property of finite character. A less trivial example of a property which is not of finite character is the following:

(6) $\langle\langle X,R\rangle\rangle$ is a w.o. class.

Clearly, if $\langle\langle X,R\rangle\rangle$ is a w.o. class, then for all finite subsets Y of X, $\langle\langle Y,R\rangle\rangle$ is a w.o. class, but the converse does not hold. To see this, let $X = \omega$ and $R = \geqq$. Every finite subset of ω has a largest element, but ω has no largest element.

A property of finite character **P** can be characterized in a more set theoretic manner as follows. Define

$$Q = \{x : \mathrm{S}(x) \ \&\ x \text{ is finite} \ \&\ \mathbf{P}(x)\}.$$

Then a class X has the property **P** if and only if every finite subset of X is in Q. Thus, we have

$$\mathbf{P} \text{ is a property of finite character} \leftrightarrow (\forall X)(\forall x)[(x \subseteq X \ \&\ x \text{ is finite}) \rightarrow x \in Q].$$

LEMMA 10.3.2.

$$(\mathbf{P} \text{ is a property of finite character} \ \&\ \mathbf{P}(X) \rightarrow (\forall Y)(Y \subseteq X \rightarrow \mathbf{P}(Y)).$$

The proof is left as an exercise.

Now we are ready to state m3.

m3: $(\mathrm{S}(x) \ \&\ \mathbf{P} \text{ is a property of finite character} \ \&\ \mathbf{P}(\emptyset)) \rightarrow$
$(\exists y)[y \subseteq x \ \&\ \mathbf{P}(y) \ \&\ (\forall z)((z \subseteq x \ \&\ \mathbf{P}(z)) \rightarrow y \not\subset z)].$

In other words, for each set x and property of finite character **P**, if **P**($\emptyset$), then there exists a $\subseteq$-maximal subset of x which has the property **P**. Note that m3 is a rule or schema rather than a proposition, since any property of finite character may be substituted for **P**. However, we shall prove that m1, m2, and m3 are all equivalent by proving

$$\text{m3} \rightarrow \text{m2} \rightarrow \text{m1} \rightarrow \text{m3}.$$

Since the property (2) above is a property of finite character, it follows that m2 is a special case of m3. Thus we have:

THEOREM 10.3.3. m3 $\rightarrow$ m2.

THEOREM 10.3.4. m2 $\rightarrow$ m1.

Proof: Suppose $\langle\langle x,R\rangle\rangle$ is a p.o. set which satisfies the hypothesis of m1. By m2, there is a y such that y is a $\subseteq$-maximal R-l.o. subset of x. It follows from the hypothesis of m1 that there is a $u \in x$ such that u is an R-upper bound of y. We claim that u is an R-maximal element of x. For suppose it is not so. Suppose there is a $v \in x$ such that

(1) $$u\,R\,v \;\&\; u \neq v.$$

Since u is an R-upper bound of y,

(2) $$(\forall w)(w \in y \rightarrow w\,R\,u).$$

It follows from (1) and (2) that $v \notin y$. Let

$$z = y \cup \{v\}.$$

From (1), (2), and the transitivity of R, it follows that z is a l.o. subset of x, and since $v \notin y$, z properly contains y as a subset. This contradicts the maximality of y. Thus, u is an R-maximal element of x. ■

THEOREM 10.3.5. m1 $\rightarrow$ m3.

Proof: Let **P** be a property of finite character and let x be a set. Let

$$y = \{u : u \subseteq x \;\&\; \mathbf{P}(u)\}.$$

Clearly, $\langle\langle y,\subseteq\rangle\rangle$ is a p.o. set. Let z be a l.o. subset of y. We shall show that $\bigcup z \in y$ and $\bigcup z$ is a $\subseteq$-upper bound of z.

Suppose $u \in \bigcup z$. Then there is a $v \in z$ such that $u \in v$. Since $z \subseteq y$, $v \in z$ implies $v \subseteq x$. Thus, $u \in v$ implies $u \in x$. This proves $\bigcup z \subseteq x$.

Let $v = \{u_1, u_2, \ldots, u_n\}$ be a finite subset of $\bigcup z$. Then there exist n elements $w_1, w_2, \ldots, w_n$ in z such that $u_i \in w_i$, $i = 1, 2, \ldots, n$. Since z is $\subseteq$-l.o., there is a $j \in \{1, 2, \ldots, n\}$ such that $u_i \in w_j$ for all $i = 1, 2, \ldots, n$. Consequently, v is a finite subset of $w_j \in z \subseteq y$. Therefore, since **P** is a property of finite character, we must have $\mathbf{P}(v)$ for each finite subset v of $\bigcup z$. Thus, $\mathbf{P}(\bigcup z)$.

It follows directly from the definition of $\bigcup$ that if $u \in z$, then $u \subseteq \bigcup z$. Therefore, $\bigcup z$ is a $\subseteq$-upper bound of z.

Hence, we have shown that $\langle\langle y,\subseteq\rangle\rangle$ satisfies the hypothesis of m1. Thus, y has a $\subseteq$-maximal element. ■

Next, we shall show that a maximal principle implies the axiom of choice.

THEOREM 10.3.6. $\text{m1} \to \text{ac1}$.

Proof: Let x be a non-empty set of non-empty sets and let C be the set of all choice functions on subsets of x. That is,

$$C = \{f: \text{Func}(f) \;\&\; (\exists y)[y \subseteq x \;\&\; \mathfrak{D}(f) = y \;\&\; (\forall u)(u \in y \to f(u) \in u)]\}.$$

We shall show that $\langle\langle C,\subseteq\rangle\rangle$ satisfies the hypothesis of m1. Clearly, $\langle\langle C,\subseteq\rangle\rangle$ is a p.o. set. Suppose D is a $\subseteq$-l.o. subset of C. We shall show that $\bigcup D \in C$ and $\bigcup D$ is an $\subseteq$-upper bound of C.

Let $f = \bigcup D$. Suppose $u \in f$. Then there is a $g \in D$ such that $u \in g$. Since $D \subseteq C$, g is a function and u is an ordered pair. Suppose $\langle u,v\rangle,\langle u,w\rangle \in f$. Then there exist $g_1, g_2 \in D$ such that

$$\langle u,v\rangle \in g_1 \;\&\; \langle u,w\rangle \in g_2.$$

Since D is $\subseteq$-l.o., both $\langle u,v\rangle$ and $\langle u,w\rangle$ belong to one of g_1 or g_2. Consequently, since g_1 and g_2 are functions, $v = w$ and f is a function. Moreover,

$$\mathfrak{D}(f) = \textstyle\bigcup_{g\in D} \mathfrak{D}(g).$$

Therefore, for each $u \in \mathfrak{D}(f), f(u) = g(u)$ for some $g \in D$. Since $g(u) \in u$, $f(u) \in u$. Therefore, we have shown that $f \in C$. Now, it follows directly from the definition of $\bigcup$ that f is a $\subseteq$-upper bound of D.

Thus, it follows from m1 that C has a $\subseteq$-maximal element, g. Suppose g is a choice function on $y \subset x$. Let $u \in x \sim y$ and let $v \in u$. Then

$$h = g \cup \{\langle u,v\rangle\}$$

is a choice function on $y \cup \{u\}$, which contradicts the maximality of g. Consequently, g is a choice function on x. ■

The proofs of 10.3.4–10.3.6 indicate how maximal principles are used in practice to prove theorems.

To conclude the proof of equivalence, we shall show that the well-ordering theorem implies the maximal principle, m2. The intuitive idea of the proof is as follows. Suppose x is a set which is p.o. by R. It follows from the well-ordering theorem that x can be w.o. We construct a $\subseteq$-maximal, R-l.o. subset y of x as follows: the first element of x, u, belongs to y; if the second element of x stands in the relation R to u, then it belongs to y, otherwise it does not; continue this process by including those elements in y which are R-connected to the elements already chosen.

THEOREM 10.3.7. $\text{w2} \to \text{m2}$.

Proof: Let x be a set which is p.o. by R. Suppose

$$f: \alpha \xrightarrow[\text{onto}]{1\text{-}1} x.$$

Define a function g on α as follows: if $\beta < \alpha$, then

$$g(\beta) = \begin{cases} f(\beta), & \text{if } (\forall\gamma)[\gamma < \beta \rightarrow (f(\beta)\ R\ g(\gamma) \text{ or } g(\gamma)\ R\ f(\beta))] \\ f(0), & \text{otherwise.} \end{cases}$$

We leave it as an exercise to prove that $\mathcal{R}(g)$ is a $\subseteq$-maximal, R-l.o. subset of x. ■

For further equivalents to the axiom of choice, the reader is referred to the exercises, Chapter 11, and Rubin (1963).

EXERCISES 10.3

1. Prove that properties (1)–(4) given at the beginning of this section are properties of finite character.
2. Prove lemma 10.3.2.
3. For each of the following, if it is a theorem prove it, if not give a counterexample:
   P is a property of finite character $\rightarrow$
   (a) $(\mathbf{P}(X)\ \&\ \mathbf{P}(Y)) \rightarrow \mathbf{P}(X \cup Y)$
   (b) $(\mathbf{P}(X)\ \&\ \mathbf{P}(Y)) \rightarrow \mathbf{P}(X \cap Y)$.
4. Prove each of the following propositions are equivalent to the axiom of choice:
   (a) $[\mathrm{S}(x)\ \&\ x \neq \emptyset\ \&$
   $(\forall y)((y \subseteq x\ \&\ y \neq \emptyset\ \&\ \langle\langle y,\subseteq\rangle\rangle \text{ is a l.o. set}) \rightarrow \bigcup y \in x)] \rightarrow$
   x has a $\subseteq$-maximal element.
   (If every non-empty nest which is a subset of a non-empty set x has its union in x, then x has a $\subseteq$-maximal element. A nest is a class which is l.o. by inclusion.)
   (b) $\mathrm{S}(x) \rightarrow (\exists y)[y \subseteq x\ \&\ \langle\langle y,\subseteq\rangle\rangle \text{ is a l.o. set}\ \&$
   $(\forall z)((z \subseteq x\ \&\ \langle\langle z,\subseteq\rangle\rangle \text{ is a l.o. set}) \rightarrow y \not\subset z)]$
   (Every set contains a $\subseteq$-maximal subset which is a nest.)
   (c) $(\langle\langle x,R\rangle\rangle \text{ is a p.o. set}\ \&\ y \subseteq x\ \&\ \langle\langle y,R\rangle\rangle \text{ is a l.o. set}) \rightarrow$
   $(\exists z)[z \subseteq x\ \&\ y \subseteq z\ \&\ \langle\langle z,R\rangle\rangle \text{ is a l.o. set}\ \&$
   $(\forall u)((u \subseteq x\ \&\ y \subseteq u\ \&\ \langle\langle u,R\rangle\rangle \text{ is a l.o. set}) \rightarrow z \not\subset u)]$.
   (Every l.o. subset of a p.o. set is a subset of a $\subseteq$-maximal l.o. set.)
   (d) $\mathrm{S}(x) \rightarrow (\exists y)[y \subseteq x\ \&\ \mathrm{Pr\ Dis}(y)\ \&\ (\forall z)((z \subseteq x\ \&\ \mathrm{Pr\ Dis}(z)) \rightarrow y \not\subset z)]$.
   (Every set contains a $\subseteq$-maximal subset whose elements are pairwise disjoint. Vaught [1952].)

*10.4. APPLICATIONS

There are applications of the axiom of choice in almost all branches of mathematics. For example, in topology there is the well-known Tychonoff compactness theorem:

The direct product of compact spaces is compact in the product topology.

[This was derived from a maximal principle by Tychonoff (1935) and shown to imply the axiom of choice by Kelley (1950).] In algebra, it has been shown by G. Klimovsky (1962) that the following statement is equivalent to the axiom of choice.

Every group contains a $\subseteq$-maximal commutative subgroup.

(Actually Klimovsky proves something weaker, but it can be extended to the form given here.) Also, the prime ideal theorem is a consequence of the axiom of choice.

Each ideal in a Boolean algebra can be imbedded in a prime ideal. [Halpern (1961) with $\mathcal{A} \neq \emptyset$ and Feferman (1965) with $\mathcal{A} = \emptyset$ have shown that the prime ideal theorem does not imply the axiom of choice.]

In analysis there is, for example, the Hahn–Banach theorem which deals with the extension of a linear functional from a subspace of a vector space to the whole space in such a manner that certain properties of the functional are preserved. A maximal principle is used in the proof of the Hahn–Banach theorem. [See, for example, Royden (1963). It can also be shown that the prime ideal theorem implies the Hahn-Banach theorem.] Even at an elementary level, in analysis there is little that can be done without using some non-constructive principle. For example, the axiom of choice is used to prove that there exists a set which is not Lebesgue measureable and that the union of a countable number of sets with Lebesgue measure zero has Lebesgue measure zero. [Royden (1963). Also see Solovay (1964) (1965a).]

In this section we shall use a form of the axiom of choice to construct what is called a *Hamel Basis* for the real numbers and derive some of its properties [Hamel (1905)]. As in Chapter 6, we let *Re* denote the set of real numbers and *Ra* denote the set of rational numbers.

Definition 10.4.1. Hamel Basis

H is a *Hamel Basis* $=_{\mathrm{Df}} [H \subseteq Re \ \& \ (\forall x)[(x \in Re \ \& \ x \neq 0) \rightarrow$
$(\exists 1 n)(\exists 1 r)(\exists 1 h)(n \in \omega \ \& \ \mathrm{Func}(r) \ \& \ \mathrm{Func}(h) \ \& \ \mathfrak{D}(r) = \mathfrak{D}(h) = n \ \&$
$\mathfrak{R}(r) \subseteq Ra \sim \{\emptyset\} \ \& \ \mathfrak{R}(h) \subseteq H \ \& \ (\forall m)(\forall p)((m,p < n \ \& \ m \neq p) \rightarrow$
$h_m \neq h_p) \ \&$

(1) $$x = r_0 h_0 + r_1 h_1 + \cdots + r_{n-1} h_{n-1})]].$$

In other words, $H \subseteq Re$ is a Hamel basis if and only if each non-zero real number is uniquely representable as a linear combination of elements of H with non-zero rational coefficients. If $H \subseteq Re$, we shall call (1) an *H-normal form* of x. Thus if $H \subseteq Re$, then H is a Hamel basis if and only if each non-zero real number has exactly one H-normal form.

We prove first that if H is a Hamel basis, then $0 \notin H$ and H cannot contain two distinct rational numbers.

THEOREM 10.4.2. H is a Hamel basis $\rightarrow$

(a) $0 \notin H$

(b) $r,s \in Ra \cap H \rightarrow r = s$.

Proof: Assume H is a Hamel basis.

(a) If $0 \in H$, then no real number has a unique H-normal form.

(b) Suppose r and s are rational numbers which belong to H. Then since $s \neq 0$,

$$r = r$$

$$r = \frac{r}{s} s.$$

Therefore, if $r \neq s$, r does not have a unique H-normal form. ■

Moreover, we can show that a Hamel basis is not countable.

THEOREM 10.4.3. H is a Hamel basis $\rightarrow H \not\preccurlyeq \omega$.

Proof: Suppose H is a Hamel basis and H is countable. Since Ra is denumerable and each real number has an H-normal form, it is easy to show without using the axiom of choice that Re is denumerable. This contradicts 6.6.5. ■

Before proving the existence of a Hamel basis, we give a preliminary definition.

DEFINITION 10.4.4. Linear Dependence and Independence

$$(\exists n)(n \in \omega \;\&\; X = \{x_i : x_i \in Re \;\&\; i < n\}) \rightarrow$$

(a) X is *Ra-linearly dependent* $=_{\text{Df}}$
$(\exists r)[\text{Func}(r) \;\&\; \mathfrak{D}(r) = n \;\&\; \mathfrak{R}(r) \subseteq Ra \;\&\; (\exists i)(i < n \;\&\; r_i \neq 0) \;\&$
$r_0 x_0 + r_1 x_1 + \cdots + r_{n-1} x_{n-1} = 0)$

(b) X is *Ra-linearly independent* $=_{\text{Df}} \neg X$ is Ra-linearly dependent.

Thus, for example, both of the following sets are Ra-linearly dependent:

$$X_1 = \{1, 1 + \sqrt{2}, 1 - \sqrt{2}\}; (-2)\cdot 1 + (1 + \sqrt{2}) + (1 - \sqrt{2}) = 0,$$
$$X_2 = \{1, 2, \sqrt{2}, \sqrt{3}\}; 1 + (-1/2)\cdot 2 + 0\cdot\sqrt{2} + 0\cdot\sqrt{3} = 0.$$

But

$$X_3 = \{1, \sqrt{2}, \sqrt{3}\},$$
$$X_4 = \{1 + \sqrt{2}, \sqrt{2}, \sqrt{3}, \sqrt{6}\},$$

are both Ra-linearly independent.

DEFINITION 10.4.5. Linear Dependence and Independence

$$X \subseteq Re \rightarrow$$

(a) X is *Ra-linearly dependent* $=_{\text{Df}}$
$(\exists y)(y \subseteq X \;\&\; y \text{ is finite} \;\&\; y \text{ is } Ra\text{-linearly dependent})$

(b) X is *Ra-linearly independent* $=_{\text{Df}}$
$(\forall y)((y \subseteq X \;\&\; y \text{ is finite}) \rightarrow y \text{ is } Ra\text{-linearly independent})$.

It follows directly from 10.4.5 that the property of being *Ra*-linearly independent is a property of finite character, while the property of being *Ra*-linearly dependent is not.

Now we are ready to "construct" a Hamel basis using a maximal principle.

THEOREM 10.4.6.© $(\exists H)(H$ is a Hamel Basis).

Proof: Since the property of being *Ra*-linearly independent is a property of finite character, it follows from m3 that there exists a $\subseteq$-maximal subset H of Re such that H is *Ra*-linearly independent. We shall prove that H is a Hamel basis.

Suppose $x \in Re$ and x does not have an H-normal form. Then, clearly, $x \notin H$, so $H \subset H \cup \{x\}$. We claim that $H \cup \{x\}$ is *Ra*-linearly independent. For suppose this is not so. Then, since H is *Ra*-linearly independent, there exist elements $h_0, h_1, \ldots, h_{n-1} \in H$ and $r_0, r_1, \ldots, r_n \in Ra$, $r_n \neq 0$, such that

$$r_0h_0 + r_1h_1 + \cdots + r_{n-1}h_{n-1} + r_nx = 0$$

or

$$x = -(r_0/r_n)h_0 - (r_1/r_n)h_1 - \cdots - (r_{n-1}/r_n)h_{n-1},$$

and this contradicts the assumption that x does not have an H-normal form. Consequently, $H \cup \{x\}$ is *Ra*-linearly independent, and this contradicts the maximality of H. Hence, every real number has an H-normal form.

Now, suppose $x \in Re$, $x \neq 0$, and suppose x has two H-normal forms:

$$x = r_0h_0 + r_1h_1 + \cdots + r_{n-1}h_{n-1}$$
$$x = s_0k_0 + s_1k_1 + \cdots + s_{m-1}k_{m-1}$$

for some $h_0, h_1, \ldots, h_{n-1}, k_0, k_1, \ldots, k_{m-1} \in H$ and some $r_0, r_1, \ldots, r_{n-1}, s_0, s_1, \ldots, s_{m-1} \in Ra$. Since $x \neq 0$, the r's and s's cannot be all zero. Consequently, the set

$$\{h_0, h_1, \ldots, h_{n-1}, k_0, k_1, \ldots, k_{m-1}\}$$

is *Ra*-linearly dependent, contradicting the *Ra*-linearly independence of H. Therefore, each non-zero real number has exactly one H-normal form, so H is a Hamel basis. ■

We have shown that a $\subseteq$-maximal, *Ra*-linearly independent subset of *Re* is a Hamel basis. The converse of this is also true:

THEOREM 10.4.7.

H is a Hamel Basis $\leftrightarrow$ H is a $\subseteq$-maximal, *Ra*-linearly independent subset of *Re*.

The proof is left as an exercise.

Suppose X is an *Ra*-linearly independent subset of *Re*. We claim that X can be extended to a Hamel basis. Define a property P as follows:

$$P(Y) \leftrightarrow X \cup Y \text{ is a } Ra\text{-linearly independent subset of } Re.$$

Since X is *Ra*-linearly independent, P is a property of finite character. Therefore, by m3, there exists a $\subseteq$-maximal subset of *Re* with the property P, and since such a subset is a $\subseteq$-maximal, *Ra*-linearly independent subset of *Re*, it is a Hamel basis. Thus we have shown, using m3, that

THEOREM 10.4.8.©

$$(X \subseteq Re \;\&\; X \text{ is } Ra\text{-linearly independent}) \rightarrow (\exists H)(H \subseteq Re \;\&\; X \subseteq H \;\&\; H \text{ is a Hamel basis}).$$

If we assume the existence of a Hamel basis, then we can show that the real numbers have some strange properties. For example, if f is a linear function on *Re*,

$$(\exists a)(a \in Re \;\&\; (\forall x)(x \in Re \rightarrow f(x) = ax)), \tag{2}$$

then f has the property,

$$(\forall x)(\forall y)(x, y \in Re \rightarrow f(x + y) = f(x) + f(y)). \tag{3}$$

In fact, it would be difficult to give an example of another function which satisfies (3). However, with the aid of a Hamel basis, a non-linear solution of the functional equation (3) can be given. Let H be a Hamel basis and let h be an irrational element in H. For each $x \in Re$, $x \neq 0$, define $F(x)$ to be the coefficient of h in the H-normal form of x. If $x = 0$, define $F(x) = 0$, and if h does not occur in the H-normal form of x, then $F(x) = 0$. It is a simple matter to prove that F satisfies (3), for if

$$x = rh + \cdots$$
$$y = sh + \cdots,$$

then

$$x + y = (r + s)h + \cdots.$$

So

$$F(x + y) = r + s = F(x) + F(y).$$

Moreover, F is not linear because $F(x)$ is zero for infinitely many real numbers x and is non-zero for infinitely many x; but a linear function is either zero for exactly one value of the argument, $x = 0$, or is identically zero.

It is not known how to construct a non-linear function which satisfies (3) without using the axiom of choice, but it can be shown without using the axiom of choice that any non-linear function which satisfies (3) is not continuous [see Sierpinski (1920)].

Using the function F, it is easy to construct a discontinuous function satisfying the functional equation

$$(4) \qquad (\forall x)(\forall y)(x, y \in Re \rightarrow f(xy) = f(x)f(y)).$$

For each $x \in Re$, $x \neq 0$, take

$$G(x) = e^{F(\log|x|)},\ G(0) = 0.$$

Then G satisfies (4) and since F is discontinuous, so is G.

Using a Hamel basis we can also prove that Re can be partitioned into a denumerable number of equipollent sets each of which is dense in Re. (See 7.5.1 for the definition of dense.)

THEOREM 10.4.9.©

$$(\exists X)(X \approx \omega \ \&\ \text{Pr Dis}(X) \ \&\ \cup X = Re \ \&\ (\forall Y)(\forall Z)(Y, Z \in X \rightarrow Y \approx Z) \ \&\ (\forall Y)(Y \in X \rightarrow Y \text{ is dense in } Re).$$

Proof: Let H be a Hamel basis and let $h \in H$. For each $r \in Re$, define

$Y_r = \{x : x \in Re$ & the coefficient of h in the H-normal form if x is $r\}$.

Let $0 \in Y_0$. If h does not appear in the H-normal form of x, then $x \in Y_0$. Define

$$X = \{Y_r : r \in Ra\}.$$

Since Ra is denumerable, then so is X. Moreover, since H is a Hamel basis, it is easy to prove that the elements of X are pairwise disjoint, $\cup X = Re$, and for all $r, s \in Ra$, $Y_r \approx Y_s$. The details are left for the reader.

Let $r \in Ra$ and $Y_r \in X$. We shall sketch the proof that Y_r is dense in *Re*. Suppose $x,y \in Re$ and $x < y$. Let $u \in Y_0$ such that $0 < u < y - x$. Such an element u is easy to construct using well-known properties of the real numbers. Now consider the real number rh. If $rh \leqq x$, then there exists an integer n such that

$$x < rh + nu < y.$$

In either case we can find an element in Y_r between x and y. ■

DEFINITION 10.4.10. Translates

$$(X \subseteq Re \ \& \ y \in Re) \rightarrow X + y =_{\mathrm{Df}} \{x + y : x \in X\}.$$

$X + y$ is called the *y-translate* of X.

Note that in the proof of theorem 10.4.9,

$$Y_r = Y_0 + rh.$$

Consequently, theorem 10.4.9 may be restated as follows:

THEOREM 10.4.11.

$$(\exists Y)[Y \subseteq Re \ \& \ (\forall X)(X = \{Y + x : x \in Re\} \rightarrow (X \approx \omega \ \& \ \text{Pr Dis}(X) \ \& \ \bigcup X = Re \ \& \ (\forall x)(x \in Re \rightarrow Y + x \text{ is dense in } Re).$$

In other words, there is a subset Y of *Re* which has the property that *Re* can be partitioned into a denumerable number of translates of Y, each of which is dense in *Re*.

For the last theorem in this section, we prove that there is a proper subset X of *Re* such that for each $y \in Re$,

$$\{X + yn : n \in \omega\}$$

is finite. It is rather difficult to imagine what such a set X would be like, but using a Hamel basis we shall "construct" it.

THEOREM 10.4.12.©

$$(\exists X)[X \subset Re \ \& \ (\forall y)(y \in Re \rightarrow \{X + yn : n \in \omega\} \text{ is finite})].$$

Proof: Let H be a Hamel basis and let

$$X = \{x : x \in Re \ \& \text{ the coefficients in the } H\text{-normal form of } x \text{ are all integers}\}.$$

Suppose $y \in Re$ and suppose the H-normal form of y is

$$r_0h_0 + r_1h_1 + \cdots + r_{n-1}h_{n-1},$$

where $r_0, r_1, \ldots, r_{n-1} \in Ra$ and $h_0, h_1, \ldots, h_{n-1} \in H$. Let d be the least common denominator of the r's. Then $yd \in X$ and $x + yd \in X$ for all $x \in X$. Therefore, it is easy to show that $X + yd = X$. Hence,

$$\{X + yn : n \in \omega\} = \{X, X + y, \ldots, X + y(d - 1)\},$$

and

$$\{X + yn : n \in \omega\} \lesssim d. \blacksquare$$

EXERCISES 10.4

1. Construct a $\subseteq$-maximal, Ra-linearly independent subset of each of the following sets:
   (a) Ra
   (b) In = set of integers
   (c) $\{1, 2, \sqrt{2}, \sqrt{3}, \sqrt{6}, 4 + 3\sqrt{2}, \sqrt{8}, 4\sqrt{2} + 3\sqrt{5}\}$
   (d) $\{1 + \sqrt{2}, \sqrt{2} + \sqrt{3}, \sqrt{2} + \sqrt{5}, \sqrt{3} - 1, \sqrt{3} - \sqrt{5}, \sqrt{5} + 1\}$.
2. For each of the following, if it is a theorem prove it, if not give a counterexample:
   (a) $(X \subseteq Re$ & X is Ra-linearly independent $Y \subseteq X) \rightarrow$ Y is Ra-linearly independent.
   (b) $(X, Y \subseteq Re$ & X & Y are Ra-linearly independent$) \rightarrow$ $X \cup Y$ is Ra-linearly independent.
   (c) $(X \subseteq Re$ & $\neg(X$ is Ra-linearly dependent$)) \rightarrow$ X is Ra-linearly independent.
   (d) $(X \subseteq Re$ & $X \neq \emptyset$ & $y \in Re) \rightarrow X \approx X + y$.
   (e) $(X \subseteq Re$ & $y \in X) \rightarrow X = X + y$.
3. Give examples without using any form of the axiom of choice of
   (a) several functions which satisfy the functional equation

$$(\forall x)(\forall y)(x, y \in Re \rightarrow f(xy) = f(x)f(y))$$

   (b) a set X such that $(X \approx \omega$ & Pr Dis(X) & $\bigcup X = Re)$.
4. Prove, using m2, that a Hamel basis exists.
5. Prove, using the well-ordering theorem, that a Hamel basis exists.

Chapter 11: Cardinal Numbers

11.1 INTRODUCTION

In this chapter and the next we shall discuss the comparative sizes of sets irrespective of ordering or other properties the sets may have. This leads to a new concept called *cardinal numbers*. It may seem pedagogically better to define cardinal numbers before ordinal numbers, to proceed from the general to the particular, but it turns out that the notion of an ordinal number will play an important role in the study of cardinal numbers.

Although there are several ways to define a cardinal number, a feature common to all definitions is a reference to the size of sets. Therefore, cardinal numbers must have the following two properties:

(1) *Every set has a unique cardinal number.*

(2) *Two sets have the same cardinal number if and only if they are equipollent.*

It is also desirable that

(3) *The cardinal number of a set is a set.*

Theorems about cardinal numbers are theorems about equipollence between sets. Thus, in theory it is not necessary to define cardinal numbers at all, but in practice it is a great convenience to have the concept.

There are several ways to define a cardinal number. One is to postulate its existence by a new axiom. The second is to define cardinal numbers as certain ordinal numbers. However, if the second definition is adopted, the axiom of choice is needed to prove (1) above. A third method is to define a cardinal number as a certain class of sets. This approach requires the axiom of regularity to prove (1) and one must assume that the class of individuals is a set (or can be partially well-ordered) to prove (3). It seems strange indeed that such powerful tools are needed to define a seemingly simple concept!

The first approach will be described in section 11.2, the second in 11.3, and the third in 11.4. (Section 11.4 may be omitted in a short course. The third definition uses the notion of rank, section 8.6.)

11.2. DEFINITION

The idea of defining a cardinal number by postulating its existence by means of a new axiom originated with A. Tarski (1924). Tarski was studying the relationship between several assertions about cardinal numbers and the axiom of choice. Thus, he needed a definition of cardinal number which did not depend on the axiom of choice. (Some of Tarski's results are discussed in Chapter 12.)

A11: $(\exists\kappa)(\mathrm{Func}(\kappa) \,\&\, (\forall x)[\mathrm{S}(x) \rightarrow (x \in \mathfrak{D}(\kappa) \,\&\, \mathrm{S}(\kappa(x)))] \,\&$
$(\forall x)(\forall y)[(\mathrm{S}(x) \,\&\, \mathrm{S}(y)) \rightarrow (\kappa(x) = \kappa(y) \leftrightarrow x \approx y)])$

Thus, we postulate the existence of a function κ which satisfies conditions (1)–(3) of section 11.1.

(1) $$\mathrm{S}(x) \rightarrow x \in \mathfrak{D}(\kappa).$$
(2) $$(\mathrm{S}(x) \,\&\, \mathrm{S}(y)) \rightarrow (\kappa(x) = \kappa(y) \leftrightarrow x \approx y).$$
(3) $$\mathrm{S}(x) \rightarrow \mathrm{S}(\kappa(x)).$$

For each set x, we shall use the symbol "$\bar{\bar{x}}$" for "$\kappa(x)$". (This notation was first given by Cantor. The double bar was used to indicate two levels of abstraction. The first bar was meant to abstract from the particular nature of the elements of the set and the second, to abstract from the order on the set. Thus, there is just one bar in the symbol for the ordinal number of a set.) $\bar{\bar{x}}$ or $\kappa(x)$ is called the *cardinal number* of x. The symbol "Cn" is used for the class of all cardinal numbers.

DEFINITION 11.2.1. Cardinal Number

(a) $\mathrm{S}(x) \rightarrow \bar{\bar{x}} =_{\mathrm{Df}} \kappa(x)$

(b) $Cn =_{\mathrm{Df}} \{y\!:\!(\exists x)(\mathrm{S}(x) \,\&\, y = \bar{\bar{x}})\}$.

An inequality relation can be defined on Cn in a natural way.

DEFINITION 11.2.2. Inequality

$$(\mathrm{S}(x) \,\&\, \mathrm{S}(y)) \rightarrow$$

(a) $\bar{\bar{x}} \mathbf{<} \bar{\bar{y}} =_{\mathrm{Df}} x \prec y$

(b) $\bar{\bar{x}} \mathbf{>} \bar{\bar{y}} =_{\mathrm{Df}} \bar{\bar{y}} \mathbf{<} \bar{\bar{x}}$

(c) $\bar{\bar{x}} \boldsymbol{\leqq} \bar{\bar{y}} =_{\mathrm{Df}} x \precsim y$

(d) $\bar{\bar{x}} \boldsymbol{\geqq} \bar{\bar{y}} =_{\mathrm{Df}} \bar{\bar{y}} \boldsymbol{\leqq} \bar{\bar{x}}$.

The bold face symbols $\mathbf{<}$, $\boldsymbol{\leqq}$, $\mathbf{>}$, and $\boldsymbol{\geqq}$ are used for inequality between cardinal number. Moreover, we shall use the convention that lower case German letters—$\mathfrak{m}$, $\mathfrak{n}$, $\mathfrak{p}$, $\mathfrak{q}$, etc.—and these letters with subscripts denote variables, each of whose range is Cn.

The following four theorems about inequality all follow from known properties of the relations $\prec$ and $\precsim$. Their proofs are left as exercises.

THEOREM 11.2.3.
(a) $(\mathfrak{m} \leqq \mathfrak{n} \ \& \ \mathfrak{n} \leqq \mathfrak{p}) \rightarrow \mathfrak{m} \leqq \mathfrak{p}$
(b) $(\mathfrak{m} \leqq \mathfrak{n} \ \& \ \mathfrak{n} \leqq \mathfrak{m}) \rightarrow \mathfrak{m} = \mathfrak{n}$.

THEOREM 11.2.4. $\quad \bar{\bar{x}} < \bar{\bar{y}} \rightarrow x \not\approx y$.

THEOREM 11.2.5. $\quad S(x) \rightarrow \bar{\bar{x}} < \overline{\overline{\mathcal{P}(x)}}$.

Proof: By theorem 3.4.6.

THEOREM 11.2.6.©

$$(\mathrm{Func}(f) \ \& \ x \subseteq \mathfrak{D}(f)) \rightarrow \overline{\overline{f''(x)}} \leqq \bar{\bar{x}}.$$

Proof: See exercise 3.5.1.

Merely using the fact that every ordinal number has a cardinal number, it can be shown that *Cn* is a proper class.

THEOREM 11.2.7. $\quad \mathrm{Pr}(Cn)$.

Proof: Let

$$X = \{\bar{\bar{\alpha}} : \alpha \in On\}.$$

Clearly, $\langle\langle X, <\rangle\rangle$ is a w.o. class. Suppose that X is a set.

Case 1. X has a $<$-last element, $\mathfrak{m}$. Let α be an ordinal number such that $\bar{\bar{\alpha}} = \mathfrak{m}$. Let

$$\beta = \Gamma(\alpha) = \{\gamma : \gamma \precsim \alpha\}.$$

It follows from 10.2.4 that β is an ordinal number. Moreover, since $\beta \notin \Gamma(\alpha)$, we must have $\alpha \prec \beta$. Therefore, by 11.2.2(a), $\mathfrak{m} = \bar{\bar{\alpha}} < \bar{\bar{\beta}}$, contradicting the definition of $\mathfrak{m}$.

Case 2. X has no $<$-last element. For each $\mathfrak{m} \in X$, let $\alpha_{\mathfrak{m}}$ be the smallest ordinal number in the set $\{\beta : \bar{\bar{\beta}} = \mathfrak{m}\}$ and let

$$\delta = \bigcup_{\mathfrak{m} \in X} \alpha_{\mathfrak{m}}.$$

By assumption, X is a set and thus δ is an ordinal number. Consequently, $\bar{\bar{\delta}} \in X$, and so $\delta \approx \alpha_{\mathfrak{m}}$ for some $\mathfrak{m} \in X$. Suppose there is an $\mathfrak{n} \in X$ such that $\mathfrak{m} < \mathfrak{n}$. Then

$$\delta \approx \alpha_{\mathfrak{m}} \prec \alpha_{\mathfrak{n}},$$

which implies $\delta < \alpha_{\mathfrak{n}}$, but this is impossible. Therefore, $\mathfrak{n} \leqq \mathfrak{m}$ for all $\mathfrak{n} \in X$, which implies that $\mathfrak{m}$ is the $<$-last element of X. However, we assumed that X has no $<$-last element. Thus, if X is a set we have arrived at a contradiction. Hence, X and therefore, *Cn*, must be a proper class. ■

EXERCISES 11.2

1. Prove each of the following:
   (a) 1–1 Func($\kappa|\omega$)
   (b) $\neg$1–1 Func($\kappa|On$).
2. Prove any theorems among the following; for each which is not a theorem give a counterexample.
   (a) $m,n \in \omega \rightarrow \overline{\overline{m \cup n}} = \overline{\overline{m + n}}$
   (b) $m,n \in \omega \rightarrow \overline{\overline{m \times n}} = \overline{\overline{m \cdot n}}$
   (c) $\overline{\overline{\omega}} = \overline{\overline{\omega \times \omega}}$
   (d) $\alpha \in On \rightarrow \overline{\overline{\alpha}} = \alpha$.

11.3. ALTERNATE DEFINITION USING THE AXIOM OF CHOICE

In section 11.2, we postulate the existence of a function which satisfies the properties of a cardinal number. In this section and the next, we shall define explicit functions which have these properties.

DEFINITION 11.3.1.

$$\kappa_1(x) =_{\mathrm{Df}} \alpha \leftrightarrow [x \approx \alpha \;\&\; (\forall\beta)(\beta \approx \alpha \rightarrow \alpha \leqq \beta)].$$

In other words, $\kappa_1(x)$ is the smallest ordinal number which is equipollent with x. Since each non-empty subclass of On has a unique first element, it follows immediately that κ_1 is a function.

THEOREM 11.3.2. Func(κ_1).

To prove that every set is in the domain of κ_1, we need the well-ordering theorem.

THEOREM 11.3.3.© $\mathrm{S}(x) \rightarrow x \in \mathfrak{D}(\kappa_1)$.

Proof: It follows from w2 that every set is equipollent with an ordinal number. ■

Each ordinal number is a set; therefore,

THEOREM 11.3.4. $x \in \mathfrak{D}(\kappa_1) \rightarrow \mathrm{S}(\kappa_1(x))$.

The final step required to show that κ_1 satisfies A11 is to prove

THEOREM 11.3.5. $x,y \in \mathfrak{D}(\kappa_1) \rightarrow (\kappa_1(x) = \kappa_1(y) \leftrightarrow x \approx y)$.

Proof: Suppose that $x,y \in \mathfrak{D}(\kappa_1)$. Then if $\kappa_1(x) = \kappa_1(y)$, x and y are equipollent to the same ordinal number so that they themselves must be equipollent.

Conversely, if $x,y \in \mathfrak{D}(\kappa_1)$ and $x \approx y$, then any ordinal number which is equipollent to x is also equipollent to y and conversely. Thus, the smallest ordinal number which is equipollent to x is the same as the smallest ordinal number which is equipollent to y. ■

Therefore, κ_1 satisfies axiom A11. Consequently, if the double bar is replaced by "κ_1" in definition 11.2.2, thus defining the inequality relation on $\mathcal{R}(\kappa_1)$, all the theorems of section 11.2 remain valid if the double bar is replaced by "κ_1" and if "*Cn*" is replaced by "$\mathcal{R}(\kappa_1)$".

There are several additional theorems about κ_1 which are true because of its explicit definition. The proofs of the first four are not difficult and are left to the reader.

THEOREM 11.3.6. $\mathcal{R}(\kappa_1) \subseteq On$.

THEOREM 11.3.7. $\omega = \{\kappa_1(x) : x \text{ is finite}\}$.

THEOREM 11.3.8. $\alpha \in \mathcal{R}(\kappa_1) \rightarrow$

(a) $\bar{\alpha} = \alpha$

(b) $\bar{\bar{\alpha}} = \alpha$.

THEOREM 11.3.9. $\alpha \in \mathcal{R}(\kappa_1) \leftrightarrow (\forall\beta)(\beta < \alpha \rightarrow \beta \prec \alpha)$.

THEOREM 11.3.10.

$(\alpha \in \mathcal{R}(\kappa_1)$ & α is infinite$) \rightarrow \alpha$ is a limit ordinal.

Proof: Suppose that α is an infinite ordinal number which is an element of the range of κ_1, and that α is not a limit ordinal. Then there is an infinite ordinal number β such that

$$\alpha = \beta^+.$$

Since β is infinite,

$$\beta \approx \beta^+.$$

Consequently, we have $\beta < \alpha$ and $\beta \approx \alpha$, contradicting 11.3.9. Thus, α must be a limit ordinal. ■

Since $\mathcal{R}(\kappa_1) \subseteq On$, there are two inequality relations defined on $\mathcal{R}(\kappa_1)$. If $x,y \in \mathfrak{D}(\kappa_1)$, then we have

$$\kappa_1(x) \leqq \kappa_1(y) \leftrightarrow x \lesssim y,$$

and

$$\kappa_1(x) \leq \kappa_2(y) \leftrightarrow (\kappa_1(x) \in \kappa_1(y) \text{ or } \kappa_1(x) = \kappa_1(y)).$$

However, it is not difficult to prove that these inequality relations are identical.

THEOREM 11.3.11. $x,y \in \mathfrak{D}(\kappa_1) \rightarrow$

$$(\kappa_1(x) \leqq \kappa_1(y) \leftrightarrow \kappa_1(x) \leq \kappa_1(y)).$$

EXERCISES 11.3

1. Give an example to show that the converse of 11.3.10 is not a theorem.
2. If the double bar is replaced by "κ_1" and "Cn" by "$\mathfrak{R}(\kappa_1)$", which of the theorems 11.2.3–11.2.7 require the axiom of choice in their proofs? Give reasons for your answer.

*3. Prove any theorems among the following; for each which is not a theorem give a counterexample.
   (a) $\alpha,\beta \in \mathfrak{R}(\kappa_1) \rightarrow \alpha + \beta \in \mathfrak{R}(\kappa_1)$
   (b) $\alpha,\beta \in \mathfrak{R}(\kappa_1) \rightarrow \alpha \cdot \beta \in \mathfrak{R}(\kappa_1)$
   (c) $\kappa_1(\alpha + \beta) = \kappa_1(\alpha) + \kappa_1(\beta)$
   (d) $\kappa_1(\alpha \cdot \beta) = \kappa_1(\alpha) \cdot \kappa_1(\beta)$
   (e) $\alpha < \beta \rightarrow \kappa_1(\alpha) < \kappa_1(\beta)$.
   (See sections 8.4 and 8.5 for the definitions of addition and multiplication of ordinal numbers.)

*11.4 ALTERNATE DEFINITION USING THE AXIOM OF REGULARITY

In intuitive set theory it was proposed that the cardinal number of a set be defined as follows: the cardinal number of a set x is the class of all sets equipollent with x (the Frege–Russell definition). However, the definition leads to difficulties since the cardinal number of a set is not necessarily a set. For example, the cardinal number of 1 would be the class of all sets which have one element,

$$\{x : x \approx 1\},$$

and this class would be equipollent with V which, by 4.5.3, is a proper class. However, the Frege–Russell definition can be modified to avoid this difficulty by using the notion of rank (section 8.6). (This modification was first proposed by A. P. Morse and D. Scott.)

DEFINITION 11.4.1. $S(x) \rightarrow$

$$\kappa_2(x) =_{\mathrm{Df}} \{y : y \approx x \;\&\; (\forall z)(z \approx x \rightarrow \rho(y) \leq \rho(z))\}.$$

If it is assumed that the class of all atoms, $\mathfrak{A}$, is a set, then it follows from 8.6.21 that $\kappa_2(x)$ is a set for each set x.

THEOREM 11.4.2. $(S(\mathfrak{A}) \;\&\; S(x)) \rightarrow S(\kappa_2(x))$.

It follows from 11.4.1 and 11.4.2 that if $\mathfrak{A}$ is a set, then κ_2 is a function.

THEOREM 11.4.3. $S(\mathcal{A}) \rightarrow \text{Func}(\kappa_2)$.

According to 11.4.1, for each set x, $\kappa_2(x)$ is the class of all sets of smallest rank which are equipollent to x. Thus if $\mathcal{A}$ is a set, the domain of κ_2 is the same as that of ρ. The axiom of regularity is needed to prove that every set is an element of the domain of ρ (8.6.6). And thus the axiom of regularity is needed to prove the following theorem.

THEOREM 11.4.4.® $(S(\mathcal{A}) \,\&\, S(x)) \rightarrow x \in \mathcal{D}(\kappa_2)$.

Hence, if it is assumed that every set has a rank and that the class of atoms is a set, it follows that κ_2 satisfies axiom A11. However, because of the directness and simplicity of the Frege–Russell definition, it is often useful to think of cardinal numbers in this way. As mentioned above, its only disadvantage is that a cardinal number is not necessarily a set; it may be a proper class. The Frege–Russell definition does satisfy the other two properties of cardinal numbers—that every set has a cardinal number, and that two sets have the same cardinal number if and only if they are equipollent (see exercise 11.4.1).

EXERCISES 11.4

1. For each set x, define

$$\kappa_3(x) = \{y : y \approx x\}.$$

Prove each of the following:
(a) $S(x) \rightarrow (\exists 1\, Y)(\kappa_3(x) = Y)$
(b) $(S(x) \,\&\, S(y)) \rightarrow (\kappa_3(x) = \kappa_3(y) \leftrightarrow x \approx y)$.

2. Show why it would be undesirable to define a cardinal number as follows:

$$S(x) \rightarrow \kappa_4(x) =_{\text{Df}} \text{The } <\text{-first element of } \{\rho(y) : y \approx x\}.$$

11.5 INITIAL ORDINALS AND ALEPHS

The equipollence relation, $\approx$, is an equivalence relation on $On \sim \omega$. Therefore, it partitions $On \sim \omega$ into pairwise disjoint classes. It follows from 10.2.2 that each of these equivalence classes is a set. The smallest element of each one of these sets is called an *initial ordinal*.

DEFINITION 11.5.1. Initial Ordinals
(a) α is an *initial ordinal* $=_{\text{Df}} (\forall \beta)(\beta < \alpha \rightarrow \beta \prec \alpha)$.
(b) $Io =_{\text{Df}} \{\alpha : \alpha \text{ is an initial ordinal}\}$.

Note that $Io = \mathcal{R}(\kappa_1) \sim \omega$, 11.3.1. The ordinal number ω is the smallest initial ordinal. The next larger initial ordinal is often denoted by Ω, the smallest non-countable ordinal number.

Since $Io = \mathcal{R}(\kappa_1) \sim \omega$, the next two theorems follow from 11.2.7 and 11.3.10, respectively:

THEOREM 11.5.2. $\Pr(Io)$.

THEOREM 11.5.3. $\alpha \in Io \rightarrow \alpha$ is a limit ordinal.

Moreover, it is easy to prove that *On* is isomorphic to *Io*.

THEOREM 11.5.4. $\langle\langle On, <\rangle\rangle \cong \langle\langle Io, <\rangle\rangle$.

Proof: By 11.5.2, *Io* is a proper class. Since $Io \subseteq On$, every initial segment of *Io* is a set. Therefore, the theorem follows from 8.2.20. ∎

Since *On* and *Io* are isomorphic w.o. classes, it follows from 7.4.5 that there is exactly one isomorphism, mapping *On* onto *Io*. Let us call this isomorphism *F*. For each $\alpha \in On$, let

$$F(\alpha) = \omega_\alpha.$$

Then ω_α is the alpha-th initial ordinal. Now it is easy to prove the following two theorems.

THEOREM 11.5.5.

(a) $\omega_\alpha = \omega_\beta \leftrightarrow \alpha = \beta$
(b) $\omega_\alpha < \omega_\beta \leftrightarrow \alpha < \beta$
(c) $\omega_\alpha \prec \omega_\beta \leftrightarrow \alpha < \beta$
(d) $\alpha < \omega_\beta \rightarrow \alpha \prec \omega_\beta$
(e) $\alpha \leqq \omega_\alpha$.

THEOREM 11.5.6.

(a) $\omega_0 = \omega$
(b) $\omega_{\alpha^+} = \Gamma(\omega_\alpha)$
(c) α is a limit ordinal $\rightarrow \omega_\alpha = \bigcup_{\beta<\alpha} \omega_\beta$.

Theorem 11.5.6 could be used as the definition of ω_α.

The cardinal number of an infinite w.o. set is called an *aleph*. (Aleph is the Hebrew letter for "A" and the symbol for it is "ℵ".)

DEFINITION 11.5.7. Alephs

(a) $\mathfrak{m}$ is an *aleph* $=_{\mathrm{Df}} (\exists\alpha)(\alpha \geqq \omega \;\&\; \overline{\overline{\mathfrak{m}}} = \alpha)$
(b) $\mathfrak{A} =_{\mathrm{Df}} \{\mathfrak{m} : \mathfrak{m}$ is an aleph$\}$.

(The lower case German letters—$\mathfrak{m}$, $\mathfrak{n}$, $\mathfrak{p}$, $\mathfrak{q}$, etc.—and these letters with subscripts denote variables, each of whose range is *Cn*, the class of all cardinal numbers.)

Since each ordinal number is equipollent with an initial ordinal, each aleph is the cardinal number of an initial ordinal.

DEFINITION 11.5.8. $\aleph_\alpha =_{\mathrm{Df}} \overline{\overline{\omega_\alpha}}$.

Hence, we have

$$\aleph_0 = \overline{\overline{\omega_0}} = \overline{\overline{\omega}}$$
$$\aleph_1 = \overline{\overline{\omega_1}} = \overline{\overline{\Omega}}.$$

"$\aleph_0$" is called aleph-zero or aleph-null; "$\aleph_1$", aleph-one; etc. Further properties of alephs are given in the next theorem. The proof is left as an exercise.

THEOREM 11.5.9.
(a) $\mathrm{w}2 \rightarrow \mathfrak{A} = Cn \sim \omega$
(b) $\mathfrak{A} = \{\aleph_\alpha : \alpha \in On\}$
(c) $\aleph_\alpha = \aleph_\beta \leftrightarrow \alpha = \beta$
(d) $\aleph_\alpha < \aleph_\beta \leftrightarrow \alpha < \beta$
(e) $\aleph_\alpha < \aleph_{\alpha^+} \,\&\, \neg(\exists \mathfrak{m})(\aleph_\alpha < \mathfrak{m} < \aleph_{\alpha^+})$
(f) $\aleph_{\alpha^+} = \Gamma(\omega_\alpha)$
(g) $\overline{\overline{\alpha}} \leqq \aleph_\alpha$
(h) $\aleph_\alpha = \overline{\overline{\{\beta : \beta < \omega_\alpha\}}}$.

EXERCISES 11.5

1. Prove theorem 11.5.5.
2. Prove theorem 11.5.6.
3. Prove theorem 11.5.9.
4. Prove $(\forall \mathfrak{m})(\forall \mathfrak{n})(\mathfrak{m} < \mathfrak{n} \,\&\, (\forall \mathfrak{p})(\mathfrak{m} < \mathfrak{p} \rightarrow \mathfrak{n} \leqq \mathfrak{p}))$. [The proof uses the axiom of choice. Tarski (1954) showed that the proposition also implies the axiom of choice.]
5. Find the smallest ordinal number α such that $\alpha = \omega_\alpha$ (see exercise 9.4.10).

*6. Prove $\alpha > 0 \rightarrow \omega_\alpha = \omega^{\omega_\alpha}$. (In other words, each initial ordinal larger than ω is an epsilon number. See section 9.5.)

11.6 CARDINAL ARITHMETIC

The symbols for the operations between cardinal numbers will be designated by bold face type,

$$\mathbf{+}, \mathbf{\cdot}, \mathbf{-}, \mathbf{\div},$$

to distinguish them from the corresponding symbols for the operations between ordinal numbers,

$$+, \cdot, -, \div.$$

In the case of exponentiation this distinction cannot be made. It is hoped that the context will clarify what is meant.

The sum of two cardinal numbers $\mathfrak{m}$ and $\mathfrak{n}$ is defined as the cardinal number of the union of two disjoint sets which have $\mathfrak{m}$ and $\mathfrak{n}$ as their cardinal numbers. To prove that the sum exists we need two preliminary lemmas.

LEMMA 11.6.1.

$$(\forall \mathfrak{m})(\forall \mathfrak{n})(\exists x)(\exists y)(S(x) \,\&\, S(y) \,\&\, x \cap y = \emptyset \,\&\, \bar{\bar{x}} = \mathfrak{m} \,\&\, \bar{\bar{y}} = \mathfrak{n}).$$

Proof: Since $\mathfrak{m}, \mathfrak{n} \in Cn$, then there exist two sets x_0 and y_0 such that $\bar{\bar{x}}_0 = \mathfrak{m}$ and $\bar{\bar{y}}_0 = \mathfrak{n}$. Let $x = x_0 \times \{0\}$ and $y = y_0 \times \{1\}$. ∎

LEMMA 11.6.2.

$$(x \approx u \,\&\, y \approx v \,\&\, x \cap y = \emptyset \,\&\, u \cap v = \emptyset) \rightarrow x \cup y \approx u \cup v.$$

Proof: See exercise 3.4.1.

DEFINITION 11.6.3. Addition

$$\mathfrak{m} + \mathfrak{n} =_{\mathrm{Df}} \mathfrak{p} \leftrightarrow (\exists x)(\exists y)(S(x) \,\&\, S(y) \,\&\, x \cap y = \emptyset \,\&\, \bar{\bar{x}} = \mathfrak{m} \,\&\, \bar{\bar{y}} = \mathfrak{n} \,\&\, \mathfrak{p} = \overline{\overline{x \cup y}}).$$

Now, it is easy to prove

THEOREM 11.6.4. $(\forall \mathfrak{m})(\forall \mathfrak{n})(\exists 1 \mathfrak{p})(\mathfrak{m} + \mathfrak{n} = \mathfrak{p})$.

Moreover, it follows immediately from the commutative and associative laws for union that the same laws hold for addition of cardinal numbers.

THEOREM 11.6.5.
(a) $\mathfrak{m} + \mathfrak{n} = \mathfrak{n} + \mathfrak{m}$
(b) $(\mathfrak{m} + \mathfrak{n}) + \mathfrak{p} = \mathfrak{m} + (\mathfrak{n} + \mathfrak{p})$.

The product of two cardinal numbers $\mathfrak{m}$ and $\mathfrak{n}$ is defined as the cardinal number of the direct product of two sets which have $\mathfrak{m}$ and $\mathfrak{n}$ as their cardinal numbers. It follows from 11.6.1 that two such sets exist; thus we need only one preliminary lemma before stating the definition.

LEMMA 11.6.6. $(x \approx u \,\&\, y \approx v) \rightarrow x \times y \approx u \times v$.

Proof: See exercise 3.4.2.

DEFINITION 11.6.7. Multiplication

$$\mathfrak{m} \cdot \mathfrak{n} =_{\mathrm{Df}} \mathfrak{p} \leftrightarrow (\exists x)(\exists y)(S(x) \,\&\, S(y) \,\&\, \bar{\bar{x}} = \mathfrak{m} \,\&\, \bar{\bar{y}} = \mathfrak{n} \,\&\, \mathfrak{p} = \overline{\overline{x \times y}}).$$

The following theorem is easy to prove.

THEOREM 11.6.8. $(\forall \mathfrak{m})(\forall \mathfrak{n})(\exists 1 \mathfrak{p})(\mathfrak{m} \cdot \mathfrak{n} = \mathfrak{p})$.

It follows immediately from exercise 3.4.3 that multiplication of cardinal numbers is both commutative and associative.

THEOREM 11.6.9.
(a) $\mathfrak{m} \cdot \mathfrak{n} = \mathfrak{n} \cdot \mathfrak{m}$
(b) $(\mathfrak{m} \cdot \mathfrak{n}) \cdot \mathfrak{p} = \mathfrak{m} \cdot (\mathfrak{n} \cdot \mathfrak{p})$.

Moreover, the distributive law follows from 3.1.23(a).

THEOREM 11.6.10. $\mathfrak{m} \cdot (\mathfrak{n} + \mathfrak{p}) = \mathfrak{m} \cdot \mathfrak{n} + \mathfrak{m} \cdot \mathfrak{p}$.

The last operation to be defined is exponentiation and this also is defined in a natural set theoretical way. First, the preliminary lemma.

LEMMA 11.6.11. $(x \approx u \;\&\; y \approx v) \rightarrow x^y \approx u^v$.

Proof: See exercise 3.5.4(a).

DEFINITION 11.6.12. Exponentiation

$$\mathfrak{m}^{\mathfrak{n}} =_{\text{Df}} \mathfrak{p} \leftrightarrow (\exists x)(\exists y)(\text{S}(x) \;\&\; \text{S}(y) \;\&\; \bar{\bar{x}} = \mathfrak{m} \;\&\; \bar{\bar{y}} = \mathfrak{n} \;\&\; \mathfrak{p} = \overline{\overline{x^y}}).$$

If x and y are sets, then

$$x^y = \{f : \text{Func}(f) \;\&\; \mathfrak{D}(f) = y \;\&\; \mathfrak{R}(f) \subseteq x\}.$$

However, if $\mathfrak{m}$ and $\mathfrak{n}$ are cardinal numbers, then $\mathfrak{m}^{\mathfrak{n}}$ will always be the cardinal number $\mathfrak{p}$ as defined in 11.6.12.

THEOREM 11.6.13. $(\forall \mathfrak{m})(\forall \mathfrak{n})(\exists 1 \mathfrak{p})(\mathfrak{m}^{\mathfrak{n}} = \mathfrak{p})$.

The next theorem gives the fundamental properties of exponentiation.

THEOREM 11.6.14.
(a) $(\text{S}(x) \;\&\; \bar{\bar{x}} = \mathfrak{m}) \rightarrow \overline{\overline{\mathcal{P}(x)}} = \bar{\bar{2}}^{\mathfrak{m}}$
(b) $\mathfrak{m}^{\mathfrak{n}+\mathfrak{p}} = \mathfrak{m}^{\mathfrak{n}} \cdot \mathfrak{m}^{\mathfrak{p}}$
(c) $(\mathfrak{m} \cdot \mathfrak{n})^{\mathfrak{p}} = \mathfrak{m}^{\mathfrak{p}} \cdot \mathfrak{n}^{\mathfrak{p}}$
(d) $(\mathfrak{m}^{\mathfrak{n}})^{\mathfrak{p}} = \mathfrak{m}^{\mathfrak{n} \cdot \mathfrak{p}}$.

Proof:
(a) By theorem 3.5.23.
(b) Suppose that x, y, and z are sets such that $\bar{\bar{x}} = \mathfrak{m}$, $\bar{\bar{y}} = \mathfrak{n}$, $\bar{\bar{z}} = \mathfrak{p}$, and $y \cap z = \emptyset$. Then,

$$\mathfrak{m}^{\mathfrak{n}+\mathfrak{p}} = \overline{\overline{x^{y \cup z}}} \;\&\; \mathfrak{m}^{\mathfrak{n}} \cdot \mathfrak{m}^{\mathfrak{p}} = \overline{\overline{x^y \times x^z}}.$$

Let $f \in x^{y \cup z}$; f is a function, $\mathfrak{D}(f) = y \cup z$, and $\mathfrak{R}(f) \subseteq x$. Let

$$f_y = f|y, f_z = f|z.$$

Define a function ψ such that for each $f \in x^{y \cup z}$,

$$\psi(f) = \langle f_y, f_z \rangle.$$

We shall show first that ψ is 1–1. Suppose that $f,g \in x^{y \cup z}$ and $\psi(f) = \psi(g)$. Then $f_y = g_y$ and $f_z = g_z$. Hence,

$$f = f_y \cup f_z = g_y \cup g_z = g.$$

To prove that ψ is onto, suppose that $\langle g,h \rangle \in x^y \times x^z$. If $f = g \cup h$ then f is a function since $y \cap z = \emptyset$, $f \in x^{y \cup z}$, and $\psi(f) = \langle g,h \rangle$. This proves (b).

The proofs of (c) and (d) are similar and are left as exercises. ■

Some monotonicity laws for cardinal arithmetic are given in the next theorem.

THEOREM 11.6.15. $(\mathfrak{m} \leqq \mathfrak{p} \;\&\; \mathfrak{n} \leqq \mathfrak{q}) \rightarrow$

(a) $\mathfrak{m} + \mathfrak{n} \leqq \mathfrak{p} + \mathfrak{q}$

(b) $\mathfrak{m} \cdot \mathfrak{n} \leqq \mathfrak{p} \cdot \mathfrak{q}$

(c) $\mathfrak{m}^{\mathfrak{n}} \leqq \mathfrak{p}^{\mathfrak{q}}$.

Proof: The proofs of (a) and (b) are not difficult; (c) follows from exercise 3.5.4(b) and (c). ■

The next theorem gives a necessary and sufficient condition for one cardinal number to be smaller than another.

THEOREM 11.6.16. $\mathfrak{m} \leqq \mathfrak{n} \leftrightarrow (\exists \mathfrak{p})(\mathfrak{m} + \mathfrak{p} = \mathfrak{n})$.

Proof: Suppose that $\mathfrak{m} \leqq \mathfrak{n}$. Let x and y be sets such that $\overline{\overline{x}} = \mathfrak{m}$, $\overline{\overline{y}} = \mathfrak{n}$, and $x \cap y = \emptyset$. Then $\mathfrak{m} \leqq \mathfrak{n}$ implies that there is a 1–1 function f mapping x into y. Let

$$z = y \sim f''x.$$

Then $x \cup z \approx y$ and $x \cap z = \emptyset$. Let

$$\mathfrak{p} = \overline{\overline{z}}.$$

Then it follows from 11.6.3 that $\mathfrak{m} + \mathfrak{p} = \mathfrak{n}$.

Conversely, suppose that $\mathfrak{m} + \mathfrak{p} = \mathfrak{n}$. Let x,y, and z be sets such that $\overline{\overline{x}} = \mathfrak{m}$, $\overline{\overline{y}} = \mathfrak{n}$, $\overline{\overline{z}} = \mathfrak{p}$, and $x \cap z = \emptyset$. By 11.6.3, there is a 1–1 function g mapping $x \cup z$ onto y. Therefore, $g|x$ is a 1–1 function mapping x into y, and thus $\mathfrak{m} \leqq \mathfrak{n}$. ■

If there is a *unique* $\mathfrak{p}$ such that $\mathfrak{m} + \mathfrak{p} = \mathfrak{n}$, then the difference $\mathfrak{n} - \mathfrak{m}$ could be defined as that unique $\mathfrak{p}$. This is exactly how subtraction is defined.

DEFINITION 11.6.17. Subtraction

$$(\exists 1 \mathfrak{p})(\mathfrak{m} + \mathfrak{p} = \mathfrak{n}) \rightarrow (\mathfrak{n} - \mathfrak{m} =_{\mathrm{Df}} \mathfrak{p} \leftrightarrow \mathfrak{m} + \mathfrak{p} = \mathfrak{n}).$$

Division can be defined in an analogous way.

DEFINITION 11.6.18. Division

$$(\exists 1\mathfrak{p})(\mathfrak{m}\cdot\mathfrak{p} = \mathfrak{n}) \rightarrow (\mathfrak{n} \div \mathfrak{m} =_{\mathrm{Df}} \mathfrak{p} \leftrightarrow \mathfrak{m}\cdot\mathfrak{p} = \mathfrak{n}).$$

In subtraction and division of cardinal numbers there is no guarantee, as in addition and multiplication, that even if $\mathfrak{m} \leqq \mathfrak{n}$, $\mathfrak{n} - \mathfrak{m}$ or $\mathfrak{n} \div \mathfrak{m}$ exists. In fact, there is no guarantee that $\mathfrak{n} \div \mathfrak{m}$ exists even if there is a $\mathfrak{p}$ such that $\mathfrak{n} = \mathfrak{m}\cdot\mathfrak{p}$. However, we shall prove in Chapter 12 that each of the following two propositions are equivalent to the axiom of choice.

$$\mathfrak{m} < \mathfrak{n} \rightarrow (\exists 1\mathfrak{p})(\mathfrak{n} - \mathfrak{m} = \mathfrak{p}).$$
$$\mathfrak{m} < \mathfrak{n} \rightarrow (\exists 1\mathfrak{p})(\mathfrak{n} \div \mathfrak{m} = \mathfrak{p}).$$

If $\mathfrak{m} = \mathfrak{n}$, then there may be many cardinal numbers $\mathfrak{p}$ such that $\mathfrak{m} + \mathfrak{p} = \mathfrak{n}$, $\mathfrak{m}\cdot\mathfrak{p} = \mathfrak{n}$, and $\mathfrak{m}^{\mathfrak{p}} = \mathfrak{n}$. For example, if $\mathfrak{m}$ is denumerable, then each of the following equations holds for all finite $\mathfrak{p}$.

$$\mathfrak{m} + \mathfrak{p} = \mathfrak{m} \tag{5.2.11}$$

$$\mathfrak{m}\cdot\mathfrak{p} = \mathfrak{m} \tag{5.2.12}$$

$$\mathfrak{m}^{\mathfrak{p}} = \mathfrak{m}. \tag{5.2.13}$$

Consequently, there are no cancellation laws for cardinal addition, multiplication, or exponentiation. Moreover, $\mathfrak{n} < \mathfrak{p}$ and $\mathfrak{m} \neq \bar{\bar{0}}$ do not necessarily imply that $\mathfrak{m} + \mathfrak{n} < \mathfrak{m} + \mathfrak{p}$, $\mathfrak{m}\cdot\mathfrak{n} < \mathfrak{m}\cdot\mathfrak{p}$, $\mathfrak{m}^{\mathfrak{n}} < \mathfrak{m}^{\mathfrak{p}}$, or $\mathfrak{n}^{\mathfrak{m}} < \mathfrak{p}^{\mathfrak{m}}$. (Why not?)

In Chapter 12 we shall show how the axiom of choice can be used to simplify addition and multiplication of transfinite cardinal numbers (cardinal numbers $\geqq \aleph_0$). It will be shown using the axiom of choice that

$$\mathfrak{m},\mathfrak{n} \geqq \aleph_0 \rightarrow \mathfrak{m} + \mathfrak{n} = \mathfrak{m}\cdot\mathfrak{n} = \max(\mathfrak{m},\mathfrak{n}).$$

In the remaining part of this section, we shall apply the results obtained in cardinal arithmetic to two familiar cardinal numbers: $\aleph_0$, the cardinal number of ω; and $\mathfrak{c}$, the cardinal number of the set of real numbers *Re*. (In the exercises we shall also consider $\mathfrak{f}$, the cardinal number of the set of all real valued functions of a real variable, $\mathfrak{f} = \overline{\overline{(Re)^{Re}}}$.)

It has previously been shown (5.1.8 and 6.6.5) that if x is finite then

$$x \prec \omega \prec Re.$$

Therefore,

$$(\forall x)(x \text{ is finite} \rightarrow \bar{\bar{x}} < \aleph_0 < \mathfrak{c}).$$

THEOREM 11.6.19. x is finite $\rightarrow$

(a) $\bar{\bar{x}} + \aleph_0 = \aleph_0 + \aleph_0 = \aleph_0$

(b) $x \neq \emptyset \rightarrow \bar{\bar{x}} \cdot \aleph_0 = \aleph_0 \cdot \aleph_0 = \aleph_0$

(c) $x \neq \emptyset \rightarrow \aleph_0^{\bar{\bar{x}}} = \aleph_0$.

Proof:

(a) By theorem 11.6.15(a),

$$\aleph_0 \leqq \bar{\bar{x}} + \aleph_0 \leqq \aleph_0 + \aleph_0. \tag{1}$$

By 5.2.10,

$$\aleph_0 = \aleph_0 + \aleph_0. \tag{2}$$

Therefore, part (a) follows from (1) and (2).

(b) Using 11.6.15(b) we obtain,

$$\aleph_0 \leqq \bar{\bar{x}} \cdot \aleph_0 \leqq \aleph_0 \cdot \aleph_0,$$

and by 5.2.12,

$$\aleph_0 = \aleph_0 \cdot \aleph_0.$$

(c) Prove that $\aleph_0^n = \aleph_0$ using part (b) and induction. ■

The next theorem gives similar properties of the cardinal number $\mathfrak{c}$.

THEOREM 11.6.20. x is finite $\rightarrow$

(a) $\bar{\bar{x}} + \mathfrak{c} = \aleph_0 + \mathfrak{c} = \mathfrak{c} + \mathfrak{c} = \mathfrak{c}$

(b) $x \neq \emptyset \rightarrow \bar{\bar{x}} \cdot \mathfrak{c} = \aleph_0 \cdot \mathfrak{c} = \mathfrak{c} \cdot \mathfrak{c} = \mathfrak{c}$

(c) $x \neq \emptyset \rightarrow \mathfrak{c}^{\bar{\bar{x}}} = \mathfrak{c}$

(d) $\bar{\bar{x}} > \bar{\bar{1}} \rightarrow \bar{\bar{x}}^{\aleph_0} = \aleph_0^{\aleph_0} = \mathfrak{c}^{\aleph_0} = \mathfrak{c}$.

Proof: The proofs of parts (a)–(c) are analogous to the proofs of (a)–(c) of 11.6.19.

(d) From 6.6.4 we have $Re \approx 2^\omega$. Therefore,

$$\mathfrak{c} = \bar{\bar{2}}^{\aleph_0}. \tag{1}$$

By theorem 11.6.15(c), if x is finite and $\bar{\bar{x}} > \bar{\bar{1}}$, then

$$\bar{\bar{2}}^{\aleph_0} \leqq \bar{\bar{x}}^{\aleph_0} \leqq \aleph_0^{\aleph_0} \leqq \mathfrak{c}^{\aleph_0}.$$

Thus, it remains to be shown that $\mathfrak{c}^{\aleph_0} = \mathfrak{c}$.

$$\begin{aligned} \mathfrak{c}^{\aleph_0} &= (\bar{\bar{2}}^{\aleph_0})^{\aleph_0} && (1) \\ &= \bar{\bar{2}}^{\aleph_0 \cdot \aleph_0} && (11.6.14d) \\ &= \bar{\bar{2}}^{\aleph_0} && (11.6.19b) \\ &= \mathfrak{c}. && (1) \ ■ \end{aligned}$$

It follows, for example from 11.6.20(c), that a Euclidean space of $n \neq 0$ dimensions has the same cardinality as a Euclidean space of one dimension. Therefore, an $n \neq 0$ dimensional Euclidean space has the same number of points as a line. Moreover, since $\mathfrak{c}^{\aleph_0} = \mathfrak{c}$, a Hilbert space has the same number of points as a line. Further properties of cardinal numbers are given in the exercises.

EXERCISES 11.6

Prove each of the following without using the axiom of choice:

1. (a) $(\aleph_0 \leqq \mathfrak{m} \ \& \ \mathfrak{n} \leqq \aleph_0) \to \mathfrak{m} + \mathfrak{n} = \mathfrak{m}$
   (b) $\mathfrak{q} + \mathfrak{r} = \mathfrak{p} \to (\mathfrak{m} + \mathfrak{n})^{\mathfrak{p}} \geqq \mathfrak{m}^{\mathfrak{q}} \cdot \mathfrak{n}^{\mathfrak{r}}$
   (c) $\mathfrak{m} + \bar{\bar{1}} = \mathfrak{m} \to \aleph_0 \leqq \mathfrak{m}$.
2. $(\mathfrak{f} = \mathfrak{c}^{\mathfrak{c}} \ \& \ x \text{ is finite}) \to$
   (a) $\bar{\bar{x}} + \mathfrak{f} = \aleph_0 + \mathfrak{f} = \mathfrak{c} + \mathfrak{f} = \mathfrak{f} + \mathfrak{f} = \mathfrak{f}$
   (b) $x \neq \emptyset \to \bar{\bar{x}} \cdot \mathfrak{f} = \aleph_0 \cdot \mathfrak{f} = \mathfrak{c} \cdot \mathfrak{f} = \mathfrak{f} \cdot \mathfrak{f} = \mathfrak{f}$
   (c) $x \neq \emptyset \to \mathfrak{f}^{\bar{\bar{x}}} = \mathfrak{f}^{\aleph_0} = \mathfrak{f}^{\mathfrak{c}} = \mathfrak{f}$
   (d) $\bar{\bar{x}} > \bar{\bar{1}} \to \bar{\bar{x}}^{\mathfrak{c}} = \aleph_0^{\mathfrak{c}} = \mathfrak{c}^{\mathfrak{c}} = \mathfrak{f}$.
3. (a) $\aleph_0 \leqq \mathfrak{m} \to \mathfrak{m} + \aleph_0 = \mathfrak{m}$
   (b) $\mathfrak{c} \leqq \mathfrak{m} \to \mathfrak{m} + \mathfrak{c} = \mathfrak{m}$
   (c) $\mathfrak{f} \leqq \mathfrak{m} \to \mathfrak{m} + \mathfrak{f} = \mathfrak{m}$.
4. $\aleph_0 \leqq \mathfrak{p} \to (\exists m)(\exists n)(\bar{\bar{2}}^{\mathfrak{p}} = 2 \cdot \mathfrak{m} = \bar{\bar{2}} \cdot \mathfrak{n} + \bar{\bar{1}})$. (In other words, if $\aleph_0 \leqq \mathfrak{p}$ then $\bar{\bar{2}}^{\mathfrak{p}}$ is simultaneously even and odd. Hint: if $\aleph_0 \leqq \mathfrak{p}$, then $\mathfrak{p} + \bar{\bar{1}} = \mathfrak{p}$.)
5. $Re \approx \{x : x \subseteq Re \ \& \ x \text{ is finite}\}$.
   (The set of all finite subsets of *Re* has cardinality $\mathfrak{c}$.)
6. A real number is called *algebraic* if it is the solution of a polynomial equation with rational coefficients. That is,

$$x \in Re \to [x \text{ is } algebraic =_{\text{Df}} (\exists n)(n \in \omega \ \& \ (\exists a)(\text{Func}(a) \ \& \ \mathfrak{D}(a) = n^+ \ \& \ (\forall m)(m < n^+ \to a_m \in Ra) \ \& \ a_n x^n + a_{n-1}x^{n-1} + \cdots + a_1 x + a_0 = 0))].$$

   Prove $\omega \approx \{x : x \in Re \ \& \ x \text{ is algebraic}\}$.
   (The cardinality of the set of all algebraic numbers is $\aleph_0$.)
7. $(Re)^{Re} \approx \{f : 1\text{–}1 \text{ func}(f) \ \& \ \mathfrak{D}(f) = \mathfrak{R}(f) = Re\}$
   (The set of all 1–1 functions mapping *Re* onto itself has cardinality $\mathfrak{f}$.)
8. The set of all continuous real valued functions of a real variable has cardinality $\mathfrak{c}$. [Hint: if g is a continuous function and x is a sequence of real numbers, then

$$\lim_{n \in \omega} g(x_n) = g(\lim_{n \in \omega} x_n).$$

   Therefore, a continuous function is completely determined if its values on the set of rational numbers are prescribed.]
9. (a) $\bar{\bar{\alpha}} + \bar{\bar{\beta}} = \overline{\overline{\alpha + \beta}}$
   (b) $\bar{\bar{\alpha}} \cdot \bar{\bar{\beta}} = \overline{\overline{\alpha \cdot \beta}}$.
10. Without using the axiom of choice, prove that the following two propositions are equivalent.
    (a) $(\aleph_0 < \mathfrak{m} \ \& \ \mathfrak{m} = \aleph_0 + \mathfrak{p} = \aleph_0 + \mathfrak{q}) \to \mathfrak{p} = \mathfrak{q}$
    (b) $\mathfrak{n} < \aleph_0$ or $\mathfrak{n} = \aleph_0$ or $\mathfrak{n} > \aleph_0$.

*Chapter 12: Cardinal Numbers and the Axiom of Choice

12.1 ADDITIONAL PROPERTIES OF CARDINAL NUMBERS

Most of the results in this section will be used in section 12.2, which treats the role played by the axiom of choice in cardinal arithmetic. However, all the results in this section are independent of the axiom of choice.

For convenience we shall identify the cardinal number of a natural number with the natural number. That is, for all $m \in \omega$ we shall replace "$\bar{\bar{m}}$" by "m". This will not lead to any inconsistency because $\kappa|\omega$ is 1–1 [exercise 11.2.1(a)].

THEOREM 12.1.1. $\qquad m,n > 1 \rightarrow m + n \leqq m \cdot n.$

Proof: Let x and y be sets such that $\bar{\bar{x}} = \mathfrak{m}$, $\bar{\bar{y}} = \mathfrak{n}$, and $x \cap y = \emptyset$. We wish to prove that

$$x \cup y \precsim x \times y.$$

Let $a,b \in x$, $a \neq b$, and $c,d \in y$, $c \neq d$. Define a mapping ψ as follows. For each $u \in x \cup y$,

$$\psi(u) = \begin{cases} \langle u,c\rangle, & \text{if } u \in x \\ \langle a,u\rangle, & \text{if } u \in y \ \&\ u \neq c \\ \langle b,d\rangle, & \text{if } u = c. \end{cases}$$

It is clear that ψ is a function mapping $x \cup y$ into $x \times y$. The proof that ψ is 1–1 is left as an exercise. ■

(Where in the preceding proof is the hypothesis, $m,n > 1$, used? The theorem is false if either m or n is $\geqq 1$ and the other is not $\leqq \aleph_0$.)

The next theorem states that for all alephs $\mathfrak{m}$, $\mathfrak{m}^2 = \mathfrak{m}$.

THEOREM 12.1.2. $\qquad m \in \mathfrak{A} \rightarrow \mathfrak{m}^2 = \mathfrak{m}.$

Proof: Let $\mathfrak{m} \in \mathfrak{A}$ and let α be an ordinal number such that $\bar{\bar{\alpha}} = \mathfrak{m}$. We shall prove that

(1) $$\alpha \times \alpha \approx \alpha$$

for all infinite ordinal numbers α.

Suppose there is an infinite ordinal number which does not satisfy (1). Let β be the smallest ordinal number such that $\beta \times \beta \not\approx \beta$.

We shall prove first that β is an initial ordinal. By 5.2.12, $\omega \times \omega \approx \omega$; therefore, $\beta \neq \omega$. Suppose there is an infinite ordinal number $\gamma < \beta$ such that $\gamma \approx \beta$. Since γ is infinite and $\gamma < \beta$, $\gamma \times \gamma \approx \gamma$. Therefore, $\beta \times \beta \approx \beta$, but this contradicts the definition of β. Thus, β must be an initial ordinal.

Let R be the ordering on $On \times On$ as defined in exercise 7.2.8(c). That is,

$$\begin{aligned} \langle\gamma_1,\delta_1\rangle\, R\, \langle\gamma_2,\delta_2\rangle \leftrightarrow [\max(\gamma_1,\delta_1) < \max(\gamma_2,\delta_2)] \text{ or } \\ (\max(\gamma_1,\delta_1) = \max(\gamma_2,\delta_2)\ \&\ \gamma_1 < \gamma_2) \text{ or } \\ (\max(\gamma_1,\delta_1) = \max(\gamma_2,\delta_2)\ \&\ \gamma_1 = \gamma_2\ \&\ \delta_1 < \delta_2). \end{aligned}$$

It follows from exercise 7.2.8(c) that $\langle\langle On \times On, R\rangle\rangle$ is a w.o. class. From exercise 7.3.4(c), it follows that for each $\gamma \in \beta$, $\gamma \times \gamma$ is an R-initial segment of $\beta \times \beta$. Moreover, if u is an R-initial segment of $\beta \times \beta$, then since β is a limit ordinal (11.5.3), there is a $\gamma \in \beta$ such that u is an R-initial segment of $\gamma \times \gamma$. Therefore,

(2) $$\bigcup_{\gamma<\beta} \langle\langle \gamma \times \gamma, R\rangle\rangle = \langle\langle \beta \times \beta, R\rangle\rangle.$$

If $\omega \leqq \gamma < \beta$, then $\gamma \times \gamma \approx \gamma < \beta$, and since β is an initial ordinal, $\gamma < \beta$ implies that $\gamma \prec \beta$. Therefore, $\overline{\langle\langle \gamma \times \gamma, R\rangle\rangle} < \beta$ for all γ such that $\omega \leqq \gamma < \beta$. Consequently,

(3) $$\bigcup_{\gamma<\beta} \langle\langle \gamma \times \gamma, R\rangle\rangle \leqq \beta.$$

It follows from (2) and (3) that

(4) $$\beta \times \beta \lesssim \beta.$$

But clearly,

(5) $$\beta \lesssim \beta \times \beta.$$

Thus, (4) and (5) contradict the assumption that $\beta \times \beta \not\approx \beta$. Therefore, (1) must hold for all infinite ordinal numbers α. ■

Using the preceding results we shall show that if the larger of two cardinal numbers is an aleph, then the sum and the product of the two cardinal numbers are each equal to the larger one. In particular, the sum of two alephs is the same as their product and is equal to the larger one.

THEOREM 12.1.3. $(\mathfrak{n} \in \mathfrak{A}\ \&\ 1 \leqq \mathfrak{m} \leqq \mathfrak{n}) \rightarrow \mathfrak{m} + \mathfrak{n} = \mathfrak{m} \cdot \mathfrak{n} = \mathfrak{n}.$

Proof:

$$\begin{aligned} \mathfrak{n} &\leqq \mathfrak{m} + \mathfrak{n} && (11.6.15a)\\ &\leqq \mathfrak{m}\cdot\mathfrak{n} && (12.1.1)\\ &\leqq \mathfrak{n}^2 && (11.6.15b)\\ &= \mathfrak{n}. && (12.1.2) \blacksquare \end{aligned}$$

Next, we shall give several lemmas concerning alephs which will be useful later.

LEMMA 12.1.4. $(\mathfrak{n} \in \mathfrak{A} \ \&\ \mathfrak{m}\cdot\mathfrak{n} \leqq \mathfrak{p} + \mathfrak{q}) \rightarrow (\mathfrak{m} \leqq \mathfrak{p} \text{ or } \mathfrak{n} \leqq \mathfrak{q})$.

Proof: Suppose $\mathfrak{n}$ is an aleph and $\mathfrak{m}\cdot\mathfrak{n} \leqq \mathfrak{p} + \mathfrak{q}$. Let x, y, and z be sets such that $\bar{\bar{x}} = \mathfrak{m}$, $\bar{\bar{y}} = \mathfrak{p}$, $\bar{\bar{z}} = \mathfrak{q}$, and $y \cap z = \emptyset$; let α be an ordinal number such that $\bar{\bar{\alpha}} = \mathfrak{n}$. Since $\mathfrak{m}\cdot\mathfrak{n} \leqq \mathfrak{p} + \mathfrak{q}$, then there is a 1–1 function ψ mapping $x \times \alpha$ into $y \cup z$.

Case 1. There is a $u \in x$ such that for all $\beta \in \alpha$, $\psi(\langle u,\beta\rangle) \in z$. Then, since ψ is 1–1, $\mathfrak{n} \leqq \mathfrak{q}$.

Case 2. For each $u \in x$, there is a $\beta \in \alpha$ such that $\psi(\langle u,\beta\rangle) \in y$. Let β_u be the smallest $\beta \in \alpha$ with this property. Then for each $u \in x$, $\psi(\langle u,\beta_u\rangle) \in y$. And since ψ is 1–1, this implies that $\mathfrak{m} \leqq \mathfrak{p}$. ∎

LEMMA 12.1.5. $(\mathfrak{p} \in \mathfrak{A} \ \&\ \mathfrak{p} \leqq \mathfrak{m}\cdot\mathfrak{n}) \rightarrow (\mathfrak{p} \leqq \mathfrak{m} \text{ or } \mathfrak{p} \leqq \mathfrak{n})$.

Proof: Let x and y be sets such that $\bar{\bar{x}} = \mathfrak{m}$ and $\bar{\bar{y}} = \mathfrak{n}$, and let α be an infinite ordinal number such that $\bar{\bar{\alpha}} = \mathfrak{p}$. Then $\mathfrak{p} \leqq \mathfrak{m}\cdot\mathfrak{n}$ implies $\alpha \precsim x \times y$. Therefore, there is a subset z of $x \times y$ such that $\alpha \approx z$. Let

$$\begin{aligned} x_1 &= \{u : (\exists v)(\langle u,v\rangle \in z)\},\\ y_1 &= \{v : (\exists u)(\langle u,v\rangle \in z)\}. \end{aligned}$$

Thus $\alpha \precsim x_1 \times y_1$, and x_1 and y_1 can be well-ordered. Let $\bar{\bar{x}}_1 = \mathfrak{q}$ and $\bar{\bar{y}}_1 = \mathfrak{r}$. Since α is infinite, the larger of $\mathfrak{q}$ and $\mathfrak{r}$ is an aleph. Therefore, it follows from 12.1.3 that

$$\mathfrak{p} = \bar{\bar{\alpha}} \leqq \mathfrak{q}\cdot\mathfrak{r} = \max(\mathfrak{q},\mathfrak{r}).$$

If $\max(\mathfrak{q},\mathfrak{r}) = \mathfrak{q}$, then $\mathfrak{p} \leqq \mathfrak{m}$, and if $\max(\mathfrak{q},\mathfrak{r}) = \mathfrak{r}$, then $\mathfrak{p} \leqq \mathfrak{n}$. ∎

COROLLARY 12.1.6. $(p \in \mathfrak{A} \ \&\ \mathfrak{p} \leqq \mathfrak{m} + \mathfrak{n}) \rightarrow (\mathfrak{p} \leqq \mathfrak{m} \text{ or } \mathfrak{p} \leqq \mathfrak{n})$.

LEMMA 12.1.7.

$$(\aleph_0 \leqq \mathfrak{m} \ \&\ \mathfrak{n} \in \mathfrak{A} \ \&\ \mathfrak{m} + \mathfrak{m} \leqq \mathfrak{m} + \mathfrak{n}) \rightarrow \mathfrak{m} + \mathfrak{m} = \mathfrak{m}.$$

Proof: Suppose that $\mathfrak{m}$ and $\mathfrak{n}$ satisfy the hypothesis. Then since $\mathfrak{m} + \mathfrak{m} \leqq \mathfrak{m} + \mathfrak{n}$, there is a $\mathfrak{p} \leqq \mathfrak{m}$ and a $\mathfrak{q} \leqq \mathfrak{n}$ such that

(1) $$\mathfrak{m} + \mathfrak{m} = \mathfrak{p} + \mathfrak{q}.$$

Since $\mathfrak{n}$ is an aleph, either $\mathfrak{q}$ is finite or an aleph.

Case 1. $\mathfrak{q} < \aleph_0$. By hypothesis $m \geqq \aleph_0$; therefore, $\aleph_0 \leqq \mathfrak{p} + \mathfrak{q}$. It follows from 12.1.6 that since $\aleph_0 \nleqq \mathfrak{q}$, $\aleph_0 \leqq \mathfrak{p}$. Since $\mathfrak{q}$ is finite and $\aleph_0 \leqq \mathfrak{p}$,

$$\mathfrak{p} + \mathfrak{q} = \mathfrak{p} \leqq \mathfrak{m}.$$

Thus, it follows from (1) that $\mathfrak{m} + \mathfrak{m} = \mathfrak{m}$.

Case 2. $\aleph_0 \leqq \mathfrak{q}$. From (1) we obtain $\mathfrak{q} \leqq \mathfrak{m} + \mathfrak{m}$. Since $\mathfrak{q}$ is an aleph, it follows from 12.1.6 that

$$\mathfrak{q} \leqq \mathfrak{m}.$$

Therefore, there is an $\mathfrak{r}$ such that

(2) $$\mathfrak{q} + \mathfrak{r} = \mathfrak{m}.$$

Since $\mathfrak{q}$ is an aleph, by 12.1.3

(3) $$\mathfrak{q} + \mathfrak{q} = \mathfrak{q}.$$

Therefore,

$$\begin{aligned} \mathfrak{m} + \mathfrak{q} &= \mathfrak{q} + \mathfrak{r} + \mathfrak{q} && (2) \\ &= \mathfrak{q} + \mathfrak{r} && (3) \\ &= \mathfrak{m}. && (2) \end{aligned}$$

Thus, it follows from (1) that

$$\begin{aligned} \mathfrak{m} + \mathfrak{m} &= \mathfrak{p} + \mathfrak{q} \\ &\leqq \mathfrak{m} + \mathfrak{q} \\ &= \mathfrak{m}. \end{aligned}$$

Consequently, $\mathfrak{m} + \mathfrak{m} = \mathfrak{m}$. ■

In definition 10.2.3 we defined Hartogs' function, Γ, for each set x:

$$\Gamma(x) = \{\alpha : \alpha \precsim x\}.$$

In theorem 10.2.4 it was shown that $\Gamma(x)$ is an ordinal number. If $\overline{\overline{x}} = \mathfrak{m}$, we use the symbol "$m^*$" for "$\overline{\overline{\Gamma(x)}}$".

DEFINITION 12.1.8. $(S(x) \;\&\; \overline{\overline{x}} = \mathfrak{m}) \rightarrow \mathfrak{m}^* =_{\mathrm{Df}} \overline{\overline{\Gamma(x)}}.$

Since $\Gamma(x)$ is an ordinal number for each set x, we have

THEOREM 12.1.9. $\aleph_0 < \mathfrak{m} \rightarrow \mathfrak{m}^* \in \mathfrak{A}.$

In fact, if $\aleph_0 \leqq \mathfrak{m}$, $\mathfrak{m}^*$ is the smallest aleph which is not less than or equal to $\mathfrak{m}$.

THEOREM 12.1.10.

$$\aleph_0 \leqq \mathfrak{m} \rightarrow [\mathfrak{m}^* \nleqq \mathfrak{m} \;\&\; (\forall \mathfrak{n})((\mathfrak{n} \in \mathfrak{A} \;\&\; \mathfrak{n}^* \nleqq \mathfrak{m}) \rightarrow \mathfrak{m}^* \leqq \mathfrak{n}^*)].$$

Proof: Suppose that $\aleph_0 \leqq \mathfrak{m}$ and x is a set such that $\bar{\bar{x}} = \mathfrak{m}$. Then $\mathfrak{m}^* \leqq \mathfrak{m}$ implies that $\Gamma(x) \precsim x$, and this implies that $\Gamma(x) \in \Gamma(x)$, which is impossible.

Suppose that $\mathfrak{n}$ is an aleph and $\mathfrak{n} \nleqq \mathfrak{m}$. Let α be an ordinal number such that $\bar{\bar{\alpha}} = \mathfrak{n}$. Then $\mathfrak{n} \nleqq \mathfrak{m}$ implies $\alpha \notin \Gamma(x)$. Therefore, $\Gamma(x) \leqq \alpha$. Thus,

$$\mathfrak{m}^* = \overline{\overline{\Gamma(x)}} \leqq \bar{\bar{\alpha}} = \mathfrak{n}. \blacksquare$$

Another property of Hartogs' function is given in the next theorem.

THEOREM 12.1.11.

$$[S(x) \& S(y) \& (\aleph_0 \leqq \bar{\bar{x}} \text{ or } \aleph_0 \leqq \bar{\bar{y}})] \rightarrow \Gamma(x \cup y) = \Gamma(x \times y) = \Gamma(x) \cup \Gamma(y).$$

The proof is left as an exercise.

Another interesting function, introduced by A. H. Kruse (1960), will have applications in the next section. It shall be called Kruse's function and denoted by "W."

DEFINITION 12.1.12. Kruse's Function

$$S(x) \rightarrow W(x) =_{\text{Df}} \{f\colon 1\text{–}1 \text{ func}(f) \& (\exists\alpha)(\mathcal{D}(f) = \alpha \& \mathcal{R}(f) \subseteq x)\}.$$

If $f \in W(x)$, then f uniquely determines a reflexive w.o. relation R on $\mathcal{R}(f)$. [If $u,v \in \mathcal{R}(f)$, $u\,R\,v \leftrightarrow f^{-1}(u) \leqq f^{-1}(v)$.] And conversely, if R reflexively w.o. a subset y of x, then by 8.2.27 there is a unique ordinal number α such that

$$\langle\langle\alpha, \leqq\rangle\rangle \cong \langle\langle y,R\rangle\rangle.$$

By theorem 7.4.5 there is exactly one isomorphism mapping α onto y. Therefore, $W(x)$ is equipollent with the set of all reflexive well-orderings of subsets of x. Thus, the symbol "W."

THEOREM 12.1.13. $S(x) \rightarrow$

$$W(x) \approx \{R\colon R \subseteq x \times x \& (\exists y)(y \subseteq x \& R|y \text{ is reflexive } \& \langle\langle y,R\rangle\rangle \text{ is a w.o. set})\}.$$

COROLLARY 12.1.14. $S(x) \rightarrow S(W(x))$.

Succeeding theorems tell us something about the relative size of $W(x)$.

THEOREM 12.1.15. $S(x) \rightarrow$

(a) $W(x) \precsim \mathcal{P}(x \times x)$

(b) $W(x) \precsim \mathcal{P}(\mathcal{P}(x))$.

Proof:

(a) By theorem 12.1.13.

(b) If $f \in W(x)$, define a function ψ as follows:

$$\psi(f) = \{\{f(\alpha) : \alpha \leqq \beta\} : \beta \leqq \mathfrak{D}(f)\}.$$

It is not difficult to prove that ψ is a 1–1 function mapping $W(x)$ into $\mathcal{P}(\mathcal{P}(x))$. ∎

The proof of the next theorem is somewhat similar to Cantor's proof of theorem 3.4.6, $\mathrm{S}(x) \rightarrow x \prec \mathcal{P}(x)$.

THEOREM 12.1.16. $\mathrm{S}(x) \rightarrow x \prec W(x)$.

Proof: Clearly $x \precsim W(x)$. Suppose that $W(x) \approx x$. Let ψ be a 1–1 function mapping $W(x)$ onto x.

$$\psi : W(x) \xrightarrow[\text{onto}]{1-1} x.$$

Let

$$K = \{f : f \in W(x) \,\&\, (\forall \alpha)[\alpha \in \mathfrak{D}(f) \rightarrow f(\alpha) = \psi(f|\alpha)]\},$$

and let

$$k = \bigcup K.$$

Since ψ is 1–1, it is rather easy to prove that $k \in K$. What can be said about $\psi(k)$? $\psi(k) \notin \mathcal{R}(k)$ because $\mathcal{R}(k) = \{\psi(k|\alpha) : \alpha \in \mathfrak{D}(k)\}$ and ψ is 1–1. Therefore, let

$$h = k \cup \{\langle \mathfrak{D}(k), \psi(k) \rangle\}.$$

Then $h \in K$. But this is impossible since for all $f \in K$, $f \subseteq k$. Clearly, $k \subset h$. Therefore, we must have $x \prec W(x)$. ∎

If x is an infinite set which can be w.o., then $W(x)$ is equipollent with the set of all subsets of x.

THEOREM 12.1.17. $(\mathrm{S}(x) \,\&\, \bar{\bar{x}} \in \mathfrak{A}) \rightarrow W(x) \approx \mathcal{P}(x)$.

Proof: Suppose that x is a set and $\bar{\bar{x}}$ is an aleph. Then, by 12.1.2, $x \times x \approx x$. Therefore, by 12.1.15,

(1) $$W(x) \precsim \mathcal{P}(x).$$

Since $\bar{\bar{x}}$ is an aleph, there exists a relation R which irreflexively w.o. x. Therefore, for each subset y of x there exists a unique ordinal number α and a unique function f such that

$$f : \langle\langle \alpha, < \rangle\rangle \cong \langle\langle y, R \rangle\rangle. \qquad (8.2.27,\ 7.4.5)$$

Consequently,

(2) $$\mathcal{P}(x) \precsim W(x).$$

The theorem follows from (1), (2) and the Schröder–Berstein theorem. ■

Some additional properties of Kruse's function are given in the following theorems.

THEOREM 12.1.18.

$$(\mathrm{S}(x) \mathbin{\&} \mathrm{S}(y) \mathbin{\&} x \cap y = \emptyset) \rightarrow W(x) \times W(y) \precsim W(x \cup y).$$

Proof: Define a function ψ on $W(x) \times W(y)$ as follows: If $f \in W(x)$ and $g \in W(y)$, then

$$\psi(\langle f,g \rangle) = h,$$

where h is a function such that

$$\mathfrak{D}(h) = \mathfrak{D}(f) + \mathfrak{D}(g),$$

and for all $\alpha \in \mathfrak{D}(h)$,

$$h(\alpha) = \begin{cases} f(\alpha), & \text{if } \alpha \in \mathfrak{D}(f) \\ g(\beta), & \text{if } \alpha = \mathfrak{D}(f) + \beta \text{ and } \beta \in \mathfrak{D}(h). \end{cases}$$

It is easy to prove that $h \in W(x \cup y)$ and ψ is 1–1. ■

If $\bar{\bar{x}} = \mathfrak{m}$, we use the symbol "$\mathfrak{m}^*$" for the cardinal number of $\Gamma(x)$. We shall use the symbol "$\mathfrak{m}^\dagger$" for the cardinal number of $W(x)$.

DEFINITION 12.1.19. $(\mathrm{S}(x) \mathbin{\&} \bar{\bar{x}} = \mathfrak{m}) \rightarrow \mathfrak{m}^\dagger =_{\mathrm{Df}} \overline{\overline{W(x)}}.$

For example,

$$0^\dagger = 1,\ 1^\dagger = 2,$$

and if $\bar{\bar{x}} = \mathfrak{m}$ and $\bar{\bar{y}} = \mathfrak{n}$, then theorem 12.1.18 could be rewritten as

$$\mathfrak{m}^\dagger \cdot \mathfrak{n}^\dagger \leqq (\mathfrak{m} + \mathfrak{n})^\dagger.$$

THEOREM 12.1.20. $\aleph_0 \leqq \mathfrak{m} \rightarrow \mathfrak{m}^\dagger + \mathfrak{m}^\dagger = \mathfrak{m}^\dagger.$

Proof: First we note that if $\aleph_0 \leqq \mathfrak{m}$, then

(1) $$\mathfrak{m} + 1 = \mathfrak{m}.$$

Moreover,

$$\begin{aligned} \mathfrak{m}^\dagger + \mathfrak{m}^\dagger &= \mathfrak{m}^\dagger \cdot 1^\dagger \\ &\leqq (\mathfrak{m} + 1)^\dagger && (12.1.18) \\ &= \mathfrak{m}^\dagger. && (1)\ ■ \end{aligned}$$

THEOREM 12.1.21. $\mathfrak{m} + \mathfrak{m} = \mathfrak{m} \rightarrow (\mathfrak{m}^\dagger)^2 = \mathfrak{m}^\dagger$.

Proof: Suppose that

(1) $$\mathfrak{m} + \mathfrak{m} = \mathfrak{m}.$$

Then

$$\begin{aligned} (\mathfrak{m}^\dagger)^2 &= \mathfrak{m}^\dagger \cdot \mathfrak{m}^\dagger \\ &\leqq (\mathfrak{m} + \mathfrak{m})^\dagger && (12.1.18) \\ &= \mathfrak{m}^\dagger. && (1) \blacksquare \end{aligned}$$

THEOREM 12.1.22.

$$(\aleph_0 \leqq \mathfrak{m} \ \& \ \mathfrak{n} \in \mathfrak{A} \ \& \ \mathfrak{m}^\dagger \leqq \mathfrak{m} + \mathfrak{n}) \rightarrow \mathfrak{m} < \mathfrak{m}^\dagger = 2^{\mathfrak{m}} \leqq \mathfrak{n}.$$

Proof: Suppose that $\mathfrak{m}$ and $\mathfrak{n}$ satisfy the hypothesis. By 12.1.16, $\mathfrak{m} < \mathfrak{m}^\dagger$. So,

$$\begin{aligned} \mathfrak{m} + \mathfrak{m} &\leqq \mathfrak{m}^\dagger + \mathfrak{m}^\dagger \\ &= \mathfrak{m}^\dagger && (12.1.20) \\ &\leqq \mathfrak{m} + \mathfrak{n}. && (\text{hypothesis}) \end{aligned}$$

Therefore, by 12.1.7,

$$\mathfrak{m} + \mathfrak{m} = \mathfrak{m}.$$

Hence, 12.1.21 implies that

(1) $$(\mathfrak{m}^\dagger)^2 = \mathfrak{m}^\dagger.$$

By hypothesis,

(2) $$\mathfrak{m}^\dagger \leqq \mathfrak{m} + \mathfrak{n}.$$

Thus, there exist cardinal numbers $\mathfrak{p}$ and $\mathfrak{q}$ such that $\mathfrak{p} \leqq \mathfrak{m}$, $\mathfrak{q} \leqq \mathfrak{n}$, and

(3) $$\mathfrak{m}^\dagger = \mathfrak{p} + \mathfrak{q}.$$

Therefore,

$$\begin{aligned} \mathfrak{m}^\dagger \cdot \mathfrak{q} &\leqq (\mathfrak{m}^\dagger)^2 && (3) \\ &= \mathfrak{m}^\dagger && (1) \\ &\leqq \mathfrak{m} + \mathfrak{n}. && (2) \end{aligned}$$

Using 12.1.4 we obtain

$$\mathfrak{m}^\dagger \leqq \mathfrak{n} \text{ or } \mathfrak{q} \leqq \mathfrak{m}.$$

If $\mathfrak{q} \leqq \mathfrak{m}$, then by (3),

$$\begin{aligned} \mathfrak{m}^\dagger &= \mathfrak{p} + \mathfrak{q} \\ &\leqq \mathfrak{m} + \mathfrak{m} \\ &= \mathfrak{m}. \end{aligned}$$

This contradicts 12.1.16. Hence, we must have $\mathfrak{m}^\dagger \leqq \mathfrak{n}$. Consequently,

$$\mathfrak{m} < \mathfrak{m}^\dagger \leqq \mathfrak{n}.$$

Therefore, since $\mathfrak{n}$ is an aleph, so too is $\mathfrak{m}$. Thus, by theorem 12.1.17, $\mathfrak{m}^\dagger = 2^{\mathfrak{m}}$, which proves the theorem. ■

To conclude this section we shall prove, without the aid of the axiom of choice, that

(1) $$\aleph_0 \leqq \mathfrak{m} \rightarrow 2^{\mathfrak{m}} - \mathfrak{m} = 2^{\mathfrak{m}}.$$

The proof is due to Sierpinski (1947).

With the aid of the axiom of choice, the proof is simple. For if the well-ordering theorem holds, then $\mathfrak{m}$ and $2^{\mathfrak{m}}$ are alephs. Thus, by 12.1.3,

$$\mathfrak{m} + 2^{\mathfrak{m}} = \max(\mathfrak{m}, 2^{\mathfrak{m}}).$$

By 3.4.6, $\mathfrak{m} < 2^{\mathfrak{m}}$. Therefore,

$$\mathfrak{m} + 2^{\mathfrak{m}} = 2^{\mathfrak{m}}.$$

Suppose that

$$\mathfrak{m} + \mathfrak{p} = 2^{\mathfrak{m}}.$$

Then $2^{\mathfrak{m}} = \max(\mathfrak{m}, \mathfrak{p})$, and since $\mathfrak{m} < 2^{\mathfrak{m}}$, we obtain $\mathfrak{p} = 2^{\mathfrak{m}}$. Consequently, there is a unique cardinal number $\mathfrak{n} = 2^{\mathfrak{m}}$ such that $\mathfrak{m} + \mathfrak{n} = 2^{\mathfrak{m}}$. Therefore, by the definition of subtraction,

$$2^{\mathfrak{m}} - \mathfrak{m} = 2^{\mathfrak{m}}.$$

Before proving (1) without use of the axiom of choice, we shall prove several lemmas.

LEMMA 12.1.23. $(S(x) \;\&\; S(y) \;\&\; x \approx y) \rightarrow (\exists v_1)(\exists v_2)(\exists w_1)(\exists w_2)$

(1) $$x \sim y = v_1 \cup v_2$$
(2) $$y \sim x = w_1 \cup w_2$$
(3) $$v_1 \cap v_2 = w_1 \cap w_2 = \emptyset$$
(4) $$v_1 \approx w_1$$
(5) $$v_2 \cap (x \cap y) = w_2 \cap (x \cap y) = \emptyset$$
(6) $$(v_2 \cup (x \cap y)) \approx x \cap y \approx (w_2 \cup (x \cap y)).$$

Proof: Suppose that x and y are sets and that $x \approx y$. Let f be a 1–1 function mapping x onto y. If $u \in x$, then $f(u) \in y$, but it may also be true that $f(u) \in x$. In this case, let

$$f^2(u) = f(f(u)).$$

In general, if $f^n(u) \in x$ for $n \in \omega$, define

$$f^{n^+}(u) = f(f^n(u)).$$

On the other hand, if $u \in y$, then $f^{-1}(u) \in x$. However, if $f^{-1}(u) \in y$, let

$$f^{-2}(u) = f^{-1}(f^{-1}(u)),$$

and in general, if $f^{-n}(u) \in y$, $n \in \omega$, define

$$f^{-n^+}(u) = f^{-1}(f^{-n}(u)).$$

Since f is 1–1, so too is f^n and f^{-n} for each $n \in \omega$.

Now we define

(7) $v_2 = \{u : u \in x \sim y \;\&\; (\forall n)((n \in \omega \;\&\; n \neq 0) \to f^n(u) \in x)\}$

(8) $w_2 = \{u : u \in y \sim x \;\&\; (\forall n)((n \in \omega \;\&\; n \neq 0) \to f^{-n}(u) \in y)\}$

(9) $v_1 = (x \sim y) \sim v_2$

(10) $w_1 = (y \sim x) \sim w_2.$

We shall show that v_1, v_2, w_1, and w_2 are the required sets. It follows from (7) and (8) that

$$v_2 \subseteq x \sim y \;\&\; w_2 \subseteq y \sim x.$$

Therefore, (1) and (2) follow from (9) and (10). Moreover, (3) also follows from (9) and (10).

For each $n \in \omega \sim \{0\}$, let

(11) $a_n = \{u : u \in x \sim y \;\&\; (\forall m)(1 \leqq m < n \to f^m(u) \in x) \;\&\; f^n(u) \in y \sim x\}.$

(12) $b_n = \{u : u \in y \sim x \;\&\; (\forall m)(1 \leqq m < n \to f^{-m}(u) \in y) \;\&\; f^{-n}(u) \in x \sim y\}.$

It is easy to see that if $n \neq m$, then $a_n \cap a_m = \emptyset$ and $b_n \cap b_m = \emptyset$. Moreover, it follows from (7)–(12) that

(13) $v_1 = \bigcup_{0<n<\omega} a_n \;\&\; w_1 = \bigcup_{0<n<\omega} b_n.$

We shall prove that for each $n \in \omega \sim \{0\}$, $f^n{}'' a_n = b_n$. Let $u \in a_n$; then $f^m(u) \in x \cap y$ for all m such that $0 < m < n$ and $f^n(u) \in y \sim x$. Therefore, if $0 < m < n$, $f^{-m}(f^n(u)) \in x \cap y$ and $f^{-n}(f^n(u)) = u \in x \sim y$. Consequently, $f^n{}'' a_n \subseteq b_n$. Similarly, $f^{-n}{}'' b_n \subseteq a_n$, so f^n is a 1–1 mapping of a_n onto b_n for each $n \in \omega \sim \{0\}$. Therefore, if $u \in v_1$, then $u \in a_n$ for exactly one $n \in \omega \sim \{0\}$. Therefore, define

$$\psi(u) = f^n(u).$$

That is,

$$\psi(u) = u_0 \leftrightarrow (\exists n)(u \in a_n \;\&\; u_0 = f^n(u)).$$

Then ψ is a 1–1 function mapping v_1 onto w_1. Consequently, (4) is true.

It remains to prove (5) and (6). By (7), $v_2 \subseteq x \sim y$, so $v_2 \cap (x \cap y) = \emptyset$.

Again by (7), if $u \in v_2$, then $f^n(u) \in x$ for all $n \in \omega \sim \{0\}$. But since f maps x onto y, $f^n(u) \in y$ for all $n \in \omega \sim \{0\}$. Therefore, if $u \in v_2$, $f^n(u) \in x \cap y$ for all $n \in \omega \sim \{0\}$. Let

$$z = (x \cap y) \sim \bigcup_{0<n<\omega} f^n{}'' v_2.$$

Thus,

$$x \cap y = z \cup \bigcup_{0<n<\omega} f^n{}'' v_2$$

and

$$v_2 \cup (x \cap y) = z \cup v_2 \cup \bigcup_{0<n<\omega} f^n{}'' v_2.$$

Define a function g on $v_2 \cup (x \cap y)$ as follows:

$$g(u) = \begin{cases} u, & \text{if } u \in z \\ f(u), & \text{if } u \notin z. \end{cases}$$

It is a simple matter to show that g is a 1–1 function from $v_2 \cup (x \cap y)$ onto $x \cap y$. Thus,

$$v_2 \cup (x \cap y) \approx x \cap y.$$

In an analogous way we can prove that

$$w_2 \cap (x \cap y) = \emptyset$$

and

$$w_2 \cup (x \cap y) \approx x \cap y.$$

Therefore, conditions (5) and (6) hold and the theorem is proved. ■

If lemma 12.1.23 is expressed in terms of cardinal numbers, it has the following form:

LEMMA 12.1.24. $\mathfrak{m} + \mathfrak{p} = \mathfrak{m} + \mathfrak{q} \to (\exists \mathfrak{n})(\exists \mathfrak{p}_1)(\exists \mathfrak{q}_1)$

(1) $\mathfrak{p} = \mathfrak{n} + \mathfrak{p}_1$

(2) $\mathfrak{q} = \mathfrak{n} + \mathfrak{q}_1$

(3) $\mathfrak{m} + \mathfrak{p}_1 = \mathfrak{m} = \mathfrak{m} + \mathfrak{q}_1.$

Proof: Let M, P, and Q be pairwise disjoint sets such that $\overline{\overline{M}} = \mathfrak{m}$, $\overline{\overline{P}} = \mathfrak{p}$, and $\overline{\overline{Q}} = \mathfrak{q}$. Let

(4) $$x = M \cup P \;\&\; y = M \cup Q.$$

Then

(5) $$P = x \sim y \;\&\; Q = y \sim x$$

and

(6) $$M = x \cap y.$$

It follows from the hypothesis that $x \approx y$; thus, lemma 12.1.23 applies. There exist sets v_1, v_2, w_1, w_2 satisfying 12.1.23. Let $\bar{\bar{v}}_1 = \bar{\bar{w}}_1 = \mathfrak{n}$, $\bar{\bar{v}}_2 = \mathfrak{p}_1$, and $\bar{\bar{w}}_2 = \mathfrak{q}_1$. Equations (1) and (2) follow from (5) and 12.1.23 (1), (2), (3). Equation (3) follows from (6) and 12.1.23 (5) and (6). ■

COROLLARY 12.1.25. $\mathfrak{m} + \mathfrak{m} = \mathfrak{m} + \mathfrak{q} \rightarrow \mathfrak{q} \leqq \mathfrak{m}.$

The proof is left as an exercise.

LEMMA 12.1.26. $(2^{\mathfrak{m}} = \mathfrak{m} + \mathfrak{p} \;\&\; \mathfrak{m} = \mathfrak{m} + \mathfrak{q}) \rightarrow 2^{\mathfrak{q}} \leqq \mathfrak{p}.$

Proof: Let x be a set such that $\bar{\bar{x}} = \mathfrak{m}$. Since $2^{\mathfrak{m}} = \mathfrak{m} + \mathfrak{p}$, there exist two sets x_1 and y such that $\bar{\bar{x}}_1 = \mathfrak{m}$, $\bar{\bar{y}} = \mathfrak{p}$, and

$$\mathcal{P}(x) = x_1 \cup y \;\&\; x_1 \cap y = \emptyset.$$

Also, since $\mathfrak{m} = \mathfrak{m} + \mathfrak{q}$, there exist two sets x_2 and z such that $\bar{\bar{x}}_2 = \mathfrak{m}$, $\bar{\bar{z}} = \mathfrak{q}$,

$$x = x_2 \cup z \;\&\; x_2 \cap z = \emptyset.$$

To prove the theorem we shall show that $\mathcal{P}(z) \lesssim y$.

We have

$$x \approx x_1 \approx x_2.$$

Let

$$f: x \xrightarrow[\text{onto}]{1-1} x_1$$

$$g: x_2 \xrightarrow[\text{onto}]{1-1} x.$$

For each $z_1 \subseteq z$, define

$$h(z_1) = z_1 \cup \{u : u \in x_2 \;\&\; u \notin f(g(u))\}.$$

Clearly, $h(z_1) \in \mathcal{P}(x)$ for all $z_1 \subseteq z$. Suppose that $h(z_1) \in x_1$ for some $z_1 \subseteq z$. Since $x_1 = f''x$, there is an $s \in x$ such that $h(z_1) = f(s)$. But $x = g''x_2$, so $s \in x$ implies there is a $t \in x_2$ such that $s = g(t)$. Therefore,

$$(\exists t)[t \in x_2 \;\&\; h(z_1) = f(g(t))].$$

Consider the element t. Since $z_1 \subseteq z$ and $x_2 \cap z = \emptyset$, $t \in x_2$ implies that $t \notin z_1$. Therefore, if $t \in h(z_1)$, then

$$t \in \{u : u \in x_2 \;\&\; u \notin f(g(u))\},$$

which implies that $t \notin f(g(t)) = h(z_1)$. On the other hand, if $t \notin h(z_1)$, then

$$t \notin \{u : u \in x_2 \;\&\; u \notin f(g(u))\}.$$

Since $t \in x_2$, this implies that $t \in f(g(t)) = h(z_1)$. Thus we arrive at a contradiction. [Note the similarity between this argument and Cantor's proof that $x \prec \mathcal{P}(x)$, theorem 3.4.6.]

We have shown that h is a function which maps $\mathcal{P}(z)$ into y. It remains to be shown that h is 1–1. Suppose that $z_1,z_2 \subseteq z$ and $h(z_1) = h(z_2)$. Let

$$w = \{u : u \in x_2 \;\&\; u \in f(g(u))\}.$$

Then

(1) $$z_1 \cup w = z_2 \cup w.$$

But $z_1,z_2 \subseteq z$, $w \subseteq x_2$, and $x_2 \cap z = \emptyset$, so

(2) $$z_1 \cap w = z_2 \cap w = \emptyset.$$

Therefore, it follows from (1) and (2) that $z_1 = z_2$. ■

Now we are ready to prove Sierpinski's theorem.

THEOREM 12.1.27. $\aleph_0 \leqq \mathfrak{m} \rightarrow 2^{\mathfrak{m}} - \mathfrak{m} = 2^{\mathfrak{m}}$.

Proof: We must prove that

(1) $$\mathfrak{m} + 2^{\mathfrak{m}} = 2^{\mathfrak{m}}$$

and

(2) $$\mathfrak{m} + \mathfrak{p} = 2^{\mathfrak{m}} \rightarrow \mathfrak{p} = 2^{\mathfrak{m}}.$$

The proof of (1) is easy since, clearly,

$$2^{\mathfrak{m}} \leqq \mathfrak{m} + 2^{\mathfrak{m}}.$$

If $\aleph_0 \leqq \mathfrak{m}$, then $\mathfrak{m} + 1 = \mathfrak{m}$, and since $\mathfrak{m} < 2^{\mathfrak{m}}$ we have

$$\begin{aligned} \mathfrak{m} + 2^{\mathfrak{m}} &\leqq 2^{\mathfrak{m}} + 2^{\mathfrak{m}} \\ &= 2 \cdot 2^{\mathfrak{m}} \\ &= 2^{\mathfrak{m}+1} \\ &= 2^{\mathfrak{m}}. \end{aligned}$$

To prove (2) suppose that

(3) $$\mathfrak{m} + \mathfrak{p} = 2^{\mathfrak{m}}.$$

Then, by (1),

(4) $$\mathfrak{m} + \mathfrak{p} = \mathfrak{m} + 2^{\mathfrak{m}}.$$

Now lemma 12.1.24 applies. Thus there exist cardinal numbers $\mathfrak{n}$, $\mathfrak{p}_1$, and $\mathfrak{q}_1$ such that

(5) $$\mathfrak{p} = \mathfrak{n} + \mathfrak{p}_1 \;\&\; 2^{\mathfrak{m}} = \mathfrak{n} + \mathfrak{q}_1 \;\&\; \mathfrak{m} + \mathfrak{p}_1 = \mathfrak{m} = \mathfrak{m} + \mathfrak{q}_1.$$

Therefore, it follows from (5) that

(6) $$\mathfrak{m} = \mathfrak{m} + \mathfrak{q}_1.$$

It follows from (3), (6), and 12.1.26 that

$$2^{\mathfrak{q}_1} \leqq \mathfrak{p}.$$

Since $\mathfrak{q}_1 < 2^{\mathfrak{q}_1}$,

(7) $$\mathfrak{q}_1 < \mathfrak{p}.$$

Also, since by (5), $\mathfrak{p} = \mathfrak{n} + \mathfrak{p}_1$, then

(8) $$\mathfrak{n} \leqq \mathfrak{p}.$$

Thus,

$$\begin{aligned}
\mathfrak{p} + \mathfrak{p} &\geqq \mathfrak{n} + \mathfrak{q}_1 && (7), (8)\\
&= 2^{\mathfrak{m}} && (5)\\
&= 2^{\mathfrak{m}+1} &&\\
&= 2^{\mathfrak{m}} + 2^{\mathfrak{m}} &&\\
&= 2^{\mathfrak{m}} + \mathfrak{m} + \mathfrak{p} && (3)\\
&= 2^{\mathfrak{m}} + \mathfrak{p} && (1)\\
&\geqq \mathfrak{p} + \mathfrak{p}. && (3)
\end{aligned}$$

Therefore,

$$\mathfrak{p} + \mathfrak{p} = 2^{\mathfrak{m}} + \mathfrak{p}$$

and 12.1.25 applies. Thus

$$2^{\mathfrak{m}} \leqq \mathfrak{p}.$$

But by (3)

$$\mathfrak{p} \leqq 2^{\mathfrak{m}}.$$

Thus we obtain $\mathfrak{p} = 2^{\mathfrak{m}}$, which completes the proof. ■

COROLLARY 12.1.28. $(\aleph_0 \leqq \mathfrak{m} \ \&\ 2^{\mathfrak{m}} \leqq \mathfrak{m} + \mathfrak{p}) \rightarrow 2^{\mathfrak{m}} \leqq \mathfrak{p}$.

Proof: If $2^{\mathfrak{m}} \leqq \mathfrak{m} + \mathfrak{p}$, then there exist cardinal numbers $\mathfrak{n}$ and $\mathfrak{q}$ such that $\mathfrak{n} \leqq \mathfrak{m}$, $\mathfrak{q} \leqq \mathfrak{p}$, and

$$\begin{aligned}
2^{\mathfrak{m}} &= \mathfrak{n} + \mathfrak{q}\\
&\leqq \mathfrak{m} + \mathfrak{q}\\
&\leqq \mathfrak{m} + 2^{\mathfrak{m}}\\
&= 2^{\mathfrak{m}}.
\end{aligned}$$

Therefore, $\mathfrak{m} + \mathfrak{q} = 2^{\mathfrak{m}}$, and so it follows from 12.1.27 that $\mathfrak{q} = 2^{\mathfrak{m}}$. ■

COROLLARY 12.1.29.

$$(\aleph_0 \leqq \mathfrak{m},\mathfrak{n} \;\&\; \mathfrak{p} \in \mathfrak{A} \;\&\; 2^{\mathfrak{m}} \leqq \mathfrak{n} + \mathfrak{p}) \rightarrow (\mathfrak{m} < \mathfrak{n} \text{ or } \mathfrak{m} < \mathfrak{p}).$$

Proof: By hypothesis,

$$(1) \qquad 2^{\mathfrak{m}} \leqq \mathfrak{n} + \mathfrak{p}.$$

Since $\mathfrak{m} < 2^{\mathfrak{m}}$, there exist cardinal numbers $\mathfrak{n}_1$ and $\mathfrak{p}_1$ such that $\mathfrak{n}_1 \leqq \mathfrak{n}$, $\mathfrak{p}_1 \leqq \mathfrak{p}$, and

$$(2) \qquad \mathfrak{m} = \mathfrak{n}_1 + \mathfrak{p}_1.$$

Hence,

$$\begin{aligned} \mathfrak{n}_1 \cdot \mathfrak{p}_1 &\leqq 2^{\mathfrak{n}_1} \cdot 2^{\mathfrak{p}_1} \\ &= 2^{\mathfrak{n}_1 + \mathfrak{p}_1} \\ &= 2^{\mathfrak{m}} && (2) \\ &\leqq \mathfrak{n} + \mathfrak{p}. && (1) \end{aligned}$$

Since $\mathfrak{p}$ is an aleph, $\mathfrak{p}_1$ is either finite or an aleph. If $\mathfrak{p}_1$ is finite, then since $\mathfrak{m} \geqq \aleph_0$, it follows from (2) that $\mathfrak{m} \leqq \mathfrak{n}$. If $\mathfrak{p}_1$ is an aleph, then 12.1.4 applies. Therefore, since $\mathfrak{n}_1 \cdot \mathfrak{p}_1 \leqq \mathfrak{n} + \mathfrak{p}$, either

$$\mathfrak{n}_1 \leqq \mathfrak{p} \text{ or } \mathfrak{p}_1 \leqq \mathfrak{n}.$$

If the first alternative holds, then it follows from (2) and 12.1.3 that

$$\mathfrak{m} \leqq \mathfrak{p} + \mathfrak{p} = \mathfrak{p}.$$

If the second alternative holds, then there is a cardinal number $\mathfrak{q}$ such that

$$(3) \qquad \mathfrak{n} = \mathfrak{q} + \mathfrak{p}_1.$$

Therefore,

$$\begin{aligned} \mathfrak{m} &= \mathfrak{n}_1 + \mathfrak{p}_1 && (2) \\ &\leqq \mathfrak{n} + \mathfrak{p}_1 \\ &= \mathfrak{q} + \mathfrak{p}_1 + \mathfrak{p}_1 && (3) \\ &= \mathfrak{q} + \mathfrak{p}_1 && (12.1.3) \\ &= \mathfrak{n}. && (3) \end{aligned}$$

We have shown that $\mathfrak{m} \leqq \mathfrak{n}$ or $\mathfrak{m} \leqq \mathfrak{p}$. Suppose that $\mathfrak{m} = \mathfrak{n}$. Then it follows from (1) that $2^{\mathfrak{m}} \leqq \mathfrak{m} + \mathfrak{p}$. Therefore, 12.1.28 implies that $2^{\mathfrak{m}} \leqq \mathfrak{p}$, which implies that $\mathfrak{m} < \mathfrak{p}$. Similarly, if $\mathfrak{m} = \mathfrak{p}$, it follows that $\mathfrak{m} < \mathfrak{n}$. ■

EXERCISES 12.1

Prove each of the following without using the axiom of choice:

1. $\aleph_\alpha^* = \aleph_{\alpha+1}$.
2. $\mathfrak{m}^* < (\mathfrak{m}^*)^*$.

3. $\mathfrak{m} \leqq \mathfrak{n} \rightarrow \mathfrak{m}^* \leqq \mathfrak{n}^*$.
4. $\aleph_0 \leqq \mathfrak{m} \rightarrow (\mathfrak{m}^2)^* = \mathfrak{m}^*$.
5. $\mathfrak{m},\mathfrak{n} \geqq \aleph_0 \rightarrow$
   (a) $(\mathfrak{m} + \mathfrak{n})^* = \mathfrak{m}^* + \mathfrak{n}^*$
   (b) $(\mathfrak{m}\cdot\mathfrak{n})^* = \mathfrak{m}^*\cdot\mathfrak{n}^*$.
6. Suppose that $\bar{\bar{x}} = \mathfrak{m}$ and $\bar{\bar{y}} = \mathfrak{n}$. We define

$$\mathfrak{m} \leqq_* \mathfrak{n} =_{\text{Df}} [(\exists f)(f{:}y \xrightarrow{\text{onto}} x) \text{ or } \mathfrak{m} = 0].$$

   Prove each of the following:
   (a) $\mathfrak{m} \leqq \mathfrak{n} \rightarrow \mathfrak{m} \leqq_* \mathfrak{n}$
   (b) $\mathfrak{m} \leqq_* \mathfrak{n} \rightarrow 2^{\mathfrak{m}} \leqq 2^{\mathfrak{n}}$
   (c) $\mathfrak{m}^* \leqq_* 2^{\mathfrak{m}^2}$
   (d) $\mathfrak{m}^* \leqq_* 2^{2^{\mathfrak{m}}}$
   (e) $\mathfrak{m} \leqq_* \bar{\bar{\alpha}} \rightarrow \mathfrak{m} \leqq \bar{\bar{\alpha}}$.
7. (a) $\mathfrak{m}^\dagger < (\mathfrak{m}^\dagger)^\dagger$
   (b) $\mathfrak{m} \leqq \mathfrak{n} \rightarrow \mathfrak{m}^\dagger \leqq \mathfrak{n}^\dagger$
   (c) $\mathfrak{m}^\dagger \leqq 2^{\mathfrak{m}^2}$
   (d) $\mathfrak{m}^\dagger \leqq 2^{2^{\mathfrak{m}}}$
   (e) $\aleph_0 \leqq \mathfrak{m} \rightarrow ((\mathfrak{m}^\dagger)^\dagger)^2 = (\mathfrak{m}^\dagger)^\dagger$.
8. $0 < n \in \omega \rightarrow n^\dagger = [n!e]$.
   ($[m]$ is the largest natural number less than or equal to m. In particular, since $e = 2.718\ldots$,

$$\begin{aligned} 1^\dagger &= [e] = 2 \\ 2^\dagger &= [2e] = 5 \\ 3^\dagger &= [6e] = 16 \end{aligned}$$

   etc.)
9. $\mathfrak{n} \neq \mathfrak{n} + 1 \leftrightarrow (\forall \mathfrak{p})(\forall \mathfrak{q})(\mathfrak{n} + \mathfrak{p} = \mathfrak{n} + \mathfrak{q} \leftrightarrow \mathfrak{p} = \mathfrak{q})$.
10. $(\mathfrak{n} \neq \mathfrak{n} + 1 \ \&\ \mathfrak{n} < \mathfrak{m}) \rightarrow (\exists 1\mathfrak{p})(\mathfrak{n} + \mathfrak{p} = \mathfrak{m})$.

12.2 CARDINAL NUMBERS AND THE AXIOM OF CHOICE

The axiom of choice plays an important role in the discussion of cardinal numbers. For example, if every set can be well-ordered, then every infinite cardinal number is an aleph. Thus, it follows from theorem 12.1.3 that

(1) $$\aleph_0 \leqq \mathfrak{m} \rightarrow \mathfrak{m} + \mathfrak{m} = \mathfrak{m}$$
(2) $$\aleph_0 \leqq \mathfrak{m} \rightarrow \mathfrak{m}^2 = \mathfrak{m}$$
(3) $$\aleph_0 \leqq \mathfrak{m},\mathfrak{n} \rightarrow \mathfrak{m} + \mathfrak{n} = \mathfrak{m}\cdot\mathfrak{n} = \max(\mathfrak{m},\mathfrak{n}).$$

Therefore, the axiom of choice makes the rules for addition and multiplication of transfinite ($\geqq \aleph_0$) cardinal numbers very simple. We shall show that (2) and (3) actually imply the axiom of choice. Altogether we shall give fourteen propositions about cardinal numbers which are equivalent to the axiom of choice.

It is assumed, unless otherwise specified, that each of the cardinal numbers in each of the fourteen propositions below is *transfinite*, $\geqq \aleph_0$.

DEFINITION 12.2.1. Transfinite

$$\mathfrak{m} \text{ is } \textit{transfinite} =_{\mathrm{Df}} \mathfrak{m} \geqq \aleph_0.$$

The first six propositions given here are due to Tarski (1924).

cn1: $\mathfrak{m} + \mathfrak{n} = \mathfrak{m}\cdot\mathfrak{n}$
cn2: $\mathfrak{m} = \mathfrak{m}^2$
cn3: $(\mathfrak{m} < \mathfrak{n} \mathbin{\&} \mathfrak{p} < \mathfrak{q}) \rightarrow \mathfrak{m} + \mathfrak{p} < \mathfrak{n} + \mathfrak{q}$
cn4: $(\mathfrak{m} < \mathfrak{n} \mathbin{\&} \mathfrak{p} < \mathfrak{q}) \rightarrow \mathfrak{m}\cdot\mathfrak{p} < \mathfrak{n}\cdot\mathfrak{q}$
cn5: $\mathfrak{m} + \mathfrak{p} < \mathfrak{n} + \mathfrak{p} \rightarrow \mathfrak{m} < \mathfrak{n}$
cn6: $\mathfrak{m}\cdot\mathfrak{p} < \mathfrak{n}\cdot\mathfrak{p} \rightarrow \mathfrak{m} < \mathfrak{n}$.

Compare cn3 and cn4 with 11.6.15(a) and (b). Also note that even though the cancellation laws for addition and multiplication of cardinal numbers do not hold, cn5 and cn6 are each equivalent to the axiom of choice.

In the preliminary discussion we have indicated how the well-ordering theorem implies cn1 and cn2. In the first two theorems we prove the converse.

THEOREM 12.2.2. cn1 $\rightarrow$ w2.

Proof: Let x be any set such that $\overline{\overline{x}} = \mathfrak{m} \geqq \aleph_0$. Then by cn1,

$$\mathfrak{m}\cdot\mathfrak{m}^* = \mathfrak{m} + \mathfrak{m}^*.$$

[Recall that $\mathfrak{m}^* = \overline{\overline{\Gamma(x)}}$ if $\overline{\overline{x}} = \mathfrak{m}$, 12.1.8.] Consequently, since $\mathfrak{m}^*$ is an aleph, it follows from 12.1.4 that

$$\mathfrak{m} \leqq \mathfrak{m}^* \text{ or } \mathfrak{m}^* \leqq \mathfrak{m}.$$

The second alternative contradicts 12.1.10 and the first implies that x is equipollent to an ordinal number.

If it should happen that $\mathfrak{m} < \aleph_0$, then replace $\mathfrak{m}$ by $\mathfrak{m} + \aleph_0$ in the preceding argument and the same result holds. ∎

The following lemma is a restatement of the proposition which is implied in the preceding paragraph.

LEMMA 12.2.3.

$$[\omega \lesssim x \mathbin{\&} (\exists R)(\mathrm{Rel}(R) \mathbin{\&} \langle\langle x,R\rangle\rangle \text{ is a w.o. set}) \mathbin{\&} \mathrm{S}(y) \mathbin{\&} \omega \not\lesssim y] \rightarrow (\exists S)(\mathrm{Rel}(S) \mathbin{\&} \langle\langle y,S\rangle\rangle \text{ is a w.o. set}).$$

The proof is left as an exercise. Henceforth, to prove the well-ordering theorem it will be sufficient to prove that every set x such that $\bar{\bar{x}} \geqq \aleph_0$ can be well-ordered.

THEOREM 12.2.4. cn2 $\rightarrow$ cn1.

Proof: Suppose that $\mathfrak{m}$ and $\mathfrak{n}$ are transfinite cardinal numbers. Then by cn2,

$$\begin{aligned} \mathfrak{m} + \mathfrak{n} &= (\mathfrak{m} + \mathfrak{n})^2 \\ &= \mathfrak{m}^2 + 2\cdot\mathfrak{m}\cdot\mathfrak{n} + \mathfrak{n}^2 \\ &\geqq \mathfrak{m}\cdot\mathfrak{n} \\ &\geqq \mathfrak{m} + \mathfrak{n}. \end{aligned} \tag{12.1.1}$$

Consequently, $\mathfrak{m}\cdot\mathfrak{n} = \mathfrak{m} + \mathfrak{n}$. ■

In the next four theorems it is shown that each of cn3 to cn6, is equivalent to some form of the axiom of choice.

THEOREM 12.2.5. cn3 $\leftrightarrow$ w2.

Proof: Let $\mathfrak{m}$, $\mathfrak{n}$, $\mathfrak{p}$, and $\mathfrak{q}$ be transfinite cardinal numbers such that $\mathfrak{m} < \mathfrak{n}$ and $\mathfrak{p} < \mathfrak{q}$. The well-ordering theorem implies that each transfinite cardinal number is an aleph. Therefore, by 12.1.3,

$$\mathfrak{m} + \mathfrak{p} = \max(\mathfrak{m},\mathfrak{p}) \ \& \ \mathfrak{n} + \mathfrak{q} = \max(\mathfrak{n},\mathfrak{q}).$$

There are four cases to consider:

Case 1. $\mathfrak{m} + \mathfrak{p} = \mathfrak{m}$ and $\mathfrak{n} + \mathfrak{q} = \mathfrak{n}$.
Case 2. $\mathfrak{m} + \mathfrak{p} = \mathfrak{p}$ and $\mathfrak{n} + \mathfrak{q} = \mathfrak{q}$.
Case 3. $\mathfrak{m} + \mathfrak{p} = \mathfrak{m}$ and $\mathfrak{n} + \mathfrak{q} = \mathfrak{q}$.
Case 4. $\mathfrak{m} + \mathfrak{p} = \mathfrak{p}$ and $\mathfrak{n} + \mathfrak{q} = \mathfrak{n}$.

In each case it is a simple matter to prove that $\mathfrak{m} + \mathfrak{p} < \mathfrak{n} + \mathfrak{q}$. The details are left as an exercise.

Conversely, suppose that cn3 is true. Let x be a set such that $\bar{\bar{x}} = \mathfrak{m} \geqq \aleph_0$. Let $\mathfrak{n} = \aleph_0\cdot\mathfrak{m}$. Then $\mathfrak{m} \leqq \mathfrak{n}$ and

$$\begin{aligned} \mathfrak{n} + \mathfrak{n} &= \aleph_0\cdot\mathfrak{m} + \aleph_0\cdot\mathfrak{m} \\ &= (\aleph_0 + \aleph_0)\cdot\mathfrak{m} \\ &= \aleph_0\cdot\mathfrak{m} \\ &= \mathfrak{n}. \end{aligned}$$

Clearly,

(1) $$\mathfrak{n} \leqq \mathfrak{n} + \mathfrak{n}^* \ \& \ \mathfrak{n}^* \leqq \mathfrak{n} + \mathfrak{n}^*.$$

Suppose that

(2) $$\mathfrak{n} < \mathfrak{n} + \mathfrak{n}^* \ \& \ \mathfrak{n}^* < \mathfrak{n} + \mathfrak{n}^*.$$

Then, cn3 implies that

$$\begin{aligned} \mathfrak{n} + \mathfrak{n}^* &< (\mathfrak{n} + \mathfrak{n}^*) + (\mathfrak{n} + \mathfrak{n}^*) \\ &= (\mathfrak{n} + \mathfrak{n}) + (\mathfrak{n}^* + \mathfrak{n}^*). \end{aligned}$$

However, we have shown above that $\mathfrak{n} + \mathfrak{n} = \mathfrak{n}$, and since $\mathfrak{n}^*$ is an aleph, it follows from 12.1.3 that $\mathfrak{n}^* + \mathfrak{n}^* = \mathfrak{n}^*$. Thus we find that $\mathfrak{n} + \mathfrak{n}^* < \mathfrak{n} + \mathfrak{n}^*$, which is clearly a contradiction. Therefore, since (2) is impossible, it follows from (1) that

$$\mathfrak{n} = \mathfrak{n} + \mathfrak{n}^* \text{ or } \mathfrak{n}^* = \mathfrak{n} + \mathfrak{n}^*.$$

The first alternative is impossible since it implies that $\mathfrak{n}^* \leqq \mathfrak{n}$. The second alternative implies that $\mathfrak{n} \leqq \mathfrak{n}^*$. Thus, $\mathfrak{n}$ is an aleph, and since $\mathfrak{m} \leqq \mathfrak{n}$, $\mathfrak{m}$ is an aleph also. ■

THEOREM 12.2.6. cn4 $\leftrightarrow$ w2.

Proof: The proof is analogous to the proof of 12.2.5. Here, choose $\mathfrak{n} = \mathfrak{m}^{\aleph_0} = \mathfrak{n}^2$ and replace "+" by "·". Details are left to the reader. ■

THEOREM 12.2.7.
(a) t $\rightarrow$ cn5
(b) cn5 $\rightarrow$ w2.

Proof:
(a) Suppose that $\mathfrak{m} + \mathfrak{p} < \mathfrak{n} + \mathfrak{p}$ but $\mathfrak{m} \not< \mathfrak{n}$. Then by the trichotomy, t, $\mathfrak{n} \leqq \mathfrak{m}$. But by 11.6.15(a), $\mathfrak{n} \leqq \mathfrak{m}$ implies that $\mathfrak{n} + \mathfrak{p} \leqq \mathfrak{m} + \mathfrak{p}$. Since this is a contradiction, we must have $\mathfrak{m} < \mathfrak{n}$.
(b) Suppose that $\bar{\bar{x}} = \mathfrak{m} \geqq \aleph_0$ and suppose that $\mathfrak{m} \not\leqq \mathfrak{m}^*$. Then

$$\mathfrak{m}^* < \mathfrak{m} + \mathfrak{m}^*.$$

Since $\mathfrak{m}^*$ is an aleph, $\mathfrak{m}^* + \mathfrak{m}^* = \mathfrak{m}^*$. Therefore,

$$\mathfrak{m}^* + \mathfrak{m}^* < \mathfrak{m} + \mathfrak{m}^*. \tag{1}$$

Thus cn5 applies, and thus (1) implies that

$$\mathfrak{m}^* < \mathfrak{m}.$$

Since this is a contradiction, then $\mathfrak{m} \leqq \mathfrak{m}^*$. ■

THEOREM 12.2.8.
(a) t $\rightarrow$ cn6
(b) cn6 $\rightarrow$ w2.

Proof: The proof is analogous to the proof of 12.2.7. Replace "+" by "·". ■

The next three propositions deal with subtraction and division of cardinal numbers. Tarski has stated without proof that cn7 is equivalent to the axiom of choice [Lindenbaum and Tarski (1926)]. The proof was given by Sierpinski (1946). The work of Tarski and Sierpinski leads to cn8 and cn9.

cn7: $\mathfrak{m} < \mathfrak{n} \rightarrow (\exists 1\mathfrak{p})(\mathfrak{m} + \mathfrak{p} = \mathfrak{n})$
cn8: $\mathfrak{m} < \mathfrak{n} \rightarrow (\exists\mathfrak{p})(\mathfrak{m} \cdot \mathfrak{p} = \mathfrak{n})$
cn9: $\mathfrak{m} < \mathfrak{n} \rightarrow (\exists 1\mathfrak{p})(\mathfrak{m} \cdot \mathfrak{p} = \mathfrak{n})$.

Thus, cn7 states that if $\mathfrak{m} < \mathfrak{n}$, then $\mathfrak{n} - \mathfrak{m}$ exists, and cn9 states that if $\mathfrak{m} < \mathfrak{n}$, then $\mathfrak{n} \div \mathfrak{m}$ exists. The following proposition is independent of the axiom of choice:

$$\mathfrak{m} < \mathfrak{n} \rightarrow (\exists\mathfrak{p})(\mathfrak{m} + \mathfrak{p} = \mathfrak{n})$$

(see 11.6.16).

Propositions cn7 and cn9 can be replaced by slightly stronger propositions.

cn7′: $\mathfrak{m} < \mathfrak{n} \rightarrow \mathfrak{n} - \mathfrak{m} = \mathfrak{n}$
cn9′: $\mathfrak{m} < \mathfrak{n} \rightarrow \mathfrak{n} \div \mathfrak{m} = \mathfrak{n}$.

Clearly, cn7′ → cn7 and cn9′ → cn9.

THEOREM 12.2.9.
(a) w2 → cn7′
(b) w2 → cn8
(c) w2 → cn9′.

Proof:
(a) Suppose that $\mathfrak{m} < \mathfrak{n}$. Then, by 11.6.16, there is a $\mathfrak{p}$ such that

$$\mathfrak{n} = \mathfrak{m} + \mathfrak{p}.$$

The well-ordering theorem and 12.1.3 imply that

$$\mathfrak{m} + \mathfrak{p} = \max(\mathfrak{m},\mathfrak{p}).$$

Since $\mathfrak{m} < \mathfrak{n}$,

$$\mathfrak{n} = \max(\mathfrak{m},\mathfrak{p}) = \mathfrak{p}.$$

Consequently, $\mathfrak{n} - \mathfrak{m}$ exists and is equal to $\mathfrak{n}$.

(b) Suppose that $\mathfrak{m} < \mathfrak{n}$. Then from w2 and 12.1.3 we get

$$\mathfrak{n} = \mathfrak{m} \cdot \mathfrak{n}.$$

(c) Suppose that $\mathfrak{m} < \mathfrak{n}$ and

$$\mathfrak{n} = \mathfrak{m} \cdot \mathfrak{n} = \mathfrak{m} \cdot \mathfrak{p}.$$

Then from w2 and 12.1.3 we get

$$\mathfrak{n} = \max(\mathfrak{m},\mathfrak{p}).$$

Since $\mathfrak{m} < \mathfrak{n}$, then $\mathfrak{p} = \mathfrak{n}$. ■

It is obviously true that cn9 → cn8. Therefore, to complete the proof that cn7, cn8, cn9, cn7′, and cn9′ are each equivalent to the axiom of choice, it is sufficient to prove that cn7 and cn8 each imply the axiom of choice.

THEOREM 12.2.10.
(a) cn7 → w2
(b) cn8 → w2.

Proof: Suppose that $\bar{\bar{x}} = \mathfrak{m} \geqq \aleph_0$. Either

$$\mathfrak{m}^* = \mathfrak{m} + \mathfrak{m}^* \text{ or } \mathfrak{m}^* < \mathfrak{m} + \mathfrak{m}^*.$$

If the first alternative holds, then $\mathfrak{m} < m^*$ and both parts of the theorem are true. Suppose, then, that the second alternative holds.

(a) By cn7, there is a unique $\mathfrak{p}$ such that

$$\mathfrak{m} + \mathfrak{m}^* = \mathfrak{m}^* + \mathfrak{p}.$$

However,

$$\mathfrak{m} + \mathfrak{m}^* = \mathfrak{m}^* + \mathfrak{m}.$$

Also, since $\mathfrak{m}^* + \mathfrak{m}^* = \mathfrak{m}^*$, then

$$\mathfrak{m} + \mathfrak{m}^* = \mathfrak{m}^* + (\mathfrak{m} + \mathfrak{m}^*).$$

Therefore, since $\mathfrak{p}$ is unique,

$$\mathfrak{m} = \mathfrak{m} + \mathfrak{m}^*.$$

But this implies that $\mathfrak{m}^* \leqq \mathfrak{m}$, which is impossible.

(b) Assuming that $\mathfrak{m}^* < \mathfrak{m} + \mathfrak{m}^*$, it follows from cn8 that there is a $\mathfrak{p}$ such that

(1) $$\mathfrak{m}^* \cdot \mathfrak{p} = \mathfrak{m} + \mathfrak{m}^*.$$

Since $\mathfrak{m}^*$ is an aleph, lemma 12.1.4 applies; thus

$$\mathfrak{m}^* \leqq \mathfrak{m} \text{ or } \mathfrak{p} \leqq \mathfrak{m}^*.$$

The first alternative is impossible, so we must have $\mathfrak{p} \leqq \mathfrak{m}^*$. Therefore,

$$\mathfrak{m}^* \leqq \mathfrak{m}^* \cdot \mathfrak{p} \leqq \mathfrak{m}^* \cdot \mathfrak{m}^* = \mathfrak{m}^*.$$

Furthermore, from (1),

$$\mathfrak{m}^* \cdot \mathfrak{p} = \mathfrak{m}^* = \mathfrak{m} + \mathfrak{m}^*,$$

which implies $\mathfrak{m} \leqq \mathfrak{m}^*$. ∎

Thus if $\mathfrak{m} < \mathfrak{n}$, then a necessary and sufficient condition for the existence of the difference, $\mathfrak{n} - \mathfrak{m}$, and the quotient, $\mathfrak{n} \div \mathfrak{m}$, is that the axiom of choice holds.

The next two propositions deal with exponentiation of cardinal numbers. It was stated without proof by Tarski [see Lindenbaum and Tarski (1926)] that each of them is equivalent to the axiom of choice.

cn10: $\mathfrak{m}^{\mathfrak{p}} < \mathfrak{m}^{\mathfrak{q}} \rightarrow \mathfrak{p} < \mathfrak{q}$.

For any cardinal number $\mathfrak{p} > 1$,

cn11($\mathfrak{p}$): $\mathfrak{m}^{\mathfrak{p}} < \mathfrak{n}^{\mathfrak{p}} \rightarrow \mathfrak{m} < \mathfrak{n}$.

cn11($\mathfrak{p}$) is actually many forms combined into one, since if it holds for any given $\mathfrak{p} > 1$, then the axiom of choice holds.

THEOREM 12.2.11.
(a) t → cn10
(b) cn10 → w2.

Proof:

(a) Suppose that $\mathfrak{m}^{\mathfrak{p}} < \mathfrak{m}^{\mathfrak{q}}$ and $\mathfrak{p} \nless \mathfrak{q}$. Then it follows from the trichotomy that $\mathfrak{q} \leqq \mathfrak{p}$. But, by 11.6.15(c), this implies that $\mathfrak{m}^{\mathfrak{q}} \leqq \mathfrak{m}^{\mathfrak{p}}$.

(b) Let x be a set such that $\bar{\bar{x}} = \mathfrak{p} \geqq \aleph_0$. Let

$$\mathfrak{m} = 2^{\mathfrak{p}^{\aleph_0}} \;\&\; \mathfrak{q} = \mathfrak{m}^*.$$

Then,

$$\begin{aligned} \mathfrak{m}^{\mathfrak{p}} &= (2^{\mathfrak{p}^{\aleph_0}})^{\mathfrak{p}} \\ &= 2^{\mathfrak{p}^{\aleph_0} \cdot \mathfrak{p}} \\ &= 2^{\mathfrak{p}^{\aleph_0 + 1}} \\ &= 2^{\mathfrak{p}^{\aleph_0}} \\ &= \mathfrak{m}. \end{aligned}$$

Consequently,

$$\mathfrak{m}^{\mathfrak{p}} = \mathfrak{m} \leqq \mathfrak{m}^{\mathfrak{m}^*} = \mathfrak{m}^{\mathfrak{q}}.$$

Suppose that $\mathfrak{m}^{\mathfrak{p}} = \mathfrak{m}^{\mathfrak{q}}$. Then since $\mathfrak{q} = \mathfrak{m}^*$ we would have

$$\mathfrak{m}^* \leqq \mathfrak{m}^{\mathfrak{q}} = \mathfrak{m}^{\mathfrak{p}} = \mathfrak{m},$$

which is impossible. Hence, $\mathfrak{m}^{\mathfrak{p}} < \mathfrak{m}^{\mathfrak{q}}$. Therefore, cn10 implies that $\mathfrak{p} < \mathfrak{q} = \mathfrak{m}^*$. ∎

THEOREM 12.2.12.

(a) $\mathfrak{t} \to \mathrm{cn11}(\mathfrak{p})$

(b) $(\exists\mathfrak{p})[\mathfrak{p} > 1 \;\&\; \mathrm{cn11}(\mathfrak{p})] \to \mathrm{w2}$.

Proof:

(a) The proof is similar to that of 12.2.11(a) and is left as an exercise.

(b) Suppose that $\mathfrak{r}$ is transfinite. Let $\mathfrak{p} > 1$ be any cardinal number for which $\mathrm{cn11}(\mathfrak{p})$ holds. Let $\mathfrak{s}$ be any cardinal number such that $\mathfrak{s} = \mathfrak{p}\cdot\mathfrak{s}$. (For example, let $\mathfrak{s} = 2^{\mathfrak{p}\cdot\aleph_0}$.) Let $\mathfrak{t} = \mathfrak{r}^{\mathfrak{s}}$. Then since $\mathfrak{p}\cdot\mathfrak{s} = \mathfrak{s}$, it is easily shown that

$$\mathfrak{t}^{\mathfrak{p}} = \mathfrak{t}. \tag{1}$$

Now define

$$\mathfrak{m} = \mathfrak{t}\cdot\mathfrak{t}^* \;\&\; \mathfrak{n} = \mathfrak{t} + ((\mathfrak{t}\cdot\mathfrak{t}^*)^{\mathfrak{p}})^*.$$

Clearly,

$$\mathfrak{n}^{\mathfrak{p}} \geqq (\mathfrak{t} + \mathfrak{t}^*)^{\mathfrak{p}}. \tag{2}$$

Since $\mathfrak{p} > 1$, there is a cardinal number $\mathfrak{q} \neq 0$ such that $\mathfrak{q} + 1 = \mathfrak{p}$. Then it follows from (2) and exercise 11.6.1(b) that,

$$\begin{aligned} \mathfrak{n}^{\mathfrak{p}} &\geqq \mathfrak{t}\cdot(\mathfrak{t}^*)^{\mathfrak{q}} && \\ &= \mathfrak{t}\cdot(\mathfrak{t}^*)^{2\mathfrak{q}} && (12.1.2) \\ &\geqq \mathfrak{t}\cdot(\mathfrak{t}^*)^{\mathfrak{p}} && \\ &= (\mathfrak{t}\cdot\mathfrak{t}^*)^{\mathfrak{p}} && (1) \\ &= \mathfrak{m}^{\mathfrak{p}}. && \end{aligned}$$

Thus, $\mathfrak{m}^{\mathfrak{p}} \leqq \mathfrak{n}^{\mathfrak{p}}$. We shall show that $\mathfrak{m}^{\mathfrak{p}} < \mathfrak{n}^{\mathfrak{p}}$.

$$\begin{aligned} (\mathfrak{m}^{\mathfrak{p}})^* &= ((\mathfrak{t}\cdot\mathfrak{t}^*)^{\mathfrak{p}})^* \\ &\leqq \mathfrak{t} + ((\mathfrak{t}\cdot\mathfrak{t}^*)^{\mathfrak{p}})^* \\ &= \mathfrak{n} \\ &\leqq \mathfrak{n}^{\mathfrak{p}}. \end{aligned}$$

Therefore, if $\mathfrak{m}^{\mathfrak{p}} = \mathfrak{n}^{\mathfrak{p}}$, then $(\mathfrak{m}^{\mathfrak{p}})^* \leqq \mathfrak{m}^{\mathfrak{p}}$, which is impossible. Hence $\mathfrak{m}^{\mathfrak{p}} < \mathfrak{n}^{\mathfrak{p}}$. Now, using cn11, we obtain $\mathfrak{m} < \mathfrak{n}$. This means that

$$\mathfrak{t}\cdot\mathfrak{t}^* \leqq \mathfrak{t} + ((\mathfrak{t}\cdot\mathfrak{t}^*)^{\mathfrak{p}})^*.$$

Therefore, by 12.1.4, we obtain

$$\mathfrak{t}^* \leqq \mathfrak{t} \text{ or } \mathfrak{t} \leqq ((\mathfrak{t}\cdot\mathfrak{t}^*)^{\mathfrak{p}})^*.$$

The first alternative is impossible and the second implies that $\mathfrak{t}$ is the cardinal number of a w.o. set. But $\mathfrak{t} = \mathfrak{r}^{\mathfrak{s}}$; thus, $\mathfrak{r} \leqq \mathfrak{t}$. Therefore, $\mathfrak{r}$ is the cardinal number of a w.o. set. ■

The next proposition asserts that the set of all subsets of a w.o. set can be w.o.

cn12: $\mathfrak{m} \in \mathfrak{A} \rightarrow 2^{\mathfrak{m}} \in \mathfrak{A}$.

Clearly, the well-ordering theorem implies cn12 since it implies that every infinite cardinal number is an aleph. H. Rubin (1960) has shown that if the class of atoms, $\mathfrak{a} = \emptyset$, or more generally, if $\mathfrak{a}$ is a set which can be w.o., then using the axiom of regularity it can be shown that cn12 implies the axiom of choice.

THEOREM 12.2.13.®

$$[S(\mathfrak{a}) \ \& \ (\exists R)(\mathrm{Rel}(R) \ \& \ \langle\langle \mathfrak{a}, R\rangle\rangle \text{ is a w.o. set})] \rightarrow (\mathrm{cn}12 \rightarrow \mathrm{w}1).$$

Proof: We shall prove by transfinite induction that for each ordinal number $\alpha > 0$ there is a function R such that for every $\beta < \alpha$, R_β w.o. the set

$$z(\beta) = \{u : \rho(u) = \beta\}.$$

This is sufficient to prove the theorem. For suppose that x is any set. Let α be an ordinal number which is larger than the rank of each element in x. [For example, let $\alpha = \rho(x)$.] We can construct a relation S on x as follows. For all $u,v \in x$,

$$u \, S \, v \leftrightarrow [\rho(u) < \rho(v) \text{ or } (\rho(u) = \rho(v) = \beta \ \& \ u \, R_\beta \, v)].$$

The relation S clearly w.o. x. Therefore, it is sufficient to construct the above mentioned function R.

Let $\alpha > 0$ be any ordinal number. By the definition of z,

$$z(0) = \mathfrak{a} \cup \{\emptyset\}.$$

By hypothesis, $\mathfrak{a}$ is a set which can be w.o. Let R_0 be a relation which w.o. $z(0)$.

Suppose that for each $\gamma < \beta \, (< \alpha)$ there is a relation R_γ which w.o. $z(\gamma)$. Let

$$w(\beta) = \{u : \rho(u) < \beta\}.$$

Since $\mathfrak{a}$ is a set, it follows from 8.6.21 that $w(\beta)$ is a set for all $\beta \in On$. Define a relation S_β on $w(\beta)$ as follows: For each $u,v \in w(\beta)$

$$u \, S_\beta \, v \leftrightarrow \rho(u) < \rho(v) \text{ or } (\rho(u) = \rho(v) = \gamma \ \& \ u \, R_\gamma \, v).$$

Then S_β w.o. $w(\beta)$. Therefore, by 8.2.27 and 8.2.28 there is a unique ordinal number δ such that

$$\overline{\langle\langle w(\beta), S_\beta\rangle\rangle} = \delta.$$

Consequently, by 7.4.5 there is exactly one isomorphism f_β mapping $w(\beta)$ onto δ. Thus, for all $u,v \in w(\beta)$, $u \neq v$,

$$f_\beta(u) < f_\beta(v) \leftrightarrow u\ S_\beta\ v.$$

Let

$$\begin{aligned}\lambda &= \Gamma(w(\alpha)) \\ &= \{\gamma : \gamma \lesssim w(\alpha)\}.\end{aligned}$$

It follows from 10.2.4 that $\lambda \in On$. Therefore, cn12 implies that there is a relation T which w.o. $\mathcal{P}(\lambda)$.

Now, for each $x \subseteq w(\beta)$ define

$$g_\beta(x) = f_\beta''x.$$

Then g_β is a function mapping $\mathcal{P}(w(\beta))$ into $\mathcal{P}(\lambda)$. Moreover, g_β is 1–1 because f_β is 1–1 (exercise 3.3.7).

If $x \in z(\beta)$, then $\rho(x) = \beta$. Therefore, by 8.6.16, if $u \in x$, then $\rho(u) < \beta$. Thus, this implies that if $u \in x$, then $u \in w(\beta)$. Hence, $x \subseteq w(\beta)$. Therefore, every element of $z(\beta)$ is a subset of $w(\beta)$, and thus

$$z(\beta) \subseteq \mathcal{P}(w(\beta)).$$

The manner by which we define R_β is now clear. If $x,y \in z(\beta)$, then

$$x\ R_\beta\ y \leftrightarrow g_\beta(x)\ T\ g_\beta(y).$$

Since T w.o. $\mathcal{P}(\lambda)$, R_β w.o. $z(\beta)$. The theorem follows by transfinite induction. ∎

The next proposition was introduced by Kruse (1962). Its importance lies in the fact that it immediately implies that both the trichotomy and the generalized continuum hypothesis (Chapter 13) imply the axiom of choice.

cn13: $\quad \mathfrak{p} \leqq \mathfrak{m},\mathfrak{n} \leqq 2^{\mathfrak{p}} \rightarrow (\mathfrak{m} \leqq \mathfrak{n} \text{ or } \mathfrak{n} \leqq \mathfrak{m}).$

In its original form Kruse's hypothesis was

$$\mathfrak{p} < \mathfrak{m},\mathfrak{n} < 2^{\mathfrak{p}}.$$

But it is clear that this makes no essential difference. The two forms are equivalent.

Clearly the trichotomy implies cn13 since cn13 is the trichotomy for cardinal numbers between $\mathfrak{p}$ and $2^{\mathfrak{p}}$. To establish the converse we shall prove a sequence of lemmas. The purpose of these lemmas is to show that cn13 implies that $2^{\mathfrak{m}}$ and $2^{\mathfrak{n}}$ are comparable for all transfinite cardinal numbers $\mathfrak{m}$ and $\mathfrak{n}$. (That is, $2^{\mathfrak{m}} \leqq 2^{\mathfrak{n}}$ or $2^{\mathfrak{n}} \leqq 2^{\mathfrak{m}}$). Then, we shall show that for each transfinite cardinal number $\mathfrak{m}$ there is an aleph $\mathfrak{n}$ such that $2^{\mathfrak{m}} \leqq 2^{\mathfrak{n}}$. Now, if it can be shown that $2^{\mathfrak{n}}$ is an aleph whenever $\mathfrak{n}$ is an aleph, it will follow that $2^{\mathfrak{m}}$, and therefore $\mathfrak{m}$, is the cardinal number of a w.o. set. Consequently, to prove that cn13 implies the axiom of choice it will be sufficient to prove that cn13 implies cn12.

LEMMA 12.2.14.

$$\text{cn}13 \rightarrow (\forall\mathfrak{m})(\forall\mathfrak{n})(\mathfrak{m},\mathfrak{n} \geqq \aleph_0 \rightarrow (2^{\mathfrak{m}} \leqq 2^{\mathfrak{n}} \text{ or } 2^{\mathfrak{n}} \leqq 2^{\mathfrak{m}})).$$

Proof: For all $\mathfrak{m}$ and $\mathfrak{n}$,

$$\mathfrak{m} + \mathfrak{n} \leqq 2^{\mathfrak{m}} + \mathfrak{n},\ \mathfrak{m} + 2^{\mathfrak{m}} \leqq 2^{\mathfrak{m}+\mathfrak{n}}.$$

Therefore, cn13 implies that $2^{\mathfrak{m}} + \mathfrak{n}$ and $\mathfrak{m} + 2^{\mathfrak{n}}$ are comparable. Thus,

$$2^{\mathfrak{m}} + \mathfrak{n} \leqq \mathfrak{m} + 2^{\mathfrak{n}} \text{ or } \mathfrak{m} + 2^{\mathfrak{n}} \leqq 2^{\mathfrak{m}} + \mathfrak{n}.$$

If the first alternative holds, then

$$2^{\mathfrak{m}} \leqq \mathfrak{m} + 2^{\mathfrak{n}}.$$

Therefore, it follows from 12.1.28 that $2^{\mathfrak{m}} \leqq 2^{\mathfrak{n}}$.

Analogously, if the second alternative holds, then $2^{\mathfrak{n}} \leqq 2^{\mathfrak{m}}$. ■

Next, we shall show that for each transfinite cardinal number $\mathfrak{m}$ there is an aleph $\mathfrak{n}$ such that $2^{\mathfrak{m}} \leqq 2^{\mathfrak{n}}$.

LEMMA 12.2.15. $(\text{cn } 13 \ \&\ \mathfrak{m} \geqq \aleph_0) \rightarrow (\exists\mathfrak{n})(\mathfrak{n} \in \mathfrak{A} \ \&\ 2^{\mathfrak{m}} \leqq 2^{\mathfrak{n}})$.

Proof: Suppose that $\mathfrak{m}$ is a transfinite cardinal number. Then by 12.2.14,

$$2^{(2^{\mathfrak{m}})^*} \leqq 2^{\mathfrak{m}} \text{ or } 2^{\mathfrak{m}} \leqq 2^{(2^{\mathfrak{m}})^*}.$$

If the first alternative holds, then since $(2^{\mathfrak{m}})^* < 2^{(2^{\mathfrak{m}})^*}$, we would have $(2^{\mathfrak{m}})^* \leqq 2^{\mathfrak{m}}$. This latter inequality is impossible. Thus, we must have $2^{\mathfrak{m}} \leqq 2^{(2^{\mathfrak{m}})^*}$. ■

The following two lemmas will be used to prove lemma 12.2.18, cn13 → cn12.

LEMMA 12.2.16.

$$\text{cn}13 \rightarrow [(\mathfrak{m}^2 = \mathfrak{m} \ \&\ \mathfrak{m}^* \leqq 2^{\mathfrak{m}}) \rightarrow (\exists\mathfrak{p})(\mathfrak{p} < \mathfrak{m}^* \leqq 2^{\mathfrak{p}} \text{ or } \mathfrak{m},2^{\mathfrak{m}} \in \mathfrak{A})].$$

Proof: Suppose that $\mathfrak{m}$ satisfies the hypothesis. Since $\mathfrak{m}^2 = \mathfrak{m}$, it follows that either $\mathfrak{m} = 0$, $\mathfrak{m} = 1$, or $\mathfrak{m}$ is infinite. If $\mathfrak{m} = 0$ or $\mathfrak{m} = 1$, then it is clear that there is a $\mathfrak{p}$ such that $\mathfrak{p} < \mathfrak{m}^* \leqq 2^{\mathfrak{p}}$. Let us suppose, then, that $\mathfrak{m}$ is infinite.

It follows from 12.1.16 and 12.1.15(a) that

$$\mathfrak{m} < \mathfrak{m}^{\dagger} \leqq 2^{\mathfrak{m}^2} = 2^{\mathfrak{m}}.$$

Also, since $\mathfrak{m}^* \leqq 2^{\mathfrak{m}}$,

$$\mathfrak{m} < \mathfrak{m} + \mathfrak{m}^* \leqq 2^{\mathfrak{m}} + 2^{\mathfrak{m}} = 2^{\mathfrak{m}}.$$

Hence, both $\mathfrak{m}^\dagger$ and $\mathfrak{m} + \mathfrak{m}^*$ are between $\mathfrak{m}$ and $2^{\mathfrak{m}}$. Thus, it follows from cn13 that either

$$\mathfrak{m}^\dagger \leqq \mathfrak{m} + \mathfrak{m}^* \text{ or } \mathfrak{m} + \mathfrak{m}^* \leqq \mathfrak{m}^\dagger.$$

If the first inequality holds, then by 12.1.22, $\mathfrak{m} < \mathfrak{m}^\dagger = 2^{\mathfrak{m}} \leqq \mathfrak{m}^*$. Thus, both $\mathfrak{m}$ and $2^{\mathfrak{m}}$ are alephs. If the second inequality holds, then $\mathfrak{m}^* \leqq \mathfrak{m}^\dagger$. Let x be a set such that $\bar{\bar{x}} = \mathfrak{m}$. Then there exists a set w such that $w \subseteq W(x)$ and

$$\Gamma(x) \approx w.$$

Each element of w is a 1–1 function from an ordinal number onto a subset of x. Let

$$y = \bigcup_{f \in w} \mathcal{R}(f).$$

Then $y \subseteq x$ and y can be w.o. Let $\mathfrak{p} = \bar{\bar{y}}$. Then

$$\mathfrak{p} < \mathfrak{p}^* \leqq \mathfrak{m}^*.$$

Moreover, $w \subseteq W(y)$; thus

$$\mathfrak{m}^* \leqq \mathfrak{p}^\dagger.$$

Since $\mathfrak{p}$ is an aleph, it follows from 12.1.17 that $\mathfrak{p}^\dagger = 2^{\mathfrak{p}}$. Therefore,

$$\mathfrak{p} < \mathfrak{m}^* \leqq 2^{\mathfrak{p}}. \blacksquare$$

LEMMA 12.2.17. $\quad$ $\text{cn13} \rightarrow \aleph_{\alpha+1} \leqq 2^{\aleph_\alpha}$.

Proof: Suppose that $\aleph_{\alpha+1} \not\leqq 2^{\aleph_\alpha}$. If $2^{\aleph_\alpha}$ is an aleph, then $\aleph_{\alpha+1} \leqq 2^{\aleph_\alpha}$ because $\aleph_{\alpha+1}$ is the smallest aleph which is larger than $\aleph_\alpha$. Suppose then that $2^{\aleph_\alpha}$ is not an aleph. Let $\mathfrak{m} = 2^{\aleph_\alpha}$. Then

$$\mathfrak{m}^2 = (2^{\aleph_\alpha})^2 = 2^{\aleph_\alpha \cdot 2} = 2^{\aleph_\alpha} = \mathfrak{m}.$$

Moreover, since $\aleph_\alpha < \mathfrak{m}$ and $\aleph_{\alpha+1} \not\leqq \mathfrak{m}$, both $\aleph_{\alpha+1}$ and $\mathfrak{m}^*$ are the smallest aleph which are $\not\leqq \mathfrak{m}$. Therefore,

$$\aleph_\alpha^* = \aleph_{\alpha+1} = \mathfrak{m}^*.$$

Hence, by exercise 12.1.6(c),

$$\mathfrak{m}^* \leqq 2^{2^{\aleph_\alpha^2}} = 2^{2^{\aleph_\alpha}} = 2^{\mathfrak{m}}.$$

Thus, $\mathfrak{m}$ satisfies the hypothesis of 12.2.16. Since $\mathfrak{m}$ is not an aleph, there is a cardinal number $\mathfrak{p}$ such that

$$\mathfrak{p} < \mathfrak{m}^* \leqq 2^{\mathfrak{p}}.$$

Since, $\mathfrak{m}^* = \aleph_{\alpha+1}$, $\mathfrak{p} \leqq \aleph_\alpha$. Therefore,

$$\aleph_{\alpha+1} = \mathfrak{m}^* \leqq 2^{\mathfrak{p}} \leqq 2^{\aleph_\alpha},$$

which contradicts the assumption that $\aleph_{\alpha+1} \not\leqq 2^{\aleph_\alpha}$. Hence, $\aleph_{\alpha+1} \leqq 2^{\aleph_\alpha}$. ∎

LEMMA 12.2.18. cn13 → cn12.

Proof: Let $\mathfrak{p}$ be any aleph. Let $\mathfrak{q}$ be an aleph such that

$$\mathfrak{p} < \mathfrak{q} \;\&\; \mathfrak{q} \not\leqq 2^{\mathfrak{p}}.$$

[For example, let $\mathfrak{q} = \overline{\overline{\Gamma(2^{\mathfrak{p}})}}$.] Then there is a $\beta \in On$ such that

$$\mathfrak{q} = \aleph_\beta.$$

Let

$$\mathfrak{r} = \aleph_{\beta+1}.$$

Then by lemma 12.2.17,

$$\mathfrak{q} < \mathfrak{r} \leqq 2^{\mathfrak{q}}.$$

Moreover,

$$\mathfrak{q} < 2^{\mathfrak{p}} + \mathfrak{q} \leqq 2^{\mathfrak{q}} + 2^{\mathfrak{q}} = 2^{\mathfrak{q}}.$$

Therefore, cn13 implies that

$$\mathfrak{r} \leqq 2^{\mathfrak{p}} + \mathfrak{q} \text{ or } 2^{\mathfrak{p}} + \mathfrak{q} \leqq \mathfrak{r}.$$

If the first inequality holds, it follows from corollary 12.1.6 that

$$\mathfrak{r} \leqq 2^{\mathfrak{p}} \text{ or } \mathfrak{r} \leqq \mathfrak{q}.$$

But neither of these inequalities is possible since $\mathfrak{q} < \mathfrak{r}$ and $\mathfrak{q} \not\leqq 2^{\mathfrak{p}}$. Therefore,

$$2^{\mathfrak{p}} + \mathfrak{q} \leqq \mathfrak{r},$$

which implies that

$$2^{\mathfrak{p}} \leqq \mathfrak{r}.$$

Since $\mathfrak{r}$ is an aleph, so too is $2^{\mathfrak{p}}$. ∎

THEOREM 12.2.19. cn13 → w1.

Proof: 12.2.14, 12.2.15, and 12.2.18. ∎

The last result to be considered in this section is due to Tarski (1964). He showed that the axiom of choice is equivalent to the following statement.

For any natural number $n \geqq 2$,

cn14(n): $(x \subseteq Cn \;\&\; \bar{\bar{x}} = n) \rightarrow (\exists p)(\exists q)(p,q \in x \;\&\; (\mathfrak{p} < \mathfrak{q} \text{ or } \mathfrak{q} < \mathfrak{p}))$.

In other words, for any natural number $n \geqq 2$, in any set of n cardinal numbers at least two distinct cardinal numbers are comparable. If $n = 2$, cn14(n) is just the trichotomy. Clearly the trichotomy implies cn14(n) for every n. We shall prove that cn14(n) implies the well-ordering theorem for each n such that $2 \leqq n < \aleph_0$. [It is not known whether cn14(n) implies the axiom of choice when $n \geqq \aleph_0$.]

THEOREM 12.2.20. $(\exists n)(n \in \omega \;\&\; n \geqq 2 \;\&\; \text{cn14}(n)) \rightarrow \text{w2}$.

Proof: Suppose that $\mathfrak{m} \geqq \aleph_0$ and that n is a natural number larger than 1 for which cn14(n) is true. Define

$$P_0(\mathfrak{m}) = 0$$
$$P_1(\mathfrak{m}) = \mathfrak{m}$$
$$P_{k+1}(\mathfrak{m}) = 2^{P_k(\mathfrak{m})}.$$

It then follows from the recursion theorem that P_k is defined for every natural number k. Let $\aleph_\alpha$ be any aleph such that

(1) $$\aleph_\alpha \nleqq P_n(\mathfrak{m}).$$

Consider the set of cardinal numbers

$$x = \{\aleph_{\alpha+j} + P_{n-j}(\mathfrak{m}) : 0 \leqq j < n\}.$$

Suppose there is a j and k, $0 \leqq j < k < n$, such that

$$\aleph_{\alpha+j} + P_{n-j}(\mathfrak{m}) = \aleph_{\alpha+k} + P_{n-k}(\mathfrak{m}).$$

Then

(2) $$\aleph_{\alpha+k} \leqq \aleph_{\alpha+j} + P_{n-j}(\mathfrak{m}),$$

and by 12.1.4, this implies that

$$\aleph_{\alpha+k} \leqq \aleph_{\alpha+j} \text{ or } \aleph_{\alpha+k} \leqq P_{n-j}(\mathfrak{m}).$$

The first inequality is impossible since $j < k$; the second contradicts (1). Thus, $\bar{\bar{x}} = n$ and cn14(n) applies. Therefore, there are natural numbers j and k, $0 \leqq j,k < n$, $j \neq k$ such that

(3) $$\aleph_{\alpha+k} + P_{n-k}(\mathfrak{m}) < \aleph_{\alpha+j} + P_{n-j}(\mathfrak{m}).$$

Suppose that $j < k$. It then follows from (3) that the inequality (2), which has been shown to be false, holds.

Suppose that $k < j$. Let $P_{n-j}(\mathfrak{m}) = \mathfrak{q}$. Then from (3),

$$\begin{aligned}\aleph_{\alpha+j} + \mathfrak{q} > \aleph_{\alpha+k} &+ P_{n-k}(\mathfrak{m}) \\ &\geqq P_{n-k}(\mathfrak{m}) \\ &\geqq P_{n-(j-1)}(\mathfrak{m}) \\ &= 2^{\mathfrak{q}}.\end{aligned}$$

It follows from 12.1.28 that $2^{\mathfrak{q}} \leqq \aleph_{\alpha+j}$, which implies that $\mathfrak{m} \leqq \aleph_{\alpha+j}$. Therefore, $\mathfrak{m}$ is an aleph. ■

There are still many unsolved problems connected with the axiom of choice. For example, it is not known if any of the following propositions imply the axiom of choice.

(1) $\mathfrak{m} \geqq \aleph_0 \rightarrow 2\mathfrak{m} = \mathfrak{m}$.

(2) $\mathfrak{m} \geqq \aleph_0 \rightarrow \mathfrak{m}^2 = \mathfrak{m}^3$.

(3) $(\exists\mathfrak{n})(\mathfrak{n}$ is infinite & cn14$(\mathfrak{n}))$.

(4) $(\forall\mathfrak{m})(\forall\mathfrak{n})(\exists\mathfrak{p})[\mathfrak{m} \leqq \mathfrak{p}$ & $\mathfrak{n} \leqq \mathfrak{p}$ & $(\forall\mathfrak{q})((\mathfrak{m} \leqq \mathfrak{q}$ & $\mathfrak{n} \leqq \mathfrak{q}) \rightarrow \mathfrak{p} \leqq \mathfrak{q})]$.

(5) $(\forall\mathfrak{m})(\forall\mathfrak{n})(\exists\mathfrak{p})[\mathfrak{p} \leqq \mathfrak{m}$ & $\mathfrak{p} \leqq \mathfrak{n}$ & $(\forall\mathfrak{q})((\mathfrak{q} \leqq \mathfrak{m}$ & $\mathfrak{q} \leqq \mathfrak{n}) \rightarrow \mathfrak{q} \leqq \mathfrak{p})]$.

Proposition (4) states that every pair of cardinal numbers has a least upper bound, and (5), that every pair of cardinal numbers has a greatest lower bound. It is not difficult to show that (1) implies (4), (5) implies (4), and the axiom of choice implies each of the propositions. (See exercise 12.2.12.) Additional results are left to the ingenuity of the reader.

EXERCISES 12.2

Prove that each of the following eight propositions is equivalent to the axiom of choice. (As in the text, it is assumed that each of the cardinal numbers is transfinite.)

1. $\mathfrak{m} + \mathfrak{n} = \mathfrak{m}$ or $\mathfrak{m} + \mathfrak{n} = \mathfrak{n}$ (Lesniewski).
2. $\mathfrak{m} \cdot \mathfrak{n} = \mathfrak{m}$ or $\mathfrak{m} \cdot \mathfrak{n} = \mathfrak{n}$ (Lesniewski).
3. $\mathfrak{m}^* = \mathfrak{n}^* \rightarrow \mathfrak{m} = \mathfrak{n}$.
4. $\mathfrak{m}^* < \mathfrak{n}^* \rightarrow \mathfrak{m} < \mathfrak{n}$.
5. $\mathfrak{m} + \mathfrak{p} = \mathfrak{m} + \mathfrak{q} \rightarrow (\mathfrak{p} = \mathfrak{q}$ or $(\mathfrak{p} \leqq \mathfrak{m}$ & $\mathfrak{q} \leqq \mathfrak{m}))$.
   [Tarski. Hint: $\mathfrak{m}^* + \mathfrak{m} = \mathfrak{m}^* + (\mathfrak{m} + \mathfrak{m}^*)$.]
6. $\mathfrak{m} + \mathfrak{m} < \mathfrak{m} + \mathfrak{n} \rightarrow \mathfrak{m} < \mathfrak{n}$ (Tarski).
7. $\mathfrak{m}^2 = \mathfrak{n}^2 \rightarrow \mathfrak{m} = \mathfrak{n}$ (Tarski).
8. $(\exists R)(\mathrm{Rel}(R)$ & $\langle\langle x,R\rangle\rangle$ is a l.o. set$) \rightarrow (\exists S)(\mathrm{Rel}(S)$ & $\langle\langle x,S\rangle\rangle$ is a w.o. set$)$.
   (H. Rubin. Hint: prove that this proposition implies cn12.)
9. Prove $(\mathrm{S}(x)$ & x is infinite$) \rightarrow (\exists y)(x = \bigcup y$ & Pr Dis(y) & $(\forall u)(u \in y \rightarrow u \approx \omega))$. (The axiom of choice is used in the proof.)
10. Prove $(\overline{\overline{x}} = \mathfrak{m}$ & $y = \{z : z \subseteq x$ & $\overline{\overline{z}} = \mathfrak{n}\}) \rightarrow \overline{\overline{y}} = \mathfrak{m}^{\mathfrak{n}}$.
    (The axiom of choice is used in the proof.)

11. Prove $(\exists\alpha)(\alpha \approx \{f{:}\text{1–1 func}(f)\ \&\ \mathfrak{D}(f) = \mathfrak{R}(f) = \beta\}) \rightarrow (\exists\gamma)(\gamma \approx \mathcal{P}(\beta))$. (The axiom of choice is *not* used in the proof. Hint: if $\beta \notin \omega$, then $\beta \approx \beta \times 2$.)
12. Prove $(S(x)\ \&\ \bar{\bar{x}} \geqq 2) \rightarrow (\exists f)(f{:}x \xrightarrow[\text{onto}]{\text{1–1}} x\ \&\ (\forall u)(u \in x \rightarrow f(u) \neq u))$. (König and Schoenflies. The axiom of choice is used in the proof.)
13. Consider the five propositions in the last paragraph of section 12.2. Prove:
    (a) The axiom of choice implies each of the propositions
    (b) (1) → (4)
    (c) (5) → (4).
    [The axiom of choice is *not* used in the proofs of (b) and (c).]

12.3 INFINITE SUMS AND PRODUCTS

Let us look at some of the problems involved in defining an infinite sum or product of cardinal numbers, such as

$$\Sigma_{u \in X}\, \mathfrak{m}_u \text{ or } \Pi_{u \in X}\, \mathfrak{m}_u.$$

To extend to the infinite case the definitions of finite sums and products as given in section 11.6, it is necessary to choose, for each $u \in X$, a set x_u such that $\bar{\bar{x}}_u = \mathfrak{m}_u$. Then define

$$\Sigma_{u \in X}\, \mathfrak{m}_u = \overline{\overline{\bigcup_{u \in X} x_u \times \{u\}}}$$
$$\Pi_{u \in X}\, \mathfrak{m}_u = \overline{\overline{\times_{u \in X}\, x_u}}.$$

The first step is difficult. The word "choose" is a key word. In general, there is no rule for choosing the sets x_u such that $\bar{\bar{x}}_u = \mathfrak{m}_u$. Consequently, if X is infinite, the axiom of choice is needed in choosing the required sets.

On the other hand, if there is a rule for choosing the sets x_u, then the axiom of choice is not needed. For example, in the case in which the cardinal numbers are all alephs, the infinite sum and product could be defined as follows:

DEFINITION 12.3.1. $(f{:}X \rightarrow On) \rightarrow$
(a) $\Sigma_{u \in X}\, \aleph_{f(u)} =_{\text{Df}} \overline{\overline{\bigcup_{u \in X} \omega_{f(u)} \times \{u\}}}$
(b) $\Pi_{u \in X}\, \aleph_{f(u)} =_{\text{Df}} \overline{\overline{\times_{u \in X}\, \omega_{f(u)}}}$.

However, even in the case where there is a rule for choosing the required sets, the axiom of choice is needed to prove the following theorem if X is infinite.

THEOREM 12.3.2.© $(\forall u)(u \in X \rightarrow x_u \approx y_u) \rightarrow$
(a) $(\forall u)(\forall v)[(u,v \in X\ \&\ u \neq v) \rightarrow (x_u \cap x_v = \emptyset\ \&\ y_u \cap y_v = \emptyset)] \rightarrow \bigcup_{u \in X} x_u \approx \bigcup_{u \in X} y_u$
(b) $\times_{u \in X}\, x_u \approx \times_{u \in X}\, y_u$.

Proof: Suppose that $x_u \approx y_u$ for all $u \in X$. Since x_u and y_u are sets, the class of all 1–1 functions which map x_u onto y_u is a set. [It is a subclass of $\mathcal{P}(x_u \times y_u)$.] Therefore, it follows from the axiom of choice that there is a function f such that for each $u \in X$, f_u is a 1–1 function mapping x_u onto y_u. Now, it is a simple matter to prove parts (a) and (b). ■

The axiom of choice is needed in the proof of the preceding theorem even in the case where x_u and y_u are w.o. sets for each $u \in X$. (See exercise 12.2.11.)

The next theorem is needed to prove that the infinite sum and product of cardinal numbers always exist. Its proof requires the axiom of choice.

THEOREM 12.3.3.©

$$(\exists x)[\text{Func}(x)\ \&\ \mathfrak{D}(x) = X\ \&\ (\forall u)(u \in X \rightarrow (\text{S}(x_u)\ \&\ \bar{\bar{x}}_u = \mathfrak{m}_u))].$$

Proof: It follows from the well-ordering theorem that $\mathfrak{m}_u$ is finite or is an aleph for each $u \in X$. Therefore, let x_u be the smallest ordinal number which has cardinality $\mathfrak{m}_u$. ■

DEFINITION 12.3.4. Infinite Sum and Product

$$(\forall u)(u \in X \rightarrow (\text{S}(x_u)\ \&\ \bar{\bar{x}}_u = \mathfrak{m}_u)) \rightarrow$$

(a) $\Sigma_{u \in X}\, \mathfrak{m}_u =_{\text{Df}} \overline{\overline{\bigcup_{u \in X} x_u \times \{u\}}}$

(b) $\Pi_{u \in X}\, \mathfrak{m}_u =_{\text{Df}} \overline{\overline{\times_{u \in X} x_u}}$.

It follows from 12.3.3 and the axiom of choice that, given any set of cardinal numbers, their sums and products exist and are themselves cardinal numbers. Moreover, it follows from 12.3.2 that the sum and product are independent of the choice of the x_u's.

It follows immediately from 12.3.4 that infinite addition and multiplication are independent of the ordering and grouping of the terms. Thus, the infinite commutative and associative laws hold for addition and multiplication of cardinal numbers. Moreover, the infinite distributive law holds.

THEOREM 12.3.5.© $\mathfrak{m} \cdot \Sigma_{u \in X}\, \mathfrak{n}_u = \Sigma_{u \in X}\, \mathfrak{m} \cdot \mathfrak{n}_u$.

The proof is left as an exercise.

Moreover, 12.3.5 may be generalized by replacing "$\mathfrak{m}$" with "$\Pi_{v \in Y}\, \mathfrak{m}_v$."

In the arithmetic of ordinal numbers, multiplication is repeated addition and exponentiation is repeated multiplication. This is also true for cardinal numbers.

THEOREM 12.3.6.© $[(\forall u)(u \in X \rightarrow \mathfrak{m}_u = \mathfrak{p})\ \&\ \overline{\overline{X}} = \mathfrak{q}] \rightarrow$
(a) $\Sigma_{u \in X}\, \mathfrak{m}_u = \mathfrak{p} \cdot \mathfrak{q}$
(b) $\Pi_{u \in X}\, \mathfrak{m}_u = \mathfrak{p}^{\mathfrak{q}}$.

Proof: We shall prove (a) and leave the proof of (b) as an exercise. Let y be a set such that $\overline{\overline{y}} = \mathfrak{p}$. Then

$$\Sigma_{u \in X}\, \mathfrak{m}_u = \overline{\overline{\bigcup_{u \in X} y \times \{u\}}}.$$

By exercise 3.5.2(b)(i),

$$\bigcup_{u \in X} y \times \{u\} = y \times \bigcup_{u \in X} \{u\}.$$

Clearly, $\bigcup_{u \in X} \{u\} = X$. Therefore,

$$\bigcup_{u \in X} y \times \{u\} = y \times X.$$

Consequently,

$$\Sigma_{u \in X}\, \mathfrak{m}_u = \overline{\overline{y \times X}} = \mathfrak{p} \cdot \mathfrak{q}. \blacksquare$$

The proofs of the following monotonicity laws for infinite sums and products are left for the reader.

THEOREM 12.3.7.© $(\forall u)(u \in X \rightarrow \mathfrak{m}_u \leqq \mathfrak{n}_u) \rightarrow$
(a) $\Sigma_{u \in X}\, \mathfrak{m}_u \leqq \Sigma_{u \in X}\, \mathfrak{n}_u$
(b) $\Pi_{u \in X}\, \mathfrak{m}_u \leqq \Pi_{u \in X}\, \mathfrak{n}_u$.

Suppose that $0 < \mathfrak{m}_p < \aleph_0$ for each $p \in \omega$. Then we claim that

$$\Sigma_{p \in \omega}\, \mathfrak{m}_p = \aleph_0.$$

Let

$$\mathfrak{n}_p = \mathfrak{m}_0 + \mathfrak{m}_1 + \cdots + \mathfrak{m}_p,$$

and let

$$x_0 = \mathfrak{n}_0 = \mathfrak{m}_0$$
$$x_{p+1} = \{\mathfrak{n}_p + p : p < \mathfrak{m}_{p+1}\}.$$

Then for each $p \in \omega$,

$$\overline{\overline{x}}_p = \mathfrak{m}_p.$$

And if $p \neq q$, $p,q \in \omega$, then

$$x_p \cap x_q = \emptyset.$$

Therefore,

$$\Sigma_{p \in \omega}\, \mathfrak{m}_p = \overline{\overline{\bigcup_{p \in \omega} x_p}} = \aleph_0.$$

Thus, for example,

$$\begin{aligned}\aleph_0 &= 1 + 2 + 3 + 4 + \cdots \\ &= 1 + 2 + 1 + 2 + \cdots \\ &= 1 + 2^2 + 3^2 + 4^2 + \cdots \\ &= 1 + 1 + 1 + 1 + \cdots.\end{aligned}$$

($\mathfrak{m}_0 + \mathfrak{m}_1 + \mathfrak{m}_2 + \mathfrak{m}_3 + \cdots = \Sigma_{p\in\omega}\, \mathfrak{m}_p$.)

Using the last sum and 12.3.5, we obtain, for any $\mathfrak{m} \in Cn$,

(1) $$\mathfrak{m}\cdot\aleph_0 = \mathfrak{m} + \mathfrak{m} + \mathfrak{m} + \mathfrak{m} + \cdots.$$

[Equation (1) can also be obtained directly from 12.3.6(a).] Take $\mathfrak{m} = \aleph_0$ in (1) and use the fact that $\aleph_0^2 = \aleph_0$. Thus we obtain

$$\aleph_0 = \aleph_0 + \aleph_0 + \aleph_0 + \aleph_0 + \cdots.$$

On the other hand, taking $\mathfrak{m} = \mathfrak{c}$ in (1) and using the fact that $\mathfrak{c}\cdot\aleph_0 = \mathfrak{c}$, we have

$$\mathfrak{c} = \mathfrak{c} + \mathfrak{c} + \mathfrak{c} + \mathfrak{c} + \cdots.$$

Using 12.3.6(b), we obtain for any $\mathfrak{m} \in Cn$ and $\mathfrak{m} > 1$,

$$\mathfrak{m}^{\aleph_0} = \mathfrak{m}\cdot\mathfrak{m}\cdot\mathfrak{m}\cdot\mathfrak{m}\cdot \cdots.$$

($\mathfrak{m}_0\cdot\mathfrak{m}_1\cdot\mathfrak{m}_2\cdot\mathfrak{m}_3\cdot \cdots = \Pi_{p\in\omega}\, \mathfrak{m}_p$.)
Since $2^{\aleph_0} = \aleph_0^{\aleph_0} = \mathfrak{c}^{\aleph_0}$,

$$\begin{aligned}\mathfrak{c} &= 2\cdot2\cdot2\cdot2\cdot \cdots \\ &= \aleph_0\cdot\aleph_0\cdot\aleph_0\cdot\aleph_0\cdot \cdots \\ &= \mathfrak{c}\cdot\mathfrak{c}\cdot\mathfrak{c}\cdot\mathfrak{c}\cdot \cdots.\end{aligned}$$

The preceding results are summarized in the following theorem:

THEOREM 12.3.8.

(a) $(\forall p)(p \in \omega \to (0 < \mathfrak{m}_p < \aleph_0 \to \Sigma_{p\in\omega}\, \mathfrak{m}_p = \aleph_0)$
(b) $(\forall p)(p \in \omega \to (\mathfrak{m}_p = \aleph_0 \to \Sigma_{p\in\omega}\, \mathfrak{m}_p = \aleph_0)$
(c) $(\forall p)(p \in \omega \to (\mathfrak{m}_p = c \to \Sigma_{p\in\omega}\, \mathfrak{m}_p = \mathfrak{c})$
(d) $(\forall p)(p \in \omega \to (1 < \mathfrak{m}_p < \aleph_0 \to \Pi_{p\in\omega}\, \mathfrak{m}_p = \mathfrak{c})$
(e) $(\forall p)(p \in \omega \to (\mathfrak{m}_p = \aleph_0 \to \Pi_{p\in\omega}\, \mathfrak{m}_p = \mathfrak{c})$
(f) $(\forall p)(p \in \omega \to (\mathfrak{m}_p = \mathfrak{c} \to \Pi_{p\in\omega}\, \mathfrak{m}_p = \mathfrak{c})$.

In conclusion we shall prove a theorem which was proposed by König (1905). [See also Zermelo (1908) and Rubin (1963).] We shall also prove that König's theorem is equivalent to the axiom of choice.

THEOREM 12.3.9.©

$$(\forall u)(u \in X \to x_u \prec y_u) \to \bigcup_{u\in X} x_u \prec \times_{u\in X}\, y_u.$$

Proof: We may assume without loss of generality that $\overline{\overline{y}}_u > 1$ for each $u \in X$ and that $x_u \cap x_v = \emptyset$ if $u,v \in X$ and $u \neq v$.

Since $x_u \prec y_u$ for each $u \in X$, the axiom of choice implies that there is a function f such that for each $u \in X$, f_u is a 1–1 function mapping x_u into y_u. Moreover, $x_u \prec y_u$ implies that $y_u \sim f_u''x_u \neq \emptyset$. Consequently, again using the axiom of choice, for each $u \in X$ we can choose an element $s_u \in y_u \sim f_u''x_u$.

Suppose that $w \in \bigcup_{u \in X} x_u$. By assumption, the x_u's are pairwise disjoint, so there is exactly one $u \in X$ such that $w \in x_u$. Define a function ψ such that

$$\psi(w) = h,$$

where, for all $v \in X$,

$$h(v) = \begin{cases} f_u(w) & \text{if } v = u.\ (f_u(w) \in y_u) \\ s_v & \text{if } v \neq u.\ (s_v \in y_v \sim f_v''x_v). \end{cases}$$

Clearly, ψ is a function mapping $\bigcup_{u \in X} x_u$ into $\times_{y \in X} y_u$. We shall prove that ψ is 1–1. Suppose that

$$\psi(w_1) = \psi(w_2) = h.$$

Then it follows from the definition of h that there is one element $u \in X$ such that both w_1 and w_2 are elements of x_u. Then $f_u(w_1) = f_u(w_2)$, and since f_u is 1–1, $w_1 = w_2$. Thus we have shown that

$$\bigcup_{u \in X} x_u \precsim \times_{u \in X} y_u.$$

It remains to be shown that the union and product are not equipollent.

Let

$$Z \subseteq \times_{u \in X} y_u \text{ and } Z \approx \bigcup_{u \in X} x_u.$$

Then Z can be represented in the form

$$Z = \bigcup_{u \in X} z_u,$$

where $z_u \approx x_u$ for each $u \in X$, and where $z_u \cap z_v = \emptyset$ for each $u,v \in X$, $u \neq v$. Let

(1) $$t_u = \{h(u) : h \in z_u\}.$$

Then

(2) $$t_u \subseteq y_u.$$

Suppose that $w \in t_u$. Then $w = h(u)$ for some $h \in z_u$. It follows from the axiom of choice that for each $u \in X$ and each $w \in t_u$ we may choose a function $h_w \in z_u$ such that $h_w(u) = w$. Since $z_u \approx x_u$ for each $u \in X$, it follows again from the axiom of choice that for each $u \in X$ there is a 1–1 function j_u mapping z_u onto x_u. Therefore, if we define a function k such that for each $w \in t_u$,

$$k(w) = j_u(h_w),$$

then since j_u is 1–1, so is k. Thus,

$$t_u \lesssim x_u. \tag{3}$$

From (2), (3), and the hypothesis that $x_u \prec y_u$, we obtain $t_u \subset y_u$. Therefore, for each $u \in X$

$$y_u \sim t_u \neq \emptyset.$$

Hence, it follows from the axiom of choice that there is a function l such that for each $u \in X$, $l(u) \in y_u \sim t_u$. Clearly, $l \in \times_{u \in X} y_u$. However, by (1) and the definition of l, it follows that $l \notin z_u$ for any $u \in X$. Therefore, $l \notin Z$ so

$$Z \subset \times_{u \in X} y_u.$$

Consequently,

$$\bigcup_{u \in X} x_u \prec \times_{u \in X} y_u. \blacksquare$$

It can be seen that König's theorem implies the axiom of choice. This is obviously so, since if we take $x_u = \emptyset$ for all $u \in X$, then König's theorem reduces to ac4.

If König's theorem is expressed in terms of cardinal numbers, it has the following form.

COROLLARY 12.3.10.©

$$(\forall u)(u \in X \rightarrow \mathfrak{m}_u < \mathfrak{n}_u) \rightarrow \Sigma_{u \in X}\, \mathfrak{m}_u < \Pi_{u \in X}\, \mathfrak{n}_u.$$

As a special case of 12.3.10 we have the result that the sum of certain strictly increasing sequences of cardinal numbers is less than the product.

COROLLARY 12.3.11.©

$$[\alpha \text{ is a limit ordinal } \& \ \mathfrak{m}_0 \neq 0 \ \& \ (\forall \beta)(\forall \gamma)((\beta, \gamma < \alpha \ \& \ \beta < \gamma) \rightarrow \mathfrak{m}_\beta < \mathfrak{m}_\gamma)] \rightarrow \Sigma_{\beta < \alpha}\, \mathfrak{m}_\beta < \Pi_{\beta < \alpha}\, \mathfrak{m}_\beta.$$

Proof: By hypothesis, $\mathfrak{m}_\beta < \mathfrak{m}_{\beta+1}$ for all $\beta < \alpha$; therefore, by corollary 12.3.10,

$$\begin{aligned} \Sigma_{\beta < \alpha}\, \mathfrak{m}_\beta &< \Pi_{0 < \beta < \alpha}\, \mathfrak{m}_\beta \\ &\leqq \Pi_{\beta < \alpha}\, \mathfrak{m}_\beta. \ \blacksquare \end{aligned}$$

EXERCISES 12.3

1. Prove theorem 12.3.5.
2. Prove theorem 12.3.6(b).
3. Prove theorem 12.3.7.
4. Show that corollary 12.3.11 may not hold if α is not a limit ordinal.
5. Prove:
   (a) $\Sigma_{\beta \leqq \alpha} \aleph_\beta = \aleph_\alpha$
   (b) α is a limit ordinal $\rightarrow \Sigma_{\beta < \alpha} \aleph_\beta = \aleph_\alpha$
   (c) $\Pi_{\beta \leqq \alpha} \aleph_\beta = \aleph_\alpha^{\bar{\bar{\alpha}}}$
   (d) α is a limit ordinal $\rightarrow \Pi_{\beta < \alpha} \aleph_\beta = \aleph_\alpha^{\bar{\bar{\alpha}}}$.
6. Prove $(f: X \rightarrow \alpha) \rightarrow$
   (a) $\aleph_\alpha = \Sigma_{u \in X} \aleph_{f(u)} \leftrightarrow \alpha = \bigcup_{u \in X} f(u)$
   (b) $\aleph_\alpha = \Sigma_{u \in X} \aleph_{f(u)} \leftrightarrow \omega_\alpha = \bigcup_{u \in X} \omega_{f(u)}$.

*Chapter 13: The Generalized Continuum Hypothesis

13.1. INTRODUCTION

Just as is the case for the axiom of choice (section 3.6), the position of the generalized continuum hypothesis in set theory has been settled once and for all. Gödel (1940) has shown that the generalized continuum hypothesis is consistent with all the other axioms of set theory and Cohen (1963) has shown that it is independent. The generalized continuum hypothesis is not a consequence of the other axioms, including the axiom of choice. (The Gödel–Cohen results are for the case $\mathfrak{a} = \emptyset$.) It has also been shown that the generalized continuum hypothesis implies the axiom of choice. [Lindenbaum and Tarski (1926), Sierpinski (1947).]

The generalized continuum hypothesis is usually stated as follows:

GCH: $(\forall \mathfrak{m})[\mathfrak{m} \geqq \aleph_0 \rightarrow \neg(\exists \mathfrak{n})(\mathfrak{m} < \mathfrak{n} < 2^{\mathfrak{m}})]$.

If $\mathfrak{m}$ is transfinite, then there are no cardinal numbers between $\mathfrak{m}$ and $2^{\mathfrak{m}}$.

In this chapter we shall prove that GCH implies the axiom of choice, give several equivalent formulations of GCH, describe the effect that GCH has on cardinal exponentiation, and finally discuss a special case of GCH, the continuum hypothesis. The continuum hypothesis is stated as follows:

CH: $\neg(\exists \mathfrak{n})(\aleph_0 < \mathfrak{n} < 2^{\aleph_0})$.

CH is of more interest to analysts than GCH because it deals with sets of cardinality $\leqq \mathfrak{c} = 2^{\aleph_0}$, which is the cardinality of the set of real numbers. One immediate consequence of CH is the following:

If a set of real numbers is not countable, then it must have the power of the continuum, cardinal number $\mathfrak{c}$.

Additional consequences of CH will be given in section 13.6. It is recommended that the student read K. Gödel's article "What is Cantor's continuum hypothesis?", Gödel (1947).

13.2. THE GENERALIZED CONTINUUM HYPOTHESIS AND THE AXIOM OF CHOICE

We shall give two proofs that GCH implies the axiom of choice. The first is due to Kruse (1962) and the second to Sierpinski (1947).

THEOREM 13.2.1. GCH $\rightarrow$ cn13.

Proof: GCH implies that for all $\mathfrak{m} \geqq \aleph_0$ there are no cardinal numbers between $\mathfrak{m}$ and $2^{\mathfrak{m}}$. Thus, cn13, which states

$$(\forall \mathfrak{p})(\mathfrak{p} \leqq \mathfrak{m}, \mathfrak{n} \leqq 2^{\mathfrak{p}} \rightarrow (\mathfrak{m} \leqq \mathfrak{n} \text{ or } \mathfrak{n} \leqq \mathfrak{m})),$$

is true. ■

THEOREM 13.2.2. GCH $\rightarrow$ w2.

Proof: Let $\mathfrak{m} \geqq \aleph_0$ and let $\mathfrak{n} = 2^{\mathfrak{m}}$. We have

$$\aleph_0 \leqq \mathfrak{m} < \mathfrak{n} < 2^{\mathfrak{n}} < 2^{2^{\mathfrak{n}}}. \tag{1}$$

It was shown in 12.1.27, without the aid of the axiom of choice, that for all $\mathfrak{p} \geqq \aleph_0$, $2^{\mathfrak{p}} - \mathfrak{p} = 2^{\mathfrak{p}}$. Therefore,

$$\mathfrak{n} - \mathfrak{m} = \mathfrak{n}, \tag{2}$$

$$2^{\mathfrak{n}} - \mathfrak{n} = 2^{\mathfrak{n}}, \tag{3}$$

$$2^{2^{\mathfrak{n}}} - 2^{\mathfrak{n}} = 2^{2^{\mathfrak{n}}}. \tag{4}$$

Moreover, it can also be shown without using the axiom of choice, that

$$\mathfrak{m}^* \leqq 2^{2^{\mathfrak{n}}} \qquad \text{[exercise 12.1.6(b),(d)].} \tag{5}$$

Thus, from (4) and (5) we obtain

$$\mathfrak{m}^* + 2^{\mathfrak{n}} \leqq 2^{2^{\mathfrak{n}}} + 2^{\mathfrak{n}} = 2^{2^{\mathfrak{n}}}. \tag{6}$$

If $\mathfrak{m}^* + 2^{\mathfrak{n}} = 2^{2^{\mathfrak{n}}}$, then it follows from (4) that $\mathfrak{m}^* = 2^{2^{\mathfrak{n}}}$. Therefore, since $\mathfrak{m}^*$ is an aleph, it follows from (1) that $\mathfrak{m}$ is an aleph.

On the other hand, if $\mathfrak{m}^* + 2^{\mathfrak{n}} < 2^{2^{\mathfrak{n}}}$, then

$$2^{\mathfrak{n}} \leqq \mathfrak{m}^* + 2^{\mathfrak{n}} < 2^{2^{\mathfrak{n}}}. \tag{7}$$

Now, GCH implies that

$$\mathfrak{m}^* + 2^{\mathfrak{n}} = 2^{\mathfrak{n}}. \tag{8}$$

This implies $\mathfrak{m}^* \leqq 2^{\mathfrak{n}}$.

Now repeat steps (6)–(8) with "$2^{2^{\mathfrak{n}}}$" replaced by "$2^{\mathfrak{n}}$" and "$2^{\mathfrak{n}}$" replaced by "$\mathfrak{n}$", and we obtain either $\mathfrak{m}$ is an aleph or $\mathfrak{m}^* \leqq \mathfrak{n}$. Then repeating the steps again with "$2^{\mathfrak{n}}$" replaced by "$\mathfrak{n}$" and "$\mathfrak{n}$" replaced by "$\mathfrak{m}$", we finally obtain that if $\mathfrak{m}$ is not an aleph, then $\mathfrak{m}^* \leqq \mathfrak{m}$. But the latter inequality is impossible. Therefore, $\mathfrak{m}$ must be an aleph. ■

13.3. THE ALEPH HYPOTHESIS

A proposition which is closely related to the generalized continuum hypothesis is Cantor's aleph hypothesis.

AH: $(\forall\alpha)(2^{\alpha} = \aleph_{\alpha+1})$

It follows from 12.2.13 that if there is a relation R such that $\langle\langle \mathcal{C}, R\rangle\rangle$ is a w.o. set and the axiom of regularity holds, then AH implies the axiom of choice because AH implies cn12.

THEOREM 13.3.1.®

$$[S(\mathcal{C}) \ \& \ (\exists R)(\langle\langle \mathcal{C}, R\rangle\rangle \text{ is a w.o. set})] \rightarrow (\text{AH} \rightarrow \text{w1}).$$

It is easy to show that GCH implies AH.

THEOREM 13.3.2. GCH $\rightarrow$ AH

Proof: Let α be any ordinal number. GCH implies the axiom of choice which implies $2^{\aleph_\alpha}$ is an aleph. Since $\aleph_{\alpha+1}$ is the smallest aleph which is larger than $\aleph_\alpha$, we have

$$\aleph_\alpha < \aleph_{\alpha+1} \leqq 2^{\aleph_\alpha}.$$

Therefore, GCH implies $2^{\aleph_\alpha} = \aleph_{\alpha+1}$. ■

Moreover, using 13.3.1 we can show that AH implies GCH.

THEOREM 13.3.3.®

$$[S(\mathcal{C}) \ \& \ (\exists R)(\langle\langle \mathcal{C}, R\rangle\rangle \text{ is a w.o. set})] \rightarrow (\text{AH} \rightarrow \text{GCH}).$$

Proof: Let $\mathfrak{m}$ be any transfinite cardinal number. It follows from the hypothesis and 13.3.1 that $\mathfrak{m}$ is an aleph. Therefore, there is an ordinal number α such that $\mathfrak{m} = \aleph_\alpha$. By AH,

$$2^{\mathfrak{m}} = 2^{\aleph_\alpha} = \aleph_{\alpha+1}.$$

Since $\aleph_{\alpha+1}$ is the smallest aleph which is larger than $\aleph_\alpha$, there are no cardinal numbers between $\mathfrak{m}$ and $2^{\mathfrak{m}}$. ■

It is an easy matter to prove that GCH is equivalent to AH and the axiom of choice. The proof does not assume that $\mathcal{C}$ is a set or the axiom of regularity or the axiom of choice.

THEOREM 13 3.4. GCH $\leftrightarrow$ (AH & w2).

The details of the proof are left as an exercise.

Let GCH($\mathfrak{m}$) be the statement that the generalized continuum hypothesis holds for the cardinal number $\mathfrak{m}$ and AH(α) be the statement that the aleph hypothesis holds for the ordinal number α. Then:

GCH($\mathfrak{m}$): $\mathfrak{m} \geqq \aleph_0 \rightarrow \neg(\exists\mathfrak{p})(\mathfrak{m} < \mathfrak{p} < 2^{\mathfrak{m}})$,

AH(α): $2^{\aleph_\alpha} = \aleph_{\alpha+1}$.

The proofs of the following two theorems are similar to the proofs of theorems 13.3.2 and 13.3.3 and are left as exercises.

THEOREM 13.3.5.© $\quad$ GCH($\aleph_\alpha$) $\rightarrow$ AH(α).

THEOREM 13.3.6. $\quad$ AH(α) $\rightarrow$ GCH($\aleph_\alpha$).

EXERCISES 13.3

1. Prove theorem 13.3.4.
2. Prove theorem 13.3.5.
3. Prove theorem 13.3.6.

13.4. COFINALITY

Before proceeding with the generalized continuum we need some results for ordinal numbers. These results will also be used in Chapter 14.

DEFINITION 13.4.1. $\quad$ Cofinality

$$\alpha \ \& \ \beta \text{ are limit ordinals} \rightarrow \alpha \ cof \ \beta =_{\mathrm{Df}} (\exists x)(\exists y)(x \subseteq \alpha \ \& \ y \subseteq \beta \ \& \ \bigcup x = \alpha \ \& \ \bigcup y = \beta \ \& \ \langle\langle x, <\rangle\rangle \cong \langle\langle y, <\rangle\rangle).$$

"α cof β" is read "α is cofinal with β." As an illustration of cofinality we have ω is cofinal with each of the following ordinal numbers: $\omega \cdot 2$, ω^2, $\omega_\alpha \cdot \omega$, and ω_ω. This is true because of the following equations:

$$\begin{aligned} \omega \cdot 2 &= \textstyle\bigcup_{n \in \omega} (\omega + n) \\ \omega^2 &= \textstyle\bigcup_{n \in \omega} \omega^n \\ \omega_\alpha \cdot \omega &= \textstyle\bigcup_{n \in \omega} (\omega_\alpha \cdot n) \\ \omega_\omega &= \textstyle\bigcup_{n \in \omega} \omega_n. \end{aligned}$$

However, ω is not cofinal with $\omega_{\alpha+1}$ for any ordinal number α.

The following theorem follows immediately from 13.4.1.

THEOREM 13.4.2.

$$(\alpha \ \& \ \beta \text{ are limit ordinals} \ \& \ \alpha \leqq \beta) \rightarrow [\alpha \text{ cof } \beta \leftrightarrow (\exists f)(f : \alpha \rightarrow \beta \ \& \ \beta = \textstyle\bigcup_{\gamma < \alpha} f(\gamma))].$$

It is clear that the relation of cofinality between limit ordinals is reflexive and symmetric. We shall prove that it is also transitive.

Suppose α, β, γ are limit ordinals such that α cof β and β cof γ. Then there exist sets $x \subseteq \alpha$, $y,z \subseteq \beta$, and $w \subseteq \gamma$ such that

(1) $$\bigcup x = \alpha, \bigcup y = \bigcup z = \beta, \bigcup w = \gamma,$$

(2) $$\langle\langle x, <\rangle\rangle \cong \langle\langle y, <\rangle\rangle,$$

(3) $$\langle\langle z, <\rangle\rangle \cong \langle\langle w, <\rangle\rangle.$$

Let $\zeta \in z$ and let $f(\zeta)$ be the smallest element of y which is larger than ζ. Since β is a limit ordinal, it follows from (1) that $f(\zeta)$ exists for each $\zeta \in z$. Let

$$y' = \mathcal{R}(f).$$

For each $\eta \in y'$ let $g(\eta)$ be the smallest element $\zeta \in z$ such that $f(\zeta) = \eta$. It is obvious that g is an isomorphism from y' into z. Define

$$z' = \mathcal{R}(g).$$

Then

(4) $$\langle\langle y', <\rangle\rangle \cong \langle\langle z', <\rangle\rangle.$$

Since $\bigcup y = \beta = \bigcup z$, it follows from the definitions of f, g, and (4) that

(5) $$\bigcup y' = \beta = \bigcup z'.$$

By (2) and (3) there are subsets x' of x and w' of w such that

(6) $$\langle\langle x', <\rangle\rangle \cong \langle\langle y', <\rangle\rangle,$$

(7) $$\langle\langle w', <\rangle\rangle \cong \langle\langle z', <\rangle\rangle.$$

Therefore, by (4), (6), and (7),

(8) $$\langle\langle x', <\rangle\rangle \cong \langle\langle w', <\rangle\rangle.$$

It follows from (1), (5), (2), (3), (6), and (7) that

(9) $$\bigcup x' = \alpha \ \& \ \bigcup w' = \gamma.$$

Now it follows from (8) and (9) that α cof γ. Hence, we have shown

THEOREM 13.4.3.

cof is an equivalence relation on $\{\alpha : \alpha \text{ is a limit ordinal}\}$.

The next theorem states that the smallest ordinal number cofinal with a given ordinal number is an initial ordinal.

THEOREM 13.4.4.

$$[\beta \operatorname{cof} \alpha \ \&\ (\forall\gamma)(\gamma \operatorname{cof} \alpha \to \beta \leqq \gamma)] \to \beta \in Io.$$

Proof: Suppose β is the smallest ordinal number which is cofinal with α. Let ω_λ be the initial ordinal which is equipollent with β. Suppose

$$f : \omega_\lambda \xrightarrow[\text{onto}]{1-1} \beta.$$

Define a subset x of ω_λ as follows.

$$\xi \in x \leftrightarrow [\xi \in \omega_\lambda \ \&\ (\forall\eta)(\eta < \xi \to f(\xi) > f(\eta))].$$

This set x has the property that

(1) $$\bigcup f''x = \beta.$$

For suppose $\eta \in \beta$. Let ξ be the smallest ordinal number in ω_λ such that $f(\xi) > \eta$. Then for all $\zeta < \xi$, $f(\zeta) \leqq \eta < f(\xi)$. Thus, by the definition of x, $\xi \in x$. Consequently, for each $\eta \in \beta$ there is a $\xi \in x$ such that $f(\xi) > \eta$. This proves (1).

Let δ be the ordinal number such that

$$\langle\langle \delta, < \rangle\rangle \cong \langle\langle x, < \rangle\rangle.$$

Then δ is cofinal with β. Since $\beta \operatorname{cof} \alpha$, it follows that $\delta \operatorname{cof} \alpha$. Now we have shown that

$$\delta \leqq \omega_\lambda \leqq \beta \leqq \delta.$$

Thus $\beta = \omega_\lambda$, so β is an initial ordinal. ∎

The smallest ordinal number which is cofinal with ω_α is an initial ordinal and we shall denote the subscript of that initial ordinal by "cf(α)."

DEFINITION 13.4.5. $\operatorname{cf}(\alpha) =_{\text{Df}} <$-first element of $\{\beta : \omega_\beta \operatorname{cof} \omega_\alpha\}$.

Thus we have

(1) $$\omega_{\operatorname{cf}(\alpha)} \operatorname{cof} \omega_\alpha$$

and cf(α) is the smallest ordinal number which satisfies (1).

The next theorem follows immediately from the reflexivity of cof.

THEOREM 13.4.6. $\operatorname{cf}(\alpha) \leqq \alpha$.

As an obvious consequence of 13.4.5 and 13.4.3, we have

THEOREM 13.4.7. $\operatorname{cf}(\alpha) = \operatorname{cf}(\beta) \leftrightarrow \omega_\alpha \operatorname{cof} \omega_\beta$.

The following theorem is also easy to prove. Its proof is left as an exercise.

THEOREM 13.4.8.

$$(\beta < \alpha \ \&\ \mathrm{cf}(\alpha) \neq \mathrm{cf}(\beta) \ \&\ x \subseteq \omega_\alpha \ \&\ \overline{\overline{x}} = \aleph_\beta) \rightarrow (\exists\gamma)(\gamma \in \omega_\alpha \ \&\ x \subseteq \gamma).$$

Next, we claim that if α is not a limit ordinal, then $\mathrm{cf}(\alpha) = \alpha$. The proof makes use of the axiom of choice.

THEOREM 13.4.9.© α is a non-limit ordinal $\rightarrow \mathrm{cf}(\alpha) = \alpha$.

Proof: Suppose α is not a limit ordinal. Then either $\alpha = 0$ and $\mathrm{cf}(\alpha) = \alpha = 0$, or there is a β such that

$$\alpha = \beta + 1.$$

Suppose ω_λ is the smallest ordinal number cofinal with ω_α. Then there is a function $f, f{:}\omega_\lambda \rightarrow \omega_\alpha$ and

(1) $$\omega_\alpha = \bigcup_{\gamma<\omega_\lambda} f(\gamma).$$

Thus, for each $\gamma < \omega_\lambda$, $\overline{\overline{f(\gamma)}} \leqq \aleph_\beta$. Consequently, if $\lambda \leqq \beta$, then

(2) $$\overline{\overline{\bigcup_{\gamma<\omega_\lambda} f(\gamma)}} \leqq \aleph_\lambda \cdot \aleph_\beta = \aleph_\beta.$$

However, (2) contradicts (1), so $\lambda = \alpha$ and $\mathrm{cf}(\alpha) = \alpha$. ■

(Where is the axiom of choice used in the proof?)

In general, if $\mathrm{cf}(\alpha) = \alpha$, then the cardinal number $\aleph_\alpha$ (or the ordinal number ω_α) is called *regular*.

DEFINITION 13.4.10. Regular

(a) $\aleph_\alpha$ is *regular* $=_{\mathrm{Df}} \mathrm{cf}(\alpha) = \alpha$

(b) ω_α is *regular* $=_{\mathrm{Df}} \mathrm{cf}(\alpha) = \alpha$.

Thus, $\aleph_\alpha$ is regular if and only if ω_α is not cofinal with any smaller ordinal number. Other necessary and sufficient conditions for an aleph to be regular are given in the next two theorems.

THEOREM 13.4.11. $\aleph_\alpha$ is regular $\leftrightarrow (\forall\beta)(\beta < \alpha \rightarrow \beta < \mathrm{cf}(\alpha))$.

Proof: By theorem 13.4.8 and definition 13.4.10.

The next theorem states that $\aleph_\alpha$ is regular if and only if the sum of less-than-ω_α cardinal numbers, each of which is less than $\aleph_\alpha$, is less than $\aleph_\alpha$. The proof uses the axiom of choice.

THEOREM 13.4.12.©

$$\aleph_\alpha \text{ is regular} \leftrightarrow (\forall\lambda)(\forall\beta)(\forall\mathfrak{m})[(\beta < \lambda < \omega_\alpha \ \&\ \mathfrak{m}_\beta < \aleph_\alpha) \rightarrow \Sigma_{\beta<\lambda}\, \mathfrak{m}_\beta < \aleph_\alpha].$$

The proof follows from exercise 12.3.6. The details are left for the reader.

The remaining theorems in this section deal with exponentiation of cardinal numbers. Most of the theorems are due to Tarski.

THEOREM 13.4.13.©

$$(\alpha \text{ is a limit ordinal } \& \operatorname{cf}(\alpha) \neq \operatorname{cf}(\beta)) \rightarrow \aleph_\alpha^{\aleph_\beta} = \Sigma_{\xi<\alpha} \aleph_\xi^{\aleph_\beta}.$$

Proof: Clearly,

$$\Sigma_{\xi<\alpha} \aleph_\xi^{\aleph_\beta} \leqq \Sigma_{\xi<\alpha} \aleph_\alpha^{\aleph_\beta} = \bar{\bar{\alpha}} \cdot \aleph_\alpha^{\aleph_\beta} = \aleph_\alpha^{\aleph_\beta}.$$

To prove the inequality the other way, we consider two cases.
Case 1. $\alpha \leqq \beta$. Then,

$$\aleph_\alpha^{\aleph_\beta} \leqq (2^{\aleph_\alpha})^{\aleph_\beta} = 2^{\aleph_\beta} \leqq \Sigma_{\xi<\alpha} \aleph_\xi^{\aleph_\beta}.$$

Case 2. $\beta < \alpha$. Let s_ξ be the set of all subsets of ω_ξ of cardinality $\aleph_\beta$. Then

$$\bar{\bar{s}}_\xi = \aleph_\xi^{\aleph_\beta}. \qquad \text{(exercise 12.2.10)}$$

Suppose $x \subseteq \omega_\alpha$ and $\bar{\bar{x}} = \aleph_\beta$. Since $\operatorname{cf}(\alpha) \neq \operatorname{cf}(\beta)$, then there is a $\gamma \in \omega_\alpha$ such that $x \subseteq \gamma$ (13.4.8). Moreover, since α is a limit ordinal, there is a $\xi < \alpha$ such that $x \subseteq \omega_\xi$. Consequently, if $x \in s_\alpha$, then there is a $\xi < \alpha$ such that $x \in s_\xi$. This implies

$$s_\alpha \subseteq \bigcup_{\xi<\alpha} s_\xi.$$

Thus,

$$\begin{aligned} \aleph_\alpha^{\aleph_\beta} &= \bar{\bar{s}}_\alpha \\ &\leqq \overline{\overline{\bigcup_{\xi<\alpha} s_\xi}} \\ &\leqq \Sigma_{\xi<\alpha} \bar{\bar{s}}_\xi \\ &= \Sigma_{\xi<\alpha} \aleph_\xi^{\aleph_\beta}. \ \blacksquare \end{aligned}$$

The next theorem gives a recursion formula for alephs.

THEOREM 13.4.14.© $\aleph_{\alpha+1}^{\aleph_\beta} = \aleph_{\alpha+1} \cdot \aleph_\alpha^{\aleph_\beta}$

Proof: First,

$$\aleph_{\alpha+1}^{\aleph_\beta} = \aleph_{\alpha+1} \cdot \aleph_{\alpha+1}^{\aleph_\beta} \geqq \aleph_{\alpha+1} \cdot \aleph_\alpha^{\aleph_\beta}.$$

To prove the inequality the other way we consider two cases.
Case 1. $\alpha + 1 \leqq \beta$. Then

$$\begin{aligned} \aleph_{\alpha+1}^{\aleph_\beta} &\leqq (2^{\aleph_{\alpha+1}})^{\aleph_\beta} \\ &= 2^{\aleph_{\alpha+1} \cdot \aleph_\beta} \\ &= 2^{\aleph_\beta} \\ &\leqq \aleph_{\alpha+1} \cdot \aleph_\alpha^{\aleph_\beta}. \end{aligned}$$

Case 2. $\beta \leqq \alpha$. Let s_γ be the set of all subsets of γ of cardinality $\aleph_\beta$. Then

$$\bar{\bar{s}}_\gamma = \bar{\bar{\gamma}}^{\aleph_\beta}. \qquad \text{(exercise 12.2.10)}$$

Since $\aleph_{\alpha+1}$ is a regular cardinal, if $x \in s_{\omega_{\alpha+1}}$, then there is a $\gamma < \omega_{\alpha+1}$ such that $x \in s_\gamma$. Thus,

$$s_{\omega_{\alpha+1}} \subseteq \bigcup_{\gamma < \omega_{\alpha+1}} s_\gamma.$$

Therefore,

$$\begin{aligned} \aleph_{\alpha+1}^{\aleph_\beta} &= \bar{\bar{s}}_{\omega_{\alpha+1}} \\ &\leqq \Sigma_{\gamma < \omega_{\alpha+1}} \bar{\bar{s}}_\gamma \\ &= \Sigma_{\gamma < \omega_{\alpha+1}} \bar{\bar{\gamma}}^{\aleph_\beta} \\ &\leqq \Sigma_{\gamma < \omega_{\alpha+1}} \aleph_\alpha^{\aleph_\beta} \\ &= \aleph_{\alpha+1} \cdot \aleph_\alpha^{\aleph_\beta}. \ \blacksquare \end{aligned}$$

Using 13.4.14, we can generalize 13.4.13.

THEOREM 13.4.15.©

$$(\text{cf}(\alpha) \neq \text{cf}(\beta) \ \& \ \alpha > 0) \rightarrow \aleph_\alpha^{\aleph_\beta} = \aleph_\alpha \cdot \Sigma_{\gamma < \alpha} \aleph_\gamma^{\aleph_\beta}.$$

Proof: Clearly,

$$\begin{aligned} \aleph_\alpha \cdot \Sigma_{\gamma < \alpha} \aleph_\gamma^{\aleph_\beta} &\leqq \aleph_\alpha \cdot \Sigma_{\gamma < \alpha} \aleph_\alpha^{\aleph_\beta} \\ &= \aleph_\alpha \cdot \bar{\bar{\alpha}} \cdot \aleph_\alpha^{\aleph_\beta} \\ &= \aleph_\alpha^{\aleph_\beta}. \end{aligned}$$

To derive the inequality the other way we consider two cases.
Case 1. α is a limit ordinal. Then by 13.4.13,

$$\begin{aligned} \aleph_\alpha^{\aleph_\beta} &= \Sigma_{\gamma < \alpha} \aleph_\gamma^{\aleph_\beta} \\ &\leqq \aleph_\alpha \cdot \Sigma_{\gamma < \alpha} \aleph_\gamma^{\aleph_\beta}. \end{aligned}$$

Case 2. α is not a limit ordinal. Then, since $\alpha \neq 0$, there is a δ such that $\alpha = \delta + 1$. Thus, by 13.4.14,

$$\begin{aligned} \aleph_\alpha^{\aleph_\beta} &= \aleph_\alpha \cdot \aleph_\delta^{\aleph_\beta} \\ &\leqq \aleph_\alpha \cdot \Sigma_{\gamma < \alpha} \aleph_\gamma^{\aleph_\beta}. \ \blacksquare \end{aligned}$$

A class of sets X is called *almost disjoint of type* $\mathfrak{m}$ if $\bar{\bar{u}} \geqq \mathfrak{m}$ for all $u \in X$, and $\overline{\overline{u \cap v}} < \mathfrak{m}$ for all $u,v \in X$. The next theorem tells something about the cardinal number of an almost disjoint set.

THEOREM 13.4.16.©

$[\overline{\overline{X}} = \aleph_\alpha \;\&\; X = \bigcup Y \;\&\; (\exists\beta)[((\forall u)(u \in Y \rightarrow \overline{\overline{u}} \geqq \aleph_\beta) \;\&$
$(\forall u)(\forall v)(u,v \in Y \rightarrow \overline{\overline{u \cap v}} < \aleph_\beta) \;\&\; \mathrm{cf}(\alpha) \neq \mathrm{cf}(\beta)) \rightarrow \overline{\overline{Y}} \leqq \aleph_\alpha \cdot \Sigma_{\eta<\alpha} \aleph_\eta^{\aleph_\beta}]]$

Proof: There is no loss of generality in assuming that $X = \omega_\alpha$. Suppose $u \in Y$. Then $u \subseteq \omega_\alpha$ and $\overline{\overline{u}} \geqq \aleph_\beta$. Therefore, there is a $v \subseteq u$ such that $\overline{\overline{v}} = \aleph_\beta$. By hypothesis, $\mathrm{cf}(\alpha) \neq \mathrm{cf}(\beta)$, so ω_α is not cofinal with ω_β. Therefore, there is a $\delta \in \omega_\alpha$ such that $v \subseteq \delta$ (13.4.8). Thus,

$$\overline{\overline{v \cap \delta}} = \overline{\overline{v}} = \aleph_\beta$$

and

$$v \cap \delta \subseteq u \cap \delta.$$

Hence, we have shown that for each $u \in Y$ there is a $\delta \in \omega_\alpha$ such that

(1) $$\overline{\overline{u \cap \delta}} \geqq \aleph_\beta.$$

Let

$$Y_\delta = \{u : u \in Y \;\&\; \delta \text{ is the smallest element of } \{\gamma : \overline{\overline{u \cap \gamma}} \geqq \aleph_\beta\}\}.$$

If $u \in Y_\delta$, then $\overline{\overline{u \cap \delta}} = \aleph_\beta$. If $\delta_1 \neq \delta_2$, then $Y_{\delta_1} \cap Y_{\delta_2} = \emptyset$. Thus,

$$Y = \bigcup_{\delta<\omega_\alpha} Y_\delta$$

and

(2) $$\overline{\overline{Y}} = \Sigma_{\delta<\omega_\alpha} \overline{\overline{Y}}_\delta.$$

Now, let

$$Z_\delta = \{u \cap \delta : u \in Y_\delta\}.$$

We claim $Y_\delta \precsim Z_\delta$. For define a function f such that for each $u \in Y_\delta$, $f(u) = u \cap \delta$. We shall show f is 1–1. Suppose $u,v \in Y_\delta$ and $u \neq v$. Then, by the definition of Y_δ, $\overline{\overline{u \cap \delta}} = \overline{\overline{v \cap \delta}} = \aleph_\beta$ and, by hypothesis, $\overline{\overline{u \cap v}} < \aleph_\beta$. Thus,

$$\overline{\overline{(u \cap \delta) \cap (v \cap \delta)}} < \aleph_\beta,$$

which implies $u \cap \delta \neq v \cap \delta$. Therefore, we have shown,

(3) $$\overline{\overline{Y}}_\delta \leqq \overline{\overline{Z}}_\delta.$$

Consequently, it follows from (2) and (3) that

(4) $$\overline{\overline{Y}} \leqq \Sigma_{\delta<\omega_\alpha} \overline{\overline{Z}}_\delta.$$

Now, if $x \in Z_\delta$, then x is a subset of δ of cardinality $\aleph_\beta$. The set of all subsets of δ of cardinality $\aleph_\beta$ has cardinality $\delta^{\aleph_\beta}$ (exercise 12.2.10). Thus

$$\overline{\overline{Z}}_\delta \leqq \overline{\overline{\delta}}^{\aleph_\beta}.$$

Substituting in (4), we obtain

$$\overline{\overline{Y}} \leqq \Sigma_{\delta < \omega_\alpha} \overline{\overline{\delta}}^{\aleph_\beta}. \tag{5}$$

If $\omega_\eta \leqq \delta < \omega_{\eta+1}$, then $\overline{\overline{\delta}} = \aleph_\eta$. Thus,

$$\Sigma_{\omega_\eta \leqq \delta < \omega_{\eta+1}} \overline{\overline{\delta}}^{\aleph_\beta} = \aleph_\eta^{\aleph_\beta} \cdot \aleph_{\eta+1}.$$

Substituting in (5)

$$\overline{\overline{Y}} \leqq \Sigma_{\eta < \alpha} (\aleph_\eta^{\aleph_\beta} \cdot \aleph_{\eta+1})$$
$$\leqq \aleph_\alpha \cdot \Sigma_{\eta < \alpha} \aleph_\eta^{\aleph_\beta}. \ \blacksquare$$

In other words, 13.4.16 states that if Y is an almost disjoint family of subsets of ω_α of type $\aleph_\beta$, then

$$\overline{\overline{Y}} \leqq \aleph_\alpha \cdot \Sigma_{\eta < \alpha} \aleph_\eta^{\aleph_\beta}.$$

EXERCISES 13.4

1. Prove theorem 13.4.2.
2. Prove theorem 13.4.7.
3. Prove theorem 13.4.8.
4. Prove theorem 13.4.12.
5. Prove $(\alpha \geqq \beta \ \& \ \mathrm{cf}(\alpha) = \mathrm{cf}(\beta)) \rightarrow$
   $(\exists f)[f{:}\omega_\beta \rightarrow \mathfrak{A} \ \& \ (\forall \gamma)(\gamma < \omega_\beta \rightarrow f(\gamma) < \aleph_\alpha) \ \& \ \aleph_\alpha = \Sigma_{\gamma < \omega_\beta} f(\gamma)]$.
6. Prove GCH $\rightarrow$
   $[\overline{\overline{X}} = \aleph_\alpha \rightarrow \neg(\exists Y)(\overline{\overline{Y}} > \aleph_\alpha \ \& \ X = \bigcup Y \ \& \ (\forall u)(u \in Y \rightarrow \overline{\overline{u}} > \aleph_\beta) \ \&$
   $(\forall u)(\forall v)(u,v \in Y \rightarrow \overline{\overline{u \cap v}} < \aleph_\beta))]$.

13.5. THE GENERALIZED CONTINUUM HYPOTHESIS AND CARDINAL NUMBERS

In section 12.2 it is shown how the axiom of choice simplifies addition, multiplication, subtraction, and division of transfinite cardinal numbers. [The axiom of choice implies,

$$\aleph_0 \leqq \mathfrak{m},\mathfrak{n} \rightarrow \mathfrak{m} + \mathfrak{n} = \mathfrak{m} \cdot \mathfrak{n} = \max(\mathfrak{m},\mathfrak{n}),$$
$$\aleph_0 \leqq \mathfrak{m} < \mathfrak{n} \rightarrow \mathfrak{n} - \mathfrak{m} = \mathfrak{n} \div \mathfrak{m} = \mathfrak{n}.]$$

In this section we shall show how GCH simplifies exponentiation of transfinite cardinal numbers.

The first theorem is a monotonicity law for exponents.

THEOREM 13.5.1. $\quad GCH \rightarrow (\aleph_0 \leqq \mathfrak{m} < \mathfrak{n} \rightarrow 2^{\mathfrak{m}} < 2^{\mathfrak{n}})$.

Proof: Suppose $\aleph_0 \leqq \mathfrak{m} < \mathfrak{n}$ and $2^{\mathfrak{m}} \not< 2^{\mathfrak{n}}$. Since GCH implies the trichotomy, $2^{\mathfrak{m}} \not< 2^{\mathfrak{n}}$ implies $2^{\mathfrak{n}} \leqq 2^{\mathfrak{m}}$. If $2^{\mathfrak{n}} < 2^{\mathfrak{m}}$, then it follows from cn10, that $\mathfrak{n} < \mathfrak{m}$. If $2^{\mathfrak{n}} = 2^{\mathfrak{m}}$, then $\mathfrak{m} < \mathfrak{n} < 2^{\mathfrak{m}}$ which contradicts GCH. ■

Now, using the generalized continuum hypothesis and the aleph hypothesis, we shall calculate the value of $\aleph_\alpha^{\aleph_\beta}$ for all α and β.

THEOREM 13.5.2. $\quad AH \rightarrow (\alpha \leqq \beta \rightarrow \aleph_\alpha^{\aleph_\beta} = \aleph_{\beta+1})$.

Proof: If $\alpha \leqq \beta$, then $\aleph_\alpha \cdot \aleph_\beta = \aleph_\beta$. Thus,

$$2^{\aleph_\beta} \leqq \aleph_\alpha^{\aleph_\beta} \leqq (2^{\aleph_\alpha})^{\aleph_\beta} = 2^{\aleph_\alpha \cdot \aleph_\beta} = 2^{\aleph_\beta}.$$

Therefore,

$$\aleph_\alpha^{\aleph_\beta} = 2^{\aleph_\beta},$$

and by AH,

$$2^{\aleph_\beta} = \aleph_{\beta+1}. \blacksquare$$

THEOREM 13.5.3.

$$GCH \rightarrow [(\alpha \geqq \beta \;\&\; \mathrm{cf}(\alpha) = \mathrm{cf}(\beta)) \rightarrow \aleph_\alpha^{\aleph_\beta} = \aleph_{\alpha+1}].$$

Proof: Suppose $\alpha \geqq \beta$ and $\mathrm{cf}(\alpha) = \mathrm{cf}(\beta)$. Then for each $\gamma < \omega_\beta$ there is a cardinal number $\mathfrak{m}_\gamma < \aleph_\alpha$ such that

(1) $$\aleph_\alpha = \Sigma_{\gamma<\omega_\beta} \mathfrak{m}_\gamma \qquad \text{(exercise 13.4.5).}$$

Since $\mathfrak{m}_\gamma < \aleph_\alpha$ for each $\gamma < \omega_\beta$, it follows from König's theorem, 12.3.10, and exercise 12.3.5(d), that

(2) $$\Sigma_{\gamma<\omega_\beta} \mathfrak{m}_\gamma < \Pi_{\gamma<\omega_\beta} \aleph_\alpha = \aleph_\alpha^{\aleph_\beta}.$$

But since $\alpha \geqq \beta$,

(3) $$\aleph_\alpha^{\aleph_\beta} \leqq (2^{\aleph_\alpha})^{\aleph_\beta} = 2^{\aleph_\alpha \cdot \aleph_\beta} = 2^{\aleph_\alpha}.$$

From (1), (2), and (3), we infer

$$\aleph_\alpha < \aleph_\alpha^{\aleph_\beta} \leqq 2^{\aleph_\alpha}.$$

Therefore, GCH implies

$$\aleph_\alpha^{\aleph_\beta} = 2^{\aleph_\alpha}.$$

However, GCH implies AH, which implies

$$2^{\aleph_\alpha} = \aleph_{\alpha+1}. \blacksquare$$

THEOREM 13.5.4.

$$\mathrm{GCH} \rightarrow ((\alpha > \beta \ \& \ \mathrm{cf}(\alpha) \neq \mathrm{cf}(\beta)) \rightarrow \aleph_\alpha^{\aleph_\beta} = \aleph_\alpha).$$

Proof: Suppose $\alpha > \beta$ and $\mathrm{cf}(\alpha) \neq \mathrm{cf}(\beta)$.
Case 1. $\alpha = \gamma + 1$. In this case

$$\begin{aligned} \aleph_\alpha^{\aleph_\beta} &= \aleph_{\gamma+1}^{\aleph_\beta} \\ &= (2^{\aleph_\gamma})^{\aleph_\beta} && \text{(AH)} \\ &= 2^{\aleph_\gamma} \\ &= \aleph_{\gamma+1} && \text{(AH)} \\ &= \aleph_\alpha. \end{aligned}$$

Case 2. α is a limit ordinal. By 13.4.13,

$$\begin{aligned} \aleph_\alpha^{\aleph_\beta} &= \Sigma_{\gamma<\alpha} \aleph_\gamma^{\aleph_\beta} \\ &\leqq \Sigma_{\gamma<\alpha} (2^{\aleph_\gamma})^{\aleph_\beta} \\ &= \Sigma_{\gamma<\alpha} 2^{\max(\aleph_\gamma, \aleph_\beta)} \\ &= \Sigma_{\gamma<\alpha} \aleph_{\max(\gamma,\beta)+1} && \text{(AH)} \\ &\leqq \Sigma_{\gamma<\alpha} \aleph_\alpha \\ &= \bar{\bar{\alpha}} \cdot \aleph_\alpha \\ &= \aleph_\alpha. \end{aligned}$$

Clearly,

$$\aleph_\alpha \leqq \aleph_\alpha^{\aleph_\beta},$$

so we must have $\aleph_\alpha^{\aleph_\beta} = \aleph_\alpha$. ■

Hence, we have shown that GCH implies,

$$\aleph_\alpha^{\aleph_\beta} = \begin{cases} \aleph_{\beta+1}, & \text{if } \alpha \leqq \beta & (13.5.2) \\ \aleph_{\alpha+1}, & \text{if } \alpha \geqq \beta \ \& \ \mathrm{cf}(\alpha) = \mathrm{cf}(\beta) & (13.5.3) \\ \aleph_\alpha, & \text{if } \alpha > \beta \ \& \ \mathrm{cf}(\alpha) \neq \mathrm{cf}(\beta). & (13.5.4) \end{cases}$$

In particular, GCH implies

(1) $$\aleph_\alpha^{\aleph_\alpha} = \aleph_{\alpha+1},$$

and

(2) $$\aleph_{\alpha+1}^{\aleph_\alpha} = \aleph_{\alpha+1}.$$

Formula (1) follows from 13.5.2 or 13.5.3 and formula (2) follows from 13.5.4. (Why?) We shall show that both (1) and (2) imply that the aleph hypothesis holds for α. In fact, (1) is equivalent to AH(α).

THEOREM 13.5.5. $\aleph_\alpha^{\aleph_\alpha} = \aleph_{\alpha+1} \leftrightarrow \mathrm{AH}(\alpha)$.

Proof: Suppose $\aleph_\alpha^{\aleph_\alpha} = \aleph_{\alpha+1}$. Then

$$\aleph_\alpha < 2^{\aleph_\alpha} \leqq \aleph_\alpha^{\aleph_\alpha} = \aleph_{\alpha+1}.$$

However, there are no cardinal numbers between $\aleph_\alpha$ and $\aleph_{\alpha+1}$, so we must have

$$2^{\aleph_\alpha} = \aleph_{\alpha+1}.$$

The proof of the converse is left as an exercise. ■

THEOREM 13.5.6. $\aleph_{\alpha+1}^{\aleph_\alpha} = \aleph_{\alpha+1} \rightarrow \mathrm{AH}(\alpha)$.

The proof is similar to the proof of 13.5.5 and is left as an exercise.

Next, we shall give several propositions which are equivalent to the generalized continuum hypothesis, but first a definition.

DEFINITION 13.5.7.

$$\mathfrak{n} \textit{ covers } \mathfrak{m} =_{\mathrm{Df}} (\mathfrak{m} < \mathfrak{n} \;\&\; \neg(\exists\mathfrak{p})(\mathfrak{m} < \mathfrak{p} < \mathfrak{n})).$$

Thus, for example, GCH could have been stated

$$(\forall\mathfrak{m})(\mathfrak{m} \geqq \aleph_0 \rightarrow 2^{\mathfrak{m}} \text{ covers } \mathfrak{m}).$$

Now the first proposition, due to H. Rubin (1959), can be stated as follows:

P1: $(\forall\mathfrak{m})(\forall\mathfrak{n})(\mathfrak{m} \geqq \aleph_0 \;\&\; \mathfrak{n} \text{ covers } \mathfrak{m}) \rightarrow (\exists\mathfrak{p})(\mathfrak{n} = 2^{\mathfrak{p}})$.

We shall show first that GCH implies P1.

THEOREM 13.5.8. GCH $\rightarrow$ P1.

Proof: Suppose $\mathfrak{m} \geqq \aleph_0$ and $\mathfrak{n}$ covers $\mathfrak{m}$. GCH implies the axiom of choice and AH. The axiom of choice implies that there is an α such that $\mathfrak{m} = \aleph_\alpha$ and there is a β such that $\mathfrak{n} = \aleph_\beta$. Since $\mathfrak{n}$ covers $\mathfrak{m}$, $\beta = \alpha + 1$. Moreover, AH implies that $\aleph_{\alpha+1} = 2^{\aleph_\alpha}$. Thus, $\mathfrak{n} = 2^{\mathfrak{m}}$. ■

To prove the converse we shall show that P1 implies AH and the axiom of choice.

THEOREM 13.5.9. P1 $\rightarrow$ AH.

Proof: Suppose P1 holds. Then for each α, $\aleph_{\alpha+1}$ covers $\aleph_\alpha$. Therefore, P1 implies that there is a $\mathfrak{p}$ such that $\aleph_{\alpha+1} = 2^{\mathfrak{p}}$.

Since $\mathfrak{p} < 2^{\mathfrak{p}}$, then there is a β such that $\mathfrak{p} = \aleph_\beta$. Let $f(\alpha)$ be the smallest β such that $\mathfrak{p} = \aleph_\beta$, then

$$(1) \qquad \aleph_{\alpha+1} = 2^{\aleph_{f(\alpha)}}.$$

Clearly, $f(\alpha) \leqq \alpha$. On the other hand,

$$\begin{aligned} \alpha_1 < \alpha_2 &\rightarrow \aleph_{\alpha_1+1} < \aleph_{\alpha_2+1} \\ &\rightarrow 2^{\aleph_{f(\alpha_1)}} < 2^{\aleph_{f(\alpha_2)}} \qquad (1) \\ &\rightarrow f(\alpha_1) < f(\alpha_2). \end{aligned}$$

Therefore, f is an isomorphism of *On* into itself, so it follows from 7.4.4 that $\alpha \leqq f(\alpha)$. Hence, we have shown that $\alpha = f(\alpha)$, which implies

$$\aleph_{\alpha+1} = 2^{\aleph_\alpha}. \blacksquare$$

Before proving **P1** implies the axiom of choice we need some help. The following lemma is due to Tarski (1954).

LEMMA 13.5.10. $\mathfrak{m} \geqq \aleph_0 \to (\mathfrak{m} + \mathfrak{m}^*$ covers $\mathfrak{m})$.

Proof: Suppose $\mathfrak{m} \geqq \aleph_0$. Clearly $\mathfrak{m} \leqq \mathfrak{m} + \mathfrak{m}^*$. If $\mathfrak{m} = \mathfrak{m} + \mathfrak{m}^*$, then $\mathfrak{m}^* \leqq \mathfrak{m}$ which is impossible. Thus, $\mathfrak{m} < \mathfrak{m} + \mathfrak{m}^*$.

Suppose

$$\mathfrak{m} \leqq \mathfrak{p} \leqq \mathfrak{m} + \mathfrak{m}^*.$$

Then there is an $\mathfrak{n}$ such that

(1) $$\mathfrak{p} = \mathfrak{m} + \mathfrak{n}.$$

Also there are cardinal numbers $\mathfrak{q}$, $\mathfrak{r}$, $\mathfrak{s}$, and $\mathfrak{t}$ such that

(2) $$\mathfrak{m} = \mathfrak{q} + \mathfrak{r} \ \& \ \mathfrak{n} = \mathfrak{s} + \mathfrak{t},$$

where

(3) $$\mathfrak{q} + \mathfrak{s} \leqq \mathfrak{m} \ \& \ \mathfrak{r} + \mathfrak{t} \leqq \mathfrak{m}^*.$$

It follows from (2) and (3) that

(4) $$\mathfrak{r} \leqq \mathfrak{m} \ \& \ \mathfrak{r} \leqq \mathfrak{m}^*.$$

Therefore, since $\mathfrak{m}$ is transfinite, it follows from (4) that

(5) $$\mathfrak{m} + \mathfrak{r} = \mathfrak{m}.$$

Now we have

$$\begin{aligned} \mathfrak{m} + \mathfrak{s} &= (\mathfrak{q} + \mathfrak{r}) + \mathfrak{s} && (2) \\ &= (\mathfrak{q} + \mathfrak{s}) + \mathfrak{r} \\ &\leqq \mathfrak{m} + \mathfrak{r} && (3) \\ &= \mathfrak{m}. && (5) \end{aligned}$$

Hence,

(6) $$\mathfrak{m} + \mathfrak{s} = \mathfrak{m}.$$

From (1),

(7) $$\begin{aligned} \mathfrak{p} &= \mathfrak{m} + \mathfrak{n} \\ &= \mathfrak{m} + \mathfrak{s} + \mathfrak{t} && (2) \\ &= \mathfrak{m} + \mathfrak{t}. && (6) \end{aligned}$$

By (3), $\mathfrak{t} \leqq \mathfrak{m}^*$. If $\mathfrak{t} = \mathfrak{m}^*$, then, from (7), $\mathfrak{p} = \mathfrak{m} + \mathfrak{m}^*$. If $\mathfrak{t} < \mathfrak{m}^*$, then, since $\mathfrak{m}^*$ is the smallest aleph which is not $\leqq \mathfrak{m}$, $\mathfrak{t} \leqq \mathfrak{m}$. Consequently, since $\mathfrak{t} < \mathfrak{m}^*$ and $\mathfrak{m}$ is transfinite, it follows from (7) that $\mathfrak{p} = \mathfrak{m} + \mathfrak{t} = \mathfrak{m}$. Thus, $\mathfrak{m} + \mathfrak{m}^*$ covers $\mathfrak{m}$. ■

COROLLARY 13.5.11.

$$(\mathfrak{m} \geqq \aleph_0 \ \& \ \aleph_{\alpha+1} \nleqq \mathfrak{m}) \rightarrow \mathfrak{m} + \aleph_{\alpha+1} \text{ covers } \mathfrak{m} + \aleph_\alpha.$$

Now we shall prove that P1 implies a form of the axiom of choice.

THEOREM 13.5.12. P1 $\rightarrow$ w2.

Proof: Suppose $\mathfrak{m} \geqq \aleph_0$. Then it follows from 13.5.11 that for all α such that $\aleph_{\alpha+1} \nleqq \mathfrak{m}$, $\mathfrak{m} + \aleph_{\alpha+1}$ covers $\mathfrak{m} + \aleph_\alpha$. Therefore, by P1 there is a $\mathfrak{p}$ such that

(1) $$2^{\mathfrak{p}} = \mathfrak{m} + \aleph_{\alpha+1}.$$

Hence, it follows from 12.1.29 that

(2) $$\mathfrak{p} < \mathfrak{m} \text{ or } \mathfrak{p} < \aleph_{\alpha+1}.$$

However, we can choose α sufficiently large so that $\mathfrak{p} \nless \mathfrak{m}$. For if α is chosen so that $\aleph_{\alpha+1} \geqq (2^{\mathfrak{m}})^*$, then it follows from (1) that

(3) $$2^{\mathfrak{p}} \geqq \mathfrak{m} + (2^{\mathfrak{m}})^* \geqq (2^{\mathfrak{m}})^*.$$

Thus, if $\mathfrak{p} < \mathfrak{m}$, then $2^{\mathfrak{p}} \leqq 2^{\mathfrak{m}}$; so it follows from (3) that $2^{\mathfrak{m}} \geqq (2^{\mathfrak{m}})^*$, which is impossible. Therefore, there is an α such that $\mathfrak{p} \nless \mathfrak{m}$, so it follows from (2) that $\mathfrak{p} < \aleph_{\alpha+1}$. Hence $\mathfrak{p}$ is an aleph. Since P1 implies AH, if $\mathfrak{p}$ is an aleph, then so is $2^{\mathfrak{p}}$. By (1), $\mathfrak{m} \leqq 2^{\mathfrak{p}}$. Consequently, $\mathfrak{m}$ is an aleph. ■

Now it follows from 13.5.9, 13.5.12, and 13.3.4 that P1 implies GCH.

With the aid of the axiom of choice we shall show that GCH($\mathfrak{m}$) is equivalent to the following statement:

P2($\mathfrak{m}$): $(\mathfrak{m} \geqq \aleph_0 \ \& \ \bar{\bar{x}} = 2^{\mathfrak{m}}) \rightarrow (\exists y)(\langle\langle y, \subseteq\rangle\rangle$ is a l.o. set &
$(\forall u)(u \in y \rightarrow \bar{\bar{u}} = \mathfrak{m})$ & $x = \bigcup y)$.

If $\mathfrak{m}$ is transfinite, then each set of cardinality $2^{\mathfrak{m}}$ is the union of a $\subseteq$-linearly ordered set each of whose elements has cardinality $\mathfrak{m}$. The proof of equivalence is due to Sierpinski (1921, 1924).

THEOREM 13.5.13.© GCH($\mathfrak{m}$) $\rightarrow$ P2($\mathfrak{m}$).

Proof: Suppose $\mathfrak{m} \geqq \aleph_0$ and $\bar{\bar{x}} = 2^{\mathfrak{m}}$. Then, by the axiom of choice, there is an ordinal number α such that $\mathfrak{m} = \aleph_\alpha$. Thus, it follows from GCH($\mathfrak{m}$) that $2^{\mathfrak{m}} = \aleph_{\alpha+1}$. Consequently, $x \approx \omega_{\alpha+1}$, so x is the union of the initial segments of x which have cardinal number $\aleph_\alpha$. ■

THEOREM 13.5.14.© $P2(\mathfrak{m}) \rightarrow GCH(\mathfrak{m})$.

Proof: Suppose $P2(\mathfrak{m})$ holds. It follows from the axiom of choice that there is an ordinal number α such that $\mathfrak{m} = \aleph_\alpha$ and

(1) $$\aleph_\alpha < \aleph_{\alpha+1} \leqq 2^{\aleph_\alpha}.$$

Let x and y be sets such that

(2) $$x \subseteq y \ \& \ \bar{\bar{x}} = \aleph_{\alpha+1} \ \& \ \bar{\bar{y}} = 2^{\aleph_\alpha}.$$

By $P2(\mathfrak{m})$, there is a set z such that $\langle\langle z, \subseteq\rangle\rangle$ is a l.o. set, each element of z has cardinality $\aleph_\alpha$, and $\bigcup z = y$.

Since $y = \bigcup z$, for each $u \in y$ there is a $v \in z$ such that $u \in v$. Therefore, using the axiom of choice, for each $u \in y$ we can choose an element $f(u) \in z$ such that $u \in f(u)$. Now, $x \subseteq y$, so let

$$w = \textstyle\bigcup_{u \in x} f(u).$$

Clearly $x \subseteq w$, so $\bar{\bar{x}} = \aleph_{\alpha+1} \leqq \bar{\bar{w}}$. Moreover, since $\overline{\overline{f(u)}} = \aleph_\alpha$ for each $u \in x$, $\bar{\bar{w}} \leqq \aleph_\alpha \cdot \aleph_{\alpha+1} = \aleph_{\alpha+1}$. Therefore,

(3) $$\bar{\bar{w}} = \aleph_{\alpha+1}.$$

To complete the proof we shall show that $y \subseteq w$. Let $u \in y$. Then $u \in f(u) \in z$ and $\overline{\overline{f(u)}} = \aleph_\alpha$. Since $\bar{\bar{w}} = \aleph_{\alpha+1}$, there is a $v \in w$ such that $v \notin f(u)$. However, $v \in f(v_1)$ for some $v_1 \in x$. Since z is $\subseteq$-linearly ordered, if $v \in f(v_1)$ and $v \notin f(u)$, we must have $f(u) \subseteq f(v_1)$. Therefore,

$$u \in f(u) \subseteq f(v_1) \subseteq w.$$

Consequently, $y \subseteq w$.

This proves the theorem because by (2), $\bar{\bar{y}} = 2^{\aleph_\alpha}$ and by (3), $\bar{\bar{w}} = \aleph_{\alpha+1}$. Consequently, since $y \subseteq w$,

$$2^{\aleph_\alpha} \leqq \aleph_{\alpha+1}.$$

But $AH(\alpha)$ implies $GCH(\aleph_\alpha)$ (13.3.6), and $\aleph_\alpha = \mathfrak{m}$. Hence, $P2(\mathfrak{m})$ implies $GCH(\mathfrak{m})$. ■

The axiom of choice was used in the proof of both 13.5.13 and 13.5.14. However, GCH implies the axiom of choice. Therefore, it is easy to see that GCH is equivalent to $(\forall\mathfrak{m})P2(\mathfrak{m})$ and the axiom of choice.

THEOREM 13.5.15. $GCH \leftrightarrow [(\forall\mathfrak{m})P2(\mathfrak{m}) \ \& \ w2]$.

We shall discuss one additional proposition in this section which deals with transitive classes. [A class X is transitive if $u \in X$ implies $u \subseteq X$ (4.1.11).] For convenience we shall let $T_\mathfrak{m}$ be the class of all transitive sets of cardinality $\mathfrak{m}$.

DEFINITION 13.5.16. $T_{\mathfrak{m}} =_{\mathrm{Df}} \{x : x \text{ is transitive } \& \ \overline{\overline{x}} = \mathfrak{m}\}$.

Now, the proposition P3($\aleph_\alpha$) can be stated as follows:

P3($\aleph_\alpha$): $\overline{\overline{T}}_{\aleph_\alpha} = \aleph_{\alpha+1}$.

Let us note, first of all, that without the axiom of regularity there is no guarantee that $T_{\aleph_\alpha}$ is a set. For without the axiom of regularity we could have that $x = \{x\}$ for a proper class of sets, and in this case T_1 would be a proper class.

We shall prove first that if $T_{\aleph_\alpha}$ is a set, then $\overline{\overline{T}}_{\aleph_\alpha} \geqq 2^{\aleph_\alpha}$.

LEMMA 13.5.17. $S(T_{\aleph_\alpha}) \rightarrow \overline{\overline{T}}_{\aleph_\alpha} \geqq 2^{\aleph_\alpha}$.

Proof: Let

$$X = \{\omega_\alpha \cup \{u\} : u \subseteq \omega_\alpha \ \& \ u \notin \omega_\alpha\}.$$

Then X is a set of transitive sets each of which has cardinality $\aleph_\alpha$. Thus,

$$\overline{\overline{X}} \leqq \overline{\overline{T}}_{\aleph_\alpha}.$$

On the other hand,

$$\overline{\overline{X}} = 2^{\aleph_\alpha} - \aleph_\alpha = 2^{\aleph_\alpha}.$$

Therefore, $\overline{\overline{T}}_{\aleph_\alpha} \geqq 2^{\aleph_\alpha}$. ■

Using 13.5.17 it is easy to show that P3($\aleph_\alpha$) $\rightarrow$ AH(α). The details are left for the reader.

THEOREM 13.5.18. P3($\aleph_\alpha$) $\rightarrow$ AH(α).

To prove the converse we use both the axiom of choice and the axiom of regularity.

THEOREM 13.5.19.©® AH(α) $\rightarrow$ P3($\aleph_\alpha$).

Proof: Since each set in $T_{\aleph_\alpha}$ has cardinality $\aleph_\alpha$, it follows from the axiom of choice that for each $x \in T_{\aleph_\alpha}$ there is a function f_x such that

$$f_x : x \xrightarrow[\text{onto}]{1\text{-}1} \omega_\alpha.$$

For each $x \in T_{\aleph_\alpha}$, define a relation R_x on ω_α such that if $\beta, \gamma \in \omega_\alpha$, then

$$\beta \, R_x \, \gamma \leftrightarrow f_x^{-1}(\beta) \in f_x^{-1}(\gamma).$$

Consequently, R is a function mapping $T_{\aleph_\alpha}$ into $\mathcal{P}(\omega_\alpha \times \omega_\alpha)$. We shall show that R is 1–1.

Suppose $R_x = R_y$. Let E_x and E_y be the epsilon relation restricted to x and y, respectively. That is,

$$u\, E_x\, v \leftrightarrow (u,v \in x \;\&\; u \in v)$$
$$u\, E_y\, v \leftrightarrow (u,v \in y \;\&\; u \in v).$$

Then $R_x = R_y$ implies

$$\langle\langle x, E_x\rangle\rangle \cong \langle\langle y, E_y\rangle\rangle.$$

Let ψ be an isomorphism mapping x onto y. Using the axiom of regularity we shall show that $\psi(u) = u$ for all $u \in x$. For suppose this is not so. Let u_0 be an element of x of smallest rank such that $\psi(u_0) \neq u_0$. Since x is transitive, then

$$u_0 = \{v : v\, E_x\, u_0\}.$$

But ψ is an isomorphism mapping x onto y, so

$$v\, E_x\, u_0 \leftrightarrow \psi(v)\, E_y\, \psi(u_0).$$

Therefore,

$$u_0 = \{v : \psi(v)\, E_y\, \psi(u_0)\}.$$

If $v \in u_0$, then $\rho(v) < \rho(u_0)$. Since u_0 is an element of smallest rank such that $\psi(u_0) \neq u_0$, we must have $\psi(v) = v$ for all $v \in u_0$. Hence,

$$u_0 = \{v : v\, E_y\, \psi(u_0)\}.$$

Therefore, it follows from the transitivity of y that $u_0 = \psi(u_0)$, which contradicts the definition of u_0. Thus, $\psi(u) = u$ for all $u \in x$, which implies $x = y$.

Consequently, R is a 1–1 function mapping $T_{\aleph_\alpha}$ into $\mathcal{P}(\omega_\alpha \times \omega_\alpha)$. Therefore,

$$\overline{\overline{T}}_{\aleph_\alpha} \leqq 2^{\aleph_\alpha{}^2} = 2^{\aleph_\alpha}.$$

However, by 13.5.17,

$$\overline{\overline{T}}_{\aleph_\alpha} \geqq 2^{\aleph_\alpha}.$$

Thus, $\overline{\overline{T}}_{\aleph_\alpha} = 2^{\aleph_\alpha}$ and so it follows from AH(α) that

$$\overline{\overline{T}}_{\aleph_\alpha} = \aleph_{\alpha+1}. \blacksquare$$

Therefore, we have shown that P3($\aleph_\alpha$) implies AH(α) and, under the assumption that the axiom of choice and the axiom of regularity hold, AH(α) implies P3($\aleph_\alpha$).

EXERCISES 13.5

1. Using GCH calculate each of the following:
   (a) $\aleph_0^{\aleph_0}$
   (b) $\aleph_\omega^{\aleph_0}$
   (c) $\aleph_{\omega_\omega}^{\aleph_0}$
   (d) $\aleph_{\omega_1}^{\aleph_0}$
   (e) $\aleph_\omega^{\aleph_{\omega_1}}$
   (f) $\aleph_{\omega_1}^{\aleph_\omega}$.
2. Finish the proof of theorem 13.5.5.
3. Prove theorem 13.5.6.
4. Prove theorem 13.5.18.
5. Using GCH determine necessary and sufficient conditions for $\mathfrak{m}^{\mathfrak{n}} = \mathfrak{n}^{\mathfrak{m}}$ when $\mathfrak{m},\mathfrak{n} \geqq \aleph_0$.
6. Prove $\mathrm{AH}(\alpha) \leftrightarrow \aleph_\alpha = \aleph_\alpha^*$.

13.6. THE CONTINUUM HYPOTHESIS

GCH($\aleph_0$) is usually called the *continuum hypothesis.* In this section we shall designate it by "CH." Thus "CH" stands for "$2^{\aleph_0}$ covers $\aleph_0$," or

CH: $\neg(\exists\mathfrak{n})(\aleph_0 < \mathfrak{n} < 2^{\aleph_0})$.

The following two theorems are special cases of 13.3.5 and 13.3.6.

THEOREM 13.6.1.© CH $\rightarrow$ AH(0).

THEOREM 13.6.2. AH(0) $\rightarrow$ CH.

Also, the following four theorems are special cases of 13.5.13, 13.5.14, 13.5.18, and 13.5.19, respectively.

THEOREM 13.6.3.© CH $\rightarrow$ P2($\aleph_0$).

THEOREM 13.6.4.© P2($\aleph_0$) $\rightarrow$ CH.

THEOREM 13.6.5. P3($\aleph_0$) $\rightarrow$ CH.

THEOREM 13.6.6. CH $\rightarrow$ P3($\aleph_0$).

In section 13.4 we mentioned almost disjoint sets of type $\mathfrak{m}$. A set Y is almost disjoint of type $\mathfrak{m}$ if for all $u \in Y$, $\overline{\overline{u}} \geqq \mathfrak{m}$ and for all $u,v \in Y$, $\overline{\overline{u \cap v}} < \mathfrak{m}$. Consider the following proposition:

P4($\aleph_\beta$): $\overline{\overline{X}} = \aleph_{\beta+1} \rightarrow \neg(\exists Y)[\overline{\overline{Y}} > \aleph_{\beta+1} \;\&\; X = \bigcup Y \;\&$
$(\forall u)(u \in Y \rightarrow \overline{\overline{u}} \geqq \aleph_\beta) \;\&\; (\forall u)(\forall v)(u,v \in Y \rightarrow \overline{\overline{u \cap v}} < \aleph_\beta)]$.

It can be shown that GCH implies P4($\aleph_\beta$) (see exercise 13.4.6). It is not known if the converse is true. However, we shall show that P4($\aleph_0$) is equivalent to AH(0). [The proof is due to Tarski (1928) and Sierpinski (1956).]

THEOREM 13.6.7.© $\quad AH(0) \to P4(\aleph_0)$.

Proof: Suppose AH(0) is true and $P4(\aleph_0)$ is false. Then there is a set X such that $\overline{\overline{X}} = \aleph_1$ and a set Y such that,

$$\overline{\overline{Y}} > \aleph_1 \tag{1}$$
$$\bigcup Y = X \tag{2}$$
$$(\forall u)(u \in Y \to \overline{\overline{u}} \geqq \aleph_0) \tag{3}$$
$$(\forall u)(\forall v)(u,v \in Y \to \overline{\overline{u \cap v}} < \aleph_0). \tag{4}$$

It follows from (3) and the axiom of choice that there exists a function F such that for each $u \in Y$, $F(u) \subseteq u$ and $\overline{\overline{F(u)}} = \aleph_0$. By (2), if $u \in Y$, then $F(u) \subseteq X$. The set of all denumerable subsets of X has cardinality $\aleph_1^{\aleph_0}$. However, AH(0) implies

$$\aleph_1^{\aleph_0} = (2^{\aleph_0})^{\aleph_0} = 2^{\aleph_0{}^2} = 2^{\aleph_0} = \aleph_1.$$

Consequently, it follows from (1) that

$$\overline{\overline{Y}} = \overline{\overline{\mathfrak{D}(F)}} > \overline{\overline{\mathfrak{R}(F)}}.$$

Therefore, F is not 1–1, so there exist $u,v \in Y$ such that $F(u) = F(v)$. Since $F(u) \subseteq u$ and $F(v) \subseteq v$, this implies $F(u) \subseteq u \cap v$. Since $\overline{\overline{F(u)}} = \aleph_0$. This contradicts (4). ■

(The proof of 13.6.7 could be modified so that the axiom of choice is not needed. The details are left as an exercise.)

The proof of the converse follows.

THEOREM 13.6.8.© $\quad P4(\aleph_0) \to AH(0)$.

Proof: Suppose $P4(\aleph_0)$ holds. Let n be a strictly increasing sequence of natural number of type ω. Let

$$D(n) = \{2^{n_0} + 2^{n_1} + \cdots + 2^{n_k} : k \in \omega\}.$$

If n and m are both strictly increasing sequences of natural numbers of type ω, then $D(n) \cap D(m)$ is finite. For if $n_k \neq m_k$, then $D(n)$ and $D(m)$ have at most k common elements.

Let

$$Y = \{D(n) : n \text{ is a strictly increasing sequence of natural number of type } \omega\},$$

and let

$$Z = \bigcup Y.$$

Clearly, $\overline{\overline{Y}} = 2^{\aleph_0}$. Since $Z \subseteq \omega$,

$$\omega_1 = Z \cup (\omega_1 \sim Z).$$

Hence, ω_1 is a union of $2^{\aleph_0}$ sets each of which has cardinality $\geqq \aleph_0$ and each pair of which has a finite intersection. Thus, it follows from P4($\aleph_0$) that $\aleph_1 \nless 2^{\aleph_0}$. Therefore, the trichotomy implies $2^{\aleph_0} \leqq \aleph_1$. However, there are no cardinal numbers between $\aleph_0$ and $\aleph_1$, so $2^{\aleph_0} = \aleph_1$. ∎

There are several interesting propositions about Euclidean spaces which are equivalent to CH. The first three are due to Sierpinski. [See Sierpinski (1956).]

An n-dimensional Euclidean space is the class of all n-tuples of real numbers. (It is assumed that the reader is familiar with elementary geometric terminology such as coordinate axes, lines, planes, parallel, perpendicular, etc. These terms will be used in their natural sense and will not be defined here.)

P5: $X = Re \times Re \rightarrow$
$(\exists Y_1)(\exists Y_2)[X = Y_1 \cup Y_2 \ \& \ Y_1 \cap Y_2 = \emptyset \ \&$
$(\forall v)(v \in Re \rightarrow \{\langle x,v\rangle : x \in Re\} \cap Y_1 \lesssim \omega) \ \&$
$(\forall u)(u \in Re \rightarrow \{\langle u,y\rangle : y \in Re\} \cap Y_2 \lesssim \omega)]$.

That is, a 2-dimensional Euclidean space can be partitioned into two sets Y_1 and Y_2 such that the intersection of any horizontal line and Y_1 is countable, and the intersection of any verticle line and Y_2 is countable.

The next two propositions are about 3-dimensional Euclidean spaces. The first one states that a 3-dimensional Euclidean space can be partitioned into three sets, Y_i, $i = 1, 2, 3$, such that if the three coordinate axes are the x_i-axes, $i = 1, 2, 3$, then the intersection of Y_i with each plane perpendicular to the x_i-axis is countable for each $i = 1, 2, 3$. The second proposition states that a 3-dimensional Euclidean space can be partitioned into three sets Y_i, $i = 1, 2, 3$, such that if the three coordinate axes are the x_i-axes, $i = 1, 2, 3$, then the intersection of Y_i with each line parallel to the x_i-axis is finite for each $i = 1, 2, 3$.

P6: $X = Re \times (Re \times Re) \rightarrow (\exists Y_1)(\exists Y_2)(\exists Y_3)[X = Y_1 \cup Y_2 \cup Y_3 \ \&$
$(\forall u)(u \in Re \rightarrow \{\langle u,y,z\rangle : y,z \in Re\} \cap Y_1 \lesssim \omega) \ \&$
$(\forall v)(v \in Re \rightarrow \{\langle x,v,z\rangle : x,z \in Re\} \cap Y_2 \lesssim \omega) \ \&$
$(\forall w)(w \in Re \rightarrow \{\langle x,y,w\rangle : x,y \in Re\} \cap Y_3 \lesssim \omega)]$.

P7: $X = Re \times (Re \times Re) \rightarrow (\exists Y_1)(\exists Y_2)(\exists Y_3)[X = Y_1 \cup Y_2 \cup Y_3 \ \&$
$(\forall v)(\forall w)(v,w \in Re \rightarrow \{\langle x,v,w\rangle : x \in Re\} \cap Y_1 \prec \omega) \ \&$
$(\forall u)(\forall w)(u,w \in Re \rightarrow \{\langle u,y,w\rangle : y \in Re\} \cap Y_2 \prec \omega) \ \&$
$(\forall u)(\forall v)(u,v \in Re \rightarrow \{\langle u,v,z\rangle : z \in Re\} \cap Y_3 \prec \omega)]$.

First, without making use of the axiom of choice we shall show that

THEOREM 13.6.9. AH(0) $\rightarrow$ P5.

Proof: Since $\overline{\overline{Re}} = 2^{\aleph_0}$, AH(0) implies

$$\overline{\overline{Re}} = \aleph_1.$$

Thus, $Re \approx \omega_1$. Let f be a 1–1 function mapping Re onto ω_1. Define a relation R on Re such that for all $x, y \in Re$,

$$x \, R \, y \leftrightarrow f(x) \in f(y).$$

Then R is an irreflexive well-ordering on Re. Define

$$Y_1 = \{\langle x,y\rangle : x,y \in Re \;\&\; (x \, R \, y \text{ or } x = y)\}$$
$$Y_2 = \{\langle x,y\rangle : x,y \in Re \;\&\; y \, R \, x\}.$$

Then

$$Y_1 \cap Y_2 = \emptyset$$
$$Y_1 \cup Y_2 = Re \times Re.$$

For each $a \in Re$, let

$$L_a = \{\langle x,a\rangle : x \in Re\}.$$

Thus, L_a is the set of all points on the line $y = a$. Then

$$L_a \cap Y_1 = \{\langle x,a\rangle : x \in Re \;\&\; (x \, R \, a \text{ or } x = a)\}.$$

But since $\langle\langle Re,R\rangle\rangle \cong \langle\langle \omega_1,<\rangle\rangle$ and $L_a \cap Y_1$ is equipollent with an R-initial segment of Re, $L_a \cap Y_1$ is countable. The proof that the intersection of a line parallel to the y-axis with Y_2 is countable is analogous. ∎

With the aid of the axiom of choice we shall prove the converse.

THEOREM 13.6.10.© P5 $\rightarrow$ AH(0).

Proof: It follows from the axiom of choice that

(1) $$\aleph_0 < \aleph_1 \leqq 2^{\aleph_0}.$$

Let Y_1 and Y_2 be two sets satisfying P5 and let Z be a set of $\aleph_1$ lines each of which is parallel to the x-axis. Then, by P5, if $L \in Z$, then $L \cap Y_1$ is countable. Let

$$K = (\bigcup Z) \cap Y_1$$
$$= \bigcup_{L \in Z} (L \cap Y_1).$$

Then, it follows from the axiom of choice that

$$\overline{\overline{K}} \leqq \aleph_0 \cdot \aleph_1 = \aleph_1.$$

Let P be the projection of K on the x-axis. That is,

$$P = \{\langle x,0\rangle : (\exists y)(y \in Re \;\&\; \langle x,y\rangle \in K)\}.$$

Since K can be mapped onto P and K can be well-ordered, $P \precsim K$. Thus,

(2) $$\overline{\overline{P}} \leqq \overline{\overline{K}} \leqq \aleph_1.$$

We shall show that every point on the x-axis belongs to P. Let $\langle a,0\rangle$ be an arbitrary point on the x-axis. Let L_a be a line through $\langle a,0\rangle$ parallel to the y-axis. Then, since Z is a set of $\aleph_1$ lines each of which is parallel to the x-axis,

$$\overline{\overline{L_a \cap \bigcup Z}} = \aleph_1.$$

But, by P5, the cardinal number of $L_a \cap Y_2$ is at most $\aleph_0$. Therefore, there must be a least one point $\langle a,b\rangle \in L_a$ such that $\langle a,b\rangle \in (\bigcup Z) \cap Y_1$. Consequently, $\langle a,b\rangle \in K$, and so $\langle a,0\rangle \in P$. Since every point on the x-axis belongs to P, we must have

(3) $$2^{\aleph_0} \leqq \overline{\overline{P}}.$$

Now AH(0) follows from (1), (2), and (3). ∎

An equivalent formulation of P5 was observed by Lusin. Every function which maps Re into Re has one point and only one point in common with each line parallel to the y-axis. Therefore, Lusin noted that P5 could be restated as follows:

P5′: $(\exists X)[(\forall f)(f \in X \rightarrow f \in (Re)^{Re} \text{ or } f^{-1} \in (Re)^{Re})\ \&$
$\overline{\overline{X}} = \aleph_0\ \&\ Re \times Re = \bigcup X]$.

The proof that P5 is equivalent to P5′ is left as an exercise. (See exercise 3.6.1.)

We shall sketch the proofs that AH(0) implies P6 and P7. The proofs of the converses are somewhat similar to the proof of 13.6.10 and will not be given here [see Sierpinski (1951, 1958)].

THEOREM 13.6.11. AH(0) → P6.

Proof: It follows from AH(0) that

$$\overline{\overline{Re}} = 2^{\aleph_0} = \aleph_1.$$

Thus, there is a relation R on Re such that

$$\langle\langle Re,R\rangle\rangle \cong \langle\langle \omega_1,<\rangle\rangle.$$

Define the three sets Y_i, $i = 1, 2, 3$, as follows:

$$Y_1 = \{\langle x,y,z\rangle : (y\ R\ x \text{ or } y = x)\ \&\ (z\ R\ x \text{ or } z = x)\}$$
$$Y_2 = \{\langle x,y,z\rangle : x\ R\ y\ \&\ (z\ R\ y \text{ or } z = y)\}$$
$$Y_3 = \{\langle x,y,z\rangle : x\ R\ z\ \&\ y\ R\ z\}.$$

The reader can easily verify that Y_1, Y_2, and Y_3 are the required sets. ■

Before proving AH(0) implies P7 we prove a preliminary lemma.

LEMMA 13.6.12.

$$(X \subseteq Re \times Re \ \&\ \overline{\overline{X}} \leqq \aleph_0) \rightarrow (\exists Y_1)(\exists Y_2)(X = Y_1 \cup Y_2 \ \& \\ (\forall v)(v \in Re \rightarrow \{\langle x,v\rangle : x \in Re\} \cap Y_1 \prec \omega\} \ \& \\ (\forall u)(u \in Re \rightarrow \{\langle u,y\rangle : y \in Re\} \cap Y_2 \prec \omega\}.$$

Proof: Since X is countable, it can be expressed in the following form:

$$X = \{\langle x_m, y_n\rangle : m,n \in \omega\}.$$

Define

$$Y_1 = \{\langle x_m, y_n\rangle : m,n \in \omega \ \&\ m \leqq n\}$$
$$Y_2 = \{\langle x_m, y_n\rangle : m,n \in \omega \ \&\ m > n\}.$$

It is easy to see that Y_1 and Y_2 are the required sets. ■

THEOREM 13.6.13. P6 → P7.

Proof: It follows from P6 that there exist three sets Z_i, $i = 1, 2, 3$, such that $X = Re \times (Re \times Re) = Z_1 \cup Z_2 \cup Z_3$, and the intersection of Z_i with each plane perpendicular to the x_i-axis is countable. Let $P_i(a)$ be the set of points on the plane $x_i = a$. That is,

$$P_1(a) = \{\langle a,y,z\rangle : y,z \in Re\}$$
$$P_2(a) = \{\langle x,a,z\rangle : x,z \in Re\}$$
$$P_3(a) = \{\langle x,y,a\rangle : x,y \in Re\}.$$

Then,

$$Z_i = \bigcup_{a \in Re} (Z_i \cap P_i(a)),\ i = 1, 2, 3.$$

Since $Z_i \cap P_i(a)$ is countable for each $a \in Re$ and each $i = 1, 2, 3$, it follows from 13.6.12 that there exist sets $A_{ij}(a)$, $i,j = 1, 2, 3$, $i \neq j$, such that

$$Z_1 \cap P_1(a) = A_{12}(a) \cup A_{13}(a)$$
$$Z_2 \cap P_2(a) = A_{21}(a) \cup A_{23}(a)$$
$$Z_3 \cap P_3(a) = A_{31}(a) \cup A_{32}(a)$$

and

$$(\forall v)(\forall w)(A_{i1} \cap \{\langle x,v,w\rangle : x \in Re\} \prec \omega),\ i = 2, 3$$
$$(\forall u)(\forall w)(A_{i2} \cap \{\langle u,y,w\rangle : y \in Re\} \prec \omega),\ i = 1, 3$$
$$(\forall u)(\forall v)(A_{i3} \cap \{\langle u,v,z\rangle : z \in Re\} \prec \omega),\ i = 1, 2.$$

Now the three sets Y_1, Y_2, and Y_3 are defined as follows:

$$Y_1 = \bigcup_{a \in Re} (A_{21}(a) \cup A_{31}(a))$$
$$Y_2 = \bigcup_{a \in Re} (A_{12}(a) \cup A_{32}(a))$$
$$Y_3 = \bigcup_{a \in Re} (A_{13}(a) \cup A_{23}(a)).$$

The proof that Y_1, Y_2, and Y_3 are the required sets is left as an exercise. ■

In 1951 Sierpinski posed the problem, to determine whether or not the following proposition is equivalent to the continuum hypothesis:

P8: $X = Re \times Re \rightarrow (\exists Y_1)(\exists Y_2)(\exists Y_3)[X = Y_1 \cup Y_2 \cup Y_3 \;\&$
$(\forall v)(v \in Re \rightarrow \{\langle x,v \rangle : x \in Re\} \cap Y_1 \prec \omega) \;\&$
$(\forall u)(u \in Re \rightarrow \{\langle u,y \rangle : y \in Re\} \cap Y_2 \prec \omega) \;\&$
$(\forall w)(w \in Re \rightarrow \{\langle z,z + w \rangle : z \in Re\} \cap Y_3 \prec \omega)].$

That is, a two-dimensional Euclidean space can be partitioned into three sets Y_1, Y_2, and Y_3 such that the intersection of Y_1 with each line parallel to the x-axis is finite, the intersection of Y_2 with each line parallel to the y-axis is finite, and the intersection of Y_3 with each line parallel to the line $y = x$ is finite. (Actually, Sierpinski stated the problem with three arbitrary non-parallel lines instead of using the three lines we chose here—the x-axis, the y-axis, and the line $y = x$. However, this makes no essential difference. P8 is equivalent to the continuum hypothesis if and only if Sierpinski's form of P8 is equivalent to the continuum hypothesis.)

Sierpinski's problem was solved by F. Bagemihl (1961) and R. O. Davies (1962). Bagemihl proved that P8 implies AH(0) and Davies proved the converse. We shall reproduce both of these proofs here.

THEOREM 13.6.14. AH(0) → P8.

Proof: AH(0) implies that there exists a 1–1 function f mapping ω_1 onto Re. Let R_α be the smallest set of real numbers which contains $f(\beta)$ for all β such that $0 \leqq \beta \leqq \alpha$, and which is closed with respect to addition and subtraction. (That is, if $u,v \in R_\alpha$, then so do $u + v$ and $u - v$.) Then, for each $\alpha \in \omega_1$,

$$R_\alpha = \{\Sigma_{i<k}\, n_i f(\alpha_i) : k \in \omega \;\&\; (\forall_i)(i < k \rightarrow n_i \in In) \;\&\; (\forall i)(i < k \rightarrow \alpha_i \leqq \alpha) \;\&\; (\forall i)(i < k - 1 \rightarrow \alpha_i < \alpha_{i+1})\}.$$

Therefore, we have

(1) $$f(\alpha) \in R_\alpha$$
(2) $$(\forall \beta)(\beta \leqq \alpha \rightarrow R_\beta \subseteq R_\alpha)$$
(3) $$\overline{\overline{R_\alpha}} = \aleph_0.$$

It follows from (1) and (2) that

(4) $$Re = R_0 \cup \bigcup_{\alpha \in \omega_1} (R_{\alpha+1} \sim R_\alpha).$$

By (3), R_α is denumerable for each α, therefore the elements of R_0 and $R_{\alpha+1} \sim R_\alpha$ can be enumerated. If $R_{\alpha+1} \sim R_\alpha \neq \emptyset$, let

(5) $R_0 = \{z_{00}, z_{10}, z_{20}, \ldots\}, R_{\alpha+1} \sim R_\alpha = \{z_{0,\alpha+1}, z_{1,\alpha+1}, z_{2,\alpha+1}, \ldots\}$.

Further, let x and y be any two real numbers. Then by (4) and (5) there exist unique natural numbers n and m and unique ordinal numbers $\alpha,\beta \in \omega_1$ such that

$$x = z_{m\alpha} \text{ and } y = z_{n\beta}.$$

Define a relation T on Re as follows:

$$z_{m\alpha}\, T\, z_{n\beta} \leftrightarrow (\alpha < \beta \text{ or } (\alpha = \beta \;\&\; m \leqq n)).$$

It is easy to see that T well-orders Re. Now define the sets Y_1, Y_2, and Y_3 as follows:

$$Y_1 = \{\langle x,y\rangle : x,y \in Re \;\&\; x\,T\,y \;\&\; (x - y)\,T\,y\}$$
$$Y_2 = \{\langle x,y\rangle : x,y \in Re \;\&\; y\,T\,x \;\&\; y \neq x \;\&\; (x - y)\,T\,x\}$$
$$Y_3 = \{\langle x,y\rangle : x,y \in Re \;\&\; x\,T\,(x - y) \;\&\; x \neq x - y \;\&\; y\,T\,(x - y) \;\& \\ y \neq x - y\}.$$

Since T well-orders Re, it is easy to prove that

$$Re \times Re = Y_1 \cup Y_2 \cup Y_3.$$

Three real numbers u, v, and w are said to be *related* if one is equal to the sum of the other two. Now we claim the following statement is true.

(6) For any real number u, there are at most a finite number of real numbers v and w such that u, v, and w are related, $v\,T\,u$ and $w\,T\,u$.

For suppose u, v, and w are related, $v\,T\,u$ and $w\,T\,u$. Then there are ordinal numbers α, β, and γ, and natural numbers m, n, and p such that

$$u = z_{m\alpha} \;\&\; v = z_{n\beta} \;\&\; w = z_{p\gamma}.$$

Since $v\,T\,u$ and $w\,T\,u$, $\beta \leqq \alpha$ and $\gamma \leqq \alpha$. Suppose $\beta < \alpha$ and $\gamma < \alpha$. Let $\delta = \max(\beta,\gamma)$. Then, by (3), $v,w \in R_\delta$. But, u, v, and w are related and R_δ is closed with respect to addition and subtraction, therefore $u \in R_\delta$. But this is impossible because $\delta < \alpha$. Therefore, either $\beta = \alpha$ or $\gamma = \alpha$. Because of symmetry, it does not matter which we choose. Suppose then that $\beta = \alpha$ and $\gamma \leqq \alpha$. Then v is an element of the finite set

$$\{z_{0\alpha}, z_{1\alpha}, \ldots, z_{p\alpha}\}.$$

Moreover, given u and v, there are at most three values of w such that u, v, and w are related. This proves (6).

Since for all real numbers x and y, the real numbers x, y, and $x - y$ are related, it follows from (6) and the definitions of Y_1, Y_2, and Y_3 that the intersection of Y_1 with any line parallel to the x-axis is finite,

the intersection of Y_2 with any line parallel to the y-axis is finite,

the intersection of Y_3 with any line parallel to the line $y = x$ is finite. ∎

THEOREM 13.6.15.© $\quad P8 \rightarrow AH(0)$.

Proof: Suppose P8 is true and AH(0) is false. Then it follows from the axiom of choice that

(1) $$\aleph_0 < \aleph_1 < 2^{\aleph_0}.$$

For each $u \in Re$ let

(2) $$R(u) = \{r + u : r \in Ra\}.$$

Since Ra, the set of rational numbers, is denumerable,

(3) $$\overline{\overline{R(u)}} = \aleph_0.$$

Moreover, it is easy to see that if $u,v \in Re$, then either $R(u) = R(v)$ or $R(u) \cap R(v) = \emptyset$. Since $Re = \bigcup_{u \in Re} R(u)$, there must be $2^{\aleph_0}$ pairwise disjoint sets of the form (2). Thus,

(4) $$\overline{\overline{\{R(u) : u \in Re\}}} = 2^{\aleph_0}$$

and

(5) $$(u,v \in Re \;\&\; R(u) \neq R(v) \rightarrow R(u) \cap R(v) = \emptyset.$$

Let S be a subset of Re of cardinality $\aleph_1$ and let

(6) $$T = \{r + s : r \in Ra \;\&\; s \in S\}.$$

Therefore, $T \subseteq Re$ and $\overline{\overline{T}} = \aleph_1$.

By P8, $Re \times Re$ can be partitioned into three sets Y_1, Y_2, and Y_3 such that the intersection of Y_1 with each line parallel to the x-axis is finite, the intersection of Y_2 with each line parallel to the y-axis is finite, and the intersection of Y_3 with each line parallel to the line $y = x$ is finite. Let L_t be the set of points on the line $x = t$. Then $L_t \cap Y_2$ is finite and since $\overline{\overline{T}} = \aleph_1$,

$$\overline{\overline{\bigcup_{t \in T} (L_t \cap Y_2)}} \leqq \aleph_1.$$

Let P be the set of ordinates of the projection of $\bigcup_{t \in T} (L_t \cap Y_2)$ on the y-axis. That is,

$$P = \{u : u \in Re \;\&\; (\exists t)(t \in T \;\&\; \langle t,u \rangle \in Y_2)\}.$$

Then

(7) $$\overline{\overline{P}} \leqq \aleph_1.$$

It follows from (1), (4), (5), and (7) that there is a $u_0 \in Re$ such that

$$R(u_0) \cap P = \emptyset.$$

Therefore, each line which is parallel to the x-axis and intersects the y-axis at a point in $R(u_0)$ intersects each line L_t with $t \in T$ in a point of $Y_1 \cup Y_3$.

Let M_t be the line parallel to the line $y = x$ which contains the point $\langle u_0, t\rangle$ with $t \in T$. If $u_1 \in R(u_0)$, then the line $y = u_1$ intersects M_t in the point

$$\langle u_1 - u_0 + t, u_1\rangle.$$

Geometrically we now have the following situation:

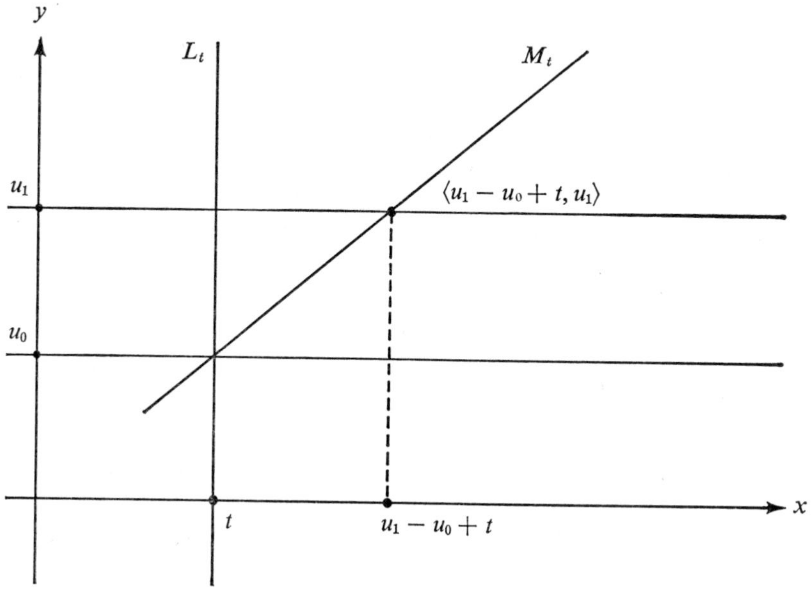

FIGURE 13.6.1

Clearly, $u_1 - u_0 + t \in T$ because $u_1 - u_0$ is rational. Hence, $\langle u_1 - u_0 + t, u_1\rangle \in Y_1 \cup Y_3$.

It follows from P8 that there are at most a finite number of real numbers $t \in T$ such that the lines M_t intersect the line $y = u_1$ in points of Y_1. Since there are only $\aleph_0$ lines of the form $y = u_1$ with $u_1 \in R(u_0)$, but $\aleph_1$ lines M_t with $t \in T$, there is an element $t_0 \in T$ such that the line M_{t_0} intersects each line of the form $y = u_1$ with $u_1 \in R(u_0)$ in a point of Y_3. This implies that $M_{t_0} \cap Y_3$ is denumerable, contradicting P8. Thus, we must have $\aleph_1 = 2^{\aleph_0}$. ∎

It follows from 3.6.14 and 3.6.15 that P8 is equivalent to the continuum hypothesis.

A Hamel basis for the real numbers was discussed in section 10.4. [A Hamel basis is a set of real numbers H which has the property that every real number different from zero is uniquely representable as a linear combination of elements from H with rational coefficients. Equivalently, a Hamel basis is a $\subseteq$-maximal Ra-linearly independent set of real numbers (10.4.7).] It was shown by Erdös and Kakutani (1943) that the continuum hypothesis is equivalent to the following statement:

P9: $$(\exists H)(\text{Func}(H)\ \&\ (\forall n)(n \in \omega \rightarrow H_n \text{ is a Hamel basis})\ \&\ Re \sim \{\emptyset\} = \textstyle\bigcup_{n\in\omega} H_n).$$

In other words, the set of all non-zero real numbers is the union of a denumerable number of Hamel bases. We shall give the proof that AH(0) implies P9. The proof of the converse can be found in the paper by Erdös and Kakutani.

THEOREM 13.6.16.© AH(0) $\rightarrow$ P9.

Proof: Suppose AH(0) holds. It follows from 10.4.3 that no Hamel basis is countable. Therefore, AH(0) implies that each Hamel basis has cardinality $\aleph_1$. Let H be a Hamel basis. Since $\overline{\overline{H}} = \aleph_1$, $\omega_1 \approx H$. Let f be a 1–1 function mapping ω_1 onto H. For each ordinal $\alpha < \omega_1$ and each $r \in Ra$, $r \neq 0$, let

$$X_{r\alpha} = \{\Sigma_{i<n}(r_i f(\beta_i)) + rf(\alpha) : n \in \omega\ \&\ (\forall i)(i < n \rightarrow (r_i \in Ra\ \&\ \beta_i < \alpha\ \&\ (i+1 < n \rightarrow \beta_i < \beta_{i+1})))\}.$$

Since $H = \mathcal{R}(f)$ is a Hamel basis,

$$(\alpha_0 \neq \alpha_1 \text{ or } r_0 \neq r_1) \rightarrow X_{r_0\alpha_0} \cap X_{r_1\alpha_1} = \emptyset.$$

Also, since $\alpha < \omega_1$, $X_{r\alpha}$ is countable for each $r \in Ra$. Consequently, for each $\alpha \in On$ and $r \in Ra$ there exists a function $g_{r\alpha}$ such that

$$g_{r\alpha} : \omega \xrightarrow{\text{onto}} X_{r\alpha}.$$

(The axiom of choice is used to obtain the function g.) For each $r \in Ra$ and $n \in \omega$, define

$$Y(r,n) = \textstyle\bigcup_{\alpha<\omega_1} \{g_{r\alpha}(n)\}.$$

The set $Y(r,n)$ consists of one and only one element from each of the sets $X_{r\alpha}$ for $\alpha < \omega_1$. We shall show that $Y(r,n)$ is an Ra-linearly independent set. That is, it is not the case that there exist m rational numbers $r_0, r_1, \ldots, r_{m-1}$ different from 0, and m ordinal numbers $\alpha_0, \alpha_1, \ldots, \alpha_{m-1} < \omega_1$ such that

$$\Sigma_{j<m}\, r_j g_{r\alpha_j}(n) = 0. \qquad (1)$$

For suppose (1) holds for some $m \in \omega$, $m \neq 0$, and suppose $\alpha_0 < \alpha_1 < \cdots < \alpha_{m-1}$. Then, since $g_{r\alpha_j}(n) \in X_{r\alpha_j}$, there exist ordinal numbers $\beta_{jk} < \alpha_{m-1}$ and rational numbers s_{jk} such that

$$\Sigma_{j<n}\, s_{j0} f(\beta_{j0}) + rr_0 f(\alpha_0) + \Sigma_{j<n}\, s_{j1} f(\beta_{j1}) + rr_1 f(\alpha_1) + \cdots + \Sigma_{j<n}\, s_{j,m-1} f(\beta_{j,m-1}) + rr_{m-1} f(\alpha_{m-1}) = 0.$$

But this contradicts the fact that H is an Ra-linearly independent set.

Thus, $Y(r,n)$ is an Ra-linearly independent set, and by 10.4.8 for each $r \in Ra$, $r \neq 0$, and for each $n \in \omega$ there is a Hamel basis $H(r,n)$ such that $Y(r,n) \subseteq H(r,n)$. Let

$$Z = \bigcup_{n\in\omega} \bigcup_{0\neq r\in Ra} H(r,n). \tag{2}$$

We claim $Z = Re$ because

$$\begin{aligned} Re &= \bigcup_{\alpha\in\omega_1} \bigcup_{0\neq r\in Ra} X_{r\alpha} \\ &= \bigcup_{n\in\omega} \bigcup_{0\neq r\in Ra} Y(r,n) \\ &\subseteq \bigcup_{n\in\omega} \bigcup_{0\neq r\in Ra} H(r,n) \\ &= Z. \end{aligned}$$

Clearly, $Z \subseteq Re$. Thus, we have obtained from (2) that $Z = Re$ is a countable union of Hamel bases. ■

EXERCISES 13.6

1. Modify the proof of theorem 13.6.7 so that the axiom of choice is not needed.
2. Prove P6 $\rightarrow$ AH(0).
3. Prove P7 $\rightarrow$ AH(0).
4. Let L_1, L_2, and L_3 be the set of points on three non-parallel lines in a 2-dimensional Euclidean space. Let

P8′: $X = Re \times Re \rightarrow (\exists Y_1)(\exists Y_2)(\exists Y_3)[X = Y_1 \cup Y_2 \cup Y_3$ &
$(\forall M_1)(M_1$ is a line parallel to $L_1 \rightarrow Y_1 \cap M_1 \prec \omega)$ &
$(\forall M_2)(M_2$ is a line parallel to $L_2 \rightarrow Y_2 \cap M_2 \prec \omega)$ &
$(\forall M_3)(M_3$ is a line parallel to $L_3 \rightarrow Y_3 \cap M_3 \prec \omega)]$.

Prove P8′ $\leftrightarrow$ AH(0).

5. Show that if $r \in Ra$ and $n \in \omega$, then the set $Y(r,n)$, as defined in the proof of theorem 13.6.16, is a Hamel basis.

Chapter 14: Additional Axioms

14.1. INACCESSIBLE CARDINALS

Inaccessible cardinals were originally defined by Tarski (1938, 1939). A survey of their properties along with an extensive bibliography is given in an article by Keisler and Tarski (1964). Inaccessible cardinals have application in the theory of Boolean algebras, measure theory, group theory, topology, and functional analysis. However, it is the purpose of this section merely to define them and to state some of their properties.

The definition of a *regular* aleph was given in 13.4.10. Moreover, theorem 13.4.12 tells us that $\aleph_\alpha$ is regular if and only if $\aleph_\alpha$ is not the sum of less than ω_α cardinal numbers each of which has cardinality less than $\aleph_\alpha$. In view of 13.4.12, the definition of "regular" can be extended to an arbitrary cardinal number as follows:

DEFINITION 14.1.1. Regular

$$\mathfrak{m} \text{ is } \textit{regular} =_{\text{Df}} [\mathfrak{m} \neq 0 \;\&\; (\forall x)((\bar{\bar{x}} < \mathfrak{m} \;\&\; (\forall y)(y \in x \rightarrow \bar{\bar{y}} < \mathfrak{m}) \;\& \; \text{Pr Dis}(x)) \rightarrow \overline{\overline{\bigcup x}} < \mathfrak{m})].$$

If $\mathfrak{m} < \mathfrak{n}$ and there are no cardinal numbers $\mathfrak{p}$ such that $\mathfrak{m} < \mathfrak{p} < \mathfrak{n}$, then $\mathfrak{n}$ is said to *cover* $\mathfrak{m}$ (see definition 13.5.7). Using the notions of regular and covers we shall define what it means for a cardinal number to be *weakly inaccessible*.

DEFINITION 14.1.2. Weakly Inaccessible

$$\mathfrak{m} \text{ is } \textit{weakly inaccessible} =_{\text{Df}} (\mathfrak{m} \text{ is regular } \& \neg(\exists \mathfrak{n})(\mathfrak{m} \text{ covers } \mathfrak{n})).$$

Thus, no finite cardinal number is weakly inaccessible. It follows from 13.4.9 and 13.4.10 that if α is not a limit ordinal, then $\aleph_\alpha$ is regular. However, if $\alpha \neq 0$ and α is not a limit ordinal, then there is a β such that $\alpha = \beta + 1$, and then $\aleph_\alpha$ covers $\aleph_\beta$. Therefore, if α is a non-limit ordinal and $\alpha \neq 0$, $\aleph_\alpha$ is not weakly inaccessible. Clearly, $\aleph_0$ is weakly inaccessible. Thus, we have the following theorem:

THEOREM 14.1.3.©

$$\aleph_\alpha \text{ is weakly inaccessible} \leftrightarrow (\alpha = 0 \text{ or } (\alpha \text{ is a limit ordinal } \& \aleph_\alpha \text{ is regular})).$$

DEFINITION 14.1.4. Strongly Inaccessible

$\mathfrak{m}$ is *strongly inaccessible* $=_{\text{Df}}$ ($\mathfrak{m}$ is regular &

$$(\forall \mathfrak{n})(\forall \mathfrak{p})(\mathfrak{n},\mathfrak{p} < \mathfrak{m} \rightarrow \mathfrak{n}^{\mathfrak{p}} < \mathfrak{m})).$$

It is easy to see that $\aleph_0$ is strongly inaccessible. Moreover, using the axiom of choice it is easy to prove that a strongly inaccessible cardinal is also weakly inaccessible.

THEOREM 14.1.5.©

$$\mathfrak{m} \text{ is strongly inaccessible} \rightarrow \mathfrak{m} \text{ is weakly inaccessible.}$$

The proof is left as an exercise.

We can also prove, assuming the generalized continuum hypothesis, that weakly inaccessible cardinals are strongly inaccessible. But first, a preliminary lemma.

LEMMA 14.1.6.©

$$\mathfrak{m} \geqq \aleph_0 \rightarrow [(\forall \mathfrak{n})(\forall \mathfrak{p})(\mathfrak{n},\mathfrak{p} < \mathfrak{m} \rightarrow \mathfrak{n}^{\mathfrak{p}} < \mathfrak{m}) \leftrightarrow (\forall \mathfrak{n})(\mathfrak{n} < \mathfrak{m} \rightarrow 2^{\mathfrak{n}} < \mathfrak{m})].$$

Proof: Clearly if $\mathfrak{m} > 2$, then

$$(\forall \mathfrak{n})(\forall \mathfrak{p})(\mathfrak{n},\mathfrak{p} < \mathfrak{m} \rightarrow \mathfrak{n}^{\mathfrak{p}} < \mathfrak{m}) \rightarrow (\forall \mathfrak{n})(\mathfrak{n} < \mathfrak{m} \rightarrow 2^{\mathfrak{n}} < \mathfrak{m}).$$

Conversely, suppose $\mathfrak{n},\mathfrak{p} < \mathfrak{m}$. Then the axiom of choice implies that $\mathfrak{n}\cdot\mathfrak{p} < \mathfrak{m}$. Consequently, by hypothesis,

$$2^{\mathfrak{n}\cdot\mathfrak{p}} < \mathfrak{m}.$$

But

$$\mathfrak{n}^{\mathfrak{p}} \leqq (2^{\mathfrak{n}})^{\mathfrak{p}} = 2^{\mathfrak{n}\cdot\mathfrak{p}}. \blacksquare$$

THEOREM 14.1.7.

$$\text{GCH} \rightarrow (\mathfrak{m} \text{ is weakly inaccessible} \rightarrow \mathfrak{m} \text{ is strongly inaccessible}).$$

Proof: Suppose $\mathfrak{m} = \aleph_\alpha$ is weakly inaccessible and suppose $\aleph_\beta < \aleph_\alpha$. Then it follows from GCH that

$$2^{\aleph_\beta} = \aleph_{\beta+1}.$$

If $\alpha = \beta + 1$, then $\aleph_\alpha$ covers $\aleph_\beta$, contradicting 14.1.2. Consequently,

$$2^{\aleph_\beta} < \aleph_\alpha,$$

so it follows from 14.1.6 that $\mathfrak{m}$ is strongly inaccessible. $\blacksquare$

Next we shall show that a transfinite cardinal $\mathfrak{m}$ is strongly inaccessible if and only if $\mathfrak{m}$ is larger than the product of less than $\mathfrak{m}$ cardinal numbers, each of which is less than $\mathfrak{m}$.

THEOREM 14.1.8.©

$$\mathfrak{m} \geqq \aleph_0 \rightarrow [\mathfrak{m} \text{ is strongly inaccessible} \leftrightarrow (\forall x)((\bar{\bar{x}} < \mathfrak{m} \ \& \ (\forall u)(u \in x \rightarrow \mathfrak{n}_u < \mathfrak{m})) \rightarrow \Pi_{u \in x}\, \mathfrak{n}_u < \mathfrak{m}).$$

Proof: Suppose $\mathfrak{m}$ is strongly inaccessible. Also suppose $\bar{\bar{x}} = \mathfrak{p} < \mathfrak{m}$ and for all $u \in x$, $\mathfrak{n}_u < \mathfrak{m}$. Then, if $v \in x$,

$$\mathfrak{n}_v \leqq \Sigma_{u \in x}\, \mathfrak{n}_u.$$

Therefore,

$$\Pi_{u \in x}\, \mathfrak{n}_u \leqq (\Sigma_{u \in x}\, \mathfrak{n}_u)^{\mathfrak{p}}.$$

Consequently, it follows from 14.1.4 that

$$\Pi_{u \in x}\, \mathfrak{n}_u < \mathfrak{m}.$$

Conversely, suppose $\mathfrak{m}$ is larger than the product of less than $\mathfrak{m}$ cardinal numbers each of which is less than $\mathfrak{m}$. Since a sum of terms cannot be larger than the product, $\mathfrak{m}$ is regular. Moreover, if $\mathfrak{n},\mathfrak{p} < \mathfrak{m}$ and $\bar{\bar{x}} = \mathfrak{p}$, then

$$\mathfrak{n}^{\mathfrak{p}} = \Pi_{u \in x}\, \mathfrak{n}.$$

By hypothesis,

$$\Pi_{u \in x}\, \mathfrak{n} < \mathfrak{m}.$$

Therefore, $\mathfrak{m}$ is strongly inaccessible. ■

The next two theorems state other necessary and sufficient conditions for a transfinite cardinal to be strongly inaccessible.

THEOREM 14.1.9.© $\mathfrak{m} \geqq \aleph_0 \rightarrow [\mathfrak{m}$ is strongly inaccessible $\leftrightarrow$

(1) $(\forall \mathfrak{n})(\forall \mathfrak{p})(\mathfrak{n},\mathfrak{p} < \mathfrak{m} \rightarrow \mathfrak{n}^{\mathfrak{p}} < \mathfrak{m})$

(2) $(\forall \mathfrak{p})(0 < \mathfrak{p} < \mathfrak{m} \rightarrow \mathfrak{m}^{\mathfrak{p}} = \mathfrak{m})]$.

Proof: Suppose $\mathfrak{m}$ is strongly inaccessible. Then it follows from 14.1.4 that (1) is true. To prove (2), suppose $\mathfrak{m} = \aleph_\alpha$. Let $\mathfrak{p}$ be a cardinal number such that $0 < \mathfrak{p} < \mathfrak{m}$. If $\mathfrak{p}$ is finite, then it follows from 12.1.2 that $\mathfrak{m}^{\mathfrak{p}} = \mathfrak{m}$. Suppose $\mathfrak{p} = \aleph_\beta$ where $\beta < \alpha$. Then, since $\mathfrak{m}$ is regular, it follows from 13.4.15 that

$$\aleph_\alpha^{\aleph_\beta} = \aleph_\alpha \cdot \Sigma_{\gamma < \alpha}\, \aleph_\gamma^{\aleph_\beta}.$$

However, since $\mathfrak{m}$ is strongly inaccessible,

$$\beta,\gamma < \alpha \rightarrow \aleph_\gamma^{\aleph_\beta} < \aleph_\alpha.$$

Thus,

$$\begin{aligned}\aleph_\alpha^{\aleph_\beta} &\leqq \aleph_\alpha \cdot \Sigma_{\gamma<\alpha} \aleph_\alpha \\ &= \aleph_\alpha \cdot \bar{\bar{\alpha}} \cdot \aleph_\alpha \\ &= \aleph_\alpha.\end{aligned}$$

This proves (2).

Conversely, suppose $\mathfrak{m}$ satisfies (2) and $\mathfrak{m} = \aleph_\alpha$. If $\mathfrak{m}$ is not regular, then there is a strictly increasing sequence f of ordinal numbers of type $\beta < \alpha$ such that $f(\xi) < \alpha$ for each $\xi < \beta$ and

$$\begin{aligned}\aleph_\alpha &= \Sigma_{\xi<\beta} \aleph_{f(\xi)} \\ &< \Pi_{\xi<\beta} \aleph_{f(\xi)} \qquad (12.3.11) \\ &\leqq \Pi_{\xi<\beta} \aleph_\alpha \\ &= \aleph_\alpha^{\bar{\bar{\beta}}}.\end{aligned}$$

This contradicts (2). ■

THEOREM 14.1.10.© $\mathfrak{m} \geqq \aleph_0 \rightarrow$ [$\mathfrak{m}$ is strongly inaccessible $\leftrightarrow$

(1) $(\forall \mathfrak{p})(0 < \mathfrak{p} < \mathfrak{m} \rightarrow \mathfrak{m}^{\mathfrak{p}} = \mathfrak{m})$ &

(2) $\neg(\exists \mathfrak{p})(2^{\mathfrak{p}} = \mathfrak{m})$].

Proof: Suppose $\mathfrak{m}$ is strongly inaccessible. Then it follows from 14.1.9 and 14.1.6 that conditions (1) and (2) hold.

Conversely suppose (1) and (2) are true. In the proof of 14.1.9 it was shown that (1) implies that $\mathfrak{m}$ is regular. Therefore, it follows from 14.1.4 and 14.1.6 that to prove that $\mathfrak{m}$ is strongly inaccessible, it is sufficient to prove that $2^{\mathfrak{p}} < \mathfrak{m}$ for all $\mathfrak{p} < \mathfrak{m}$.

Suppose that $\mathfrak{p} < \mathfrak{m}$, then, since $\mathfrak{m} \geqq 2$, $2^{\mathfrak{p}} \leqq \mathfrak{m}^{\mathfrak{p}}$. By (1), $\mathfrak{m}^{\mathfrak{p}} = \mathfrak{m}$. Therefore, $2^{\mathfrak{p}} \leqq \mathfrak{m}$. If $2^{\mathfrak{p}} = \mathfrak{m}$, this contradicts (2). Thus we must have $2^{\mathfrak{p}} < \mathfrak{m}$. ■

The axiom for inaccessible cardinals states that there exist arbitrarily large strongly inaccessible cardinals.

IC: $(\forall \mathfrak{n})(\exists \mathfrak{m})(\mathfrak{m}$ is strongly inaccessible & $\mathfrak{m} \geqq \mathfrak{n})$.

An equivalent formulation of IC can be given in terms of sets as follows [see Tarski (1939)].

IC′: $(\forall x)(S(x) \rightarrow (\exists y)(S(y)$ &

(1) $x \lesssim y$ &

(2) $\{u : u \subseteq y \ \&\ \bar{\bar{u}} \neq \bar{\bar{y}}\} \approx y$ &

(3) $\neg(\exists w)(S(w) \ \&\ \mathcal{P}(w) \approx y)$).

It follows from theorem 14.1.10 that IC and IC′ are equivalent. The details are left to the reader (exercise 14.1.1). Thus, we have

THEOREM 14.1.11.© $\quad IC \leftrightarrow IC'$.

IC′ is quite a powerful proposition. If there exists a set, it clearly implies A10, the axiom of infinity; and together with A6, the axiom of replacement, it implies A4, the power set axiom. We shall prove that it also implies the axiom of choice.

THEOREM 14.1.12. $\quad IC' \rightarrow w1$.

Proof: Let x be any set. Then by IC′, there is a set y satisfying conditions (1)–(3) of IC′. We shall prove that (2) implies that y can be well-ordered. Then it follows from (1) that x can be well-ordered.

Since

$$z = \{u : u \subseteq y \;\&\; \bar{\bar{u}} \neq \bar{\bar{y}}\} \approx y,$$

there is, a 1–1 function f mapping z onto y:

$$f : z \xrightarrow[\text{onto}]{1\text{–}1} y.$$

Define a function g on *On* as follows:

$$\begin{aligned} g(\alpha) &= f(g''\alpha) \text{ if } g''\alpha \in z \\ &= u \notin y \text{ if } g''\alpha \notin z. \end{aligned}$$

It follows from the recursion theorem 8.3.4 that g exists and is unique.

We claim that for all α such that $g''\alpha \in z$, $g(\alpha) \notin g''\alpha$. For suppose otherwise. Let

$$\beta = <\text{-smallest element of } \{\alpha : g''\alpha \in z \;\&\; g(\alpha) \in g''\alpha\}.$$

Then $g(\beta) \in g''\beta$, so there is a $\gamma < \beta$ such that $g(\beta) = g(\gamma)$. Since f is 1–1, $g(\beta) = g(\gamma)$ implies $g''\beta = g''\gamma$. Thus, $g(\gamma) \in g''\gamma$, which contradicts the definition of β.

Suppose $g''\alpha, g''\beta \in z$ and $g''\alpha = g''\beta$. Then, if $\alpha < \beta$, $g(\alpha) \in g''\alpha$, which contradicts the preceding result. Thus, we have shown

$$(g''\alpha, g''\beta \in z \;\&\; g''\alpha = g''\beta) \rightarrow \alpha = \beta.$$

Therefore, g is 1–1 on $\{\alpha : g''\alpha \in z\}$. Consequently, there is an ordinal number α such that $g''\alpha \notin z$. Otherwise the set y would contain a subclass equipollent with *On*. Let

$$\gamma = <\text{-smallest element of } \{\alpha : g''\alpha \notin z\} \text{ and } w = g''\gamma.$$

We claim $w \approx y$. First, $w \subseteq y$, because if $\alpha < \gamma$, then $g''\alpha \in z$, so $g(\alpha) \in y$. However, $w \notin z$, because of the definition of γ. Therefore, $w \subseteq y$ and $\bar{\bar{w}} = \bar{\bar{y}}$. Consequently,

$$y \approx w = g''\gamma.$$

Since g is 1–1 on γ, y can be well-ordered. ■

Note the similarity between the proof of theorem 14.1.12 and the proof that the axiom of choice implies the well-ordering theorem, 10.1.3.

It has been shown by R. Solovay (1965) that if IC′ is consistent with the other axioms of set theory, then it does not imply either the generalized continuum hypothesis or its negation. Thus the generalized continuum hypothesis is independent of IC′ and the other axioms of set theory. [See Gödel (1947).]

If set theory is consistent, the existence of an inaccessible cardinal cannot be proved from the other axioms. For if $\aleph_\alpha$ is an inaccessible cardinal, then we can construct a model for set theory as follows. Define

$$V = \tau(\omega_\alpha)$$
$$\mathrm{P}\mathcal{T}\,(X) \leftrightarrow X \subseteq V \text{ and } \rho(X) = \omega_\alpha.$$
$$\mathrm{S}(X) \leftrightarrow X \subseteq V \text{ and } \rho(X) < \omega_\alpha.$$
$$\in\, = E|\tau(\omega_\alpha).$$

(See Section 8.6 for the definition of τ and ρ and 8.2.1 for the definition of E.) In this manner we can construct a model for the NBG system within the system, contradicting Gödel's incompleteness theorem.

The reader is referred to the work of P. Mahlo (1911, 1912, 1913) and A. Levy (1960) for additional results about inaccessible cardinals.

EXERCISES 14.1

1. Prove IC $\leftrightarrow$ IC′. (The axiom of choice is used in the proof.)
2. Prove $(\exists x)\mathrm{S}(x) \rightarrow (\mathrm{IC}' \rightarrow \mathrm{A10})$.
3. Prove $(\mathrm{IC}' \;\&\; \mathrm{A6}) \rightarrow \mathrm{A4}$.
4. Prove that IC′ is equivalent to each of the following two propositions:

IC″: $(\forall x)(\mathrm{S}(x) \rightarrow (\exists y)(\mathrm{S}(y)\;\&$

(1) $x \in y$
(2) $(\forall u)(\forall v)((u \in y \;\&\; v \subseteq u) \rightarrow v \in y)$
(3) $(\forall u)(u \in y \rightarrow \mathcal{P}(u) \in y)$
(4) $(\forall u)((u \subseteq y \;\&\; \bar{\bar{u}} \neq \bar{\bar{y}}) \rightarrow u \in y)$

IC‴: $(\forall x)(\mathrm{S}(x) \rightarrow (\exists y)(\mathrm{S}(y)\;\&$

(1) $x \subseteq y$
(2) $(\forall u)(u \in y \rightarrow u \subseteq y)$
(3) $(\forall u)[u \in y \rightarrow (\exists z)(z \in y \;\&\; (\forall v)(v \subseteq u \rightarrow v \in z))]$
(4) $(\forall u)[(u \subseteq y \;\&\; (\forall v)(v \subseteq u \rightarrow v \not\approx y)) \rightarrow u \in y]$.

Where in the proof of equivalence is the axiom of choice used?

14.2. THE AXIOM OF CONSTRUCTIBILITY

This section is devoted to the work of Gödel. While proving the consistency of the generalized continuum hypothesis and the axiom of choice with the other axioms of set theory, Gödel proposed another axiom, called the axiom of *constructibility*. He proved that the axiom of constructibility is consistent with the other axioms of set theory and that it implies both the axiom of choice and the generalized continuum hypothesis. It is with this latter problem that we shall concern ourselves in this section. The discussion follows that of Gödel (1940).

Axiom schema A3 states the rules for constructing classes. If A3 is replaced by

A3′: If **P** is a wff in which X is not a free variable and in which there are no bound class variables, then the following statement is an axiom,

$$(\exists X)(\mathrm{Cl}(X) \;\&\; (\forall u)(u \in X \leftrightarrow \mathbf{P}))$$

(see footnote page 31). Gödel has shown that the axiom schema A3′ can be replaced by a finite number of axioms. We list these axioms below.

B1: The Axiom for $\in$
$(\exists X)(\forall u)(\forall v)(\langle u, v\rangle \in X \leftrightarrow u \in v)$.

B2: The Axiom for Intersection
$(\forall X)(\forall Y)(\exists Z)(\forall u)(u \in Z \leftrightarrow (u \in X \;\&\; u \in Y))$.

B3: The Axiom for the Complement
$(\forall X)(\exists Y)(\forall u)(u \in Y \leftrightarrow u \notin X)$.

(Note that it follows from de Morgan's law, 2.6.12, that union may be defined in terms of intersection and complement.)

B4: The Axiom for the Domain
$(\forall X)(\exists Y)(\forall u)(u \in Y \leftrightarrow (\exists v)(\langle u,v\rangle \in X))$.

B5: The Axioms for the Direct Product
$(\forall X)(\exists Y)(\forall u)(\forall v)(\langle u,v\rangle \in Y \leftrightarrow u \in X)$.

B6: The Axiom for the Inverse
$(\forall X)(\exists Y)(\forall u)(\forall v)(\langle u,v\rangle \in Y \leftrightarrow \langle v,u\rangle \in X)$.

B7: An Axiom for the Ternary Inverse
$(\forall X)(\exists Y)(\forall u)(\forall v)(\forall w)(\langle u,v,w\rangle \in Y \leftrightarrow \langle v,w,u\rangle \in X)$.

B8: An Axiom for the Ternary Inverse
$(\forall X)(\exists Y)(\forall u)(\forall v)(\forall w)(\langle u,v,w\rangle \in Y \leftrightarrow \langle u,w,v\rangle \in X)$.

Next we define eight operations corresponding to axiom A5, the pairing axiom, and B1–B8. They will be called the *fundamental operations*.

DEFINITION 14.2.1. Fundamental Operations

(1) $\mathfrak{F}_1(X,Y) =_{\mathrm{Df}} \{X,Y\}$
(2) $\mathfrak{F}_2(X,Y) =_{\mathrm{Df}} \{\langle u,v\rangle : \langle u,v\rangle \in X \;\&\; u \in v\}$
(3) $\mathfrak{F}_3(X,Y) =_{\mathrm{Df}} X \sim Y$
(4) $\mathfrak{F}_4(X,Y) =_{\mathrm{Df}} X \cap (Y \times V)$
(5) $\mathfrak{F}_5(X,Y) =_{\mathrm{Df}} X \cap \mathfrak{D}(Y)$
(6) $\mathfrak{F}_6(X,Y) =_{\mathrm{Df}} X \cap Y^{-1}$
(7) $\mathfrak{F}_7(X,Y) =_{\mathrm{Df}} \{\langle u,v,w\rangle : \langle u,v,w\rangle \in X \;\&\; \langle v,w,u\rangle \in Y\}$
(8) $\mathfrak{F}_8(X,Y) =_{\mathrm{Df}} \{\langle u,v,w\rangle : \langle u,v,w\rangle \in X \;\&\; \langle u,w,v\rangle \in Y\}$.

The operations are relativized in order to insure that when applied to sets they will yield sets [and also for reasons which will appear later (theorems 14.2.12–17)]. The axiom for intersection, B2, is not used because

$$X \cap Y = X \sim (X \sim Y).$$

Moreover, since

$$E = \{\langle u,v\rangle : u \in v\} \qquad (8.2.1)$$
$$X|Y = \{\langle u,v\rangle : \langle u,v\rangle \in X \;\&\; u \in Y\} \qquad (3.2.17)$$
$$Y^{-1} = \{\langle u,v\rangle : \langle v,u\rangle \in Y\} \qquad (3.2.12),$$

parts (2), (4), and (6) can be rewritten as follows:

$$\mathfrak{F}_2(X,Y) = X \cap E$$
$$\mathfrak{F}_4(X,Y) = X|Y$$
$$\mathfrak{F}_6(X,Y) = \{\langle u,v\rangle : \langle u,v\rangle \in X \;\&\; \langle v,u\rangle \in Y\}.$$

A set is called constructible if it can be obtained by iterated applications of the fundamental operations. What this actually means is described below and the formal definition of a constructible set is given in 14.2.11.

We shall need two relations which will be designated by "R^*" and "S^*." [The relation R^* was defined earlier in exercise 7.2.8(c), but we shall repeat the definition here for convenience.]

DEFINITION 14.2.2.

(a) $R^* \subseteq On \times On \;\&\; (\langle\alpha,\beta\rangle\, R^*\, \langle\gamma,\delta\rangle \leftrightarrow$
$[\max(\alpha,\beta) < \max(\gamma,\delta)$ or $(\max(\alpha,\beta) = \max(\gamma,\delta) \;\&\; \alpha < \gamma)$ or
$(\max(\alpha,\beta) = \max(\gamma,\delta) \;\&\; \alpha = \gamma \;\&\; \beta < \delta)])$

(b) $S^* \subseteq 9 \times (On \times On) \;\&\; (\langle m,\alpha,\beta\rangle\, S^*\, \langle n,\gamma,\delta\rangle \leftrightarrow$
$[(m,n < 9 \;\&\; \langle\alpha,\beta\rangle\, R^*\, \langle\gamma,\delta\rangle)$ or $(\langle\alpha,\beta\rangle = \langle\gamma,\delta\rangle \;\&\; m < n < 9)])$.

It follows from exercise 7.2.8(c) that R^* and S^* are w.o. relations and it follows from exercise 7.3.4(c) that each S^*-initial segment of $9 \times (On \times On)$ is a set. Moreover, since $9 \times (On \times On)$ is a proper class and S^* is irreflexive, it follows from 8.3.5 that,

THEOREM 14.2.3. $\langle\langle 9 \times (On \times On), S^*\rangle\rangle \cong \langle\langle On, <\rangle\rangle$.

By 7.4.5, there is exactly one isomorphism mapping $9 \times (On \times On)$ onto On. We shall call the isomorphism "J."

DEFINITION 14.2.4. $J: \langle\langle 9 \times (On \times On), S^*\rangle\rangle \cong \langle\langle On, <\rangle\rangle$.

Thus, J is a 1–1 function mapping $9 \times (On \times On)$ onto On, and if $\langle m,\alpha,\beta\rangle, \langle n,\gamma,\delta\rangle \in 9 \times (On \times On)$, then

$$\langle m,\alpha,\beta\rangle\; S^*\; \langle n,\gamma,\delta\rangle \leftrightarrow J(m,\alpha,\beta) < J(n,\gamma,\delta).$$

For example, if $m < 9$,

$$\begin{aligned} J(m,0,0) &= m \\ J(m,0,1) &= 9 + m \\ J(m,1,0) &= 18 + m \\ J(m,1,1) &= 27 + m \\ J(m,0,\omega) &= \omega + m \\ J(m,0,\omega_1) &= \omega_1 + m, \text{ etc.} \end{aligned}$$

LEMMA 14.2.5.
(a) $0 < m < 9 \rightarrow J(m,\alpha,\beta) > J(0,\alpha,\beta)$
(b) $J(0,0,\alpha) \geqq \alpha$
(c) $m < 9 \rightarrow J(m,\alpha,\beta) \geqq J(m,0,\alpha)$
(d) $m < 9 \rightarrow J(m,\alpha,\beta) \geqq J(m,0,\beta)$
(e) $(m < 9 \;\&\; J(m,\alpha,\beta) < J(0,0,\gamma)) \rightarrow \alpha,\beta < \gamma$.

The proof is left as an exercise.

For notational convenience, we make the following definition:

DEFINITION 14.2.6. $m < 9 \rightarrow$
(a) $J_m(\alpha,\beta) =_{\mathrm{Df}} J(m,\alpha,\beta)$
(b) $K_1(J_m(\alpha,\beta)) =_{\mathrm{Df}} \alpha$
(c) $K_2(J_m(\alpha,\beta)) =_{\mathrm{Df}} \beta$.

For each $m < 9$, J_m is a function, $\mathfrak{D}(J_m) \subseteq On \times On$, and $\mathfrak{R}(J_m) \subseteq On$. Also, K_1 and K_2 are each functions from On onto On.

THEOREM 14.2.7.
(a) $m < 9 \rightarrow J_m(\alpha,\beta) \geqq \max(\alpha,\beta)$
(b) $0 < m < 9 \rightarrow J_m(\alpha,\beta) > \max(\alpha,\beta)$
(c) $K_1(\alpha) \leqq \alpha \;\&\; K_2(\alpha) \leqq \alpha$
(d) $\alpha \notin \mathfrak{R}(J_0) \rightarrow (K_1(\alpha) < \alpha \;\&\; K_2(\alpha) < \alpha)$.

Proof: Parts (a) and (b). Let $\gamma = \max(\alpha,\beta)$. Then if $0 < m < 9$,

$$\begin{aligned} J_m(\alpha,\beta) &> J_0(\alpha,\beta) && (14.2.5a) \\ &\geqq J_0(0,\alpha) && (14.2.5c) \\ &\geqq \gamma. && (14.2.5b) \end{aligned}$$

Parts (c) and (d). Since J is a 1–1 function mapping $9 \times (On \times On)$ onto On, for each $\alpha \in On$ there exist unique ordinal numbers β and γ and a unique natural number $m < 9$ such that

$$\alpha = J_m(\beta,\gamma).$$

Thus,

$$K_1(\alpha) = \beta \ \&\ K_2(\alpha) = \gamma.$$

It follows from part (a) of this theorem that

$$K_1(\alpha) \leqq \alpha \ \&\ K_2(\alpha) \leqq \alpha,$$

and it follows from part (b) that if $\alpha \notin \mathcal{R}(J_0)$, then

$$K_1(\alpha) < \alpha \ \&\ K_2(\alpha) < \alpha. \ \blacksquare$$

THEOREM 14.2.8. $(m < 9 \ \&\ \alpha,\beta < \omega_\gamma) \rightarrow J_m(\alpha,\beta) < \omega_\gamma.$

Proof: Suppose $m < 9$, and $\alpha,\beta < \omega_\gamma$. Let x be the S^*-initial segment of $9 \times (On \times On)$ generated by $\langle m,\alpha,\beta\rangle$. Then, since J is an isomorphism,

(1) $$x \approx J_m(\alpha,\beta).$$

Let $\delta = \max(\alpha,\beta)$. It follows from the definition of S^* that

$$x \subseteq 9 \times ((\delta + 1) \times (\delta + 1)).$$

If $\gamma = 0$, then δ is finite, so that x, and also, $J_m(\alpha,\beta)$ is finite. If $\gamma > 0$, then $\delta + 1$ is infinite. Thus,

(2) $$\overline{\overline{x}} \leqq \overline{\overline{\delta + 1}}.$$

Since $\delta + 1 < \omega_\gamma$,

(3) $$\overline{\overline{\delta + 1}} < \aleph_\gamma.$$

Therefore, it follows from (1), (2), and (3) that

$$J_m(\alpha,\beta) < \omega_\gamma. \ \blacksquare$$

THEOREM 14.2.9. $\omega_\alpha = J_0(0,\omega_\alpha).$

Proof: By 14.2.7(a),

$$\omega_\alpha \leqq J_0(0,\omega_\alpha).$$

Suppose

$$\omega_\alpha < J_0(0,\omega_\alpha).$$

Then there is a natural number $m < 9$ and ordinal numbers β and γ such that

$$\omega_\alpha = J_m(\beta,\gamma).$$

By 14.2.5(e), $J_m(\beta,\gamma) < J_0(0,\omega_\alpha)$ implies $\beta,\gamma < \omega_\alpha$. But by 14.2.8, $\beta,\gamma < \omega_\alpha$ implies $J_m(\beta,\gamma) < \omega_\alpha$. ∎

The symbol "F" will be used in this section for the specific function defined as follows.

DEFINITION 14.2.10.

$$F =_{\text{Df}} \{\langle\alpha,x\rangle : (\alpha \in \mathcal{R}(J_0) \ \& \ x = F''\alpha) \text{ or } (\exists m)(0 < m < 9 \ \& \ \alpha \in \mathcal{R}(J_m) \ \& \ x = \mathfrak{F}_m(F(K_1(\alpha), F(K_2(\alpha))))\}.$$

Since J is a 1–1 function from $9 \times (On \times On)$ onto On, it follows from 14.2.7(d) and the recursion theorem that F is a function and $\mathfrak{D}(F) = On$.

The constructible sets are those sets which are elements of the range of F.

DEFINITION 14.2.11. Constructible Sets

(a) x is *constructible* $=_{\text{Df}} x \in \mathcal{R}(F)$

(b) $L =_{\text{Df}} \{x : x \text{ is constructible}\}$.

Thus, a set is constructible if it can be obtained from two constructible sets by applying one of the fundamental operations, or if it is a certain set of constructible sets. The axiom of constructibility states that every set is constructible.

Con: $(\forall x)(S(x) \rightarrow x \text{ is constructible})$.

We shall prove first that if every set is constructible, then there are no atoms.

THEOREM 14.2.12. $\text{Con} \rightarrow \mathcal{A} = \emptyset$.

Proof: Suppose u is an atom, then $\{u\}$ is a set. We shall show that there is no ordinal number α such that $F(\alpha)$ has an atom as an element. Otherwise, let α_0 be the smallest ordinal number in the class:

$$\{\alpha : (\exists u)(u \in \mathcal{A} \ \& \ u \in F(\alpha))\}$$

For some m, $0 \leqq m < 9$, $\alpha_0 \in \mathcal{R}(J_m)$.

If $m = 0$,

$$F(\alpha_0) = \{F(\beta) : \beta < \alpha_0\}.$$

Therefore, if $u \in F(\alpha_0)$, then $u = F(\beta)$ for some $\beta < \alpha_0$. However, by the definition of F, for all ordinal numbers β, $F(\beta)$ is a set.

Similarly, if $m = 1$,

$$F(\alpha_0) = \{F(K_1(\alpha_0)), F(K_2(\alpha_0))\},$$

so that each element of $F(\alpha_0)$ is a set.

If $1 < m < 9$, then $u \in F(\alpha_0)$ implies that $u \in F(K_1(\alpha_0))$. But, by 14.2.7(d), $K_1(\alpha_0) < \alpha_0$. Thus, if u is an atom, this contradicts the definition of α_0. ∎

Because of 14.2.12, Con can be stated in a more common form, namely,

$$V = L.$$

It is a relatively easy matter to prove that Con implies the axiom of choice. For, F being a mapping from On onto L, induces a well-ordering relation on L. Therefore, if every element of a constructible set is constructible, then every constructible set can be well-ordered. We shall prove that not only is every element of a constructible set constructible, but that each element of a constructible set appears earlier than the set itself in the enumeration given by F.

THEOREM 14.2.13. $F(\alpha) \subseteq F''\alpha$.

Proof: Suppose the theorem is true for all $\beta < \alpha$. If $\alpha \in \mathfrak{R}(J_0)$, then $F(\alpha) = F''\alpha$, so the theorem is true for α. Suppose then that $\alpha \in \mathfrak{R}(J_m)$ for some m such that $0 < m < 9$. Then there exist ordinal numbers β and γ such that

(1) $$\alpha = J_m(\beta,\gamma).$$

It follows by 14.2.7(d) that $\beta,\gamma < \alpha$. Hence,

(2) $$F(\beta) \subseteq F''\beta \subseteq F''\alpha$$

and

(3) $$F(\gamma) \subseteq F''\gamma \subseteq F''\alpha.$$

If $m = 1$, then $F(\alpha) = \{F(\beta), F(\gamma)\}$. Since $\beta,\gamma < \alpha$, $F(\beta), F(\gamma) \in F''\alpha$. Therefore, $F(\alpha) \subseteq F''\alpha$.

If $1 < m < 9$, then $F(\alpha) \subseteq F(\beta)$, so it follows from (2) that $F(\alpha) \subseteq F''\alpha$. ∎

COROLLARY 14.2.14. L is transitive.

COROLLARY 14.2.15.

$$(x = F(\alpha) \;\&\; y \in x) \rightarrow (\exists\beta)(\beta < \alpha \;\&\; y = F(\beta)).$$

COROLLARY 14.2.16. $F''\alpha$ is transitive.

Using 14.2.15 we can prove that the axiom of constructibility implies the axiom of regularity, A9.

THEOREM 14.2.17. Con $\rightarrow$ A9.

Proof: Let α be an ordinal number such that $F(\alpha) \neq \emptyset$. Then it follows from 14.2.15 that there is a $\beta < \alpha$ such that $F(\beta) \in F(\alpha)$ and for all $\gamma < \beta, F(\gamma) \notin F(\alpha)$. Therefore, if $x \in F(\beta) \cap F(\alpha)$, then there is a $\gamma < \beta$ such that $x = F(\gamma)$. But $\gamma < \beta$ implies $F(\gamma) \notin F(\alpha)$. Thus, $F(\beta) \cap F(\alpha) = \emptyset$. ■

For each constructible set x there may be many ordinal numbers α such that $F(\alpha) = x$. The smallest such ordinal number is called the *order of* x, od(x).

DEFINITION 14.2.18. Order

$$x \in L \rightarrow od(x) =_{\mathrm{Df}} <\text{-smallest element of } \{\alpha : F(\alpha) = x\}.$$

Using the notion of order, it is clear how L can be well-ordered:

$$x,y \in L \rightarrow (x\, T\, y \leftrightarrow od(x) < od(y)).$$

Since T well-orders L, it follows from 14.2.15 and 14.2.18 that each constructible set can be well-ordered. Therefore,

THEOREM 14.2.19. Con $\rightarrow$ W1.

The remaining part of this section deals with the formidable problem of proving that the axiom of constructibility implies the generalized continuum hypothesis.

It turns out that it is advantageous to study the notion of order a little more closely. We shall denote by "$C(\alpha)$," the order of the element of smallest order in $F(\alpha)$.

DEFINITION 14.2.20.

$$(\forall x)[(x \in F(\alpha) \ \ \& \ \ (\forall y)(y \in F(\alpha) \rightarrow od(x) < od(y))) \rightarrow C(\alpha) =_{\mathrm{Df}} od(x)] \ \& \ (F(\alpha) = \emptyset \rightarrow C(\alpha) =_{\mathrm{Df}} \emptyset).$$

The following theorem gives some properties of *od* and *C*.

THEOREM 14.2.21.

(a) $(x \in L \ \& \ y \in x) \rightarrow od(y) < od(x)$

(b) $x \in F(\alpha) \rightarrow od(x) < \alpha$

(c) $C(\alpha) \leqq \alpha$

(d) $(x,y \in L \ \& \ od(x),od(y) < \omega_\alpha) \rightarrow od(x \cap y) < \omega_\alpha$.

Proof: The proof of (a)–(c) follows from theorem 14.2.13 and its corollaries, and the proof of (d) follows from theorem 14.2.8. The details are left as an exercise. ■

Next we show that the set of all constructible sets which correspond to elements in an initial ordinal is equipollent with that initial ordinal.

THEOREM 14.2.22. $F''\omega_\alpha \approx \omega_\alpha$.

Proof: Since F is a function, $F''\omega_\alpha \lesssim \omega_\alpha$. Let

$$\beta = \omega_\alpha \cap \mathcal{R}(J_0).$$

Suppose $\gamma,\delta \in \beta$ and $\gamma < \delta$. Then $F(\delta) = F''\delta$ and $F(\gamma) \in F(\delta)$. It follows from 14.2.17, that $F(\gamma) \in F(\delta)$ implies $F(\gamma) \neq F(\delta)$. Thus, $F|\beta$ is a 1–1 function.

It follows from 14.2.8 that

$$J_0''(\omega_\alpha \times \omega_\alpha) \subseteq \omega_\alpha \cap \mathcal{R}(J_0) = \beta.$$

Since $J_0|\beta$ is 1–1,

$$J_0''(\omega_\alpha \times \omega_\alpha) \approx \omega_\alpha \times \omega_\alpha \approx \omega_\alpha.$$

Thus,

(1) $$\omega_\alpha \lesssim \beta.$$

But $F|\beta$ is 1–1, so

(2) $$\beta \approx F''\beta \subseteq F''\omega_\alpha.$$

Therefore, it follows from (1) and (2) that $\omega_\alpha \lesssim F''\omega_\alpha$. ■

An equivalent formulation of the aleph hypothesis is

$$(\forall\alpha)(\mathcal{P}(\omega_\alpha) \approx \omega_{\alpha+1}).$$

Moreover, it follows from the axiom of choice that

$$\omega_{\alpha+1} \lesssim \mathcal{P}(\omega_\alpha).$$

Consequently, in view of theorem 14.2.22, in order to prove that Con implies the aleph hypothesis, it is sufficient to prove

$$\mathcal{P}(F''\omega_\alpha) \subseteq F''\omega_{\alpha+1}.$$

This is now the objective.

DEFINITION 14.2.23. Closure

(a) X is *1-closed with respect to* $R =_{\text{Df}} R''X \subseteq X$

(b) X is *2-closed with respect to* $R =_{\text{Df}} R''(X \times X) \subseteq X$

(c) $(f\colon w \to \{1,2\}) \to Y$ is the *(w,f)-closure of* $X =_{\text{Df}}$

(1) $X \subseteq Y$

(2) $(\forall R)(R \in w \rightarrow Y$ is $f(R)$-closed with respect to $R)$

(3) $(\forall Z)[(X \subseteq Z \ \& \ (\forall R)(R \in w \rightarrow Z$ is $f(R)$-closed with respect to $R)) \rightarrow Y \subseteq Z]$.

Thus, the closure of a class X with respect to a set of relations is the smallest class which contains X as a subclass and is closed with respect to the relations. We shall be dealing with the closure of a class only when the class is a set and the relations are functions. In this case we have the following theorem:

THEOREM 14.2.24.

$[n < \omega \ \& \ (\exists T)(\langle\langle x,T\rangle\rangle$ is a w.o. set$) \ \& \ (\forall m)(m < n \rightarrow \text{Func}(R_m)) \ \& \ (f\colon \{R_m : m < n\} \rightarrow \{1,2\})] \rightarrow (\exists y)(\text{S}(y) \ \& \ y$ is the $(\{R_m : m < n\}, f)$ closure of $x \ \& \ (x$ is infinite $\rightarrow y \approx x))$.

Proof: Let z be a set and let

$$G(z) = z \cup \bigcup_{m<n} R_m'' z^{f(R_m)},$$

where $z^1 = z$ and $z^2 = z \times z$. Therefore, if z is a set, then so also is $G(z)$, and if z can be well-ordered, then so can $z \times z$, and $R_m'' z^{f(R_m)}$ and, hence, $G(z)$. Now define a function g on ω as follows:

$$g(0) = x$$
$$g(m + 1) = G(g(m)),$$

and let

$$y = \bigcup g''\omega.$$

Then y is a set and it is easy to prove that y is the closure of x with respect to $\{R_m : m < n\}$. The details are left as an exercise.

As for the cardinality of y—if z is infinite and z can be well-ordered, then

$$\overline{\overline{G(z)}} = \bar{\bar{z}}.$$

Thus, if x is infinite and can be well-ordered,

$$\overline{\overline{g(m)}} = \overline{\overline{g(0)}} = \bar{\bar{x}}.$$

Therefore,

$$\bar{\bar{y}} = \overline{\overline{\bigcup g''\omega}} \leqq \bar{\bar{x}} \cdot \bar{\bar{\omega}} = \bar{\bar{x}}$$

and

$$\bar{\bar{y}} = \overline{\overline{\bigcup g''\omega}} \geqq \overline{\overline{g(0)}} = \bar{\bar{x}}. \ \blacksquare$$

THEOREM 14.2.25.

$[x \subseteq On$ & (x is 1-closed with respect to K_1 & K_2) & $(\forall m)(m < 9 \rightarrow$ x is 2-closed with respect to J_m) & $G:\langle\langle x,<\rangle\rangle \cong \langle\langle \alpha,<\rangle\rangle] \rightarrow$

(1) $(\forall\beta)(\forall\gamma)(\forall m)[(\beta,\gamma < \alpha \;\&\; m < 9) \rightarrow J_m(G(\beta),G(\gamma)) = G(J_m(\beta,\gamma))]$ &

(2) $(\forall m)(m < 9 \rightarrow \alpha$ is 2-closed with respect to J_m).

Proof: Suppose x, G, and α satisfy the hypothesis. Let

$$j = J|9 \times (x \times x).$$

Then, since x is 1-closed with respect to K_1 and K_2 and 2-closed with respect to J_m for $m < 9$, $\mathfrak{R}(j) = x$. Therefore,

$$j:\langle\langle 9 \times (x \times x),S^*\rangle\rangle \cong \langle\langle x,<\rangle\rangle.$$

Define a function g on $9 \times (\alpha \times \alpha)$ as follows:

$$(\beta,\gamma \in x \;\&\; m < 9) \rightarrow g(m,G(\beta),G(\gamma)) = G(j(m,\beta,\gamma)).$$

Since j and G are isomorphisms, it is easy to see that g is also an isomorphism,

$$g:\langle\langle 9 \times (\alpha \times \alpha),S^*\rangle\rangle \cong \langle\langle \alpha,<\rangle\rangle.$$

Let

$$h = J|9 \times (\alpha \times \alpha).$$

We shall show that $h = g$. Clearly, $\mathfrak{D}(h) = 9 \times (\alpha \times \alpha)$. Moreover, since J is an isomorphism and $9 \times (\alpha \times \alpha)$ is an S^*-initial segment of $9 \times (On \times On)$, $\mathfrak{R}(h)$ is an $<$-initial segment of On which is an ordinal number. It follows from theorem 7.4.5 that there is exactly one such isomorphism mapping $9 \times (\alpha \times \alpha)$ onto an ordinal number, so we must have $h = g$. Therefore, it follows from the definitions of h and g that for all $\beta,\gamma < \alpha$ and $m < 9$,

$$J(m,G(\beta),G(\gamma)) = G(J(m,\beta,\gamma)),$$

which proves (1).

Moreover, since $h = g$ and $\mathfrak{R}(g) = \alpha$, (2) follows from the definition of h. ■

The next result is a symmetric formulation of theorem 14.2.25 (1).

COROLLARY 14.2.26.

$[x,x' \subseteq On$ & (x,x' are 1-closed with respect to K_1 & K_2) & $(\forall m)(m < 9 \rightarrow$ x,x' are 2-closed with respect to J_m) & $G:\langle\langle x,<\rangle\rangle \cong \langle\langle x',<\rangle\rangle] \rightarrow$ $(\forall\beta)(\forall\gamma)(\forall m)[(\beta,\gamma \in x \;\&\; m < 9) \rightarrow J_m(G(\beta),G(\gamma)) = G(J_m(\beta,\gamma))]$.

Proof: It follows from hypothesis that both x and x' are isomorphic to the same ordinal number. The proof is completed by applying 14.2.5(1). ∎

As a direct consequence of 14.2.26 we have,

COROLLARY 14.2.27.

$$[x,x' \subseteq On \ \&\ (x,x' \text{ are 1-closed with respect to } K_1 \ \&\ K_2) \ \&\ (\forall m)(m < 9 \rightarrow x,x' \text{ are 2-closed with respect to } J_m) \ \&\ G{:}\langle\langle x,<\rangle\rangle \cong \langle\langle x',<\rangle\rangle] \rightarrow (\forall\alpha)(\forall m)((\alpha \in x \ \&\ m < 9 \ \&\ \alpha \in \mathfrak{R}(J_m)) \rightarrow G(\alpha) \in \mathfrak{R}(J_m)).$$

The next theorem is the most difficult one to prove and the most important one in the group.

THEOREM 14.2.28.

$$[x,x' \subseteq On \ \&\ (x,x' \text{ are 1-closed with respect to } K_1, K_2 \ \&\ C) \ \&\ (\forall m)(m < 9 \rightarrow x,x' \text{ are 2-closed with respect to } J_m) \ \&\ G{:}\langle\langle x,<\rangle\rangle \cong \langle\langle x',<\rangle\rangle] \rightarrow$$

(1) $(\forall\alpha)(\forall\beta)[\alpha,\beta \in x \rightarrow (F(\alpha) \in F(\beta) \leftrightarrow F(G(\alpha)) \in F(G(\beta)))]$ &

(2) $(\forall\alpha)(\forall\beta)[\alpha,\beta \in x \rightarrow (F(\alpha) = F(\beta) \leftrightarrow F(G(\alpha)) = F(G(\beta)))]$.

Proof: Suppose x,x', and G satisfy the hypothesis. Suppose $\alpha,\beta \in x$ and let

$$\eta = \max(\alpha,\beta).$$

The proof is by transfinite induction on η. Therefore, assume the theorem is true for all $\alpha_1,\beta_1 \in x$ such that $\alpha_1,\beta_1 < \eta$. In what follows we shall use the following abbreviations:

$$(\forall\gamma)(\gamma \in x \rightarrow \gamma' =_{\text{Df}} G(\gamma))$$
$$r =_{\text{Df}} F''x, \qquad r' =_{\text{Df}} F''x'$$
$$r_\eta =_{\text{Df}} F''(x \cap \eta),\ r'_\eta =_{\text{Df}} F''(x' \cap \eta').$$

We note first of all that the theorem is clearly true if $\alpha = \beta$. Hence we must show that (1) and (2) hold if either

$$\alpha < \eta \ \&\ \beta = \eta,$$

or

$$\alpha = \eta \ \&\ \beta < \eta.$$

Thus, we must prove

(3) $(\forall\alpha)[\alpha \in x \cap \eta \rightarrow (F(\alpha) \in F(\eta) \leftrightarrow F(\alpha') \in F(\eta'))]$

(4) $(\forall\beta)[\beta \in x \cap \eta \rightarrow (F(\eta) \in F(\beta) \leftrightarrow F(\eta') \in F(\beta'))]$

(5) $(\forall\beta)[\beta \in x \cap \eta \rightarrow (F(\eta) = F(\beta) \leftrightarrow F(\eta') = F(\beta'))]$,

under the conditions

(6) $(\forall\alpha)(\forall\beta)[\alpha,\beta \in x \cap \eta \to (F(\alpha) \in F(\beta) \leftrightarrow F(\alpha') \in F(\beta'))]$

(7) $(\forall\alpha)(\forall\beta)[\alpha,\beta \in x \cap \eta \to (F(\alpha) = F(\beta) \leftrightarrow F(\alpha') = F(\beta'))]$.

Let

(8) $$H = (F \circ G \circ F^{-1})|r_\eta.$$

It follows from (7) that H is a 1–1 function, for if $u \in r_\eta$, then there is an $\alpha \in x \cap \eta$ such that $u = F(\alpha)$. Then $H(u) = F(\alpha')$. By (7), if $\beta \in x \cap \eta$, $F(\alpha) = F(\beta)$ if and only if $F(\alpha') = F(\beta')$. Thus, H is a 1–1 function from r_η onto r'_η. Moreover, it follows from (6) that H is an isomorphism.

(9) $(\forall u)(\forall v)[u,v \in r_\eta \to (u \in v \leftrightarrow H(u) \in H(v))]$.

We also wish to show that H preserves unordered pairs, ordered pairs, and ordered triplets. To prove this, however, we need some preliminary material.

(10) $(\forall m)(0 < m < 9 \to r$ is 2-closed with respect to $\mathfrak{F}_m)$.

For suppose $u,v \in r$. Then there are ordinal numbers $\alpha,\beta \in x$ such that $u = F(\alpha)$ and $v = F(\beta)$. Since x is 2-closed with respect to J_m, $m = 0, 1, 2, \ldots, 8$, $\gamma = J_m(\alpha,\beta) \in x$. If $m \neq 0$, then $F(\gamma) = \mathfrak{F}_m(u,v)$. Since $\gamma \in x$, $\mathfrak{F}_m(u,v) \in r$.

In particular, it follows from (10) that

(11) $(\forall u)(\forall v)(\forall w)(u,v,w \in r \to \{u\}, \{u,v\}, u \sim v, \langle u,v\rangle, \langle u,v,w\rangle \in r)$.

Moreover,

(12) $(\forall u)(u \in r \to od(u) \in x)$.

For suppose $u \in r$. Then by (11), $\{u\} \in r$. Thus there is an $\alpha \in x$ such that $F(\alpha) = \{u\}$. Let $\beta = C(\alpha)$. Then by the definition of C, $\beta = od(u)$, and since x is 1-closed with respect to C, $od(u) \in x$.

(13) $(\forall u)((u \in r \;\&\; u \neq \emptyset) \to u \cap r \neq \emptyset)$.

For, if $u \in r$, then there is an $\alpha \in x$ such that $u = F(\alpha)$. Since $u \neq \emptyset$, it follows from the definition of C that

$$F(C(\alpha)) \in F(\alpha) = u.$$

Moreover, x is 1-closed with respect to C, so $C(\alpha) \in x$ and $F(C(\alpha)) \in r$. Consequently, $F(C(\alpha)) \in u \cap r$.

Now, using (13) we can prove

(14) (a) $(\forall u)(\{u\} \in r \to u \in r)$

(b) $(\forall u)(\forall v)(\{u,v\} \in r \to u,v \in r)$

(c) $$(\forall u)(\forall v)(\langle u,v\rangle \in r \rightarrow u,v \in r)$$
(d) $$(\forall u)(\forall v)(\forall w)(\langle u,v,w\rangle \in r \rightarrow u,v,w \in r)$$
(e) $$(\forall u)(\forall v)(\langle u,v\rangle \in r \rightarrow \langle v,u\rangle \in r)$$
(f) $$(\forall u)(\forall v)(\forall w)(\langle u,v,w\rangle \in r \rightarrow \langle v,w,u\rangle \in r)$$
(g) $$(\forall u)(\forall v)(\forall w)(\langle u,v,w\rangle \in r \rightarrow \langle u,w,v\rangle \in r).$$

Part (a) follows directly from (13) for if $\{u\} \in r$, then, since $\{u\} \neq \emptyset$, $\{u\} \cap r \neq \emptyset$, which implies $u \in r$. To prove (b), suppose $\{u,v\} \in r$. Then by (13), either $u \in r$ or $v \in r$. Suppose $u \in r$. Then by (11) $\{u\} \in r$ and $\{v\} = \{u,v\} \sim \{u\} \in r$. Thus, by (a), $v \in r$. Parts (c) and (d) follow from (a) and (b), for $\langle u,v\rangle = \{\{u\},\{u,v\}\}$ and $\langle u,v,w\rangle = \{\{u\},\{u,\{\{v\},\{v,w\}\}\}\}$. Part (e) follows from (c) and (11), and parts (f) and (g) follow from (d) and (11).

Next we claim that

(15) $$(\forall u)(\forall v)((u \in r_\eta \ \&\ v \in u \cap r) \rightarrow v \in r_\eta).$$

For, let $\alpha = od(v)$. Then, by (12), $\alpha \in x$. Moreover, it follows from 14.2.21(a), $v \in u$ implies $\mathrm{od}(v) < od(u)$. Since $u \in r_\eta$, $u = F(\beta)$ for some $\beta \in x \cap \eta$. Therefore, $od(u) < \eta$. Thus, $\alpha = od(v) < \eta$. Hence, $\alpha \in x \cap \eta$ and $v = F(\alpha) \in r_\eta$.

(16) $$(\forall u)(u \in F(\eta) \cap r \rightarrow u \in r_\eta).$$

Because 14.2.15 implies that if $u \in F(\eta)$, then $od(u) < \eta$, and (12) implies that if $u \in r$, then $od(u) \in x$. Therefore $u \in r_\eta$.

Next, it is easy to show that

(17) (a) $$(\forall u)(\forall v)(\{u,v\} \in r_\eta \rightarrow u,v \in r_\eta)$$
(b) $$(\forall u)(\forall v)(\langle u,v\rangle \in r_\eta \rightarrow u,v \in r_\eta)$$
(c) $$(\forall u)(\forall v)(\forall w)(\langle u,v,w\rangle \in r_\eta \rightarrow u,v,w \in r_\eta).$$

To prove (a), note that $\{u,v\} \in r_\eta$ implies $\{u,v\} \in r$. Therefore, it follows from (14)(b) that $u,v \in r$. Thus, $\{u,v\} \in r_\eta$ and $u,v \in \{u,v\} \cap r$, and so (15) implies $u,v \in r_\eta$. The proof is similar for (b) and (c).

Now, we are ready to prove that the isomorphism H also preserves unordered pairs, ordered pairs, and ordered triplets.

(18) $$(\forall u)(\forall v)(\forall w)(\forall z)(u,v,w,z \in r_\eta \rightarrow$$
(a) $$z = \{u,v\} \leftrightarrow H(z) = \{H(u),H(v)\}$$
(b) $$z = \langle u,v\rangle \leftrightarrow H(z) = \langle H(u),H(v)\rangle$$
(c) $$z = \langle u,v,w\rangle \leftrightarrow H(z) = \langle H(u),H(v),H(w)\rangle.$$

Because of symmetry, it is sufficient to establish each of the above equivalences in one direction. Therefore, to prove (a) it is sufficient to show that the right side implies the left. Suppose that $H(z) = \{H(u),H(v)\}$. Then, $H(u) \in H(z)$ and $H(v) \in H(z)$. Since H is an isomorphism, this implies that $u \in z$ and $v \in z$. Thus, $\{u,v\} \subseteq z$. Suppose further that $z \sim \{u,v\} \neq \emptyset$. Then, by (11), $z \sim \{u,v\} \in r$. Therefore, by (13), there is a $w \in (z \sim \{u,v\}) \cap r$. Since $z \in r_\eta$ and $w \in z \cap r$, it follows from (15) that $w \in r_\eta$. Therefore, $H(w) \in H(z)$, which implies $H(w) = H(u)$ or $H(w) = H(v)$. Thus, $w = u$ or $w = v$, which is impossible. Hence, $z = \{u,v\}$. Parts (b) and (c) follow from (a).

Returning now to the original problem of proving (3)–(5), we shall show that (3) implies (4) and (5).

First to prove (3) implies (5), suppose that $\beta \in x \cap \eta$ and $F(\eta) \neq F(\beta)$.

Case 1. $F(\eta) \sim F(\beta) \neq \emptyset$. By (11) $F(\eta) \sim F(\beta) \in r$. Therefore, by (13), there is a $u \in r$ such that $u \in F(\eta) \sim F(\beta)$. Since $u \in F(\eta) \cap r$, it follows from (16) that $u \in r_\eta$. Thus, there is a $\gamma \in x \cap \eta$ such that $u = F(\gamma)$. Since $u \in F(\eta) \sim F(\beta)$, $F(\gamma) \notin F(\beta)$. Therefore, by (6),

$$F(\gamma') \notin F(\beta').$$

But $F(\gamma) \in F(\eta)$, so by (3),

$$F(\gamma') \in F(\eta').$$

Consequently, $F(\eta') \neq F(\beta')$.

Case 2. $F(\beta) \sim F(\eta) \neq \emptyset$. Starting as in case 1, there is a $u = F(\gamma) \in (F(\beta) \sim F(\eta)) \cap r$. Since $u \in r$ and $u \in F(\beta) \in r_\eta$, it follows from (15) that $u \in r_\eta$. Since $F(\gamma) \in F(\beta)$, it follows from (6) that

$$F(\gamma') \in F(\beta'),$$

and since $F(\gamma) \notin F(\eta)$, it follows from (3) that

$$F(\gamma') \notin F(\eta').$$

Thus, $F(\eta') \neq F(\beta')$. The proof in the other direction follows by symmetry.

Next, we shall show that (5) implies (4). Suppose $\beta \in x \cap \eta$ and $F(\eta) \in F(\beta)$. Let $\alpha = od(f(\eta))$. Then by 14.2.21(b) and hypothesis, $\alpha < \beta < \eta$. By (12), $\alpha \in x$, therefore, $\alpha \in x \cap \eta$. Since $F(\eta) = F(\alpha)$, it follows from hypothesis that $F(\alpha) \in F(\beta)$. By (5),

$$F(\eta) = F(\alpha) \rightarrow F(\eta') = F(\alpha').$$

And by (6),

$$F(\alpha) \in F(\beta) \rightarrow F(\alpha') \in F(\beta').$$

Thus, $F(\eta') \in F(\beta')$. The inverse implication follows by symmetry.

Now, the remaining problem is to prove (3), and by symmetry, it is sufficient to prove

$$(\forall\alpha)[\alpha \in x \cap \eta \rightarrow (F(\alpha) \in F(\eta) \rightarrow F(\alpha') \in F(\eta'))]$$

Suppose then that $\alpha \in x \cap \eta$ and $F(\alpha) \in F(\eta)$.

Case 1. $\eta \in \mathcal{R}(J_0)$.

By 14.2.27, $\eta' \in \mathcal{R}(J_0)$. Thus, $F(\eta) = F''\eta$ and $F(\eta') = F''\eta'$. Since $\alpha' < \eta$ and $\alpha' < \eta'$, we must have both $F(\alpha) \in F(\eta)$ and $F(\alpha') \in F(\eta')$.

Case 2. $\eta \in \mathcal{R}(J_1)$.

Then, since x is 1-closed with respect to K_1 and K_2, there exist $\beta,\gamma \in x$ such that $\eta = J_1(\beta,\gamma)$. By 14.2.7(b), $\beta,\gamma < \eta$ and by 14.2.25(1), $\eta' = J_1(\beta',\gamma')$. It follows from the definition of F that

$$F(\eta) = \{F(\beta),F(\gamma)\},$$

and by (18)(a),

$$F(\eta') = \{F(\beta'),F(\gamma')\}.$$

Therefore, if $F(\alpha) \in F(\eta)$, then $F(\alpha) = F(\beta)$ or $F(\alpha) = F(\gamma)$, which implies by (7) that $F(\alpha') = F(\beta')$ or $F(\alpha') = F(\gamma')$. Thus,

$$F(\alpha') \in \{F(\beta'),F(\gamma')\} = F(\eta').$$

Case 3. $\eta \in \mathcal{R}(J_m)$, $2 \leqq m < 9$.

Since x is 1-closed with respect to K_1 and K_2, there exist $\beta,\gamma \in x$ such that $\eta = J_m(\beta,\gamma)$. Moreover, 14.2.7(b) implies $\beta,\gamma < \eta$, and 14.2.25(1) implies $\eta' = J_m(\beta',\gamma')$. Therefore, it follows from the definition of F that

$$F(\eta) = F(\beta) \cap \Phi_m(F(\gamma))$$

and

$$F(\eta') = F(\beta') \cap \Phi_m(F(\gamma)).$$

If $F(\alpha) \in F(\eta)$, then $F(\alpha) \in F(\beta)$ and $F(\alpha) \in \Phi_m(F(\gamma))$. If $F(\alpha) \in F(\beta)$, then it follows from (6) that $F(\alpha') \in F(\beta')$. Suppose $F(\alpha) \in \Phi_m(F(\gamma))$.

If $m = 2$,

$$\Phi_m(F(\gamma)) = E = \{\langle u,v\rangle : u \in v\}.$$

Thus, $F(\alpha) \in \Phi_2(F(\gamma))$, implies $F(\alpha) = \langle u,v\rangle$, where $u \in v$. Since $F(\alpha) \in r_\eta$ it follows from (17)(b) that $u,v \in r_\eta$. By (18)(b),

$$F(\alpha') = \langle H(u),H(v)\rangle.$$

Since H is an isomorphism, $u \in v$ implies $H(u) \in H(v)$. Therefore, $F(\alpha') \in E$ so $F(\alpha') \in F(\eta')$.

If $m = 3$, then

$$\Phi_m(F(\gamma)) = (F(\gamma))' = \{u : u \notin F(\gamma)\}.$$

Thus, $F(\alpha) \in \Phi_3(F(\gamma))$ implies $F(\alpha) \notin F(\gamma)$. Therefore it follows from (6) that $F(\alpha') \notin F(\gamma')$. Consequently, $F(\alpha') \in F(\eta')$.

If $m = 4$, then

$$\Phi_m(F(\gamma)) = F(\gamma) \times V.$$

If $F(\alpha) \in \Phi_4(F(\gamma))$, then there are elements u and v such that $u \in F(\gamma)$ and $F(\alpha) = \langle u,v \rangle$. Since $F(\alpha) \in r_\eta$, by (17)(b), $u,v \in r_\eta$. Therefore, by (18)(b),

$$F(\alpha') = \langle H(u),H(v) \rangle.$$

Since $u \in F(\gamma)$, then $H(u) \in F(\gamma')$. Thus, $F(\alpha') \in F(\gamma') \times V$, and so $F(\alpha') \in F(\eta')$.

If $m = 5$, then

$$\Phi_m(F(\gamma)) = \mathfrak{D}(F(\gamma)).$$

If $F(\alpha) \in \mathfrak{D}(F(\gamma))$, then $F(\gamma)''\{F(\alpha)\} \neq \emptyset$. Thus, by (10), $F(\gamma)''\{F(\alpha)\} \in r$. Therefore, by (13), there is a $u \in r$ such that $u \in F(\gamma)''\{F(\alpha)\}$. This implies that $\langle f(\alpha),u \rangle \in F(\gamma)$. Since $F(\alpha),u \in r$, by (11), $\langle F(\alpha),u \rangle \in r$. Then, since $F(\gamma) \in r_\eta$ and $\langle F(\alpha),u \rangle \in F(\gamma) \cap r$, it follows from (15) that $\langle F(\alpha),u \rangle \in r_\eta$. Therefore, by (17)(b), $u \in r_\eta$. Using the fact that H is an isomorphism and (18)(b), it follows from $\langle F(\alpha),u \rangle \in F(\gamma)$ and $F(\alpha),u,F(\gamma) \in r_\eta$ that $\langle F(\alpha'),H(u) \rangle \in F(\gamma')$. Thus, $F(\alpha') \in \mathfrak{D}(F(\gamma'))$, so $F(\alpha') \in F(\eta')$.

If $m = 6$, then

$$\Phi_m(F(\gamma)) = (F(\gamma))^{-1}.$$

If $F(\alpha) \in \Phi_6(F(\gamma))$, then there exist elements u and v such that $F(\alpha) = \langle u,v \rangle$ and $\langle v,u \rangle \in F(\gamma)$. Since $\langle u,v \rangle \in r$, it follows from (14)(e) that $\langle v,u \rangle \in r$. Therefore, $\langle v,u \rangle \in F(\gamma) \cap r$ and $F(\gamma) \in r_\eta$, so by (15), $\langle v,u \rangle \in r_\eta$. Hence, by (17)(b), $u,v \in r_\eta$. Thus, by (18)(b),

$$H(\langle v,u \rangle) = \langle H(v),H(u) \rangle.$$

Since H is an isomorphism and $\langle v,u \rangle \in F(\gamma)$, it follows that

$$\langle H(v),H(u) \rangle \in F(\gamma').$$

Since $F(\alpha) = \langle u,v \rangle$, again by (18)(b),

$$F(\alpha') = \langle H(u),H(v) \rangle.$$

Therefore, $F(\alpha') \in (F(\gamma'))^{-1}$ so $F(\alpha') \in F(\eta')$.

For the cases in which $m = 7$ and $m = 8$ the proofs are similar to the preceding one, so the details are left to the reader. ■

The next theorem follows from 14.2.28.

THEOREM 14.2.29.

$[x \subseteq On \;\&\; (x \text{ is 1-closed with respect to } K_1,K_2 \;\&\; C) \;\&\; (\forall m)(m < 9 \rightarrow x \text{ is 2-closed with respect to } J_m) \;\&\; G{:}\langle\langle x,<\rangle\rangle \cong \langle\langle \alpha,<\rangle\rangle] \rightarrow (\forall\beta)(\forall\gamma)[\beta,\gamma \in x \rightarrow (F(\beta) \in F(\gamma) \leftrightarrow F(G(\beta)) \in F(G(\gamma))]$.

Proof: Let $\alpha = x'$. By 14.2.25(2), α is closed with respect to J_m, $m < 9$; by 14.2.7(c), α is closed with respect to K_1 and K_2; and by 14.2.21(c),

α is closed with respect to C. Consequently, 14.2.29 follows from 14.2.28(1). ■

We are now ready to prove the main result.

THEOREM 14.2.30. Con $\rightarrow$ AH.

Proof: We shall prove that 14.2.29 implies,

(1) $$\mathcal{P}(F''\omega_\alpha) \subseteq F''\omega_{\alpha+1}.$$

We have previously shown that (1) implies the aleph hypothesis (see the remarks following 14.2.22).

Suppose $u \in \mathcal{P}(F''\omega_\alpha)$. Then

(2) $$u \subseteq F''\omega_\alpha.$$

Con implies that u is constructible. Therefore, there is an ordinal number δ such that

(3) $$u = F(\delta).$$

Let x be the closure of $\omega_\alpha \cup \{\delta\}$ with respect to C, K_1, K_2, and J_m, $m = 0$, $1, \ldots, 8$. By 14.2.24, x is a set and $\bar{\bar{x}} = \aleph_\alpha$. Let β be the ordinal number which is isomorphic to x and let G be the isomorphism mapping x onto β:

(4) $$G\colon \langle\langle x,<\rangle\rangle \cong \langle\langle \beta,<\rangle\rangle.$$

Then by 14.2.29,

(5) $$(\forall\xi)(\forall\eta)[\xi,\eta \in x \rightarrow F(\xi) \in F(\eta) \rightarrow F(G(\xi)) \in F(G(\eta))].$$

Since $\delta \in x$ and $\bar{\bar{x}} = \aleph_\alpha$, it follows from (4) that $G(\delta) \in \beta$ and $\bar{\bar{\beta}} = \aleph_\alpha$. Thus, $\beta < \omega_{\alpha+1}$ and

(6) $$G(\delta) < \omega_{\alpha+1}.$$

Now, by (5),

(7) $$(\forall\xi)[\xi \in x \rightarrow (F(\xi) \in F(\delta) \leftrightarrow F(G(\xi)) \in F(G(\delta)))].$$

Since $\omega_\alpha \subseteq x$, ω_α must be a $<$-initial segment of x. Consequently, since G is an isomorphism, it follows that $\xi \in \omega_\alpha \rightarrow G(\xi) = \xi$. Thus, from (7),

(8) $$(\forall\xi)[\xi \in \omega_\alpha \rightarrow (F(\xi) \in F(\delta) \leftrightarrow F(\xi) \in F(G(\delta))].$$

This implies,

(9) $$F(\delta) \cap F''\omega_\alpha = F(G(\delta)) \cap F''\omega_\alpha.$$

Using (2), (3), and (9), we obtain

$$(10) \qquad u = F(\delta) = F(G(\delta)) \cap F''\omega_\alpha.$$

By theorem 14.2.9, $\omega_\alpha \in \mathcal{R}(J_0)$. Thus, $F''\omega_\alpha = F(\omega_\alpha)$. Substituting in (10),

$$(11) \qquad u = F(G(\delta)) \cap F(\omega_\alpha).$$

It follows from (11), (6), and 14.2.21(d) that $od(u) < \omega_{\alpha+1}$. Therefore, $u \in F''\omega_{\alpha+1}$. ∎

A class X is said to be constructible if $X \subseteq L$ and for all $u \in L$, $u \cap X \in L$. Gödel (1940) has shown that the constructible classes form a model for set theory. Thus, if axioms A1, A2, A3′, A4–A7, and A10 are consistent, it follows from theorems 14.2.17, 14.2.19, and 14.2.30 that

A1, A2, A3′, A4–A10, GCH, and Con

are all consistent. The relative consistency of these axioms has not been demonstrated if A3′ is replaced by A3. The development in this section closely follows that given in Gödel (1940) and we feel that this is a natural approach when working in NBG set theory. However, there is a large group of mathematicians and logicians who prefer the approach which was suggested in Gödel's original paper in 1939. For an excellent exposition of this approach the reader is referred to Carol Karp's paper, "A proof of the relative consistency of the continuum hypothesis."

EXERCISES 14.2

1. For all $m < 9$, calculate
   (a) $J(m, 0, 2)$
   (b) $J(m, 1, 2)$
   (c) $J(m, 2, 2)$
   (d) $J(m, 2, 0)$
   (e) $J(m, 2, 1)$
   (f) $J(m, 1, \omega)$.
2. Prove lemma 14.2.5.
3. Prove corollaries 14.2.14, 14.2.15, and 14.2.16.
4. Complete the proof of 14.2.21.
5. Complete the proof of 14.2.28.
6. Prove each of the following:
   (a) $\emptyset \in L$
   (b) $u,v \in L \rightarrow (\forall m)(m < 9 \rightarrow \mathfrak{F}_m(u,v) \in L)$
   (c) $u,v \in L \rightarrow u \cap v \in L$
   (d) $u,v \in L \rightarrow \langle u,v \rangle \in L$
   (e) $u \subseteq L \rightarrow (\exists v)(v \in L \ \&\ u \subseteq v)$.
7. Prove each of the following:
   (a) L is a constructible class

(b) X is a constructible class $\rightarrow$
  (i) $X \cap E$ is a constructible class
  (ii) X^{-1} is a constructible class
  (iii) $\mathfrak{D}(X)$ is a constructible class
  (iv) $\mathfrak{R}(X)$ is a constructible class

(c) X & Y are constructible classes $\rightarrow$
  (i) $X \sim Y$ is a constructible class
  (ii) $X \cap Y$ is a constructible class
  (iii) $X \cup Y$ is a constructible class.

Bibliography

Bachmann, H. (1955) *Transfinite Zahlen*, Springer-Verlag, Berlin.

Bagemihl, F. (1961) "A proposition of elementary plane geometry that implies the continuum hypothesis," Z. Math. Logik Grundlagen Math., **7,** 77–79.

Banach, S. (1920) "Sur l'équation fonctionelle $f(x + y) = f(x) + f(y)$," Fund. Math., **1,** 123.

Banach, S. and Tarski, A. (1924) "Sur la decomposition des ensembles de points en parties respectivement congruentes," Fund. Math., **6,** 244–277.

Bell, E. T. (1937) *Men of Mathematics*, Simon and Schuster, New York.

Bernays, P. (1937) "A system of axiomatic set theory, I," J. Sym. Logic, **2,** 65–77.
(1941) "II," **6,** 1–17.
(1942) "III," **7,** 65–89.
(1942) "IV," **7,** 133–145.
(1943) "V," **8,** 89–106.
(1948) "VI," **13,** 65–79.
(1954) "VII," **19,** 81–96.

Bernays, P. and Fraenkel, A. A. (1958) *Axiomatic Set Theory*, North-Holland, Amsterdam.

Bourbaki, N. (1951) *Théorie des Ensembles*, (Act. Sc. Ind. 1141) 2nd Edition, Hermann, Paris.
(1954) *Théorie des Ensembles*, (Act. Sc. Ind. 1212) Hermann, Paris.
(1956) *Théorie des Ensembles*, (Act. Sc. Ind. 1243) Hermann, Paris.

Cantor, G. (1895) "Betrage zur Begrundung der transfiniten Mengenlehre, I," Math. Annal. **46,** 481–512.
(1897) "II", **49,** 207–246.
(1915) *Contributions to the Founding of the Theory of Transfinite Numbers*, translated by P. E. B. Jourdain. Chicago. Reprinted by Dover Publications Inc.

Cohen, P. (1963) "The independence of the continuum hypothesis," Proc. Natl. Acad. Sci. U.S.A., **50,** 1143–1148.
(1963) "The independence of the continuum hypothesis II," Proc. Natl. Acad. Sci. U.S.A., **51,** 105–110.
(1966) *Set Theory and the Continuum Hypothesis* W. A. Benjamin Inc., New York.

Collins, G. (1954) "Distributivity and an axiom of choice," J. Sym. Logic, **19,** 275–277.

Copi, I. (1954) *Symbolic Logic*, Macmillan, New York.

Davies, R. O. (1962) "Equivalence to the continuum hypothesis of a certain proposition of elementary plane geometry," Z. Math. Logik Grunlagen Math., **8,** 109–111.

Erdös, P. and Kakutani, S. (1943) "On non-denumerable graphs," Bull. Amer. Math. Soc., **49,** 457–461.

Feferman, S. (1964) "Independence of the axiom of choice from the axiom of dependent choices," J. Sym. Logic, **29,** 226.

(1965) "Some applications of the notions of forcing and generic sets," Fund. Math. **56,** 325-345.

Feferman, S. and Levy, A. (1963) "Independence results in set theory by Cohen's method, II," Notices Amer. Math. Soc. **10,** 593.

Fitch, F. (1952) *Symbolic Logic*, Macmillan, New York.

Fraenkel, A. A. (1922) "Über den Begriff 'definit' und die Unabhängigkeit des Auswahlaxioms," Sitz. Preuss. Akad. Wiss., 253–257.

(1922) "Zu den Grundlagen der Cantor-Zermeloschen Mengenlehre," Math. Annal. **86,** 230–237.

(1937) "Über eine abgeschwächte Fassung des Auswahlaxioms," J. Sym. Logic, **2,** 1–25.

(1953) *Abstract Set Theory*, North-Holland, Amsterdam.

Fraenkel, A. A. and Bar-Hillel, Y. (1958) *Foundations of Set Theory*, North-Holland, Amsterdam.

Gentzen, G. (1934) "Untersuchungen über das logische Schliessen," Math. Z., **3,** 176–210, 405–431. [French translation with commentary, *Recherches sur la Déduction Logic* by R. Feys and J. Ladriere, Paris, 1955.]

Gödel, K. (1931) "Über formal unentscheidbare Sätze der *Principia Mathematica* und verwandter Systeme," Monatsh. Math. Phil., **38,** 173–198.

(1934) *On undecidable propositions of formal mathematical systems* (Mimeographed) Princeton University Press, Princeton.

(1939) "Consistency-proof for the generalized continuum hypothesis," Proc. Natl. Acad. Sci. U.S.A., **25,** 220–224.

(1940) *The consistency of the axiom of choice and of the generalized continuum-hypothesis with the axioms of set theory*, Princeton University Press, Princeton. Revised edition 1951.

(1947) "What is Cantor's continuum problem?" Amer. Math. Monthly, **54,** 515–525.

Halpern, J. (1961) "The independence of the axiom of choice from the Boolean prime ideal theorem," Notices Amer. Math. Soc. **8,** 279–80.

(1964) "The independence of the axiom of choice from the Boolean prime ideal theorem," Fund. Math., **55,** 56–66.

Halpern, J. and Levy, A. (1964) "The ordering theorem does not imply the axiom of choice," Notices Amer. Math. Soc. **11,** 56.

Halmos, P. (1960) *Naive Set Theory*, Van Nostrand, Princeton.

Hartogs, F. (1915) "Über das Problem der Wohlordnung," Math. Annal., **76,** 436–443.

Hausdorf, F. (1914) *Grundzüge der Mengenlehre*, W. de Gruyter, Leipzig. 2nd Revised Edition Berlin & Leipzig, 1927; English translation, 2nd Edition Chelsea, New York, 1962.

Kamke, E. (1950) *Theory of sets*, Dover, New York.

Keisler, H. and Tarski, A. (1964) "From accessible to inaccessible cardinals," Fund. Math., **53,** 225–308.

(1965) "Corrections to the paper 'From accessible to inaccessible cardinals'," Fund. Math., **57,** 119.

Kelley, J. L. (1950) "The Tychonoff product theorem implies the axiom of choice," Fund. Math., **37,** 75–76.

(1955) *General Topology*, Van Nostrand, Princeton.

Kleene, S. (1952) *Introduction to Metamathematics*, Van Nostrand, New York.

Klimovsky, G. (1962) "El axioma de elección y la existencia de subgrupos commutativos maximales," Rev. Union Matem. Argentina Asoc. Fis. Argentina, **20,** 267–287.

König, J. (1905) "Zum Kontinuum problem," Math. Annal., **60,** 177–180.

Kruse, A. (1960) "Some developments in the theory of numerations," Trans. Amer. Math. Soc., **97,** 523–553.

(1962) "Some observations on the axiom of choice," Z. Math. Logik Grundlagen Math., **8,** 125–146.

Kuratowski, C. (1922) "Une méthode d'élimination des nombres transfinis des raisonnements mathematiques," Fund. Math., **3,** 76–108.

Kurepa, G. (1952) "Sur la relation d'inclusion et l' axiome de choix de Zermelo," Bull. Soc. Math. France, **80,** 225–232.

Landau, E. (1946) *Grundlagen der Analysis*, Chelsea, New York.

Levy, A. (1960) "Axiom schemata of strong infinity in axiomatic set theory," Pacific J. Math., **10,** 223–238.

(1963) "Independence results in set theory by Cohen's method I, III, IV" Notices Amer. Math. Soc., **10,** 592–593.

Lindenbaum, A. and Tarski, A. (1926) "Communication sur les recherches de la théorie des ensembles," Compt. Rend. Varsovie, **19,** 299–330.

Mahlo, P. (1911) "Über lineare transfinite Mengen Berichte über die Verhandlungen der Königlich Sächseschen," Gesellschrift der Wissenschaften zu Leipsig, Math-Physische Klasse, **63,** 187–225.

(1912) "Zur theorie und Anwendung der ρ_0-Zahlen," **64,** 108–112.

(1913) "II," **65,** 268–282.

Mendelson, E. (1956) "Some proofs of independence in axiomatic set theory," J. Sym. Logic, **21,** 291–303.

(1956a) "The independence of a weak axiom of choice," J. Sym. Logic, **21,** 350–366.

Mirimanoff, D. (1917) "Remarques sur la théorie des ensembles et les antinomies cantoriennes," L'Ens. Math., **19,** 209–217.

Moore, R. L. (1932) "Foundations of point set theory," Amer. Math. Soc. Colloq. Publ., **13,** New York.

Mostowski, A. (1939) "Über die Unabhängigkeit des Wohlordnugssatzes vom Ordnungsprinzip," Fund. Math., **32,** 201–252.

(1948) "On the principle of dependent choices," Fund. Math., **35,** 127–130.

(1952) *Sentences undecidable in formalized arithmetic*, North-Holland, Amsterdam.

(1953) "On models of axiomatic systems," Fund. Math., **39,** 133–158.
Neumann, J. von (1923) "Zur Einführung der transfiniten Zahlen," Acta Szeged, **1,** 199–208.
(1925) "Eine Axiomatisierung der Mengenlehre," J. reine angew. Math., **154,** 219–240.
(1928) "Die Axiomatisierung der Mengenlehre," Math. Z., **27,** 669–752.
(1929) "Über eine Widerspruchsfreiheitsfrage in der axiomatischen Mengenlehre," J. reine angew. Math., **160,** 227–241.
Quine, W. V. (1937) "New foundations for mathematical logic," Amer. Math. Monthly, **44,** 70–80.
(1951) *Mathematical Logic*, Revised Edition, Harvard University Press, Cambridge, Mass.
(1951a) "On the consistency of 'New Foundations'," Proc. Natl. Acad. Sci. U.S.A., **37,** 538–540.
Robinson, R. M. (1937) "The theory of classes. A modification of von Neumann's system," J. Sym. Logic, **2,** 29–36.
Royden, H. (1963) *Real Analysis*, Macmillan, New York.
Rubin, H. (1959) "A new form of the generalized continuum hypothesis," Bull. Amer. Math. Soc., **65,** 282–283.
(1960) "Two propositions equivalent to the axiom of choice only under both the axioms of extensionality and regularity," Notices Amer. Math. Soc., **7,** 381.
Rubin H. and Rubin, J. E. (1963) *Equivalents of the Axiom of Choice*, North Holland, Amsterdam.
Russell, B. (1906) "On some difficulties in the theory of transfinite numbers and order types," Proc. London Math. Soc., (2), **4,** 29–53.
Schoenfield, J. R. (1955) "The independence of the axiom of choice," J. Sym. Logic., **20,** 202.
Scott, D. (1954) "The theorem on maximal ideals in lattices and the axiom of choice," Bull. Amer. Math. Soc., **60,** 83.
(1955) "Definitions by abstraction in axiomatic set theory," Bull. Amer. Math. Soc., **61,** 442.
Shepherdson, J. C. (1951) "Inner models for set theory," J. Sym. Logic, **16,** 161–190.
(1952) **17,** 225–237.
(1953) **18,** 145–167.
Sierpinski, W. (1918) "L'axiome de M. Zermelo et son role dans la Théorie des Ensembles et l'Analyse," Bull. Acad. Sci. Cracovie, 97–152.
(1921) "Les exemples effectives et l'axiome du choix," Fund. Math., **2,** 112–118.
(1946) "Sur une proposition équivalente à l'axiome du choix," Actas Acad. Ci. Lima, **11,** 111–112.
(1947) "L'hypothèse généralisée du continu et l'axiome du choix," Fund. Math., **34,** 1–5.
(1947a) "Démonstration de l'égalite $2^m - m = 2^m$ pour les nombres cardinaux transfinis," Fund. Math., **34,** 113–118.

(1947b) "Sur la difference de deux nombres cardinaux," Fund. Math., **34,** 119–126.
(1950) *Leçons sur les nombres transfinis*, Gauthier-Villars, Paris, 2nd edition.
(1956) *Hypothèse du Continu* (containing as an appendix a number of research papers 1934–56) Chelsea, New York, 2nd Edition.
(1958) *Cardinal and Ordinal Numbers*, Panstwowe Wydawnictwo Naukowe, Warszawa.
Skolem, T. (1922) "Einige Bemerkungen zur axiomatischen Begrundung der Mengenlehre," Wiss. Vorträge gehalten aug dem 5. Kongress der Skandenav. Mathemaliken in Helsingfors, 217–232.
Solovay, R. (1963) "Independence results in the theory of cardinals **I, II**," Notices Amer. Math. Soc., **10,** 595.
(1964) "The measure problem," J. Sym. Logic, **29,** 227–228.
(1965) "Measurable cardinals and the continuum hypothesis," Notices Amer. Math. Soc., **12,** 132.
(1965a) "The measure problem," Notices Amer. Math. Soc., **12,** 217.
Specker, E. (1953) "The axiom of choice in Quine's 'New foundations for mathematical logic'." Proc. Natl. Acad. Sci. U.S.A., **39,** 972–975.
(1957) "Zur Axiomatik der Mengenlehre (Fundierungs- und Auswahlaxiom)." Z. Math. Logik Grundlagen Math., **3,** 173–210.
Suppes, P. (1957) *Introduction to Logic*, Van Nostrand, Princeton.
(1960) *Axiomatic Set Theory*, Van Nostrand, Princeton.
Szele, T. (1950) "On Zorn's lemma," Public. Math. Debrecen, **1,** 254–256.
Tarski, A. (1924) "Sur quelques théorèmes qui équivalent à l'axiome du choix," Fund. Math., **5,** 147–154.
(1925) "Quelques théorèmes sur les alephs," Fund. Math., **7,** 1–14.
(1928) "Sur la décomposition des ensembles en sousensembles presque disjoints," Fund. Math., **12,** 188–205.
(1929) "Sur la décomposition des ensembles en sousensembles presque disjoints," Fund. Math., **14,** 203–215.
(1938) "Über unerreichbare Kardinalzahlen," Fund. Math., **30,** 68–89.
(1938a) "Eine äquivalente Formulierung des Auswahlaxioms," Fund. Math., **30,** 197–201.
(1939) "On well-ordered subsets of any set," Fund. Math., **32,** 176–183.
(1948) "Axiomatic and algebraic aspects of two theorems on sums of cardinals," Fund. Math., **35,** 79–104.
(1949) "Cancellation laws in the arithmetic of cardinals," Fund. Math., **36,** 77–92.
(1949a) *Cardinal Algebras*, Oxford University Press, New York.
(1951) "On a statement related to the principle of choice," Bull. Amer. Math. Soc., **57,** 81.
(1954) "Theorems on the existence of successors of cardinals and the axiom of choice," Indag. Math., **16,** 26–32.
(1955) "The notion of rank in axiomatic set theory and some of its applications," Bull. Amer. Math. Soc., **61,** 443.

(1964) "The comparability of cardinals and the axiom of choice," Notices Amer. Math. Soc., **11,** 578.

Teichmüller, O. (1939) "Braucht der Algebraiker das Auswahlaxiom?" Deutsche Math., **4,** 567–577.

Tukey, J. W. (1940) "Convergence and uniformity in topology," Ann. Math. Studies, No. 2, Princeton.

Vaught, R. (1952) "On the equivalence of the axiom of choice and a maximal principle," Bull. Amer. Math. Soc., **58,** 66.

Whitehead, A. N. (1902) "On cardinal numbers", Amer. J. Math., **24,** 367–394.

Whitehead, A. N. and Russell, B. (1910–13) *Principia Mathematica,* 3 vols., Cambridge University Press, 2nd Edition 1925, 1927, 1927. Reprinted 1950. Paperback edition 1962.

Zermelo, E. (1904) "Beweis, das jede Menge wohlgeordnet werden kann," Math. Annal., **59,** 514–516.

(1908) "Untersuchungen über die Grundlagen der Mengenlehre I," Math. Annal., **65,** 261–281.

(1929) "Über den Begriff der Definitheit in der Axiomatik," Fund. Math., **14,** 339–344.

(1930) "Über Grenzzahlen und Mengenbereiche," Fund. Math., **16,** 29–47.

Zorn, M. (1935) "A remark on method in transfinite algebra," Bull. Amer. Math. Soc.. **41,** 667–670.

Index of Symbols

Index of Terms